THE **GUIDE** TO UK Company Giving

2009/10

JOHN SMYTH

Additional research by:
Alan French

Contributions from:
DEL REDVERS

'Charity of the Year' and Smaller Organisations

DIRECTORY OF SOCIAL CHANGE

Published by
Directory of Social Change
24 Stephenson Way
London NW1 2DP
Tel. 08450 77 77 07; Fax 020 7391 4808
email publications@dsc.org.uk
www.dsc.org.uk
www.companygiving.org.uk
from whom further copies and a full publications list are available.

Directory of Social Change is a Registered Charity no. 800517

First published 1998
Second edition 1999
Third edition 2000
Fourth edition 2002
Fifth edition 2004
Sixth edition 2007
Seventh edition 2009

ISBN 978 1 906294 32 8

British Library Cataloguing in Publication Data
A catalogue record for this book is available from the British Library

Cover design by Gabriele Kern
Text designed by Gabriele Kern
Typeset by Marlinzo Services, Frome
Printed and bound by CPI Antony Rowe, Chippenham

Other Directory of Social Change departments in London:
General enquiries 08450 77 77 07

Directory of Social Change Northern Office:
Federation House, Hope Street, Liverpool L1 9BW
Research 0151 708 0136

Contents

Introduction   v

Contributions

'Charity of the Year' and Smaller Organisations
by Del Redvers   ix

Facts & figures   xiii

Applying to companies   xvii

Alphabetical listing of companies   xxiv

Alphabetical listing of companies entries   1

Member organisations

Arts & Business   366

Business in the Community/Scottish BitC   371

London Benchmarking Group   377

ProHelp   378

Company activity listing   380

Geographical listing of head offices   385

Useful contacts   389

Index   393

Welcome to the seventh edition of *The Guide to UK Company Giving*, which continues to provide relevant, updated policy information and commentary on the current state of corporate community involvement in the UK.

This edition features 490 companies, which together gave around £808 million in community support (including £500 million in cash donations) in 2007/08. We continue with the familiar layout format to help make the task of identifying potential new sources of corporate support both easier and, ultimately, more fruitful.

As ever, most of the guide consists of the individual company entries, but it also contains additional sections offering advice and information for fundraisers, voluntary organisations, community groups and companies.

Company information

Our basic criterion for inclusion of a company is that it must have made cash donations of £20,000 or more in support of the community in its latest financial year. A limited number of companies gave less than this, but have been included either because they give substantial help in other ways (at least £100,000 of in kind support) or because in previous years they have met our criteria and there is no obvious reason for suspecting the recent decrease to be the start of a downward trend.

Wherever possible, we have quoted the UK charitable donations figure declared by the company in its annual report and accounts, as it continues to provide a tangible and unambiguous indicator of its commitment to the community. Failing this, we quote the worldwide donations figure while making it clear that this is the case. As acknowledged above, however, cash donations are not the only way in which a company can provide support for charities and community groups.

Where made available to us, we have included an additional figure for total community contributions. However, the means of measuring the value of these contributions, and even what should be included under this heading, are open to debate. In our view, the term should cover a company's charitable donations, plus support such as good-cause

sponsorship and the value of gifts in kind, secondments and employee volunteering during company time.

If calculated and provided by the company, we quote management costs separately because we do not consider it valid to include this as part of total community contributions. Obviously, companies incur certain costs in running their community investment programmes, but inclusion in the overall figure gives the impression of the available funding being greater than it actually is.

Finally, if possible, we give a figure for any cause-related marketing initiatives a company may have undertaken. Again, we do not include this in the total community contributions figure because of its obvious commercial benefit to the company concerned.

Entry layout

The layout used for the entries in this guide is described in the breakdown of the 'Fictitious Company' entry on pages xxvi and xxvii. We hope that this will enable users to access the information they require on the various types of support that each company may offer more readily.

Geographical and activity indexes

Most companies state that there must be a link for any appeal to be considered – the most obvious of these being geographical, business activity or employee involvement. To help you prepare a preliminary list of companies to look at further (not to immediately write to!), we have included a geographical listing of head offices (page 385) and company activity listing (page 380). While the head office index is geographically biased towards London, it provides a useful starting point.

Comprehensive search facilities are available at the subscription-based website: www.companygiving.org.uk, which also lists the directors, brands and subsidiaries of each company.

Company listings

Our research probably accounts for 80–90% of all giving by companies. However, there are companies that, by virtue of membership of one or more specific organisations, have declared an interest in supporting the community. We have therefore listed all current corporate members of Arts & Business, Business in the Community, London Benchmarking Group and Scottish Business in the Community, even though the companies concerned do not necessarily have an entry in this guide.

We have also included details of ProHelp (formerly, the Professional Firms Group): potentially a very useful source of support for charities. ProHelp is made up of a group of professional practices (including surveyors, architects, accountants and solicitors), each of which has offered to provide their professional services free of charge (or at minimal cost) to voluntary and community groups in their locality. Rather than provide a list of ProHelp members, we have given the regional office contacts, as they are best able to provide up-to-date information on what is happening in their area and explain how you can access their services.

A brief explanation of each of these organisations is given at the start of the relevant section.

Company comparisons

The level of giving by companies in this guide varies greatly (from around £20,000 to over £75 million). Perhaps because of this, we tend to equate 'big giver' with 'most generous', but this may not actually be the case. While very large companies may be applauded for giving say £4 million in donations, smaller companies giving a few hundred thousand pounds, may actually be contributing a far greater proportion of their profits to charity.

To give an example, although GlaxoSmithKline plc and Littlewoods Shop Direct Home Shopping Ltd appear towards opposite ends of the cash donations scale (£6.0 million compared with £600,000 in 2007/08), when this is expressed as a percentage of pre-tax profits their positions are reversed, giving 0.08% and 18%, respectively. While the usefulness of comparisons made in this way is a matter for dispute (profits can go down as well as up), it does show how, taken at face value, figures can be misleading as far as which company is making the greater gift to the community.

Corporate social responsibility

Corporate social responsibility (CSR) continues to be the focus of much debate. Some people simply don't like the concept, believing that to put it into effect will have damaging consequences for business. Others dislike the term, which they see as confusing and limited in scope, excluding other important factors beyond the social (hence the increasing use of the wider reaching 'corporate responsibility').

Our research deals with one aspect of CSR which, broadly speaking, is the philanthropic. However, usage of the term will no doubt continue to develop until it either establishes itself with a generally accepted meaning or is replaced by a newer form of words.

Nevertheless, our concern is not so much with the label, but whether there is any substance to back it up. Examples abound of company annual reports that glibly trot out statements of ethical intent or concern for the local community. More often than not, however, such statements fail to be substantiated with examples. For a number of companies the right to count themselves amongst established good corporate citizens appears to have been earned not through positive community action, but by signing up to any one of a number of self-congratulatory CSR membership bodies. In fact, there are so many standards and institutions that companies can adopt or join in order to present themselves as socially responsible that there is a danger of these standards and institutions' credibility being undermined.

Measuring corporate support

The methods we use to gather information on companies' charitable support are relatively straightforward. Basic financial details and the level of cash donations for a particular year are obtained from published annual reports or information lodged at Companies House. For other support in addition to cash donations (gifts in kind, employee volunteering and so on) and the specifics of a company's charitable support policy, we use a questionnaire and/or speak to the relevant person. (With the larger companies such information is increasingly to be found on their websites, sometimes at great length.)

The inclusion of policy details within a company entry is a very important aspect of our work as it provides fundraisers with the information necessary to make an informed decision about which companies to target. As ever, we do not sanction the scatter-gun approach, believing this to be not particularly successful, a waste of time for the parties concerned and potentially damaging to other, more qualified applicants.

Our ability to provide this service is, of course, reliant to a large extent on the cooperation of the companies whose details we intend to publish. In researching this edition we experienced a questionnaire return rate of around 22%, which, although the highest for a couple editions, did not always provide the depth of information requested (see comments made in the 'Facts & figures' chapter).

The main differences between the Directory of Social Change (DSC) and organisations such as the London Benchmarking Group (LBG) and Business in the Community (BitC) when it comes down to publishing figures on companies' support for voluntary and community groups is with regard to the inclusion, or not, of management cost figures as part of total community contributions.

Notwithstanding this, and primarily through the efforts of the LBG, which was established in 1995 and now consists of over a hundred members, some agreement has been reached concerning what actually constitutes Corporate Community Involvement (CCI) and how its value should be measured.

Of these two relatively high profile organisations, only the LBG appears to be willing to ask the difficult questions of businesses. The continual monitoring and fine tuning of its measurement techniques and its push to standardise the way in which companies calculate total community contributions is enabling us to present a more accurate and comprehensive picture of corporate support.

Business in the Community on the other hand has chosen to drop its long-standing PerCent Club standard (which sought to encourage companies to give at least 1% of pre-tax profits in support of charitable/community initiatives) and no longer makes public any figures for individual companies. Its recently introduced 'CommunityMark' provides companies with a self-assessment method of benchmarking their community investment, with the process being complemented by 'additional feedback from community partners and relevant employee volunteers, selected by the company'. Twenty-one businesses have apparently met this new national standard, investing £600 million in a range of community projects in the last year. Cross-checking of what appears to be a highly inflated figure is not possible as, **'Companies are not required to publicly benchmark'** (BitC's emphasis); i.e. to make the information openly available.

People may accuse DSC of still living in the dark ages of so-called 'cheque-book' philanthropy when, according to IBM's Celia Moore, 'It was a contest of who was giving the most' (quoted in *The Value of Giving*, published by the Ethical Corporation, September 2008). Now, as she goes on to state, 'It's about the effectiveness of what you do', with larger companies, particularly, looking at the creation of long-term partnerships and the leverage of additional resources from elsewhere.

While DSC acknowledges the benefits of such partnerships, only a relatively small number of voluntary sector organisations appear to reap the rewards. For those without the necessary matching profile or fundraising resources, our research provides straightforward evidence of the level of corporate community support and points the way for small- and medium-sized organisations to make informed decisions about which companies to approach. Conversely, in creating the CommunityMark to meet the demands of business and for a more holistic means of measuring what companies do in the community, BitC appears happy to quote an overall investment figure and yet is unwilling to show how this was arrived at. This lack

of transparency echoes that which is shown by numerous companies in this guide and does not assist those seeking funding.

Evidence drawn from research for the Ethical Corporation report mentioned earlier suggests that many companies are in fact wary of talking publicly about their community investment activity. DSC, however, has always maintained that it is in the public and the sector's interest to know about individual company policy so that a clearer picture may be made of what support is available, where and for what purposes.

In line with this and our policy principles (particularly 'Responsible Giving and Regulation'), DSC embarked in 2008 on two projects. One which sought to clarify the obstacles presented to applicants by the lack of access to the terms and conditions that govern grant funding and the other to map the geographical distribution of funding in the UK from trusts and foundations, companies and government departments. Although there is insufficient space here to go into any great detail, certain issues have become clear from our initial findings.

For example, the lack of access to terms and conditions at the point of application can have a number of negative consequences for voluntary sector organisations. These include: an inability to make an informed decision about whether to apply; the possibility of having to negotiate aspects of the terms and conditions from a position of weakness; having to choose to decline an offer having invested time and effort in applying; and difficulty in subjecting terms and conditions to public scrutiny and challenge.

The full findings of our research into this area will be presented as a report later in the year.

The results of our geographical mapping of funding in the UK were published in November 2008 as *The Funders' Almanac* – the first step in a long-term project. Our aim is to build a comprehensive picture of funding in the voluntary sector that provides vital intelligence to funders and policy makers across the board.

As part of this, we want funders to understand the wider environment in which they and the recipients of their funding operate and be able to respond effectively to change. We believe that funders' objectives and agendas, including those of companies, should be set by the needs of the ends users, not the other way around.

Trends in corporate support

With Britain facing arguably its worst economic downturn in 60 years, it may be more useful to try to look at what might be, rather than what has been with regard to trends in corporate support. However, with the bailing out of some of the UK's largest givers by the British government, e.g. HBOS plc, Northern Rock plc and Royal Bank of Scotland plc, the loss of three companies to administrators between the completion of our research in December 2008 and writing this introduction in January 2009, and the general economic uncertainty that exists, the task is not easy.

In 2008, some commentators expressed their concern that companies no longer saw community investment as a priority as they focused on the bigger issue of long-term sustainability. The recent SEE (Social, Environmental and Ethical) Potential report, 'CSR – Pragmatism or Tokenism', for example, noted that 79% of respondents thought business should be tackling environmental issues in the future, compared to the 59% in favour of tackling social issues.

Somewhere along the line community investment appears to have been marginalised and yet, as Jon Lloyd, a consultant at Corporate Citizenship has said, 'The fact is that well managed strategic community investment can be one of the sharpest tools in the CSR toolbox'. David Grayson, Director of the Doughty Centre for Corporate Responsibility at Cranfield University, agrees with this view. In Salter Baxter's 2008 Directions Report – 'Sustainability Gets Tough', he expresses the view that the present hard times will further sharpen the contrast between those companies committed to investing in the community and those which have merely paid lip service to the idea.

Socially responsible businesses are not going to abandon their hard won reputations because of the economic downturn. Indeed, he sees the downturn as an impetus to speed up innovation and find more cost-effective ways of advancing their commitment to being responsible businesses. To quote: 'Doing good in the good times takes vision. Sticking with it in the tough times takes vision and determination'.

For example, FT.com reported on 6 January 2009 that, in contrast to most retailers who were cutting back on capital expenditure, the Co-operative Group planned to spend £2 billion on its food business in the coming year. Results for the three weeks to 3 January showed sales were up by 5.2%, something which chief executive Peter Marks believes is partly down to the company's reputation as an ethical business.

In conclusion, it seems that for every pessimistic view about the effect of the current economic climate on community investment, there is an optimistic one. We prefer to look, therefore, towards the vision and determination that many companies are demonstrating. We hope that their numbers are sufficient to offset any shortfall created by the less committed ones and that, as a result of these difficult times, we see an even stronger base of responsible companies emerging in the future.

Warning!

We are told that companies continue to receive many unsolicited or inappropriate appeals for support. While many bring this upon themselves due to a lack of clear guidelines for potential applicants, this should not be seen as an excuse to conduct blanket mailings.

One of the findings of the report 'An Evaluation of Corporate Community Investment in the UK' published by the Charities Aid Foundation, was that companies support a relatively narrow set of causes and issues and do not tend to change this chosen set over time. This coupled with a survey which found that the biggest frustration charities face in attempting to work with companies is limited access to decision makers, means it is vitally important to do your research thoroughly.

Further information on how to approach businesses for support successfully is given in the 'Applying to companies' section. In general, however, before approaching any company in this guide its entry should be read carefully. As we have stated previously, unless there is a clear link with a company or your project is clearly within its defined areas of support, you should *not* be applying.

We would also recommend that you download a copy of 'Charities Working with Business', published by the Institute of Fundraising. This gives a good overview of the issues involved in undertaking a relationship with a company and is available at: www.institute-of-fundraising.org.uk

Acknowledgements

We would like to thank all the companies that have helped to compile this guide. Each was sent a questionnaire and a draft entry, following the return of which corrections were noted and incorporated. Failing any cooperation in this respect, information was gathered from sources in the public domain. Notwithstanding this, the text and any mistakes within it, remain ours rather than theirs.

And finally ...

If you have any comments about the guide, positive or negative, please get in touch with us at the Research Department of the Directory of Social Change, Federation House, Hope Street, Liverpool L1 9BW; Tel: 0151 708 0136; fax: 0151 708 0139; email: research@dsc.org.uk

'Charity of the Year' and Smaller Organisations

Del Redvers

This article was included in the last edition of the guide; subsequently Business Community Connections has ceased operating. Nevertheless, we think the content of the article will still be of interest and use to certain readers.

Charity of the Year is a label increasingly applied to all manner of partnerships, but what does it really mean? Business Community Connections (BCConnections) researched how different charities and businesses use the Charity of the Year concept and in doing so identified several critical factors for success.

There are many forms of Charity of the Year partnership but with certain common themes. Most obviously and significantly they are time limited relationships although certainly not always one year in duration. The most widespread understanding of the term is a partnership in which the staff from a business undertake a range of activities to raise money for the identified charity. At the end of the year businesses often feel the need to replace the charity they support in order to prevent fundraising fatigue, and to ensure wider appeal to staff and customers as no one charity will be relevant to all stakeholders. This also gives the business the opportunity to support another charity.

Increasingly, however, other elements are added to the staff fundraising concept, such as cash donations, employee volunteering or other in-kind donations, sponsorship, cause related marketing or lobbying and campaigning. Sometimes these partnerships involve very little or no staff fundraising at all. Many businesses involved in these other types of Charity of the Year relationship would not be able to support a staff fundraising partnership, perhaps because they have smaller numbers of higher paid staff with less free time. Similarly, it makes sense for companies with relevant goods or services to donate them in-kind to the charity as part of their contribution. The term Charity of the Year is used to brand a relationship, because although it can be misleading, it is a widely understood and accepted term.

For smaller organisations

Traditionally Charity of the Year relationships have been the preserve of large charities, frequently those able to offer national exposure to large corporate partners. There is, however, evidence to suggest a growing trend in the number of smaller charities seeking and successfully establishing Charity of the Year partnerships. The BCConnections research shows no reason why Charity of the Year should be out of bounds to small or medium sized charities and by the same token to Small and Medium Enterprises (SMEs). There are however a number of risks which can offset the many benefits available to both charities and businesses and which need to be weighed very carefully irrespective of the size of the organisation.

The advantages ...

The research suggests that in general Charity of the Year partnerships do work for both partners. On the whole charities tend to put a financial value on the relationship of 6 or 7 times the cost of establishing and managing the partnership. Whilst larger charities frequently net income in excess of £100,000 through these relationships, smaller charities also tend to consider them worthwhile activities even if they are very unlikely to achieve a 6 figure financial contribution. A Charity of the Year partnership can ...

1. Provide a reasonably predictable and often large income stream over a fixed period of time.
2. Provide an excellent opportunity to significantly increase the profile and reputation of the charity.
3. Create a track record of working with the corporate sector.
4. Lever support from other businesses and customers.
5. Increase fundraising activity from existing supporters.
6. Educate the workforce and customers of the business about the charity or its cause.
7. Offer access to employees as a new market of potential supporters.

8. Last longer than 1 year. There is a growing trend towards the "Charity of 2 or 3 years" giving the security of a longer-term income stream.
9. Generate unrestricted income, although there is a developing trend towards restricted funds in these relationships.
10. Increase the morale at the charity, especially amongst the fundraising team.

And Pitfalls ...

There are many issues for a charity to consider before deciding whether or not to pursue a Charity of the Year relationship.

These partnerships can be resource intensive to manage, most significantly in terms of staff time. The cost benefit analysis section of the BCConnections research reveals that managing a small Charity of the Year partnership often takes at least 10% of one person's time. A large partnership can occupy from 1 to 3 employees on a full time basis. There may also be costs associated with legal agreements for joint promotions, licencing and sponsorship arrangements.

Pitching for major Charity of the Year partnerships can be a significant undertaking in itself, requiring the investment of resources at an early stage, with no promise of a return. Once a partnership is agreed there is often a lengthy planning period before it is launched. Consequently, there exists a time lag between investing resources to develop the partnership and receiving the support. This can create a cashflow problem, particularly for smaller charities but also where a charity is expected to cover early costs such as producing badges and promotional material. Despite what can amount to considerable set up costs, these partnerships will always be time limited and therefore, for most charities, cannot be considered a sustainable source of income.

Frequently, businesses use voting schemes to engage staff in selecting the Charity of the Year. This often results in the exclusion of many types of charities from the selection process as in an unrestricted ballot, staff have a tendency to vote for charities such as children, cancer and other health related charities with poignant issues.

There is always an element of risk on both sides in any corporate community relationship as a link is forged between the reputations of the two partners. With Charity of the Year this link is likely to be well publicised and consequently the relationship can backfire if it is considered to be unethical.

Getting a Charity of the Year partnership

If your organisation is seeking a Charity of the Year partnership, there are some things you should bear in mind ...

1. Be strategic in your approach. Focus on the good fit between your charity and your target companies. Start building relationships with these businesses and try to grow the company contacts you already have. Think ahead and plan which business may adopt you next year or the year after that.
2. Decide on the cost benefit ratio you are prepared to accept. This is usually not just a financial exercise as it may involve judgements about intangible benefits and the potential worth of a partnership with the company in the longer term.
3. Be prepared to walk away. One of the most important messages to come out of the research is that charities need to assess at an early stage the potential value of the partnership, and then negotiate and decide whether or not it is worthwhile pursuing.
4. Consider approaching new businesses not previously involved in Charity of the Year partnerships.
5. Consider the benefits and drawbacks of a Charity of the Year partnership from the business point of view. Try to gain an understanding of why your target business might want a Charity of the Year partnership and more specifically with your organisation. This can help you to value your charity's worth and feel more confident about negotiating with the business.
6. If possible seek advice from a previous Charity of the Year of your target business. This should increase your understanding of the company, how they work and what they may want out of the partnership. This should be supplemented by in-depth research on the company from published sources.
7. Ask the business for a meeting at an early stage. This will give you more guidance about what they want from the partnership, before you invest significant resources. It will also help start to develop a relationship.
8. Be flexible about including other types of involvement for the partnership, apart from staff fundraising.
9. Consider at the outset how you could monitor the impact of your proposed Charity of the Year partnership on the wider community.

The Pitch

When pitching for a Charity of the Year partnership, a key consideration is how the charity will be selected. If it is a management decision, there needs to be a focus on benefits to the business whilst for a staff ballot the proposal should be more emotive. Where possible engage the beneficiaries of the charity in the process.

Proposals should be tailored specifically to the business you are approaching and stick to any brief given. Should the pitch fail, always ask for feedback and if appropriate a contribution; it is worth asking if the business can compensate you in any way for the time and resources invested. However, always be mindful of possible future relationships with that business.

For smaller Charity of the Year partnerships there is often no formal pitch process. Businesses that already engage in small scale Charity of the Year partnerships are more likely to use existing contacts or staff recommendations to identify future partners. Smaller businesses that have never had a Charity of the Year may need some guidance from the charity to help them appreciate the potential of the relationship.

Setting up the Partnership

Planning

The importance of development time prior to publicising the partnership cannot be underestimated. In the BCConnections research over a quarter of the organisations did not plan the partnerships. Many larger businesses now select their Charity of the Year 6 months to 1 year before the publicised partnership year begins. For smaller partnerships however, 1 or 2 months can provide ample planning time.

Agreement

A written agreement outlining the parameters of the relationships (objectives, targets, timeframes and budgets) plays an important role in managing the expectations of your partner. Clearly allocate responsibility for tasks and costs.

Seek to maximise the mutual benefit of the partnership. The greater the benefit for your business partner, the more seriously they will take the relationship and the greater the likelihood they will invest in Charity of the Year partnerships in the future.

Develop a plan of events, and a process for regular communication and review. Use the expertise of charity fundraisers to generate ideas for activities. Most charities find it easier to have a phased programme of fundraising events rather than doing everything at once.

Financial Return

Consider whether there should be a minimum guaranteed return to the charity from the partnership. Some charities recommended including minimum guarantees in any documentation to protect against risk such as a minimum amount of cash to be raised. In addition agree what percentage of money raised will be restricted. Some charities will ask for a percentage of funding to be unrestricted to cover the costs of running the partnership. Also establish the timings of payments to the charity throughout the year and consider the impact on cashflow. Whilst a single large cheque handed over at the end of the year may look impressive, it is often not a practical option, particularly for smaller charities.

Communications

Establish who will be responsible for the overall publicity of the partnership. If a logo is to be designed for the new partnership who will pay for it? Ensure that use of logos is agreed in advance.

There is also the issue of internal communication with the company's employees. Several charities have commented that it takes time to motivate and inspire staff to get involved in a programme of fundraising or other activities and the timetable should allow for this. The appointment of charity champions amongst the staff of the business can help to co-ordinate activity and provides a communication channel, particularly for multi-site operations.

Thinking Ahead

Discuss the sustainability of the partnership and develop an exit strategy early on in the relationship. During review meetings consider whether it is beneficial to both partners to keep the relationship going beyond the year. Even if the charity is not designated Charity of the Year going forward, it may be possible to maintain and develop specific elements of the relationship, such as relationships with suppliers and payroll giving.

Measuring and Monitoring

There has been an increasing emphasis on measuring the impact and benefits of Charity of the Year partnerships as with all other aspects of corporate community involvement. Like other types of relationship, there need to be mechanisms for measuring the social impact, benefits to the business and benefits to the charity. Significantly, Charity of the Year partnerships require careful measurement of the relationship itself as it is often more involved than other types of corporate community partnership.

Critically both parties need to know if there was a positive benefit compared to the cost of their involvement. Effective measurement of the partnership enables both parties to decide whether to undertake similar ventures in the future and identifies areas for improvement. Knowing what you want to measure at the outset allows for the correct accounting procedures to be put in place. For instance, without prior planning it may be easy for a company to breakdown staff fundraising by office or team but not by individual activities. This would make it impossible to measure the effectiveness of each activity.

The following represent some of the measures used by the businesses and charities we interviewed during the course of the research to assess the success of the partnership.

- Targets met or exceeded in planning and preparation.
- Financial target met or exceeded.
- % of company branches involved.
- Outcome of the partnership for charity beneficiaries; e.g. number of individuals helped as a result, or number of pieces of equipment purchased, amount of research time enabled etc.
- Positive PR; e.g. the number of articles/column cms or amount of television time.
- Number of contacts the charity has developed.
- Staff and customer surveys; e.g. awareness and perceptions of business and charity.
- Feel good factor; e.g. for business – number of letters, comments received in chat room etc.
- Number of charity champions that come forward in the business.

Conclusions

Charity of the Year relationships are a popular and highly visible way for charities and businesses to work together for mutual benefit and to target the social impact of corporate support for the voluntary sector. Whilst there are no hard and fast rules about establishing and managing Charity of the Year partnerships, a considered and strategic approach will help to maximise the many advantages offered by this type of relationship whilst minimising the risk.

Smaller charities should be encouraged to consider how they can adapt the models developed by larger organisations. Although there is definitely the opportunity for charities of all sizes to benefit from Charity of the Year relationships, they are not necessarily appropriate for all organisations and represent just one of several types of relationship that can form between the voluntary and corporate sectors.

The Charity of the Year research conducted by BCConnections is available in full with the cost-benefit analysis template and case studies at www.bcconnections.org.uk. The BCConnections website also has information to help charities or community organisations considering any form of partnership working with the corporate sector.

BCConnections would like to gratefully acknowledge the help of all the charities and businesses that participated in the Charity of the Year research.

Del Redvers is the Joint Chief Executive at Business Community Connections.

How much do companies give?

Given that there is a statutory obligation for companies to declare their charitable donations where the total exceeds £200 in any one year, getting a figure is relatively easy. You just ask a company for a copy of its annual report or download it from the company website and look (generally speaking) in the Directors' Report section. The figure for community contributions, however, is more difficult to obtain and less precisely calculated, if at all. While the work of the London Benchmarking Group (LBG) has had success in addressing this by providing clear guidelines for and assessing the various elements that make up in kind support, this hasn't guaranteed that figures for individual companies reach the public domain.

Although many companies' level of donations remains fairly constant year on year, others fluctuate significantly, and for no apparent reason, which can make predicting trends in company giving difficult. Furthermore, in trying to provide an accurate picture of the level of company support *in the UK*, we have been hindered by the unwillingness of a significant number of the biggest givers to provide UK-specific figures.

In 2008, around 107 companies, or just below 22% of those initially contacted, replied to our questionnaire requesting details of their UK community support. Based on these returns and further research, the total cash donations made in 2007/08 by the 490 companies in this guide amounted to £500 million, compared to £367 million in 2005/06. With a further £308 million (2005/06: £367 million) declared for in kind support, this gives a total community contributions figure of £808 million compared to £734 million in 2005/06. Surprisingly, these figures show that the level of cash donations has risen by over 36%, compared to a 26% rise in the last edition, while the in-kind portion has actually fallen by 16% following a 26% increase in 2005/06.

We cannot say categorically, however, that these figures are indicative of a move by companies towards giving the greater portion of their support via cash donations. This is primarily due to two factors.

i) The inclusion of a number of 'new' companies with exceptional or high levels of giving, e.g. HESCO Bastion (£11.5 million) and RAB Capital (£5.3 million), the cash donations of a group of ten 'new' companies totaling £27 million and the almost doubling of Barclays' donations to over £30 million.

ii) The lack of information regarding the full extent of in kind support in the UK and its value. As mentioned earlier, not only is this not generally available, but in some instances there is a deliberate decision not to release details even when specifically asked for.

Nevertheless, based solely on the returns received and information in the public domain, we see for the second edition running that, contrary to the trend earlier in the millennium, the percentage rise in cash donations (and this year in monetary terms too) is outstripping that of in kind support. Whether this will continue to be the case in 2009, given the current economic downturn, remains to be seen.

In truth, the figures quoted above are probably a little short of what is actually given in total, but even so, it may be useful to try and put this into perspective. Polls over a number of years have shown that in general the public tends to overestimate the level of support received by the voluntary sector from big business (around one-quarter of total income in one case). In fact, according to calculations by organisations such as NCVO and the Charities Aid Foundation, just 4–5% is contributed by companies. Out of a total voluntary sector income of £31 billion in 2005/06, this equates to around £1.2 billion, which is somewhat closer to our researched figure than certain other published estimates.

Community contributions
Total amount given

Previous research has shown that around 99% of the total community contributions made by the companies listed in past guides could be accounted for by the top 400. In this edition that number has dropped dramatically, with the top 300 now accounting for 99% (£799 million), the top 50 companies for 79% (£638 million) and the 'Top 25' (see Table 1) 37% (£298 million) of total

<table>
<tr><td colspan="3">*Table 1*</td></tr>
</table>

Top 25 by UK community contribution

2007/08

(1)	Barclays PLC	£38.9 million
(2)	Lloyds TSB Group plc*	£37.5 million
(3)	HBOS plc	£18.6 million
(4)	HSBC Holdings plc*	£18.4 million
(5)	Marks and Spencer Group plc	£15.0 million
(6)	Northern Rock plc*	£14.3 million
(7)	Ecclesiastical Insurance Group plc*	£14.1 million
(8)	Shell*	£13.0 million
(9)	Fidelity Investment Management Limited*	£11.8 million
(10)	HESCO Bastion Limited*	£11.5 million
(11)	Diageo plc*	£10.7 million
(=12)	British Nuclear Fuels plc*	£10.0 million
(=12)	The Co-operative Group plc	£10.0 million
(14)	J Sainsbury plc	£7.6 million
(15)	ITV plc	£7.0 million
(16)	PricewaterhouseCoopers LLP	£6.8 million
(17)	Vodafone Group plc*	£6.7 million
(18)	Unilever UK	£6.3 million
(19)	Deloitte	£6.1 million
(=20)	British Sky Broadcasting Group plc	£6.0 million
(=20)	GlaxoSmithKline plc*	£6.0 million
(=22)	BUPA Limited*	£5.7 million
(=22)	KPMG	£5.7 million
(24)	Man Group plc*	£5.5 million
(25)	RAB Capital plc*	£5.3 million

Note: 2007/08 community contribution figures were unavailable for those companies marked with an asterisk. However, their level of UK charitable donations alone merits inclusion.

contributions. The minimum figure required to gain entry to this select group of 25 rose to £5.3 million (up from £4.4 million in the last edition), although as indicated below this could have been even higher.

As mentioned earlier, obtaining a figure for total community contributions (as opposed to purely cash donations) can be difficult, especially as we make the 'Top 25' UK-specific. In order to achieve the latter, we had to omit 13 of the largest givers as they chose to provide worldwide contribution figures only.

Those companies omitted from 'Table 1' contributed £288 million, or nearly 36% of the total in the guide and included the likes of Tesco, Royal Bank of Scotland, BT Group, Cadbury and National Grid. We could have made an estimate based, for example, on the figures provided by Barclays plc which gave around 75% of its total support in the UK. Why, however, should there be the need to do this and who is to say it would be an accurate reflection of reality in any case? It would be far better for this information to be provided openly by all companies in the first place.

It appears then, for the present at least, that the effect of the Companies Act 2006 on reporting levels is yet to be seen. (The Act aimed to strengthen the

requirements in the legislation on social and environmental reporting so that the 1,300 companies quoted on the UK stock market must report on environmental matters, employees, social and community issues and risks down company supply chains where they are necessary to understanding the company's business.)

Changes in giving

Despite previous indications that businesses were more accurately calculating their in kind support, our latest findings rather turn that on its head (although this is most probably due to figures not being reported rather than not being calculated). Nevertheless, some observations can be made.

For the first time in the history of the guide Barclays plc heads our top 25 following a 10% increase in its community contributions in the UK (up from £35.3 million in 2005/06). Companies in the table that have increased their total contributions substantially include Ecclesiastical Insurance Group plc (7) – up from £5.4 million to £14.1 million, and Marks and Spencer Group plc (5) – up from £9.3 million to £15 million.

Six companies are new to the 'Top 25', including PricewaterhouseCoopers LLP (16) and Deloitte (19),

Table 2

Top 25 by UK charitable donation

2007/08

(1)	Lloyds TSB Group plc	£37.5 million
(2)	Barclays plc	£30.4 million
(3)	HSBC Holdings plc	£18.4 million
(4)	Northern Rock plc	£14.3 million
(5)	Ecclesiastical Insurance Group plc	£14.1 million
(6)	Shell	£13.0 million
(7)	HBOS plc	£12.7 million
(8)	Fidelity Investment Management Ltd	£11.8 million
(9)	HESCO Bastion Ltd	£11.5 million
(10)	Diageo plc	£10.7 million
(11)	British Nuclear Fuels plc	£10.0 million
(12)	The Co-operative Group plc	£8.3 million
(13)	Vodafone Group plc	£6.7 million
(14)	GlaxoSmithKline plc	£6.0 million
(15)	BUPA Ltd	£5.7 million
(16)	Man Group plc	£5.5 million
(17)	Marks and Spencer Group plc	£5.4 million
(18)	RAB Capital plc	£5.3 million
(19)	British Sky Broadcasting Group plc	£5.2 million
(20)	Deutsche Bank	£4.8 million
(21)	Centrica plc	£4.1 million
(=22)	John Lewis Partnership plc	£2.8 million
(=22)	Apax Partners LLP	£2.8 million
(24)	EDF Energy plc	£2.7 million
(25)	Alliance Boots	£2.6 million

Note: These 2007/08 figures are for statutorily declared UK charitable donations only. This can understate total community contributions, particularly for the largest companies.

both of which provide professional services on a pro bono basis. Of particular note, however, is HESCO Bastion plc (10) which made an exceptional donation of £10 million to the Leeds Community Foundation to establish a fund and Man Group plc (24) which donated £5.5 million. In 2008/9, the latter will contribute around £16 million to charities, the majority of which will be donated through the Man Group plc Charitable Trust.

Contributions as a percentage of profit

As a percentage of pre-tax profits, community contributions for the top 300 stood at 0.38%. This figure is down from 0.49% in the last edition and may be seen as the effect of the 16% drop in in-kind support.

Though now defunct, the former PerCent Club standard of giving 1% of pre-tax profits to good causes was reached by 93 companies; up from 78 in the last edition.

Charitable donations
Total amount given

Of the £500 million given in cash by the companies in the guide the top, 300 account for over 98% of the total (£492 million), the top 50 for nearly 77% (£384 million) and the 'Top 25' (see Table 2) for over 50% (£252 million). The minimum figure required to gain entry to this select group of 25 remained at the same level as for the last edition – £2.6 million.

However, given that this table is also UK-specific, the same criteria for inclusion applied as that for Table 1. The nine companies omitted gave a total of £96 million in cash donations, or just over 19% of the total and included Royal Bank of Scotland, Tesco, WPP Group and the Prudential.

Changes in giving

Lloyds TSB Group plc regained the top spot following a £5.8 million rise in its donations, although this may not have been the case had the Royal Bank of Scotland supplied UK figures.

Seven new companies are listed in the 'Top 25' including RAB Capital plc (18), Apax Partners LLP

(=22) and EDF Energy plc (24). In addition, some familiar names have reentered after an absence, e.g. BUPA Ltd (15) and Alliance Boots (25).

Donations as a percentage of profit

As a percentage of pre-tax profits, cash donations for the top 300 stood at 0.24%. Slightly down on the 0.25% of the last edition, the indication being that despite the significant leap in cash donations, profits have increased at a greater rate.

The potential for company giving

We believe companies have the capacity, if not the will, to put a whole lot more back into society. Normally, when asked what the total contributions figure is for all companies in the UK (on top of that given by those in the guide), we estimate there to be around a further £100 million available. (This would come from the numerous small- or medium-sized enterprises whose level of giving is too low to be included, and from professional firms that are not obliged to publish such information.)

Given the current economic climate as we enter 2009 the likelihood is that some companies will choose to cut back on their community investment (thus raising questions about their commitment in the first place), while for others it will remain static or increase at a slower rate than has been the case. However, we do not necessarily think it will be all doom and gloom as some commentators would have us believe.

According to an article in *The Times* (1 November 2008), Ipsos MORI recently looked at the financial performance of 33 FTSE companies that have measured and managed their corporate responsibility through Business in the Community's Corporate Responsibility Index. Overall, these companies were able to show increased shareholder return of between 3.3% and 7.7% throughout 2002 to 2007 when compared to the FTSE 350.

The writer concluded that: 'Responsible business is plainly good business'. Whether this maxim will hold during the coming year is unknown, but we sincerely hope it does.

This section gives basic information on identifying potential companies to approach, how to establish contact with them and how to put together a proposal for them to consider.

Corporate social responsibility

Corporate social responsibility (CSR) is a much bandied about phrase which seeks to define what an increasing number of people and groups believe the wider role of business in society should be. This guide deals with one aspect of CSR which, broadly speaking, is the philanthropic. The meaning of this term can also include respect for human rights and the environment, for example. Despite the increasing interest in the issue of CSR (as witnessed by the number of articles, journals and conferences appearing around the topic), it should be remembered that company giving is way below that of the general public and, to a lesser extent, charitable trusts. According to calculations by organisations such as NCVO and the Charities Aid Foundation, between 4 and 5% is contributed by companies. Out of a total voluntary sector income of £31 billion in 2005/06, this equates to just £1.2 billion. Nevertheless, ethical issues aside, companies remain an important target for both national and regional fundraisers.

To make an effective appeal to industry you must have a basic understanding of why firms give. This will enable you to put forward good reasons why they should support your work. Many companies, especially the larger, higher profile ones, receive hundreds if not thousands of requests for support from charities, voluntary sector organisations and local community groups each year. For your appeal to be successful it needs to be more than a general plea to 'put something back into the community'. You can help a company justify its charitable support by telling them not just why you want the money, but why giving you support should be of interest to them. You can also tell them about any benefits they will get in return for their money and about the impact their donation will have on your work. At the very least you should be able to demonstrate a clear link with the company through a geographical, product or employee contact or other relevant connection.

Some basic don'ts when applying to companies

✗ Don't write indiscriminate 'Dear Sir/Madam' circular letters to any company you come across.

✗ Don't use any guide you may have access to as a simple mailing list.

✗ Don't write to a company that specifically says it does not support your kind of work.

✗ Don't write to a company unless *at least one* of the following applies:

▷ The company has a declared policy indicating a specific interest in your group's area of work.

▷ The company operates in the same locality as your group and a clear product link exists between your needs and its supplies.

▷ You have a strong personal link with a senior company officer, or a member of staff is actively involved in your work.

▷ There is some good reason to write to that particular company. The fact that the company makes a profit and your group needs money is not a sufficiently strong link.

Why companies give

Most companies give out of *enlightened self-interest* rather than for pure altruistic or philanthropic reasons, and see their giving in terms of 'community involvement' or 'community investment'. The main reasons why companies give are:

▷ To *create goodwill*. Companies like to be seen as good citizens in the communities in which they operate and as a caring company by society at large.

▷ To *be associated with causes that relate to their business*. Mining or extraction companies often like to support environmental projects, for example.

▷ To *build good relations with employees*. Support for employee volunteering is a growing area of company giving, creating a 'feel good' factor among employees and a sense of loyalty to their socially responsible employer. Increasingly, some preference is given to those charities for which staff are raising money or for which staff members are doing volunteer work. Funds raised may be matched (usually up to a set limit) and/or employees given work time off in which to volunteer.

Because they are asked or *it is expected of them.* They also don't want to be seen as mean in relation to other rival companies in their particular business sector. They are concerned that the quantity and quality of their giving is appropriate to their status as a company.

Because the *chair/senior directors are interested in a particular cause* (and perhaps support it personally). This is quite often the case with smaller companies where, as a result, it can be difficult to get a donation for causes outside of this criterion. Unless you know a friend of the managing director to plead your case, success is unlikely.

Because *they have always given.* Some companies never review their donation policy. They see their donations more as an annual subscription to a list of charities they wish to support each year. Your aim should be to get your charity's name on to such a list, where it exists.

It is worth pointing out that a certain amount of chaos exists in company giving. Outside the largest givers, few companies have any real policy for their charitable giving. Mostly they cover a wide range of causes, or attempt to deal with each appeal on its merits. For privately-owned or family-controlled companies their giving is often little different from personal giving. For public companies, where it is the shareholders' funds that are being given away, there is pressure to dress up what they are doing, perhaps by claiming to give according to some well-defined criteria.

However, some companies do have clear policies. **Where such policies are printed, please respect them.** Dealing with a mass of clearly inappropriate applications is the single biggest headache in corporate giving and has caused some companies to consider winding-up their charitable support programme altogether. Don't jeopardize someone else's chance of success by your own indiscriminate applications.

What companies give

Many charities are unrealistic about what they might obtain from companies. To use an oft-quoted phrase, 'the business of business is business'. In other words, corporate charitable support is often only a sideline, accounting for around 4% of the voluntary sector's income.

However, much company support lies outside cash donations. In fact, for many of the larger donors cash donations are a decreasing percentage of their total giving. For smaller givers, however, cash will continue to remain their most common form of support for charities. Here, then, are a variety of ways in which companies can support charities:

Support in kind, which includes giving company products or surplus office equipment; providing use of company facilities, including meeting rooms, printing or design facilities, help with mailings

'Secondment' of a member of staff to work with the charity, where a member of the company's staff helps on an agreed basis while remaining employed (and paid) by the company

Providing expertise and advise, whether by contributing a senior member of staff to the charity's management board, or over the telephone on a one-off basis

Encouraging employees to volunteer, undertake fundraising drives, or support a payroll giving scheme

Sponsorship of an event, activity or award scheme

Sponsorship of promotional or educational activities. **Note:** Some companies handle sponsorship through their community affairs department, while others do so through the marketing department. In smaller firms donations and sponsorship are usually handled by the managing director.

Cause-related marketing, where, to encourage sales of a particular product, the company contributes a donation to a specified charity in return for each linked product sold. This is becoming an increasingly common form of support, but not usually to the benefit of smaller, less attractive charities.

Advertising in charity brochures, newsletters, annual reports and so on. Smaller companies are often prepared to give in this way, if asked. For larger companies, however, it is usually something they exclude as standard as the initial approach is often made by a third-party who would also receive a share of the donation.

The types of companies that give

Multinational companies – Most multinational companies have global giving programmes, generally tied to areas where they have or are developing business interests. Some multinational companies have an international structure for managing their giving, with budgets set for each area and a common policy regarding what they wish to support. With others, community investment remains at the discretion of local company management in the country concerned.

Geographically speaking, the further out from the centre (i.e. the company's headquarters) you are, the less you can expect to get. This can be broken down as follows: (i) most money is spent in the headquarters' town or region; (ii) most money is spent in the home country of the company; (iii) more money is spent in developed countries than developing ones.

Leading national companies – These will be supporting large national charities; have their own sponsorship schemes; make smaller donations to local charities in the area in which they are headquartered or have a major business presence. Numerous national companies will make grants through regional offices, while retail stores such as B&Q will use the local store manager to give advice on a local application. Such stores may also provide the manager with a small budget to spend at their discretion.

Larger local companies – In any city or region there will be large companies that are important to the local economy. They will often feel a responsibility to support voluntary action and community initiatives in those areas, and value the good publicity this provides.

There are also companies with a regional remit. The water, electricity and independent television companies all have a specific geographical area within which they operate, even if they are part of a multinational company.

Smaller local companies – There are a myriad of companies that make up the local business community. Referred to as small and medium enterprises (SME's), they are often overlooked in the rush to target the large companies on which good information is generally available. However, from manufacturers on trading estates to accountants and solicitors in the high street, the majority of SME's claim to be involved with their local community. Following a MORI poll which surveyed 200 managing directors of firms ranging in size from 20 to 1,000 employees, 16% said they are involved 'a great deal' with their local community and 45% said they are involved 'a fair amount'. Many of these companies are privately owned, so the best approach will often be through the managing director or senior partner.

Key factors in approaching companies
Research

Research is very important, not just into companies, but also into personal contacts. When planning an appeal, an important first step is to find which of the people associated with your charity have influence or know people who have. If you can find a link between one of your supporters and a particular company – use it.

▶ One of your trustees/members may be on the board of directors or have contacts there – it will prove useful for them to write or sign the appeal letter.

▶ One of your volunteers or supporters may be an employee of the company.

▶ Your clients/users (or their parents) may work for the company.

Alternatively, you might be able to tie your appeal in to a known personal interest of a director.

Getting in touch

Generally an appeal through a personal contact will work the best. But if you haven't got a contact and can see no way of developing one, then you will have to come up with another link.

As a first step you might contact the company to find out the following:

▶ who is responsible for dealing with charitable appeals

▶ their name and job title

▶ what information they can send regarding their company

▶ any procedure or timetable for submitting applications

▶ whether they might be interested in coming to see your organisation at work.

Visits are useful when discussing bigger donations with the larger companies, but are difficult to arrange for anything small.

Almost certainly your appeal will be in the form of a letter. Make this as personal as you can. Circular letters tend to end up in the bin. Make the letter short and to the point.

Be specific in your approach

Rather than sending out a circular mailing to 100 or 1,000 companies, you will be more successful if you select a few companies you believe will be particularly interested in your project, and target your application to them and their policy. (Many companies will not consider circular appeals as a point of policy.)

Find a good reason why you believe the company should support you and include this prominently in your letter. You may be able to relate what you are doing as a charity to companies that have some relevance to your work: for example, a children's charity can appeal to companies making children's products; a housing charity to construction companies, building societies, etc. Any relationship, however tenuous, creates a point of contact on which you can build a good case for obtaining the company's support. If there is no relationship, should you be approaching that company at all?

There may be occasions when a charity will not want to accept money from a company in a related industry. A health education charity may not want to accept money from a tobacco company or brewery or from the confectionery industry, or an environmental group may not wish to accept a donation from a nuclear power company. Such charities may feel that if they did so they would be seen to be compromised. Similarly, a local charity might not want money from a company that has made people in the area redundant. Each charity has to judge where it draws the line.

Be clear about why you need the money

You must be clear about the objectives of the work you are raising money for, particularly its timescale and how it relates to your overall programme of work. Try to think in project terms rather than seeking money to cover basic administration costs. This can be difficult, because most people spend most of their money on administration in one form or another, so you need to conjure up projects out of your current activities to present to potential donors. You can build a percentage of administration costs into the costs of a project. If you relate what you are doing to a specific timescale, this again makes what you are applying for appear more of a project than a contribution to your year-on-year core costs.

Be persistent

Do not underestimate the persistence factor. If you do not receive a donation in the first year, do not assume that the company will never support you. Go back a second and even a third time.

If you are going back, mention the fact that you have applied to the company previously, perhaps saying that you are now presenting something different which may be (you hope) of more interest.

If the company gives you reasons for refusing support, use these to help you put in more appropriate applications in the future. If the response is that the company does not give to your particular type of activity, then you know that it is absolutely no use in your going back. If the company said its funds were fully committed, you can try to find out when would be a better time to apply (although this might only have been a convenient excuse because the company did not want to give to you).

Note the response to your appeal and use any information you can glean to improve your chances the next time. People respect persistence, so it really is important to go back again and again.

Identifying which firms to approach

The firms to approach will depend on what sort of organisation you are. If you are a national organisation then an appeal to the country's leading companies is appropriate. Local groups should approach local firms and local branches of national companies that have a presence in their area. All organisations can approach companies in allied fields: for example, theatres can appeal to fabric companies.

You will find the names and other details of companies in a whole series of useful directories.

Sources of information

The Kompass Register of British Industry and Commerce (available in regional sections)
Key British Enterprises
The Waterlow Stock Exchange Year Book
Major Unquoted Companies

Individual company websites

To find key contacts in companies:

The Directory of Directors and *Who's Who* are useful for finding out more about company directors.
Corporate Register – updated quarterly – a guide to decision makers in UK Stockmarket companies.

The best sources of information on which companies exist in your area are:

▷ The local Chamber of Commerce, where most of the more prominent local companies will be members.

▷ *The Kompass Register* (available at main libraries), in which companies are organised regionally.

▷ The local council: the Rating Department might produce a list of major business ratepayers. The Economic Development section may have a list of major employers.

▷ The local newspaper(s), which will carry stories from time to time that mention the success or expansion of existing firms, or details of new ones planning to set up in the area

▷ The Confederation of British Industry regional office.

Companies you have existing contact with. This could include those companies that supply you with goods, your bank, solicitors and/or accountants. Emphasise your organisation's value as a good customer. Ask them if they can provide any useful contacts.

Don't forget, most of these local companies have no donations policy and give to projects that catch the fancy of the managing director or senior partner. Some may never have given anything before, and may not know it is possible to give charitable gifts tax-effectively (via Gift Aid, for example), so you may need to try and persuade them to give. Alternatively, it might be easier to approach these companies for in kind support in the first instance, and later on, once they have given something, ask them to make a cash donation.

Lastly, one big problem you may face involves the ownership of seemingly independent companies. Many companies are in fact part of much larger concerns. In recent years there has been a substantial number of mergers and takeovers, plus the buying and selling of business between corporations. A useful source of information is the directory *Who Owns Whom*, (published by Dun & Bradstreet), which has a subsidiary index listing most subsidiaries of companies included in this guide. You can also use company annual reports, which (for most companies) can be obtained on request. These reports provide good background information on the company concerned, and occasionally information on its corporate support programme. Some private (and occasionally public) companies will not send out annual reports except to shareholders; in such cases you can go to Companies House to get hold of a copy. Offices are situated in Cardiff, Edinburgh and London.

Before writing a letter of appeal ...

You obviously should try to find out as much as you can about the companies you have identified as potential donors. But, remember that:

- Companies generally have less well defined policies than trusts, although you can often determine a pattern in their giving.

- The chance of an application made 'out of the blue' getting substantial support is low. Appeals made towards the end of a company's financial year are also less likely to succeed.

- Companies are more conservative in their giving and are less likely to support innovative projects (at least until they have got established) or anything that is risky or controversial.

- Companies' policies change more frequently than those of trusts because of mergers, takeovers, or a fall or rise in profits. So ensure your research is bang up to date. Consulting one of the above mentioned directories or even a copy of the company's latest annual report and accounts is not necessarily enough; it may have been taken over since then. Check the financial press on a regular basis, or make a quick telephone call to see if anything has changed, such as company name, address (they may have kept the same telephone number, but moved), your contact, and so on.

Writing a letter of appeal

First, put yourself in the position of the company. Why should they want to give their shareholders' funds to you? Why should they choose your charity's appeal ahead of any others they might receive? Second, think about the benefits they will get from supporting you and mention these in your letter (for sponsorship proposals these benefits will be central to your success or failure). Then consider the following important points:

- Think up a project or aspect of your work that the business sector might like to support. Generally, do not appeal for administration costs or a contribution to an endowment fund (although there will be cases where this approach will succeed). Recognise that companies are likely to be interested in some ideas and not others. For example, a drugs charity would be more likely to get money for education than rehabilitation. An appreciation of the kind of projects that companies like to support will be very helpful to you.

- Your letter should be as short as possible. Try to get it all on one side of A4. You can always supply other information as attachments. Company people are busy. You can help them by making your appeal letter short and to the point. It should be written clearly and concisely and be free from jargon. Someone not acquainted with what you are doing should be able to read and understand it and be persuaded to act on it. Give your letter in draft to someone outside your charity to read and comment on before finalising it and sending it out.

- You should state why you need the money and exactly how it will be spent. The letter itself should be straightforward. It should include the following information (not necessarily in this order): what the organisation does and some background on how it was set up; whom the organisation serves; why the organisation needs funds; how the donation would be spent if it were to be forthcoming; and why you think the company might be interested in supporting you.

You should attempt to communicate the urgency of your appeal. Fundraising is an intensively competitive business; there is a limited amount of money to give away, and you have to ensure that some of it comes your way. If it appears that although you would like the money now it would not matter terribly much if you got it next year, this will put people off. But don't give the impression you are fundraising at the last minute. Show them you are professional and you have carefully planned your fundraising appeal. You should also try to show that your charity is well-run, efficient and cost-effective in how it operates.

You should mention why you think the company should support your cause. This could range from rather generalised notions of corporate responsibility and the creation of goodwill in the local community, to much more specific advantages such as preventing children painting graffiti on its factory walls or the good publicity companies will get from supporting your cause. If the firm's generosity is to be made public – for example, through advertising or any publicity arising from the gift – then emphasize the goodwill that will accrue to the company. Most companies would say that they do not require any public acknowledgement for the contributions they make, but most will appreciate and welcome this.

Ask for something specific. It is all too easy to make a good case and then to mumble something about needing money. Many companies, having been persuaded to give, are not sure how much to give. You can ask a firm to give a donation of a specific amount (matched to what you believe its ability to contribute to be), or to contribute the cost of a particular item. You can suggest a figure by mentioning what other companies are giving. You can mention a total and say how many donations you will need to achieve this. Don't be unreasonable in your expectations. Just because a company is large and rich, it doesn't mean that it makes big grants.

If you can demonstrate some form of 'leverage' this will be an added attraction. Company donations on the whole are quite modest, but companies like to feel they are having a substantial impact with the money they spend. If you can show that a small amount of money will enable a much larger project to go ahead, or will release further funds, say, on a matching basis from another source, this will definitely be an advantage.

Having written a very short appeal letter, you can append some background support literature. This should not be a 50-page treatise outlining your latest policies but, like your letter, it should be crisp and to the point: a record of your achievements,

your latest annual report, press cuttings, or even a specially produced brochure to accompany your appeal.

Make sure that the letter is addressed to the correct person at the correct address. It pays to do this background research. Keep all the information on file as it will make your job much easier next time.

If you are successful, remember to say thank you; this is an elementary courtesy which is too often forgotten. If the company gives you any substantial amount of money, then you should try to keep it in touch with the achievements related to its donation (such as a brief progress report or copies of your annual report or latest publications).

If you do not succeed, go back again next year (unless the company says that it is not its policy to support your type of organisation or to give to charity at all). Persistence can pay. If you have received a donation, go back again next year. The company has demonstrated that it is interested in what you are doing and in supporting you. It may well do it again next year, especially if you have thanked it for the donation and kept it in touch with how the project developed.

How companies reply to you

Many companies will not even reply to your appeal. A few may acknowledge receipt of your letter, and occasionally you will get thanked for your request and be told that it is being considered and you will only hear the outcome if you are successful. Up to half of the companies you approach will write back, depending on the spread of the companies you approach. Larger companies have a system for dealing with charity mail, and most will see it as good PR to give a reply. Smaller companies that do not give much charitable support will not have the time or resources to do anything but scan the mail and throw most of it in the bin.

The application letter – checklist

▷ Is it only one side of A4?

▷ Does it state what your link is with the company?

▷ Does it stress the benefits to the company?

▷ Is it clear why you need the money?

▷ Is it clear what you are asking for?

▷ Is it addressed to the correct contact?

▷ Is it attractive to the company?

▷ Is it endorsed?

What sort of reply should you expect? If you do an extensive appeal, you will inevitably get a lot of refusals. These will normally be in the form of a pre-printed or word-processed letter or a postcard. Occasionally you will get an individually typed letter of reply. If the company says yes, you will get a cheque or a Charities Aid Foundation or Charities Trust voucher. But more often companies will say no.

There may be various reasons given or phrases used by a company that refuses your request. The company may not mean what it says. Funds may still be available for those appeals it wishes to support; it may be able to give support and just not want to; or it may not want to now or in the future. You should try to read between the lines. Companies, in trying to be polite, may in fact be misleading you if you take what they say at face value.

An overview of commercial sponsorship

'Sponsorship' is a widely misused term in fundraising. A 'sponsored silence' or 'sponsoring a child' in the developing world is not truly commercial sponsorship. They are simply donations that provide additional benefits to the donor.

Background

In recent years the sponsorship marketplace has expanded sharply. Commercial sponsorship now has a higher profile and there are greater expectations about what it can achieve.

You have to accept the following if you want a commercial sponsorship to work:

It is a commercial exchange

You have to give the sponsor something which is worthwhile. This could be:

- access to a new market
- an improved reputation
- the potential of income.

A sponsorship is a legal agreement. It will be laid out in a formal contract, so you must deliver what you have promised.

Because it is a business relationship, *you will have to pay VAT.*

You will have to approach the sponsor

This is almost always the case. You will have to sell your organisation and the idea of sponsorship. You might want to tell a sponsor:

- who you reach and influence (your audience)
- how you measure that information

- how a sponsorship could affect the way your audience view you
- your position in relation to similar organisations.

You will have to prove your worth

Sponsors do not want to be associated with a failing or ineffective organisation. You will need to be able to display financial stability and good business practice.

You will need the right people

It takes time to organise an effective sponsorship arrangement. It requires staff with a real sense of business requirements and expectations. Sponsorship is not for the faint-hearted or for newly established organisations. It requires serious planning and strategic thinking.

It could take a while

Most commercial organisations plan at least nine months ahead. Commercial sponsorship is a medium-term income stream. You should only consider it once you've secured grants, individual donors and other more traditional funding sources.

It is worth the effort

Sponsorships usually involve greater income than many other fundraising sources. They also require much less detailed budgeting.

Sponsorship money is usually unrestricted so can be used anywhere it is needed. You can spend the cash wherever and however you want, as long as you deliver on your side of the agreement.

Alphabetical listing of companies

This section gives information on 490 companies from all sectors of industry, gathered from a combination of annual reports and company websites and supplemented by our own research. The general layout showing the information on each company is on pages 36–37.

Types of company

A company may be: a public limited company (designated plc), normally a company with shares quoted on the stock exchange; a privately owned company; or a subsidiary company. If it is a subsidiary it may have retained its own identity for charitable donations and we would include an entry in this guide. Other subsidiaries included are British-based subsidiaries of an overseas-based company.

Where a company has been recently acquired it may not yet have decided whether it will continue to manage its own donations budget.

Through acquisitions and mergers, companies may now be owned by a holding company, a conglomerate or a transnational company. We usually only give the name of the holding company. You may have to do your own research to link local companies and plants with the head office that may have ultimate control over their donations. The company annual report, usually available free on request, lists subsidiary and associate (less than 50% owned) companies and reports on the activity of the company during the year. We have included the main subsidiaries of each company within the entry. However, for many companies this is taken from the latest annual report, which can be several months out of date. The *Who Owns Whom* directory (published by Dun & Bradstreet) also lists subsidiaries of UK companies, and more up-to-date information can often be found on company websites.

Interpreting financial information

The charitable donations figure given is that published by the company in the 'Director's Report' section of its annual report and accounts. As far as we know this legally should relate only to cash donations. However, we have noticed an increasing trend for companies to include the value of secondments, gifts in kind, advertising or sponsorship which, customarily, are included in the total contributions figure. Furthermore, a company's present level of donations does not necessarily indicate future commitments. Sending an appeal to less generous companies may actually persuade them to increase their donations. Certainly if they never receive appeals there will be no outside pressure on them to change their policy, although in general if a company is only giving a little your chances of success are reduced.

Normally a coordinated company donor will budget a certain sum for its charitable donations and stick within this amount. Some allocate all their budget at an annual meeting; others spread donations throughout the year. Some give to causes they wish to support until the budget is used up and then stop; others continue to give even after the budget is spent if an appeal takes their fancy. If they reply to your appeal, many will write and say that their budget is 'fully committed'. Often this is simply a polite way of refusing support.

The year-end is important in that if you get your appeal in soon afterwards, the company will not have spent its charitable budget for the coming year. However, if a company allocates its budget evenly throughout the year and receives a flood of applications at the start of its new financial year, some which would have been supported later in the year now miss out. There is no fail-safe answer to this problem. However, your chances of success are usually improved by sending the application earlier rather than later in the company's financial year.

How to interpret the donations policy

There are certain standard phrases that appear in the policy of the company entries.

No response to circular appeals
This means that 'Dear Sir/Madam' letters, whether they are hand-signed or use photocopied signatures, are probably not even read, let alone replied to.

Preference for local charities in areas of company presence
Preference for appeals relevant to company business
Preference for charities where a member of staff is involved

These are self-explanatory. Local charities should check whether appeals can be made locally or must be sent to head office. Any link with the company should be highlighted.

Preferred areas of support are ...
We asked companies to tick preferred areas of support to indicate the sort of appeals most likely to interest them

Exclusions (*No grants for ...*)
The same list was used as for the preferred areas, with common exclusions being: fundraising events, advertising in charity brochures, appeals from individuals, denominational (religious) appeals, political/campaigning activity, and bricks and mortar appeals.

Before applying, potential applicants should always consider whether there is a particular reason why the company might want to support them.

Fictitious Productions plc

Company registration number 001122

---

68 Nowhere Street, Anytown AN6 2LM
0151 000 0000; Fax: 0151 100 0000
Website: www.fictprod.co.uk

Correspondent: A Grant, CSR Manager 0151 000 0001

Chief officer: T Story
Chief Executive: S Yarn

Year end	Turnover	Pre-tax profit
31/12/2008	£837,300,000	£292,000,000

Nature of company business
The company is involved in production of fictitious information. Subsidiaries and locations include Cashflow Industries (Grimsby), False Publications (Liverpool), Sundry Matters (Bristol), and Wage Packet Co (Perth).

UK employees: 3,872

Charitable donations
2008: £420,000
2007: £350,000
2006: £225,000
2005: £184,000
2004: £243,000
Total community contributions: £575,000
Membership: BitC, L B Group

Company name: The full name of the company is given with the companies listed in alphabetical order. Its registration number at Companies House is also included.

Address: Head office, to which appeals should be sent unless otherwise stated.

Telephone: Appeals should be submitted *in writing*, but you may wish to ask for details of the appeals procedure, check the contact for charitable donations or request a copy of the latest annual report. The latter, along with community support information, may also be obtained via the quoted website address, if available.

Contact for appeals: Only the very large corporate donors have specialist staff dealing with appeals (a direct line number may be given in such instances). However, the company secretary or public relations department will deal with appeals to many companies.

Chief officers: We give the names of the *Chief officer, Chair, Chief Executive* and/ or *Managing Director.* There is not room to list all members of the main board.

Financial statistics: The *year-end, turnover* and *pre-tax profit* (a figure in brackets denotes a loss). Most relate to 2007/08. The figures give an indication of the scale of the company's giving relative to its size.

Nature of company business: The main area of activity is given, together with subsidiaries and locations (where known). This can be useful if you are looking for a product or geographical link. We also state the number of UK employees, where available.

Charitable donations: Figures for the last five years are given, together with a figure for total community contributions (which includes the cost of in kind giving, arts sponsorship, secondments, etc), where available. May state additional figures relating to management costs and cause-related marketing promotions.

Membership: Indicates whether the company is a member of Arts & Business, Business in the Community, and the London Benchmarking Group.

Community involvement

The company prefers to support local organisations in areas of company presence. It focuses its giving on sickness and disability, the arts, heritage, social welfare, education and youth, and environment.

Community involvement: This provides an overview of the company's community support policy (if one exists), detailing preferred causes and any geographical areas that are favoured.

Exclusions

No response to circular appeals. No grants for fundraising events, purely denominational (religious appeals), local appeals not in areas of company presence, large national appeals, overseas projects, political activities or individuals. Non-commercial advertising is not supported. It does not sponsor individuals or travel.

Exclusions: Listing any areas, subjects or types of grants the company will not consider.

Applications

In writing to the correspondent. Applications are considered by a donations committee which meets three times a year.

Applications: Including how to apply and when to submit an application. We also state whether there is further information available from the company.

Corporate giving

The company's community contributions totalled £575,000 in 2008. This included in kind giving, the cost of secondments and arts sponsorship and charitable donations of £420,000. National grants range from £250 to £5,000. Local grants range from £25 to £500.
Major grant recipients in 2008 included Any Town Disability Network (for information leaflets), Perth Parent & Toddler Association (towards play equipment) and the local wildlife trust.

Corporate giving: Quotes total cash donations made and, if available, total community contributions.

Typical grants range, to indicate what a successful applicant can expect to receive.

Examples of grants, listing where possible the purpose and size of the grants. Large grants are often a good indicator of the company's priorities.

In-kind support

The company donates surplus or used furniture/equipment to local causes.
Enterprise: The company supports local enterprise agencies and considers secondment of employees to local economic development initiatives.

In kind support: Some companies give gifts in kind, which can be anything from used stock to printing facilities.

Employee-led support

A charity is selected each year to benefit from employee fundraising, with the company making a contribution.
Payroll giving: A scheme is operated by the company.

Employee-led support: Many company employees give time and money to local causes, including fundraising and expertise. If a payroll giving scheme is operated, we state so.

Commercially-led support

Sponsorship: *The arts* – The typical sponsorship range is from £1,000 to £25,000. It sponsors Southport Sinfonietta and supported festivals in Grimsby and Perth.

Commercially-led support: Covers arts and good-cause sponsorship, if undertaken, together with a contact, if different from the main correspondent. Provides information on cause-related marketing promotions, if applicable.

3i Group plc

Company registration number 1142830

16 Palace Street, London SW1E 5JD

020 7928 3131; Fax: 020 7928 0058

Website: www.3igroup.com

Correspondent: Kevin Dunn, Company Secretary

Chairman: The Baroness Sarah Hogg

Chief Executive: Philip Yea

Year end	Turnover	Pre-tax profit
31/03/2008	£1,041,000,000	£834,000,000

Nature of company business
The group's principal activity is investment in a wide range of growing independent businesses.

Subsidiaries include: Garden Pensions Trustees Ltd

Main locations: Aberdeen, Manchester, London, Glasgow, Reading, Solihull, Leeds, Cambridge, Bristol, Birmingham

Total employees: 772

Charitable donations

2008: £454,130
2007: £429,409
2006: £390,570
2004: £253,419

Membership: A & B, BitC

Community involvement

The company continues to favour charitable initiatives with which members of staff are personally involved and local charities where 3i has an office. There is a preference for education, young people and organisations engaged in the relief of poverty and/or work of benefit to the community.

In addition to charitable donations, the company undertakes some arts sponsorship and occasional secondment to charities, as well as contributing through gifts in kind.

The company has offices in the UK in Aberdeen, Birmingham, Bristol, Cambridge, Glasgow, Leeds, London, Manchester, Reading, and Solihull. Each of these offices is allocated a tranche of the company's charitable budget which is administered centrally.

Exclusions

No support for appeals from non-charities, advertising in charity brochures, animal welfare charities, appeals from individuals, children/youth, elderly people, enterprise and training, environment/heritage, fundraising events, overseas projects, political appeals, religious appeals, sickness/disability charities or sport.

Applications

In writing to the correspondent.

Information available: The company produce a corporate social responsibility report within its annual report and accounts.

Corporate giving

In 2007/08, the company made charitable donations of £454,130 (2006/07: £429,409) to a variety of charities. Approximately 29% of this figure was in matched donations of staff Give As You Earn contributions.

Two examples of 3i's support are a series of programmes with The Old Vic theatre in London. The other is 3i's support for The Passage, a charity focused on the homeless, which is based close to 3i's London office.

In kind support

3i continued to support the charity In Kind Direct, which distributes donated surplus products to other UK voluntary organisations.

Employee-led support

3i supports the charitable activities of its staff by matching donations made under the Give As You Earn scheme and through their own fundraising efforts. In 2007/08, this amounted to £129,733.

Payroll giving: The Give As You Earn scheme is operated by the company.

Commercially-led support

Sponsorship: *The arts* – The company's major involvement continues to be sponsorship of the senior student orchestra of the Royal Academy of Music.

It has also supported the Young Vic Theatre scheme which enables children, otherwise denied the opportunity, to be inspired by theatre.

3M United Kingdom plc

Company registration number 241888

3M Centre, Cain Road, Bracknell RG12 8HT

08705 360036; Fax: 01344 858278

Website: www.3M.com/uk

Correspondent: Heather McMahon, Community Relations Manager 01344 858632; Fax: 01344 862367

Managing Director: Doug Mitchell

Year end	Turnover	Pre-tax profit
31/12/2006	£560,067,000	£70,902,000

Nature of company business
The principal activity of the company is the manufacture and marketing of a range of coated materials and other related products and services. These include abrasives, adhesives, cleaning materials, tapes, reflective materials and office stationery products.

Subsidiaries include: Biotrace International plc

Main locations: Bangor, Bedford, Aycliffe, Atherstone, Bracknell, Loughborough, Manchester, Clitheroe, Hillington, Gorseinon, Bridgend, Runcorn, Northallerton

UK employees: 2,227

Charitable donations

2006: £301,676
2005: £358,331
2004: £338,491
2003: £267,938

Total community contributions: £494,504

Membership: BitC

Community involvement

3M requested that they not be listed as part of our research into corporate community support in the UK. As ever, however, we believe in including all relevant companies, of which 3M is one, and have therefore taken much of the following information from their website and annual report.

3M in the UK focuses its community giving, nationally, around road safety programmes for children and, at a local level, on organisations serving the communities where 3M operates. Support for the latter concentrates on two areas – education and the environment – although grants are also given for relief of suffering.

In aiming to help the communities closest to its UK and Ireland sites, 3M provides support in a number of ways including:

- financial donations/grants
- in kind gifts of 3M products and services
- volunteer services of its employees and retirees
- use of 3M facilities.

In 2008, 3M facilities in the UK were based in: Atherstone; Aycliffe; Bangor; Bedford; Bracknell; Bridgend; Clitheroe; Gorseinon; Hillington; Loughborough; Manchester; Northallerton; and Runcorn.

Exclusions

No support for appeals from individuals, third party fundraisers, local appeals not in areas of company presence, large national appeals or overseas projects.

Applications

In writing to the correspondent. To be considered for support, local projects must fall within one or both of the topic areas (education and the environment) and relate to a community in which 3M has a site presence. Additionally, proposals must fulfil one or more of the following criteria:

- be from a registered UK charitable concern
- address a specific identified local community need
- involve 3M volunteers
- on completion, show measurable results.

Information available: A comprehensive Environmental, Social and Economic Sustainability Report is available online.

Corporate giving

In 2006, the company made cash donations in the UK and Ireland (effectively, Dublin) totalling £301,676. The purposes for which these donations were given were broken down as follows:

Category	Grant total
Environment	£16,196
Education	£201, 018
Relief of suffering	£10,610
Other	£73,852

In addition to cash donations, a further £195,828 was contributed in the form of employee volunteering (£119,564) and gifts in kind (£73,264) making total community contributions in the UK and Ireland of £494,504.

In kind support

The main areas of non-cash support are mentoring, gifts in kind of 3M products and services, and the use of 3M facilities.

In 2006, in support of its national road safety programme, the company developed a free web-based educational tool – 3M Streetwise – to help schools throughout the UK to teach road safety messages, as well as looking at the scientific principles of light, sound and forces.

Employee-led support

Through the 3M 4 Good programme, 3M encourages its employees to spend one day a year volunteering in their community. Whilst the company's Care & Share programme matches donations and fundraising by 3M employees up to £100 per employee per year to charities registered in the UK.

Payroll giving: The Give As You Earn scheme is available to employees.

Commercially-led support

Sponsorship: 3M is a headline sponsor of National Road Safety Week.

Abbey

Company registration number 2294747

PO Box 911, Milton Keynes MK9 1AD

0870 608 0104

Website: www.aboutabbey.com

Correspondent: Alan Eagle, Trust Secretary, Abbey Charitable Trust 0870 608 0104; Fax: 01908 344257 Email: alan.eagle@abbey.com

Chief Executive: Antonio Horta-Osorio

Year end	Pre-tax profit
31/12/2007	£866,000,000

Nature of company business
Provision of an extensive range of personal financial services.

Subsidiaries include: Scottish Mutual Assurance plc, Carfax Insurance Ltd, Cater Allen International Ltd, Scottish Mutual Investment Managers Ltd, Scottish Provident Ltd, Scottish Mutual Pension Funds Investments Ltd

Main locations: Glasgow, Milton Keynes, London, Sheffield, Bradford

UK employees: 16,000

Charitable donations

2007: £1,950,000
2005: £1,556,947
2004: £1,672,493
2003: £1,500,000

Total community contributions: £2,016,689
Management costs: £387,711

Membership: A & B, BitC, L B Group

Community involvement

Abbey's community relations programme encompasses four areas of activity:

- Abbey Charitable Trust
- employee volunteering
- fundraising
- social sponsorship.

The Abbey Charitable Trust

The company's charitable support is given through The Abbey Charitable Trust (Charity Commission no. 803655). This was set up with an initial donation from Abbey National plc (now simply 'Abbey') of £5 million following the sale of shares unclaimed since the company's flotation. This endowment fund received a further £750,000 from Abbey Housing Association Ltd, increasing the endowment fund to £5.75 million.

Further information about the trust is available at: www.aboutabbey.com then go to Abbey corporate > CSR > Charitable trust.

The charitable trust is committed to supporting local communities and disadvantaged people, particularly in areas where Abbey has a significant presence. Its priorities currently are:

- education and training
- local regeneration projects which encourage cross-community partnerships
- financial advice to help with money management.

The trust, however, is looking to increase support through the Abbey Community Partnerships Groups programme, which aims to establish staff community partnership groups in areas with a branch presence.

Only organisations with charitable status will be supported. There is a preference to fund whole projects rather than make a partial donation.

Employee volunteering – see 'Employee led support' section.

Fundraising – Abbey's Charity of the Year 2008 – Great Ormond Street Hospital Children's Charity.

Social sponsorship – Abbey arranges a small number of partnerships with national charities every year to supplement and compliment the work of its charitable trust and employee community activities.

In 2008 Abbey are supporting the following charities: Whizz-Kidz – London Marathon team; and Help the Aged – Big Spring Walk.

Exclusions

The company cannot make donations which:

- are for a specific individual
- support lobbying or political parties
- would benefit a single religious or ethnic group
- help causes outside the UK
- replace statutory funding
- last for more than one year
- help schools gain specialist schools status
- sponsor events, conferences or advertising
- fund salaries, core costs or holidays.

Applications

All you need to do is write a letter to the correspondent on the official headed notepaper of your charity.

You should include a statement that you are authorised to make an application on behalf of your charity. Please don't forget to get it signed by a trustee as well as a member of staff. Abbey regrets that it cannot accept on-line applications.

If you require confirmation that Abbey have received your application then please enclose a self addressed envelope or postcard with your application. Abbey like to save paper whenever they can, so please do not send your annual report and accounts as they can either access these online, or will request them if they feel it will help them to make a decision. If you want any of your enclosures returned please enclose a self-addressed envelope.

Remember, only registered charities or organisations with charitable status can be considered.

Information available: Further and full information about what you need to include in your letter of application are available on the company's website (see 'Community involvement – overview).

Corporate giving

In 2007, Abbey (the company) donated £1,950,000 to the Abbey Charitable Trust and gave additional in kind support of £66,689. In turn, the trust made grants totalling £2,701,959, broken down as follows:

	£	No. of grants
financial literacy	742,851	53
community regeneration	426,933	124
education and training	1,015,129	344
relief of suffering	375,852	587
disability	100,792	51
other	40,402	76

Major beneficiaries during the year included: Princess Royal Trust for Carers, Radar, Shelter, St Pancras Humanist Housing Association, and Bradford Community Environmental Project.

Abbey Community Partnership Groups currently exist in a number of areas around the country (Camden, Glasgow, Bradford, Sheffield, Teeside, Milton Keynes and Northern Ireland) and have a budget allocation of around £100,000 each.

Employee-led support

Abbey's commitment to volunteering spans over 16 years, with opportunities co-ordinated in its seven major UK office locations. To support staff that volunteer it offers a matched time scheme which enables staff involved in out of working hours volunteering to have up to 35 hours a year of paid work time in which to volunteer. With the matched donation scheme an individual can claim up to a maximum of £500 and a group of four or more employees up to £2,500.

Payroll giving: The company operates the Charities Trust scheme.

Abbott Mead Vickers – BBDO Ltd

Company registration number 1935786

151 Marylebone Road, London NW1 5QE

020 7616 3500; Fax: 020 7616 3600

Website: www.amvbbdo.com

Correspondent: Colin Fleming, Finance Director

Chair and Chief Executive AMV Group: Cilla Snowball

Chief Executive Officer: Farah Ramzan Golant

Year end	Turnover	Pre-tax profit
31/12/2006	£40,521,000	£6,341,000

Nature of company business
Advertising agency.

Subsidiaries include: Proximity, Drury Communications, Redwood Publishing, Electronic Solutions, Minerva, Hammond Communications, Fishburn Hedges, OMD, PHD, Rocket, Craik Jones Watson Mitchell Voelkel, Telecom Express Ltd, Aurelia Public Relations, Drum PHD

Main locations: London

UK employees: 315

Charitable donations

2006: £59,000
2005: £64,000
2004: £90,000
2002: £50,000

Community involvement

No longer a member of Business in the Community, we understand the company continues to supports both national and local charities, with a preference towards those based in London.

Applications

In writing to the correspondent who can provide further information.

Corporate giving

In 2006, AMV made cash donations totalling £59,000. We have no details about which organisations benefited from the donations.

In kind support

AMV encourages staff to involve themselves with community projects.

Employee-led support

Payroll giving: The company operate the Give As You Earn scheme.

Commercially-led support

Sponsorship: *The Arts* – Contact Colin Fleming, Finance Director.

Accenture UK Ltd

Company registration number 4757301

60 Queen Victoria Street, London EC4N 4TW

020 7844 4000; Fax: 020 7844 4444

Website: www.accenture.com

Correspondent: Mary Jane Smith, Accenture Foundation
Email: corpcitizenship@accenture.com

Chairman and Managing Director: D Thomlinson

Year end	Turnover	Pre-tax profit
31/08/2007	£1,928,919,000	£4,963,000

Nature of company business
Management consulting and technology services organisation.

Main locations: Newcastle upon Tyne, Manchester, London, Aberdeen, Edinburgh

Charitable donations

2007: £432,904
2006: £603,373
2005: £484,000
2004: £573,989
2003: £584,265

Membership: BitC

Community involvement

Accenture believe in: 'Giving our people opportunities to engage in community-investment programmes is an excellent means to make a difference to local communities, enhance the skills of Accenture professionals and build talented teams that create successful outcomes for all involved

'The strategic aim of our community investment programmes is to promote sustainable livelihoods through skills development. By addressing skills or capacity shortages we can help to build better futures for all the communities in which we operate directly or indirectly.

'Our efforts to create better communities fall into two categories:

'Time and Skills

'We believe we can make the greatest contribution by playing to our strengths. So we give employees the opportunity to contribute actively and have the greatest possible positive impact at a personal level by giving their time and skills.

'We bring to our community work the same principles of high performance that we apply to our client work and believe that the most sustainable way of empowering our communities is by leveraging our core business competencies and building organisational capacity for our partners as well as upskilling individuals.

'Giving

'Guided by our community objectives, Accenture aims to promote positive social transformation through carefully targeted giving to community partners that share our vision of creating a sustainable, diverse and skilled society.

'To put this objective into effect, Accenture supports a number of organisations through financial grants, as well as facilitating tax-effective giving through our payroll schemes for our employees. We also encourage individual fundraising efforts for worthwhile causes by matching fundraising and allowing time off to organise or take part in such activities, and also maintain an employee nominated payroll giving charity scheme, Making a Difference.'

Donations in the UK are made through The Accenture Foundation (Charity Commission no. 1057696). In addition there is a UK Employee Charity Committee that gives out approximately a quarter of a million pounds a year based on employee proposals. There are also matching schemes and payroll schemes available for employees. Greatest support is via our time and skills offering where every Accenture employee is entitled to three days a year to spend on charitable activity of their choice.

Exclusions

No support for political appeals or religious appeals.

Applications

Proposals are generally invited by the trustees or initiated at their request. Unsolicited applications are discouraged and are unlikely to be successful, even if the fall within the areas in which the trustees are interested (see below).

The UK Foundation will consider proposals from UK registered charities which align with the overarching theme of 'Building Skills for Better Futures'. This covers proposals from registered charities working within the following areas: Education; Employability; and Enterprise.

In addition, the proposals should:

- be conducive to Accenture employees involvement (or potential for it)
- have a visible cause and effect in the UK (i.e. demonstrable impact)
- not lead the supported organisation to become dependent/reliant on Accenture.

Potential grantees must be registered UK charities or equivalent.

Information available: Corporate Citizenship Review 2007

Corporate giving

The Accenture Foundation

The Accenture Foundation supports registered or exempt charities working in education and training and disadvantaged communities, especially when on behalf of children/young people and in areas local to Accenture offices.

In 2006/07, the Accenture Foundation had assets of £11 million, an income of just over £1 million. Of this the firm donated £432,904 with a similar amount coming from senior company executives.

Grants were made to organisations totalling £1.3 million. Beneficiaries included: VSO (£258,000); Kids Company (£144,000); Oxfam (£126,000); UK Youth and The Prince's Trust (£50,000 each); Springboard (£30,000); and National Information Forum (£10,000).

In kind support

Accenture actively seeks opportunities that will allow it to best utilise its key skills and so have the most beneficial impact on society and its people. It does this through:

- Pro bono programmes
- voluntary service overseas placements
- projects conducted with Accenture Development Partnerships
- three day community allowance
- secondments.

Each of the above is explained in detail on Accenture's website.

Employee-led support

Making a Difference – This Accenture employee-run charity scheme donates money to charities nominated by employees. The money is collected through payroll giving and pooled together to make a difference. Details of the causes supported through this scheme are available on the firm's website.

Payroll giving: *Give As You Earn* – Employees are able to sign up to donate to charities of their choice through tax effective payroll giving. Ten percent of people in the United Kingdom are now contributing.

Commercially-led support

Sponsorship: Accenture has sponsored numerous high profile community events and institutions over the past few years. The organisation claims that these associations help promote their business, while allowing them to enjoy the benefits of supporting worthwhile organisations that a make a positive impact on local culture and community.

The arts: Accenture sponsors numerous arts organisations and initiatives including: Sponsorship of Innovation at the National Theatre which includes the provision of expertise and in kind support for a number of innovative technology projects; a three-year corporate membership agreement with the Tate Britain and Tate Modern Galleries; Northern Ballet Theatre based in Leeds – this sponsorship aims to provide support to increasing business growth in the North of England and Scotland; Royal Shakespeare Company has been chosen as Accenture's latest global sponsorship initiative.

ADC Krone (UK)

Company registration number 1776843

Runnings Road, Kingsditch Trading Estate, Cheltenham, Gloucestershire GL 51 9NQ

01242 264400; Fax: 01242 264488

Website: www.adc.com

Correspondent: Mrs Sam Naylor-Howell, ADC Cares

Year end
31/10/2007

Nature of company business
Telecommunications company.

Main locations: Glenrothes, Cheltenham

Total employees: 8,200

Community involvement

Donations are made through the ADC Foundation (the charitable arm of ADC Telecommunications, Inc.) which was founded in 1999. The foundation's goal is to provide social and economic value by encouraging employee contributions and by making direct grants in two strategic focus areas: mathematics and science education, and non-profit access to technology.

Funding is available to groups in Cheltenham, with a preference for projects involving collaboration between more than one organisation. Areas of work which can be funded are:

- science, technology, engineering or mathematics education, at any level
- access to technology, where improved technology for an organisation will bring direct results to the beneficiaries of the group's work.

Exclusions

The ADC Foundation will not consider requests for in kind giving, general operating grants, capital grants or fundraisers including customer-sponsored charity benefit events. Nor does it make grants to individuals, for religious purposes, or to address generic quality of life issues.

Applications

Having determined that your intended proposal fits with one of the foundation's focus areas (see 'Community Involvement' above), you should first fill out the online 'Letter of Inquiry'. These are accepted throughout the year with decisions being made quarterly. Details can be found at: www.adc.com/aboutadc/adcfoundation/howtoapply/index.jsp

Please note, however, that to gain input and ideas from every level and in all geographical locations, the foundation has established numerous advisory Community Connections Committees comprising of local ADC employees who make recommendations to the foundation regarding local grants that fit the foundation's chosen focus. It may, therefore, benefit your applications success if you have access to members of the said committee.

Corporate giving

In 2006, the ADC Foundation made worldwide cash donations of US$1,625,983 (around £800,000). Of this, nearly 60% went towards supporting education initiatives and 20% towards matching employees giving. No breakdown figure covering the UK was available. However, wed o know that the company has supported Well Child, as per the following extract from the foundation's 2006 annual report:

'Following a successful online healthcare education project targeted at young people, in 2006, WellChild was ready to tackle the daunting task of establishing its own internet presence, which would serve as a single, comprehensive reference for children's and young people's health. Additionally, WellChild hoped to pilot the use of portable new media devices to further engage children with chronic illness.

'The ADC Cares Cheltenham committee saw Well Child's project as an excellent opportunity to build and enhance the technological capacity of an important organization, thereby better equipping it to achieve its mission.

'The ADC Cares Cheltenham committee saw WellChild's project as an excellent opportunity to build and enhance the technological capacity of an important organization, thereby better equipping it to achieve its mission.'

Employee-led support

Employee giving is encouraged and supported via ADC Foundation programmes including employee 'Matching gifts' of up to $1,000 (£500). We are unsure if this applies in the UK. The company will also help employee volunteer projects which support community needs, campaigns or foundation giving goals.

Addleshaw Goddard

Company registration number 4673315

100 Barbirolli Square, Manchester M2 3AB

0161 934 6000; Fax: 0161 934 6060

Website: www.addleshawgoddard.com

Correspondent: The Trustees, Addleshaw Goddard Charitable Trust 020 7788 5504; Fax: 0161 934 6060

Email: karen.sinclair@addleshawgoddard.com

Senior Partner: Paul Lee

Year end	Turnover	Pre-tax profit
30/04/2007	£176,700,000	£61,700,000

Nature of company business
Legal firm.

Main locations: Leeds, London, Manchester

UK employees: 1,475

Charitable donations

2007: £75,000
2006: £66,491

Total community contributions: £275,000

Membership: BitC

Community involvement

Addleshaw Goddard is a leading UK law firm specialising in advice to corporate clients across the full range of services. There are 176 Partners and over 1,300 staff located in offices in Leeds, London and Manchester. Support is given through various pro bono and community based activities. Every member of the firm is given two days of paid time per annum for such activities. Financial help is given via the Addleshaw Goddard Charitable Trust (Charity Commission no. 286887) which aims to promote any charitable purpose in the communities in the City of London, Leeds and Manchester.

Addleshaw Goddard Charitable Trust

The trust was established for any objects and purposes which are charitable according to the laws of England & Wales. Current practice is to support community projects local to each of its offices (Leeds, London & Manchester), to support and develop links with a national charity partner selected every 2–3 years and to help a wider variety of charities by matching Addleshaw Goddard staff fundraising.

Exclusions

No support for general or circular appeals, local appeals not in the areas of company presence, animal welfare, individuals or political/religious appeals.

Applications

In writing to the correspondent.

Corporate giving

During the financial year 2006/07, Addleshaw Goddard LLP donated £75,000 to its associated trust (the Addleshaw Goddard Charitable Trust) and the trust in turn made donations totallng £55,376 in line with its constitution and objects.

In 2007/08, the trustees established a structure for the trust's future activities which led to:

- links being established locally in Leeds with Mencap and Barnardos, in London with Centrepoint and London Sports Forum for Disabled People, and in Manchester with St Ann's Hospice and Groundwork Trust. The firm's.links with Business in the Community in Leeds, London and Manchester have also been maintained during the year

- the trustees reviewing potential national charity partners and inviting four charities to submit their proposals to be the national charity selected to work with Addleshaw Goddard for the two year period from May 2008. At the time of writing (April 2008), the trustees were nearing the end of that exercise and anticipated that the successful charity would be appointed shortly

- the trust continuing to support employee fundraising, matching individual efforts to a maximum of £500 per event, with a maximum of £3,000 per group of employees entering the same event in support of the same charity.

Grant beneficiaries during 2006/07 included: The Prince's Trust (£10,500); Business in the Community (£8,225); Thomas Rhys Pryce Memorial Trust (£3,000); and Meningitis Research Foundation (£2,500).

In kind support

The firm operates a wide range of initiatives, information on which can be accessed through the firm's website: ww.addleshawgoddard.com/csr.

In kind support is not formally recorded at present, but the figure is estimated to be in the region of £200,000 a year (excluding cash donations).

Employee-led support

Staff are encouraged to become involved with their local communities through fund raising activities and volunteer work.

Each office has a Community Involvement Team which runs a programme of activity, including the firm's *Big Week Out* which provides opportunities to 25–30% of the firm's people to become involved in the same concentrated period of time.

Payroll giving: The firm operate the Work Place Giving scheme.

Commercially-led support

Sponsorship: Arts and good-cause sponsorship are undertaken 'via the structures and remit of the Addleshaw Goddard Charitable Trust.'

adidas (UK) Ltd

Company registration number 1075951

The adidas Centre, Pepper Road, Hazel Grove, Stockport SK7 5SD

0161 419 2500; Fax: 0161 419 2603

Website: www.adidas-group.com

Correspondent: Lauren Cruse, Customer Care Manager

Managing Director: Gil Steyaert

Year end	Turnover	Pre-tax profit
31/12/2006	£305,456,000	£33,220,000

Nature of company business
The distribution and retail of sports goods to the sports trade in the UK.

Subsidiaries include: Reebok

Main locations: Stockport, Bolton, Basingstoke, Chelmsford

UK employees: 790

Charitable donations

2006: £18,235
2005: £42,235
2004: £14,201

Community involvement

At group level adidas publish a set of comprehensive corporate giving guidelines from which we have quoted.

Corporate Giving at the adidas group can take the form of:
- cash donations
- donations in kind
- products
- equipment
- services
- know-how
- corporate volunteering.

These are provided selectively and focus on the following areas:
- sports within a social context
- kids and youth
- education
- preventative health projects – preferably sports related
- relief efforts.

Charity of the year: Action Heart (Midlands) and In Kind Direct (2008).

Exclusions

No support for individuals; political parties or advocacy groups; discriminatory groups (race, creed, gender, sexual orientation, or age); religious causes; cultural festivals projects in association with film, music or theatre sponsoring; research projects of any kind; or, advertising and promotion.

In addition, no grants will be made if there is a relevant risk that products will be perceived as bribery, or if the brand name or image could be jeopardised or misused.

Applications

Applications are accepted and reviewed throughout the year in the order in which they are received. Requests must be submitted in writing. The request should be sent to the company's closest subsidiary or liaison office.

Project proposals should be no longer that two pages and the following information needs to be included:
- a description of the organisation and its goals and the specified project
- brief information which indicates the stability of the organisation, such as a list of board members, financial statements and other funding sources for the fiscal year/project
- the amount, product, equipment or service requested
- the specific purpose for which the donation is to be used
- confirmation that the donation is tax-deductible
- proof of the impact and results of the project
- format of reporting and post-event-documentation for the adidas group.

Note: Although the group website states, as above, that applications may be sent to the company's closest subsidiary or liaison office for consideration, this may not be the case in the UK.

Our request for updated information on adidas's community support in the UK was sent to the head office in Stockport. The reply, however, came from the customer care department in Chelmsford and informed us that the charity budget was fully committed to two chosen charities.

Should you therefore still wish to proceed with a grant application, it is perhaps better to send it to the following contact: Lauren Cruse, Customer Care Manager, adidas (UK) Ltd, PO Box 1512, Chelmsford, Essex CM1 3YB.

A decision regarding the status of your application is normally sent within four weeks of it being submitted.

Corporate giving

In 2006, the company made cash donations to UK charities totalling £18,235 (2005: £42,235). No figure for in kind support was available. We assume the recipients of this support to be the two chosen charities named above.

As an indication to potential applicants of the likelihood of success, we quote the following information provided by adidas: During the year the adidas group in the region EMEA (Europe, Middle East and Africa) received 3,841 donation requests, of which 206 were supported. Cash donations were made to 178 of these and three involved employee volunteering totalling 362 hours. The total number of products donated was 142,484 units.

In kind support

Donations in kind may be given in the form of products, equipment, services or know how.

Employee-led support

Company staff are encouraged to carry out voluntary work where aligned with the group's aims.

Commercially-led support

Cause-related marketing: The adidas Group joins with charities or good causes to market products that make a positive impact on social issues, whilst achieving business objectives. We have no examples from the UK.

Admiral Group plc

Company registration number 3849958

Capital Towers, Greyfriars Road, Cardiff CF10 3AZ

0871 882 8282

Website: www.admiralgroup.co.uk

Correspondent: Justin Beddows, Assistant Communications Manager

Chairman: Alastair Lyons

Chief Executive: Henry Engelhardt

Chief Operating Officer: David Stevens

Year end	Turnover	Pre-tax profit
31/12/2007	£364,134,000	£182,098,000

Nature of company business
The company is the holding company for the Admiral Group of companies. The group's principal activity continues to be the selling and administration of private motor insurance and related products.

Subsidiaries include: EUI Ltd, Able Insurance Services, Inspop.com Ltd

Main locations: Swansea, Cardiff

UK employees: 2,364

Charitable donations
2007: £87,000
2006: £38,000
2005: £108,000
2004: £75,000
Membership: A & B

Community involvement

The company's charitable donations are directed into two main areas: sponsorship of national charities and support of local community-based organisations.

There is some preference for helping organisations based in South Wales and groups involved with arts and culture, animal welfare and sport/recreation. Support is also considered for general charitable purposes.

Exclusions

No support for local appeals not in areas of company presence or political appeals.

Applications

In writing to the correspondent. Please note, however, that local support tends to be directed towards organisations involved with Admiral employees or their immediate family.

Corporate giving

In 2007, the company made cash donations of £87,000 (2006: £38,000). Nationally, two main charities were supported – the Born Free Foundation and the South Wales-based Ty Hafan Children's Hospice. Locally, 110 organisations received grants totalling £25,000.

Employee-led support

The group encourages its employees to become involved with their local communities. In support of this, it launched 'Harry's Pot' in 1999, a fund to which staff can apply for a donation or sponsorship toward an organisation of their choice. In 2005, over 100 organisations received help through the scheme including: 1054 Air Training Cadets; Childline Cymru; Cross Keys Silver Band; Morriston Hospital Radio; St Peter's Under 11s Rugby; and Swansea Little Theatre.

Commercially-led support

Sponsorship: *The arts* – Some recent events sponsored by the company include: Admiral Comedy Festival; Cardiff Lesbian and Gay Mardi Gras; SeaSwansea Festival; South Wales Echo Community Championship Awards; Mumbles Mostly Jazz and Blues Festival; and Welsh National Opera.

Adnams plc

Company registration number 31114

Sole Bay Brewery, Southwold, Suffolk IP18 6JW

01502 727200; Fax: 01502 727201

Website: www.adnams.co.uk

Correspondent: Rebecca Abrahall, Charity Administrator

Chairman: Jonathan Adnams

Managing Director: Dr Andy Wood

Year end	Turnover	Pre-tax profit
31/12/2007	£47,368,000	£3,795,000

Nature of company business
The principal activities of the company are brewing, retailing and wholesaling beer, wines, spirits and minerals, property ownership and hotel management.

UK employees: 301

Charitable donations

2007: £40,000
2006: £39,000
2005: £30,000
2004: £35,000

Membership: BitC

Community involvement

Adnams plc is committed to giving not less than 1% of its annual profits to charitable causes. The company is a member of the Good Corporation.

In addition to providing in kind support to local organisations, cash donations are made through The Adnams Charity (Charity Commission no. 1000203) which supports worthwhile causes within a 25-mile radius of St Edmund's Church in Southwold, Suffolk.

Applicants should also note the following:

- the trustees prefer applications for specific items
- grants are generally of a one-off nature
- grants are not made in successive years
- the trustees are reluctant to give grants to cover ongoing running costs, however, in very exceptional circumstances they may do so
- the Adnams Charity does not provide sponsorship of any kind
- the Adnams Charity does not provide raffle prizes
- the Adnams Charity does not give funds indirectly to charities, for example, by sponsoring the fundraising efforts of individuals.

Exclusions

The Adnams Charity does not normally make grants to religious organisations or private clubs unless these can demonstrate that the purpose of the grant is for something of clear public benefit, accessible to all. No grants to individuals, although public bodies and charities may apply on behalf of individuals.

Applications

An application form is available from the Charity Administrator by emailing charity@adnams.co.uk, telephoning 01502 727200 or writing to the Charity Administrator.

Applicants will be asked to provide information on:

- what the grant is for
- who will benefit
- how much the item(s) will cost – please provide a detailed quotation
- other fundraising activities being undertaken and amount raised so far
- to whom cheques should be made payable in the event of a grant being made.

In addition, where possible, the most recent set of audited accounts should be enclosed with the application.

A copy of your 'reserves policy' if you are applying from a registered charity is also required.

The trustees meet quarterly, normally in January, April, July and October. Applications should be submitted early to ensure they are placed on the review list.

Corporate giving

In 2007, the company made cash donations of £40,000 the majority of which went through The Adnams Charity.

The Adnams Charity

Primarily funded by the company, from which it receives an annual income, in 2006/07 the charity had a total income of £52,000 and made grants totalling just over £41,000. 46 good causes were supported, including a number of schools and pre-schools with outdoor play equipment. Funding was also provided for the development of several community recreation facilities.

The grants were broken down in the accounts under six categories – education, health and social welfare, the arts, recreation, buildings and community facilities, and environment and conservation. Besides stating the amount given to each beneficiary, a brief outline of the purpose for which the grant was given is included.

In January 2008, the trustees approved the following grants: £2,000 to the Suffolk Foundation towards the cost of the additional IT equipment; £1,100 to Coldair Green Primary School for the purchase of two laptop computers; and £500 to the May Centre towards the cost of installing a ramp between the lounge and the patio at the centre.

Adobe Systems UK

Company registration number SC101089

3 Roundwood Avenue, Stockley Park, Uxbridge UB11 1AY

020 8606 1100; Fax: 020 8606 4004

Website: www.adobe.com

Correspondent: See 'Applications'

Year end	Turnover	Pre-tax profit
30/11/2006	£33,266,000	£1,395,000

Nature of company business
THe marketing and support of communication computer software.

Main locations: Uxbridge, London, Edinburgh, Glasgow

UK employees: 205

Charitable donations

2007: £54,000

Community involvement

Adobe's philanthropic support in the UK appears to be mainly focused on its Youth Voices initiative. Launched in June 2006, Adobe Youth Voices is described as being designed to help underserved middle and high school aged youth develop the critical skills necessary to become active and engaged members of their communities. The programme will provide young people with access to multimedia tools and training, so enabling them to explore and communicate their ideas, concerns and aspirations. By engaging with their communities in this way, young people can further develop the critical skills needed for success in school, career and life.

Although Adobe's US-community support programmes (Adobe Action Grants and Adobe Community Investment Grants) no longer appear to be open to *direct applications* from UK organisations, Adobe grants are available through the Thames Community Foundation. An emphasis is placed on the following criteria:

- arts and cultural organisations with the mission or principal focus on the creation, promotion and exhibition of visual arts, multimedia or video
- providing services to reduce hunger and homelessness and provide affordable housing
- protecting the natural environment and improving public spaces for the enjoyment of the community
- improving access to electronic information for people with disabilities.

In addition to the above, in kind support is available to qualifying organisations through Adobe's international software donation programme.

Applications

Adobe community investment grants (Thames Community Foundation) – If your organisation meets the eligibility criteria and you would like to apply for an 'Adobe Community Investment Grant', please download the application form and guidelines for applicants notes from the foundation's website: www.thamescommunityfoundation.org.uk/funds.htm

For further information regarding Youth Voices email: youthvoices@adobe.com

To apply to the software donation programme see: https://adobeprograms.giftsinkind.org/default1.htm

Corporate giving

In 2007, Adobe donated $9.5 million to its foundation, $7.5 million to community groups, schools and universities worldwide, and $18 million of software (at 'fair market value'). The company's grant report for the year does mention support for the Thames Community Foundation, but to what extent we do not know.

According to the latest accounts available for the Thames Community Foundation (2006/07), Adobe provided £54,000 for the fund it holds with them. Grant amounts range from £3500–£5000 and are for one year only. No details of the beneficiaries were available.

Adobe Youth Voices

Participating sites for 2007/08 were:

London Quintin Kynaston School, London Borough of Westminster; The Grey Coat Hospital CE Comprehensive School for Girls, London Borough of Westminster; St Charles Catholic Sixth Form College, London Borough of Kensington and Chelsea; St Marylebone CE School, London Borough of Westminster; Dunraven School, London Borough of Lambeth; South Camden Community School, London Borough of Camden; and Plashet School, London Borough of Newham.

Further details can be found on the company's website or by emailing: youthvoices@adobe.com

In kind support
Software donation programme

Adobe's International Software Donation Program is managed in partnership with Gifts In Kind International. A processing and shipping fee will be charged for all software donations.

Who may apply – In the United Kingdom: primary and secondary schools and qualified non-profit organisations/ NGOs.

How to apply – Download and complete the application for the region in which your organisation is located. The application is available on the Gifts In Kind International website. (https://adobeprograms.giftsinkind.org/default1.htm)

Send the application, along with payment for required processing and shipping fees, to Gifts In Kind International as instructed on the application. Adobe offices are unable to process software donation applications.

Selection and notification process for all programmes

Because Adobe has a limited amount of software to donate, priority is given to those non-profit organisations, schools, and programmes that are most closely aligned with Adobe's corporate giving focus areas.

Applications are processed by Adobe's distribution partners, Gifts In Kind International and TechSoup. All applicants will be notified directly by the distribution partners to confirm whether they have been selected to receive a donation within one month of submitting an application. Adobe offices are unable to process software donation applications.

Further in kind support such as the provision of meeting space and other facilities in its offices can also be made available to voluntary groups where appropriate. Surplus office equipment can also be donated.

Employee-led support

Employees are encouraged to volunteer for non-profit organisations and educational establishments whose aim's closely mirror those of the company's community support programme.

Payroll giving: Schemes exist in the company's UK offices, with employee's contributions being matched by the company.

AEA Technology plc

Company registration number 3095862

Harwell Business Centre, Didcot, Oxfordshire OX11 0QJ

0870 190 1900; Fax: 0870 190 8109

Website: www.aeat.co.uk

Correspondent: Martin Millson

Chairman: Dr Bernard Bulkin

Chief Executive: Andrew McCree

Year end	Turnover	Pre-tax profit
31/03/2008	£80,900,000	£8,000,000

Nature of company business
AEA Technology plc and its subsidiaries offer a range of advanced technology products and services, and expert consultancy, based on deep industry understanding and close customer relationships.

Subsidiaries include: AGM Batteries Ltd, Waste Management Technology Ltd

Main locations: Derby, Harlow, Harwell, Glengarnock, Risley, London, Winfrith, Barnsley

UK employees: 2,175

Charitable donations

2008: £8,957
2007: £25,483
2006: £28,380
2005: £48,942
2004: £18,422

Community involvement

AEA's policy is to focus community involvement in energy and environmental improvements.

Exclusions

Previously no support for advertising in charity brochures, animal welfare, appeals from individuals, elderly people, fundraising events, medical research, overseas projects, political appeals, religious appeals, sickness/disability, social welfare or sport.

Applications

In writing to the correspondent.

Corporate giving

The group donated £8,957 (2007: £25,483) plus payments in kind for charitable purposes. No figure for the latter was available.

Previous beneficiaries have included: Young Foresight; Junior Research Fellow, Cambridge University; a Research Professor in micro-analytical techniques at Oxford University; and ICRS-6 Conference.

In kind support

Previously the three main areas of non-cash support were gifts in kind, staff secondments and training schemes.

Employee-led support

In the past the company has operated a staff volunteering scheme. Employees' volunteering/charitable activities have been supported by the company through financial help and by allowing time off to volunteer.

Payroll giving: The company has been involved with the Give As You Earn scheme.

Commercially-led support

Sponsorship: Local schools close to company locations in the UK have received sponsorship through a 'school link' programme and School Governor Award scheme. The Salters Institute A-level Physics project also received support.

Aegis Group plc

Company registration number 1403668

180 Great Portland Street, London W1W 5QZ

020 7070 7700; Fax: 020 7070 7800

Website: www.aegisplc.com

Chairman: Lord Sharman of Redlynch

Chief Executive Officer: Robert Lerwill

Year end	Turnover	Pre-tax profit
31/12/2007	£9,351,200,000	£132,700,000

Nature of company business
The principal activity of the group is the provision of a wide range of services in the areas of media communications and market research.

Subsidiaries include: Carat International, Synovate Europe, Vizeum, Isobar Communications

Main locations: London

UK employees: 43

Charitable donations

2007: £200,000
2006: £300,000
2005: £400,000
2004: £200,000

Membership: BitC

Community involvement

Aegis declined to participate in our survey, stating that: 'At present, we do not wish to be included in your publication'. However, we maintain our policy of including all relevant companies.

In the main, support is given at local operating company level to a range of charities and community projects. At group level, both local and national charities are given help. There is some preference for supporting children with particular needs.

Staff are also encouraged to engage with their local communities.

Exclusions

No support for local appeals not in areas of company presence.

Applications

We were unable to obtain the name of the person responsible for considering requests for support. Unless you have personal knowledge of a company employee willing to speak on your behalf, success is unlikely.

Corporate giving

In 2007, the company made charitable donations of £200,000. Whilst this excludes fundraising by staff, the figure may well be a global one. Limited details of the beneficiaries were available.

In the UK, Carat [a subsidiary] remains the only media agency to be a member of Business in the Community, with 2007 charitable projects including pro bono strategy consultancy and media planning for the Breast Cancer Campaign.

In kind support

Aegis Media UK's charitable programmes include a reading scheme for the Gateway School and time giving for Time & Talents Westminster.

Employee-led support

Staff are allowed company time off in which to carry out volunteer work on behalf of charities and community projects.

Payroll giving: A scheme is in operation.

AEGON Scottish Equitable plc

Company registration number 144517

Lochside House, Edinburgh Park, Edinburgh EH12 9SE

0131 339 9191

Website: www.aegonse.co.uk

Correspondent: Ian Young, Director & Group Secretary

Chairman: Otto Thoresen

Year end	Pre-tax profit
31/12/2007	£230,900,000

Nature of company business
The transaction of life assurance, pensions and other long-term insurance business in the UK.

Subsidiaries include: Guardian Financial Services

Main locations: Lytham St Annes, Edinburgh

Charitable donations

2007: £109,844
2006: £161,384
2004: £81,208
2003: £61,665

Community involvement

AEGON state that it is: 'Very much a part of the local communities that we live and work in. To make sure we have a positive effect on these communities, we've developed the community involvement programme. This focuses on three main areas:

- projects in the community
- employee volunteering
- sharing AEGON resources and skills.'

Exclusions

No support for circular appeals, fundraising events, advertising in charity brochures, appeals from individuals, purely denominational (religious) appeals, local appeals not in areas of company presence or overseas projects.

Applications

In writing to the correspondent.

Corporate giving

In 2007, the company made charitable donations in the UK of just under £110,000. Although we have no details of the

beneficiaries, the company's website gave the following examples regarding its community involvement:

'*AEGON Breakfast Club* – In 2007, we launched the AEGON Breakfast Club in Edinburgh, in partnership with the Heart of Midlothian Education and Community Trust and the City of Edinburgh Council. This exciting initiative aims to fund breakfast clubs in every primary school in the city, giving the children a healthy start to the day, and is something our staff are very involved with.

'*Lytham Young Enterprise Scheme* – In Lytham, we're one of the sponsors of the Young Enterprise Scheme. This initiative helps 15 to 18-year-olds start up and manage their own business, giving them invaluable experience. Our own employees are on hand to offer advice and insight.'

Employee-led support

AEGON offers teams within its business the chance to have a day out working with a charity. For example, in November 2007 the corporate service team spent a day with the Scottish Wildlife Trust, building paths at the wildlife centre.

Aggregate Industries Ltd

Company registration number 5655952

Bardon Hall, Copt Oak Road, Markfield, Leicestershire, United Kingdom LE67 9PJ

01530 816600; Fax: 01530 816666

Website: www.aggregate.com

Correspondent: Mrs Mary Ford, Company Secretary
01530 816600; Fax: 01530 816666

Chairman: Benoit-Henri Koch

Chief Executive: Bill Bolsover

Year end
31/12/2007

Nature of company business
Aggregate Industries and its subsidiaries are engaged in the exploitation of land and mineral reserves principally for the supply of heavy building materials for construction activities.

The company became part of the Holcim Group in 2005.

Subsidiaries include: Supreme Concrete, Brown & Potter Ltd, Stoneflair Ltd, Three Counties Concrete Ltd, Ronez Ltd, Paragon Materials Ltd, London Concrete Ltd

Main locations: Coalville

UK employees: 6,000

Total employees: 6,200

Charitable donations

2007: £63,000
2006: £55,000
2005: £112,000
2004: £269,000
2003: £323,000

Membership: BitC

Community involvement

The company's policy is to provide financial support to charities which benefit the local areas and communities of Leicestershire and within the aggregates/construction industry.

In addition, the company has sites all over the UK, particularly in the East and West Midlands, London, the South West, Scotland and northern England. It supports charities local to those sites, especially those involved with children/youth, education, older people, enterprise/training, environment/heritage, or allied to the construction industry, medical research, science/technology, sickness/disability and social welfare.

Exclusions

No support for advertising in charity brochures, animal welfare, appeals from individuals, the arts, fundraising events, overseas appeals, political appeals or religious appeals.

Applications

In writing to the correspondent.

Corporate giving

In 2007, the company made charitable donations amounting to £63,000. No information on how this was distributed was made available.

Commercially-led support

Sponsorship: The company undertakes good-cause sponsorship.

Agilent Technologies UK Ltd

Company registration number 3809903

South Queensferry, West Lothian EH30 9TG

0131 331 1000; Fax: 0131 331 3000

Website: www.agilent.com

Correspondent: Rosalind Bryant

Year end	Turnover	Pre-tax profit
31/10/2007	£210,095,000	£32,357,000

Nature of company business
The design, manufacture, marketing and servicing of products and system for measurement, communication and chemical analysis.

Main locations: Winnersh, Queensferry

UK employees: 901

Charitable donations
2007: £53,873

Community involvement

The company supports projects to increase student interest and achievement in science education, with an emphasis on women and groups under-represented in the technology industry. Agilent also aims to increase the ability of communities to effectively address local health and human services needs, and environmental issues.

Exclusions

Agilent are unable to fulfil donation requests from organisations or programmes that preclude participation or involvement based on criteria such as race, colour, age, religion, national origin, sexual orientation or disability.

Applications

Local appeals should be made in writing to the correspondent.

For further information about the Agilent Foundation, please write to: Agilent Technologies Foundation, MS 1B-07 , 5301 Stevens Creek Blvd , Santa Clara, CA 95051, USA.

Corporate giving

Agilent Technologies UK Ltd made charitable donations of £53,873 in 2007. We have no details of the beneficiaries.

In line with the company's overall objectives concerning science and mathematics, grants have been provided through the pre-university science education programme for the purchase of laboratory equipment and towards curriculum support. Awards have also gone to a number of institutions including Beaumont School in St Albans and Queensferry Primary Scotland in West Lothian.

Aligent Technologies Foundation

The Agilent Technologies Foundation is a separate, non-profit organisation funded by Agilent Technologies which focuses on advancing pre-university science education around the world. The foundation makes pre-selected, foundation-initiated grants in countries where Agilent is located.

The foundation supports:

- programmes for strategic initiatives linked to change and improvement in student learning and engagement
- events and initiatives that strengthen the science education process
- programmes that include diversities of race, gender, class and ethnicity and support underrepresented segments of the population.

Worldwide, the foundation made donations of $5,105,797 in 2007.

Employee-led support

The Agilent Employee Giving Campaign is supported by the foundation which matches funds raised by employees on behalf of health and human care organisations in their local communities.

Commercially-led support

Sponsorship: *Science/technology* – In 2007 the company jointly-sponsored Edinburgh University Science Festival.

Air Products Group Ltd

Company registration number 3101747

Hersham Place Technology Park, Molesey Road, Walton-on-Thames, Surrey KT12 4RZ

01932 249 200; Fax: 01932 258 565

Website: www.airproducts.co.uk

Year end	Turnover	Pre-tax profit
30/09/2007	£479,712,000	£48,862,000

Nature of company business

The manufacture and sale of industrial gases, the design and construction of equipment for the production and use of industrial gases, and the manufacture and sale of speciality chemicals.

Subsidiaries include: Anchor Chemical (UK) Ltd, Ancomer Ltd, Magictalk Ltd, The Oxygen Therapy Company Ltd, Prodair Services Ltd, On-site Engineering Services Ltd, Rimer-Alco International Ltd, Unoco (UK) Ltd, Gardner Cryogenics Ltd

Main locations: Crewe, Walton-on-Thames

UK employees: 2,057

Charitable donations

2007: £153,584
2006: £89,235
2005: £100,000

Community involvement

The following information is taken from the company's website, which now provides clear guidelines regarding its community support policy.

'At Air Products, we believe for our social investment to be successful, it is important to understand the needs of the communities we operate in. This is done through discussion and consultation with individuals, employees, community groups and other key stakeholders. Our aim is to respond to these needs through a targeted social responsibility programme, which helps to develop fruitful relationships and sustainable communities in a meaningful way.

'Our focus is to assist local charities and non-profit making organisations that have a direct impact on the communities in which we operate and where our employees live and work.'

Air Products' support is concentrated on five specific areas:

▶ education
▶ environment and safety
▶ arts and culture
▶ community investment
▶ fitness, health and welfare.

The company's support for these areas may take a number of forms: Monetary donations; Employee matching scheme; In kind goods and services; Raffle prizes; and/or, obsolete PC donations.

Exclusions

The company regrets that it is unable to support:

▶ personal appeals on behalf of individuals
▶ advertising
▶ organisations whose prime function is entertainment for profit
▶ sectarian or denominational organisations or their sponsored activities or programmes, as its employees, stakeholders and customers represent all religious and ethnic groups (except where the organisation is seeking funds in the direct interest of the entire community or is offered and readily available on a non-restricted, non-sectarian basis – Aid to Education is exempt from this provision)
▶ political parties, public office holders, political committees, or political candidates.

Applications

If your charity or not-for-profit organisation fits Air Products' criteria and you would like to apply for support, please complete the online application form on the company's website.

Information available: The company produce an annual corporate social responsibility report.

Corporate giving

In 2006/07, the company's charitable donations amounted to £153,534 (2006: £89,235). Some of the projects/organisations supported during the year included: Rydens School, Surrey – Young Apprentice competition; London Schools Hydrogen Challenge; Wildlife Aid – Surrey; Manchester Camerata; The Police Community Clubs of Great Britain; Overton Rugby Festival; and Elmbridge Sports Awards.

In kind support

Education: The company provides work experience schemes for pupils and educational materials for schools. Used equipment is passed on to schools, as are products with the company logo for use as raffle prizes.

Discounts on balloon gas are offered to charities.

Employee-led support

Employees who are active in charitable fundraising frequently have funds matched (50% of the amount raised up to a maximum of £500) by the company, primarily in the health and welfare fields. Staff are encouraged to become volunteers in their own time and to become school governors. Staff are also seconded to voluntary organisations such as Home-Start.

Payroll giving: The company operates a payroll giving scheme for employees.

Commercially-led support

Sponsorship: The company will consider undertaking arts and good cause sponsorship.

Akzo Nobel UK Ltd

Company registration number 128124

28th Floor Portland House, Bressenden Place, London SW1E 5BG

020 7932 9800; Fax: 020 7932 9932

Website: www.akzonobel.uk.com

Correspondent: Company Secretary

Chief Executive: Hans Wijers

Year end
31/12/2007

Nature of company business
The group is an industrial materials company involved in polymer technology and surface science. Business areas are: pharmaceuticals; coatings; and chemicals.

Subsidiaries include: Akcros Chemicals Ltd, Diosynth Ltd, Organon Laboratories Ltd, Eka Chemicals Ltd, Mason Vehicle Graphics, Nobilas UK Ltd, International Paint Ltd, Biosynth Ltd, Intervet UK Ltd, Organon Laboratories Ltd, Eka Chemicals, Intervet UK Ltd

Main locations: London, Newhouse, Gateshead, Southampton, Plymouth, Brentwood, Buckhaven, Milton Keynes, Cambridge, Beith, Henley-on-Thames, Congresbury, Blackburn

UK employees: 4,100

Total employees: 61,300

Charitable donations

2006: £6,000

Community involvement

From the contents of the company's website it is clear that Akzo Nobel acknowledges its wider responsibilities to society, though there is little specific reference to its UK programme. Perhaps with the 2008 takeover of ICI this will change.

The focus of the company's community programme for sponsorship and donations is to stimulate young talent, while the corporate projects the company is involved in are mainly international in character. The local units, meanwhile, have adopted a more regional approach.

Support through sponsorship and donations are given to selected activities in the fields such as education, sports, science, healthcare, culture and the arts.

Exclusions

The company provides no support for political parties, their institutions, agencies or representatives.

Applications

In writing to the correspondent.

Information available: The company produce an annual sustainability report.

Corporate giving

Unfortunately, we have been unable to obtain full financial and community investment figures for Akzo Nobel businesses in the UK. The company details given here are for the holding company which declared charitable donations of around £6,000 in 2006. Given that there are a further 16 company sites around the UK (excluding those for ICI), it seems reasonable to assume that overall the company gives sufficient to be included.

Education: The company started its Education-Industry Partnership Programme in 1991. This aims to interest young students in science and technology through a closer collaboration between the company's sites and the educational system.

Employee-led support

According to the company's website its community programme is a worldwide initiative that encourages employees to get involved in their local communities. It states:

'[The community programme is] an opportunity for Akzo Nobel colleagues to contribute to local projects that need hands-on, professional support. We hope that over time these initiatives will become self-supporting.

'The success of the community programme relies on the enthusiasm of our employees – and so far, more than 2,500 of them have got involved in over 500 projects around the world.'

Although there are numerous examples of successful projects from around the world, none of them are from the UK.

Commercially-led support

Sponsorship: Beneficiaries have included The Coulthard Institute of Art, Museum of the Chemical Industry, The Royal Society, The National Museum of Science & Industry, The Museum of Film, Photography & Television and The National Railway Museum.

Alcoa UK Holdings Ltd

Company registration number 499001

1 Park Row, Leeds LS1 5AB

Website: www.alcoa.com

Correspondent: (See 'Applications')

Year end	Turnover	Pre-tax profit
31/12/2006	£589,109,000	(£23,416)

Nature of company business
Alcoa is a world leading producer of primary aluminium, fabricated aluminium, and alumina. Active in all major aspects of the industry.

Subsidiaries include: Reynolds Food Packaging, AFL Automotive, Howmet Ltd, AFL Telecommunications, ASA, Kawneer UK

Main locations: Telford, Runcorn, London, Laindon, Exeter, Coalville, Birmingham

UK employees: 2,850

Charitable donations

2006: £55,582
2005: £39,000
2004: £32,000

Membership: BitC

Community involvement

The company's main support for local voluntary and community groups in England is via the Alcoa Foundation; although a small amount comes from within the UK. Based in the United States., the foundation's website provides a comprehensive breakdown of its grant making worldwide.

Alcoa's grant making is focused around what it terms 'Areas of Excellence', i.e. conservation and sustainability, safe and healthy children and families, global education and workplace skills, and business and community partnerships.

Priority is given to projects and organisations in or near communities where Alcoa offices or plants are located, currently: Birmingham, Coalville, Exeter, Laindon. London, Runcorn and Telford.

Exclusions

Generally, no support for individuals, political or religious organisations, local appeals not in areas of company presence, capital campaigns, endowment funds or funds directed towards deficit reduction or operating reserves, advertising, fundraising events, trips, documentaries, videos, conferences or sponsorships, indirect or overhead costs, multi-year grants.

Applications

In writing to your local foundation contact (situated at each Alcoa site), who will then make recommendations to the Alcoa Foundation for grant awards.

Full details of grant giving guidelines and procedures are available at: www.alcoa.com/global/en/community/info_page/ Request_grant_community-based.asp

Corporate giving

Through the combined efforts of Alcoa UK and the Alcoa Foundation, total cash donations to charitable/community organisations in the UK in 2006 amounted to just under £199,000 (£56,000 from the company and £143,000 from the foundation). Beneficiaries of foundation grants included: Alphington Primary School, Exeter (environmental education programme); Deafway, Leyland (British sign-language and online communication programme); Pontybrenin Primary School, Swansea (self-sufficiency and workforce readiness programme); and The Police Community Clubs of Great Britain, Birmingham (anti-bullying campaign for middle schools).

In 2007, the foundation made grants totalling nearly £246,000. Examples of beneficiaries include: Devon Wildlife Trust (Devon bat conservation project); Glebe Farm Library, Birmingham (community health lifestyles choices workshops); and London School of Economics & Political Science.

Interestingly, the company/foundation also makes what they call 'Exit grants'. These are made to assist local organisations whenever Alcoa have businesses or locations that will or might be affected by a plant divestiture or closing. The purpose is to leave a grant commitment behind in the affected community. These strategies consider the timing of the action, multi-year grants already committed to not-for-profit organisations in the community, historical grantmaking levels, community needs and expectations, and other commitments that are in effect.

To this effect in 2007, a grant of £15,000 was given to the Blaenymaes, Portmead, Penplas Development Trust Ltd, Swansea, for a workforce development and food service programme. Cynically, one could say that this was just a sop to appease the local community. However, whilst it will never replace the jobs lost, it does acknowledge that a company's responsibility to a community doesn't necessarily end once it has upped and left.

Employee-led support

In addition to grant-based activities, two global programmes have been developed to recognize the volunteer efforts of Alcoa employees through special Alcoa grants. ACTION (Alcoans Coming Together In Our Neighbourhoods) encourages Alcoans to work as a team to help a local non-profit, while Bravo! recognizes individual employee volunteer efforts.

ACTION – The programme encourages teams of five or more Alcoa employees to spend a minimum of four hours on a community service project for a local non-profit organisation or NGO. As recognition of their efforts, Alcoa will make either a US$1,500 £750) or a US$3,000 (31,500) unrestricted grant (depending on the size of the team) to the organisation.

Bravo! – The Bravo! programme recognizes the volunteer efforts of individual Alcoa employees in their communities. For each Alcoa employee who volunteers at least 50 hours at a non-profit or NGO, a yearly US$250 (£125) grant is awarded to that organisation.

Qualifying organisations include non-profit civic, health, social welfare, educational, cultural, community, or governmental organisations that provide a charitable service.

A further initiative is Alcoa's annual worldwide 'Month of Service' which is a company-wide event that recognises and encourages the efforts of the thousands of Alcoa employees who volunteer in their communities around the world. Employees' volunteer time is matched with grants from Alcoa.

Allen & Overy LLP

Company registration number OC306763

One Bishops Square, London E1 6AO

020 3088 0000; Fax: 020 3088 0088

Website: www.allenovery.com

Correspondent: Louise Zekaria, The Pro Bono & Community Affairs Senior Manager
Email: louise.zekaria@allenovery.com

Managing Partner: Wim Dejonghe

Senior Partner: David Morley

Year end 30/04/2008	Turnover £1,015,800,000	Pre-tax profit £447,200,000

Nature of company business
International law firm.

Main locations: London

UK employees: 2,227

Total employees: 4,475

Charitable donations

Total community contributions: £16,600,000

Membership: BitC, L B Group

Community involvement

Allen & Overy are an international law firm with an extensive pro bono community affairs programme – 'Values into Community Action' – which supports a broad range of initiatives. The firm state:

'By working with our local communities we are able to identify and respond to their needs, offering help that makes an enduring impact, whether it be helping with literacy or numeracy schemes in the inner city or providing access to justice for those who cannot afford it.

'The programme also provides a valuable opportunity for personal and professional development. It responds to the desire of many individuals to use their skills and experience to help others and put something back into societies around the world.'

To oversee its pro bono work, Allen & Overy has appointed a Pro Bono and Community Work Committee. In each of the offices outside London, it has a programme contact and partner responsible for local programmes.

Charitable giving

The Allen & Overy Foundation is administered by the London Charities Committee which is comprised of partners within the firm.

The charities committee will make donations to charities that:
- are law related
- are based in its neighbouring boroughs of Tower Hamlets and Hackney
- have Allen & Overy volunteers participating in their activities.

The committee has recently given greater emphasis to the third option, to recognise the dedication of staff to the firm's pro bono and community activities.

Charity or Community Partner of the Year

Each year, the London office chooses a charitable or community organisation to support.

When determining its community partner of the year, Allen & Overy look for a charity or community organisation whose work follows the theme of: Diversity or Children and Education.

The organisation should:
- be small and not as high profile or well-funded as many others
- provide a high quality service and be greatly in need of the firm's support to continue its service
- be located near the firm's Spitalfields office and preferably based in Tower Hamlets
- offer varied, interesting and flexible opportunities for staff volunteering
- have professional staff that are easy to work with.

Charity/ Community Partner of the year: The Whitechapel Mission (2008/09).

Applications
Charitable giving (London)

If your organisation falls within the guidelines given and you wish an application to be considered, please send a letter and supporting documents to the correspondent.

Please set out details of your organisation, the project for which sponsorship is required, the amount being requested and the charitable registration number. Short listed requests are considered by the Allen & Overy Charities Committee in their quarterly meetings.

Outside of London each Allen & Overy office has a community programme contact and partner who are responsible for their local initiatives.

Charity or Community Partner of the Year

If you would like to nominate a charity or community organisation, please send a note addressed to Louise Zekaria, setting out the following:
- how the organisation meets the criteria
- potential volunteering opportunities with the organisation for its staff
- suggested ways in which Allen & Overy could support the organisation.

As in previous years, Allen & Overy's Charities Committee will make the final decision. Applications are considered in February/March of each year.

Information available: The firm produce two excellent reports on its work with its local communities; these are 'Values into Action' 2007/08, which details its pro bono and community affairs, and 'Artbeat' which covers its community arts initiative. Both are downloadable from the firm's website.

Corporate giving

In 2007/08, the total value of lawyer hours spent of pro bono and community affairs work was equivalent to £16.6 million in billings. We do not know what proportion of this is attributable to the firm's UK offices. However, some of the organisations to benefit from pro bono work included: Advocates for International Development (A4D); Battersea Legal Advice Centre; Interrights; Liberty; and Toynbee Hall.

The firm's community affairs work in London is centred on the Tower Hamlets area through its Access to Education and Access to Employment programmes. These provide a clear strategy linked to its staff's aspirations to help children through educational and regeneration projects. Young people's basic skills are enhanced, their self-confidence and self-esteem is raised, and they have a better chance of breaking the cycle of poverty and unemployment.

Allen & Overy work with local organisations and local schools including St John's Primary School, Bethnal Green Technology College, School Governors, CityGateway and The Brokerage CityLink.

More general community work has included collaboration with Maxitech, Streetshine, and Habitat for Humanity.

Comprehensive details of the above and other community initiatives are included in the report 'Values into Community Action 2007/08'.

We have been unable to obtain any information regarding the total value of grants made by the firm as part of its charitable giving.

In kind support
The Library in Allen & Overy's London office regularly donates old editions of books within its collections to a number of different organisations, including Battersea Legal Advice Centre, the International Book Facility, the Statute Law Revision Society and the English-speaking Polish Law Club based in Debora, Poland.

Employee-led support
In addition to the extensive pro bono work the firm conduct, opportunities for non-lawyers to participate in community (non-legal) volunteering have also been developed, based on staff aspirations to help children through educational and regeneration projects.

If you have a specific query or you would like to find out about volunteering opportunities, please email probonoteam@allenovery.com.

Alliance & Leicester plc

Company registration number 3263713

Building 1, Floor 2, Carlton Park, Narborough, Leicester LE19 0AL

0116 201 1000

Website: www.alliance-leicester-group.co.uk

Correspondent: Anoushka Lander, CSR/Investor Relations Co-ordinator
Email: csr@alliance-leicester.co.uk

Chairman: Roy Browm

Chief Executive: D J Bennett

Year end	Turnover	Pre-tax profit
31/12/2007	£1,425,800,000	£399,200,000

Nature of company business
Principal activity: provision of a range of personal financial services.

Main locations: Bootle, Leicester

UK employees: 7,223

Charitable donations

2007: £810,000
2005: £1,020,000
2003: £512,000

Total community contributions: £1,444,000

Membership: BitC

Community involvement

Alliance & Leicester supports a range of good causes and projects in its local communities and has continued to focus on four areas:

- supporting initiatives aimed at improving both local and national education
- supporting its staff efforts in raising money for charity through the group's matched donation scheme
- supporting organisations that help those who are experiencing financial difficulties
- supporting charities and organisations that aim to improve the links between businesses and the communities in which they operate.

Exclusions

No support for circular appeals, advertising in charity brochures, animal welfare, appeals from individuals, the arts, education, older people, environment/heritage, fundraising events, medical research, overseas projects, political appeals, religious appeals, science/technology, sickness/disability, sport or local appeals not in areas of company presence.

Applications

In writing to the correspondent, who has stated that the charities committee selects charities to support and, as such, is unable to encourage other appeals. Unsolicited applications will not be acknowledged.

Corporate giving

In 2007, Alliance & Leicester continued to support local charities and community activities. Donations for charitable purposes in the year amounted to £810,000 (including £100,000 donated by the group to the NSPCC). In addition to this, in kind support, e.g. use of office space, staff volunteering and non-financial gifts was estimated to be worth £270,000 with a further £364,000 being given in good-cause sponsorship to support local community events and programmes. (This latter figure excludes the commercial sponsorship of the European Capital of Culture Celebrations in Liverpool.)

In the North West of England the majority of the group's charitable donations continue to be made via the Alliance & Leicester Fund managed on the group's behalf by the Community Foundation for Merseyside. In addition, in 2007 we have set up an additional smaller fund managed by the Greater Manchester Community Foundation, to support community and charitable organisations in Manchester.

In kind support

As part of Business in the Community's 'Cares' scheme, the company is active in encouraging and supporting staff engaged in volunteering activities. Staff at the Leicester, Liverpool, Leeds and Manchester operations participate in the Right to Read scheme which aims to improve literacy standards by volunteers listening to primary school children read.

Management secondments, organising fundraising events, and the use of office space were also part of the in kind support provided by the company.

Employee-led support

During 2007, the group donated around £90,000 to charities through its Matched Donation Scheme, which matches funds raised by staff and their children.

Payroll giving: A payroll giving scheme is in operation.

Commercially-led support

Sponsorship: *Good-causes* – In 2007, Alliance & Leicester provided £364,000 of support for local community events and programmes,

Alliance Boots Holdings Ltd

Company registration number 4452715

D90 Building West G14, Nottingham NG90 1BS

0115 949 2185

Website: www.boots-uk.com/csr

Correspondent: Rachel McGuire, Community Affairs Manager
Email: rachel.mcguire@boots.co.uk

Chairman: Stefano Pessina

Year end	Turnover	Pre-tax profit
31/03/2008	£11,865,000,000	(£64,000,000)

Nature of company business
The group's principal activities are: retailing of chemists' merchandise; the development, manufacture and marketing of healthcare and consumer products; the provision of opticians' and other healthcare services.

Main locations: Nottingham

UK employees: 76,000

Charitable donations

2008: £2,620,330
2007: £1,458,000
2006: £1,420,000
2005: £1,652,000
2004: £2,364,000

Total community contributions: £4,454,499
Management costs: £360,456

Membership: BitC

Community involvement

Note: All of the information contained herein, except the year end financial figures, refers to Boots UK.

The company's priority is to contribute positively to the communities that it serves. Community health is at the centre of this activity and the focus is on building active partnerships that will produce projects and initiatives with real health benefits. In the UK Boots is working with two key charity partners in the areas of women's cancer – The Eve Appeal and Breast Cancer Care. In addition the company has supported Children in Need for a number of years.

Employees are encouraged to share their expertise to help people lead healthier lifestyles and provided with opportunities to devote their time and energy to supporting causes that matter. Employees' fundraising efforts are also supported and the company provides a matched giving scheme to staff, enabling them to claim up to £500 to match their own funds raised. The company also offers the Give as You Earn payroll giving facility.

The Boots Charitable Trust is an independent grant making trust wholly funded by the company. Since it was established in the 1970's the Trust has donated over £9 million to charitable causes. Currently the Trust's giving is focused in the county of Nottinghamshire, in recognition of Boots long history with the area.

See www.boots-uk.com.

Exclusions
The trust will not support the following:
- projects benefiting people outside Nottinghamshire
- individuals
- organisations that are not registered charities and who have income or expenditure of more than £5,000 per year
- charities seeking funds to redistribute to other charities
- projects for which there is a legal statutory obligation.

Applications
Boots Charitable Trust

Applications to the trust are only accepted on the official application form which must be accompanied by your latest annual report and detailed accounts. Letters of support from partnership and statutory organisations, local CVS's and so on will go to support your application, as will statistics on the numbers of people benefiting from your activities.

The application form can be downloaded as a Word document, or it can be posted out to you by the correspondent, to whom it should be returned once completed. All applications are responded to.

The correspondent is: Rachel McGuire, Boots Charitable Trust, D90 Building G14 West, Nottingham NG90 1BS (Tel: 0115 949 2185; email: rachel.mcguire@boots.co.uk).

For amounts under £2,000 there is no deadline for applications and the decision period is 1–2 months.

For amounts over £2,000 the trustee meetings are held bi-monthly in January, March, May, July, September and November. The deadline for receipt of applications is the 7th of the month preceding the meeting i.e. February 7th for the March meeting, April 7th for the May meeting and so on. The decision period is 2–4 months.

Corporate giving

In 2007/08, the company made UK community contributions of over £4.8 million including management costs. A large proportion of these contributions were made to healthcare related projects reflecting its focus on pharmacy. Donations are usually made either at a national or a local level within the countries that the company operate. Contributions were broken down as follows:
- cash donations (£2,620,330)
- employee time (£1,104,885)
- in kind donations (£729,284)
- management costs (£360,456).

Out of a total worldwide contributions figure of £5.1 million, £4.1 million went in support of national organisations, £660,000 to local organisations and £380,000 to international organisations.

The Boots Charitable Trust

During the year to March 2008 the company donated £220,000 to the trust which made donations of £226,115.

On average the trust gives between 50 and 60 grants per year to charities and voluntary organisations benefiting people living in Nottinghamshire. Trustees are especially keen on projects with the capacity to deliver significant impact and which reach the greatest number of people.

Major donations during the year include £15,000 towards a new minibus at the Nottinghamshire Hospice, the only hospice in the county that offers palliative care services for patients that are suffering from any type of life limiting illness. Transport services are essential to patients accessing the vital care and support services that they receive at the hospice's daycare facility.

Other major donations include an award of £10,000 to the Wheelbase Motor Project which works with young people aged 14–25 who have been or are at risk of offending or social exclusion, or who are excluded from mainstream education. Participatory and interactive sessions are run in the classroom while practical motor vehicle skills are taught in the workshop.

A donation of £11,171 from the trust will enable Think Children, a charity which supports young children who have emotional and social difficulties, to deliver focused play sessions in the school environment.

In kind support
Since 2001 unwanted products such as damaged or end of line stock have been donated to charities as gifts in kind. As well as being of benefit to the voluntary sector this reduces the amount of waste sent to landfill. National and international charities providing humanitarian aid and medical assistance are supported in this way.

In 2007/08 in kind donations were valued at £729,284.

Employee-led support
Volunteering programmes enable Boots employees to participate in a range of community activities in company time, sharing their skills and expertise with schools, hospitals and voluntary organisations. Boots No. 7 Beauty consultants volunteer to run beauty workshops for women cancer patients in 50 UK hospitals through their involvement with the charity Look Good ... Feel Better.

In 2006/07 the company joined forces with Home-Start family support charity, to match Boots volunteers with projects that make a real difference to families in their area. Volunteers at the Nottingham support office continue to give their support to literacy schemes in city primary schools.

The company continues to provide work experience opportunities to students in its stores, enabling them to learn more about the retail sector and the qualities required by employers.

Payroll giving: The company offers the Give As You Earn payroll giving facility.

Commercially-led support

Sponsorship: After two successful years of helping thousands of customers to stick to their healthy New Year's resolutions with the Change One Thing campaign, the company developed a free on line resource for PSHE/PSE/Home Economics and Science teachers of 11–14 year olds. The website is dedicated to helping students make positive changes to their lifestyles and links to the curriculum in this area.

See www.boots.com/changeonethingschools

Allianz Insurance plc

Company registration number 84638

57 Ladymead, Guildford, Surrey GU1 1DB

01483 568161; Fax: 01483 300952

Website: www.allianzcornhill.co.uk

Correspondent: Fran Everist, Community Affairs Consultant
Email: fran.everist@allianzcornhill.co.uk

Chairman: Clem Booth

Chief Executive: Andrew Torrance

Year end	Turnover	Pre-tax profit
31/12/2007	£1,582,100,000	£197,100,000

Nature of company business
The group undertakes all classes of insurance business. It has 13 UK branches.

Subsidiaries include: Trafalgar Insurance plc, British Reserve Insurance Co. Ltd, Pet Plan Ltd, Domestic Insurance Services Ltd, DBI Insurance Co. Ltd

Main locations: Brentford, Liphook, Guildford, Bristol, Tunbridge Wells

UK employees: 10,865

Charitable donations

2007: £146,095
2006: £132,048
2005: £89,314
2004: £153,498
2003: £102,852

Membership: A & B

Community involvement

Allianz's policy is to consider all applications for support and to provide help where appropriate. There is a preference for charities where the business is located (Guildford, London, Tunbridge Wells, Bristol, Brentford and Liphook), and in which a member of staff is involved. Previously, we were advised that there is some preference for charities working in the fields of children and youth, education, older people, enterprise/training, environment/heritage, fundraising events, science/technology, sickness/disability charities and social welfare.

In 2006, Allianz launched a new fund with the Surrey Community Foundation. The Allianz Fund has been established to benefit communities in Guildford and the surrounding areas. The fund supports projects that build capacity and skills within the community through training and development. Other fund criteria include disadvantaged, older people, drugs and the environment.

Each year, as part of its community investment programme, Allianz adopts a national charity. This is done through staff elections that begin in October. After initial category selection a shortlist of national charities that fit Allianz's criteria is then put forward for a second staff vote. The successful charity is named in December and the fundraising campaign begins the following spring.

Charity of the Year: Breast Cancer Care (2007).

Exclusions

No response to circular appeals. No support for advertising in charity brochures, appeals from individuals, the arts, medical research, overseas projects, political appeals, religious appeals, sport or local appeals not in areas of company presence.

Applications

For further details please contact the correspondent.

Information Available: Further tailored advice for applicants is available from the company on request.

Corporate giving

In 2007, the company made donations of just over £146,000 (2006: £132,000). Besides supporting Breast Cancer Care (around £90,000 was given through a combination of company donations and employee fundraising), the group also supported The Prince's Trust, The Jubilee Sailing Trust and A Chance to Shine.

Support was also provided through the Allianz Fund at the Surrey Community Foundation, with donations going to Oakleaf, Normandy Community Therapy Garden and Lakeview Community Action Group.

In kind support

Non-cash support is given in the form of gifts in kind and may take the form of one or more of the following:

- donation of surplus office furniture or equipment
- donation of in-house design and print services
- use of office space for meetings
- donation of the expertise and time of a relevantly qualified employee
- teams of volunteers
- Items for raffles and auctions
- donation of unwanted paper and stationery to schools and community groups.

Employee-led support

Allianz operate a 'Helping Hands' scheme as part of its community investment programme. This scheme marries teams of employees with local charities and community groups in need of help.

Staff are also involved in mentoring students and businesses in the Surrey area.

Payroll giving: The company operates the Give As You Earn scheme to which the company adds 10%.

Commercially-led support

Sponsorship: In 2007, in the Guildford area, the company sponsored:

- the Guildford Sports Awards – community team award
- Keep Yourself Safe initiative organised by SCC Traffic and Road Safety and Guildford Borough Council
- firewise scheme – operated in schools by Surrey Fire and Rescue
- Guildford Book Festival – sponsors of the adult short story competition
- Disability Challengers six-a-side football tournament
- Spectrum Customer Achievement Awards.

Funding for these activities is supplemented by the income from the recycling of toner cartridges and mobile telephones.

Allied London Properties Ltd

Company registration number 104394

1 Cavendish Place, London W1G 0QD

020 7291 7970; Fax: 020 7291 7971

Website: www.alliedlondon.com

Correspondent: John Ashurst, Company Secretary
Email: info@alliedlondon.com

Chief Executive: M J Ingall

Year end	Turnover	Pre-tax profit
31/12/1998	£7,260,000	£5,515,000

Nature of company business
Principal activity: property investors.

Subsidiaries include: Pellam Homes Ltd, Gough Cooper Properties Ltd, Hamiltonhill Estates Ltd

Main locations: London

UK employees: 38

Charitable donations
1998: £47,000

Community involvement

Previous information suggested that support is given to a wide range of charitable organisations, especially in the fields of education, health and community affairs.

Exclusions

No support for appeals from individuals or overseas projects.

Applications

The company stated that it does not wish to receive unsolicited requests for donations.

Corporate giving

Recent information on the company's community involvement was not available.

In 1998, the company donated £47,000 to charitable organisations. Grants to national organisations ranged from £100 to £10,000. Grants to local organisations ranged from £50 to £500.

Support has been given to Industry in Education, Prince's Youth Business Trust, Action on Addiction, WellBeing, British Red Cross, Variety Club and NSPCC.

In kind support

In May 2005, Allied London's Spinningfields development in Manchester (close to the site of the city's first ever children's hospital) was used as the launch site for fundraising 'Balloon Race' on behalf of children's hospitals.

AMEC plc

Company registration number 1675285

76–78 Old Street, London EC1V 9RU

020 7539 5800; Fax: 020 7539 5900

Website: www.amec.com

Correspondent: Charities Committee

Chairman: Jock Green-Armytage

Chief Executive: Samir Brikho

Year end	Turnover	Pre-tax profit
31/12/2007	£2,356,200,000	£151,600,000

Nature of company business
AMEC's provides a broad range of services to the oil and gas industry worldwide. The company has regional; offices throughout England, Scotland and Wales.

Subsidiaries include: CV Buchan

Main locations: Aberdeen, Ashford, London, Birchwood, Birmingham, Manchester

UK employees: 17,368

Charitable donations
2007: £188,000
2006: £186,000
2005: £108,000
2003: £69,000

Total community contributions: £334,000

Membership: BitC

Community involvement

AMEC states on its website that: 'Investing in our communities involves more than making charitable donations, but requires taking an active interest and making a positive contribution, whether it is in time, materials, or another form of giving. Our approach is based on providing support for the communities in which we live and work, leaving benefits in project locations long after we leave.'

To help achieve this goal AMEC established a charities committee made up of members of the senior management team, including the chairman, chief executive and finance director. Throughout the year the charities committee monitors the effectiveness of the company's charitable donation policy and reviews the investments made through the employee matched funding scheme.

Unusually, for a corporate, details of these internal reviews, together with related documents, are available online within the Sustainability Report 2007 > Community investment section of the company's website; and fascinating reading they make too!

Without going into too much detail, it appears that in early 2007 AMEC withdrew matched funding for charities on behalf of which individual employees were fundraising and, instead, established a group of six nominated charities. This, according to the review notes, was 'to ensure that funds were raised for none controversial charitable institutions [and] to ensure money was diverted to worthy causes'.

However, although these charities were chosen by each division of AMEC, applications for matched funding dropped from over 300 in 2006 to 33 in 2007. As a result, it was agreed to reinstate the employee choice matched funding in 2008 and to split the community investment budget in half (50% towards supporting employee nominated 'local' charities and 50% towards a small number of AMEC 'strategic' charities).

A decision was also taken by the committee to support charities which 'uphold human rights through education, access to health care, entrepreneurship, improved environmental quality and work which supports the UN millennium development goals'.

Exclusions

Non-charitable grants cannot be considered.

Applications

In writing to the correspondent.

Information available: The company's latest sustainability report (2007) is available online at www.amec.com.

Corporate giving

The company's annual report and accounts for 2007 states that it made donations to UK charities of £446,000 (2006: £186,000). We assume this figure to include in kind support as the charitable investment budget set for the year by the charities committee was £300,000. Furthermore, of the latter, some £112,000 is accounted for by a donation to United Way – a North American voluntary network. We have, therefore adjusted the figures shown under 'Financial information' accordingly, although even now we think these may contain an element of funds raised by AMEC employees.

The six nominated charities for 2007 were as follows (donations in brackets):

- United Way (£112,300)
- CLAN (£12,325)
- Engineers without Borders (£12,000)
- Children with Leukaemia (£5,380)
- Engineers Against Poverty (£5,000)
- WaterAid (£5,000)
- all other charities (£24,500).

Following these donations, around £115,000 remained in the community investment budget due to the lack of matched funding applications. The charities committee therefore decided to identify a small number of charities it was felt would benefit significantly from a contribution.

The remaining monies were split equally between the following charities: SOS Children's Village; World Medical Health Fund; HopeHIV; and IMPACT Foundation.

In kind support

The group tries to ensure that many of its waste products, such as toner cartridges and inkjets, are re-used to the advantage of worthwhile causes. There has also been a pledge of in kind support to Engineers Against Poverty (see above).

Employee-led support

The AMEC plc board charities committee has, as of 2008, pledged to support, up to a capped amount, charity fundraising undertaken by groups of employees through fund matching grants.

Amey UK plc

Company registration number 4736639

Sherard Building, Edmund Halley Road, Oxford OX4 4DQ

01865 713 100

Website: www.amey.co.uk

Correspondent: Communications Department

Email: group.hse@amey.co.uk

Chairman: Sir Richard Mottram

Chief Executive: Mel Ewell

Year end	Turnover	Pre-tax profit
31/12/2007	£1,371,456,000	£103,013,000

Nature of company business
A leading provider of support services in the UK, ranging from transportation and education, to defence and health.

Main locations: Birmingham, Belfast, Preston, Manchester, Newport, Glasgow, Edinburgh, Bristol

UK employees: 10,029

Charitable donations

2007: £60,783
2006: £46,070

Membership: BitC

Community involvement

Amey has over 200 sites located throughout the UK. In July 2005, it published its 'Community Involvement Policy' which, according to the company's website, was still valid as at September 2008. The document states that Amey's express policy is:

- to seek to explain its objectives and business practices to communities in which it works and, where appropriate, to consult with representatives of those communities to establish their needs and priorities
- that the contribution to communities will be made both by the company itself and by the enthusiasm, creativity, skills and personal time of its employees and, in some instances, those of our business partners
- to encourage employees to be active in the community and to be involved with relevant charitable organisations. Amey will, wherever practical, support such endeavours
- to focus corporate charitable support primarily on a charity chosen by its staff, with the selection reviewed every two years, where Amey undertakes to match funds raised by employees. The support for a nominated charity does not preclude fundraising at a more local level in support of any communities in which Amey is active as a business, or for charities clearly of relevance to the business.

Charity of the year: Wooden Spoon (2008)

Exclusions

No provision for funding or other support to political organisations of any sort, and only exceptionally to provide funding or support to religious organisations as part of an initiative to the general benefit of a community. No funding or support will be given to individuals outside the business.

Applications

In writing to the correspondent.

Corporate giving

In 2007, the company gave £60,783 (2006: £46,070) in grants to organisations. We have no details of the beneficiaries outside of the stated 'charity of the year'

Employee-led support

Employees are encouraged to be active in the community. The company's charitable support is focused on a charity chosen by its staff, with the selection reviewed every two years. Amey matches funds raised by its employees.

Anglesey Aluminium Metals Ltd

Company registration number 909645

Penrhos Works, PO Box 4, Holyhead, Gwynnedd LL65 2JJ

01407 725000; Fax: 01407 725001

Website: www.angleseyaluminium.co.uk

Correspondent: Jennifer Snelson, Community Relations Officer

Managing Director: David Bloor

Year end	Turnover	Pre-tax profit
31/12/2007	£203,342,000	£38,800,000

Nature of company business
The company owns and operates an aluminium smelter.

UK employees: 567

Charitable donations
2007: £21,155
2006: £15,240

Community involvement

The following information is taken from the company's website (September 2008):

'Anglesey Aluminium Metal Ltd (AAM) aims to expand and strengthen relationships with the Anglesey community through regular consultation and engagement. AAM sets out to build enduring relationships with neighbours that are characterised by mutual respect, active partnership and long term commitment.

'The board of Anglesey Aluminium Metal Ltd agrees the financial allocation for the donations and sponsorship committee in the annual board meeting. The donations committee members administrate the fund allocated by the board of directors. Preference is given to local organisations rather than individuals and donations are given to support a specific aim or function. In addition to applications received on an 'ad hoc' basis, it is proposed that 50 per cent of the donations budget will be managed more actively by the committee targeting projects that will build the community profile of AAM.'

Exclusions

No support for individuals, political or religious appeals, or local appeals not in areas of company presence.

Applications

In writing to the correspondent.

Corporate giving

In 2007, the company made charitable donations of £21,155. We have no details of the beneficiaries.

In kind support

Education: 'Anglesey Aluminium Metal Ltd and the Friends of Anglesey Red Squirrrels'' hold a number of educational visits with local schools as part of the Red Squirrel introduction programme. The visits are referred to as 'Red Squirrel Talk and Walk', during which the Friends of Anglesey Red Squirrels give an onsite talk about the Red Squirrels to the school children then take the participants for a walk near the woodland area to spot some squirrels.'

Environment: 'Anglesey Aluminium Metal Ltd is the custodian of a 200 acre coastal park that provides a natural shelter for many varieties of flora and fauna. Each year about 100,000 people visit the park. In early 2006 AAM appointed Kehoe Countryside Ltd (a countryside management company) to manage the AAM owned Penrhos Coastal Park and ensure it remains a beautiful and safe place for both the local community and visitors to enjoy.'

Anglia Regional Co-operative Society Ltd

Company registration number IP08644R

Westgate House, Park Road, Peterborough PE1 2TA

01733 563151; Fax: 01733 313078

Website: www.arcs.co.uk

Correspondent: Ron Douglas, Secretary
Email: executive.officer@arcs.co.uk

Chairman: Jean Humphreys

Chief Executive: John Chillcott

Year end	Turnover	Pre-tax profit
01/09/2007	£349,767,000	£2,779,000

Nature of company business
Co-operative society trading in food, household goods, furniture and funerals.

Main locations: Peterborough

UK employees: 3,406

Total employees: 3,406

Charitable donations
2007: £67,000
2005: £75,000
Membership: BitC

Community involvement

The mutual society supports national and local charities at a regional level, and has an effective policy of soliciting charitable donations from its customers via its dividend scheme which sees the trading profit of the organisation shared between those customers who have enrolled as a member. Members then have an opportunity at the point of sale to donate their dividend to share account number 600 (Share 600), the proceeds of which are presented each year to three or four charities, which are agreed by the board of directors.

A sub-committee of the board meets quarterly to consider charitable claims and to recommend those worthy of Share 600 funds to the full board. In addition to the three or four main charities supported each year, consideration is given to other claims, which may be met by Share 600 funds. The main recipients are often national charities, but the donations are made to branches in its trading areas as the society looks to support the local community where it can.

Exclusions

No grants for: running costs; causes deemed to promote a particular religious viewpoint; statutory services, such as schools, libraries, hospitals and so on; improvements to property not owned by the applicant charity; party political causes; or causes they believe conflict with the ethos of the co-operative movement. No support for animal welfare, the arts, enterprise/training, heritage, overseas projects, religious appeals, science/technology, sickness/disability, social welfare or sport.

The society does not consider 'charity of the year' applications.

Applications

In writing to the correspondent.

Corporate giving

In 2006/07 the company donated £67,000 to charitable causes, mainly through match funding of monies raised in its stores for worthwhile causes. These included: Cancer Research – Fakenham; St John's Ambulance – Beccles; and East Anglian Air Ambulance.

Members' donations to the share account, Share 600, were donated to the following organisations in the company's trading areas during 2007: Anthony Nolan Trust; Multiple Sclerosis Society; Parkinson's Disease Society; Breast Cancer Care – Waveney Region; Macmillan Nurses – Beccles and Lowestoft; CRUSE Bereavement Care – Peterborough; Children with Leukaemia – Spalding; Pilgrim Hospital (CT scanner appeal) – Spalding/Boston; Against Breast Cancer – Abingdon; and Linchfield Primary School – Market Deeping.

Employee-led support

The society matches employee fundraising from Share 600 funds up to a maximum of £2,000 per employee.

Commercially-led support

Sponsorship: – *Good-cause sponsorship* may be considered. Applications should be by letter, addressed to the board of directors.

Anglian Water Services Ltd

Company registration number 2366656

Anglian House, Ambury Road, Huntingdon, Cambridgeshire PE29 3NZ

01480 323000; Fax: 01480 323115

Website: www.awg.com

Correspondent: Sustainable Development Department

Chairman: Jonson Cox

Chief Executive: Jonson Cox

Year end	Turnover	Pre-tax profit
31/03/2008	£969,200,000	£331,900,000

Nature of company business
Water supply and distribution, waste water collection and treatment, and process engineering.

Subsidiaries include: Maintenance & Property Care Ltd, Power Services HVDE Ltd, Ambury Developments Ltd, PURAC Ltd, Rutland Insurance Ltd, Alpheus Environmental Ltd, Morrison International Ltd, MVM Holdings Ltd

Main locations: Peterborough, Huntingdon

UK employees: 7,432

Charitable donations

2008: £1,040,000
2007: £1,040,000
2006: £1,000,000
2005: £1,000,000
2004: £1,180,000

Membership: BitC

Community involvement

Anglian Water Group (of which Anglian Water Services is the principal subsidiary) is owned by a private consortium, Osprey, comprising of Canada Pension Plan Investment Board, Colonial First State Global Asset Management, Industry Funds Management and 3i Group plc. Following the acquisition of AWG by Osprey, the company was officially delisted from the stock exchange on 21 December 2006.

The company states that it is the group's policy that it has adopted a coordinated approach to the management of its community investment throughout the group businesses. The community programme is predominantly based on employee involvement at all levels throughout the business with some financial support for special projects.

Anglian water also operates a charitable trust: The Anglian Water Trust Fund (Charity Commission no.1054026), aims to help people in conditions of need in the area it operates. Grants to individuals are in the form of paying household bills or purchasing essential household items, with many grants being made to pay the water/sewage bills issued by Anglian Water. Grants are also made to organisations which can help such people move out of debt, such as those wishing to install or improve money advice services. Further information can be found in *A Guide to Local Trusts in the Midlands*, also published by DSC, or on the trust's website (www.awtf.org.uk).

Exclusions

No support for advertising in charity brochures, appeals from individuals, political appeals or sport (unless at educational level), animal welfare, medical research or religious appeals.

Applications

If you are looking for support for your organisation, please contact the AWG group sustainable development department for further information.

Applications to the Anglian Water Trust Fund should be sent to: 3rd Floor, Midgate House, Midgate, Peterborough PE1 1TN (Tel: 01733 421 021; email: awtf@charisgrants.com).

Full details of the funding criteria and how to apply are available at: www.awtf.org.uk

Corporate giving

In 2007/08, the company made its usual donation of £1 million to The Anglian Water Trust Fund. However, we understand that this commitment expired on 31 March 2008 and that the funding requirements of the fund are being reviewed, although no decision has yet been made.

In addition to its donation to the trust fund, the company also gave £40,000 in support of WaterAid.

No figure was available with regard to the company's in kind support.

In kind support

On occasion the company, due to upgrades on IT systems, has redundant computer hardware which it is no longer able to use. In support of its re-use/recycle ethos it can usually offer this equipment to charity/community organisations in the vicinity of its local offices. Equally, in some cases where office upgrades are necessary, some furniture (e.g. desks, chairs, filing cabinets) become surplus to requirement and are therefore offered to the local community rather than simply disposed of.

To find out if there is a current recycling programme running in your area, please contact the sustainable development department.

Employee-led support

The company operates a ' give me five' scheme which allows employees to take up to 30 work time hours to get involved in community activities. Designed with personal development at the heart, any new skills, competencies and relevant experience gained can be linked with the employee's annual appraisal and personal development plan. Employees give their time, skills and expertise to many organisations including: The Prince's Trust, Young Enterprise, Education Business Link organisations, mentoring programmes, CITB, Special Constables, Age Concern, WaterAid and many more

This year nearly 100 'give me five' volunteers supported the Community Service Volunteer's Make A Difference Day campaign across the UK. A total of 10 AWG Community projects were registered across the divisions. In addition to the financial support for materials etc., employees gave their time, skills and expertise in all sorts of ways including designing and building a sensory garden for a special needs school, transforming a disused piece of land into a road safety/play area for a nursery school and making over a reception area for a local hospice.

Payroll giving: The company operates the Give As You Earn scheme.

Anglo American plc

Company registration number 3564138

20 Carlton House Terrace, London SW1Y 5AN

020 7968 8888

Website: www.angloamerican.co.uk

Correspondent: Edward Bickham, Group Head of Extenal Relations
Email: ebickham@angloamerican.co.uk

Chairman: Sir Mark Moody-Stuart

Year end	Turnover	Pre-tax profit
31/12/2007	£12,735,000,000	£4,410,500,000

Nature of company business
The company, and its subsidiaries, joint ventures and associates, is a worldwide group in gold, platinum group metals and diamonds, with significant interests in coal, base and ferrous metals, industrial minerals and forest products.

Subsidiaries include: Mondi Packaging (UK) Ltd, Cleveland Potash Ltd, Tarmac Group Ltd

Main locations: London

UK employees: 11,000

Total employees: 100,000

Charitable donations

2007: £1,545,000
2005: £824,402

Membership: BitC, L B Group

Community involvement

The company's charitable donations in the UK are primarily made through the Anglo American Foundation (Charity Commission no. 1111719). The foundation welcomes applications from organisations involved with the following areas: education; international development; health/HIV; environment; and London-based community development.

Exclusions

No support for appeals from individuals, medical research, political appeals, religious appeals or sport.

Applications

Applications to the foundation should be made in writing to: Miss Catherine Louise Marshall, Anglo American Group Foundation, 20 Carlton House Terrace, London SW1Y 5AN.

Corporate giving

In 2007, Anglo American, its subsidiaries and the Anglo American Group Foundation made donations for charitable purposes or wider social investments amounting to $60.5 million (£30,250,000 – 0.7% of pre-tax profit). Charitable donations of $3.09 million (£1,545,000) were made in the UK, consisting of payments in respect of education, sport and youth $1.321 million (£660,500); community development $0.642 million (£321,000); health and HIV/AIDS $0.28 million (£140,000); environment $0.135 million (£67,500); arts, culture and heritage $0.241 million (£120,500), and other charitable causes $0.469 million (£234,500).

Anglo American Group Foundation

In 2007, the foundation received £1,051,615 from Anglo American Services (UK) Ltd pre-tax profits. This is likely to remain the foundation's major source of income in the future. Beneficiaries included: CARE International (£65,000); Plan International (£50,000); International Women's Health Coalition (£38,000); Aidspan (£15,000); Fairbridge (£10,000) and Cecily's Fund (£5,000).

In kind support

The company may, from time to time, provide additional support through gifts in kind. We have no details of the form this may take.

Employee-led support

The company has an employee volunteering scheme and allows company time off for community support activities to take place. Employee fundraising is matched by the company up to a maximum of £500 per employee.

Payroll giving: A scheme is operated by the company on behalf of its employees.

Commercially-led support

Sponsorship: Arts and good-cause sponsorship is undertaken.

AOL UK Ltd

Company registration number 3462696

62 Hammersmith Road, London W14 8YW

020 7348 2500; Fax: 020 7348 8002

Website: www.aol.co.uk

Correspondent: Head of Corporate Responsibility

Email: ukcharity@aol.com

Year end	Turnover	Pre-tax profit
31/12/2006	£177,552,285	£282,543,858

Nature of company business
Launched in the UK in 1996, AOL UK is an interactive service company and a division of AOL Europe – the internet, online and e-commerce services company.

Main locations: London

UK employees: 646

Charitable donations
2006: £76,676
2005: £72,290
Membership: L B Group

Community involvement

'The community investment programme at AOL seeks to extend the benefits of the internet to those who would most benefit from the medium but are often the least likely to obtain access through traditional means. This is often addressed by providing direct funding, advice and support in kind to charities and community groups going online to demonstrate innovative use of the medium.

'AOL UK has longstanding relationships with a number of UK charities in order to extend the benefits of the internet to their users. Our priority areas are young people and people with disabilities.'

The former AOL Innovation in the Community Awards, run in conjunction with Citizen's Online, are now offered under the TalkTalk brand following the acquisition of AOL's broadband business in the UK by the Carphone Warehouse. Full details are available at: www.citizensonline.org.uk

Exclusions

No funding or support for individuals (including, for example, overseas events and marathons), advertising or sponsorship in charity brochures (including calendars and ball programmes).

Applications

AOL UK does not accept unsolicited applications.

Corporate giving

In 2006, AOL made charitable donations in the UK of £76,676 (2005: £72,290). Although not explicitly stated, we assume the beneficiaries to have included the following longstanding charity partners:

John Groomes – supporting John Grooms' development of an award-winning lifestyle portal for people with disabilities; *NCH* – funding computer and internet classes at an NCH centre in West London, which help local people to gain confidence and crucial ICT skills; *Mencap* – Working with Mencap on Web projects for people with learning disabilities; *Citizens Online* – teaming up with the digital inclusion charity Citizens Online to run a national awards scheme that encourages charities and community groups to use the internet to connect, support and inspire their users; and *CAF* – supporting online giving through the Charities Aid Foundation, including initiatives such as National Giving Week.

In kind support

AOL supports GiveNow.org which is hosted by CAF (Charities Aid Foundation) and the Time Warner Foundation. GivenNow.org is the UK's first website to enable donors to give both their time and money to the charities of their choice.

Employee-led support

AOL UK offers each employee up to two days paid leave per year to volunteer for good causes, be it AOL's partner charities or their own chosen charity. There is also an annual Time Warner Volunteer Day (Time Warner own AOL) with past projects including planting trees, painting playgrounds, and working on a city farm.

AOL UK also helps employees to raise funds for their chosen charities by offering matched funding for individuals and teams. Recent fundraising initiatives range from completing the Great North Run to organising a second hand book sale, climbing Ben Nevis to competing in World Cup fantasy football.

Payroll giving: The Give As You Earn scheme is offered by the company, enabling employees to donate to good causes directly from their salary, before tax is deducted.

Apax Partners LLP

Company registration number OC303117

33 Jermyn Street, London Sw1Y 6DN

020 7872 6300; Fax: 020 7666 6441

Correspondent: David Marks, Trustee, Apax Foundation
Email: foundation@apax.com

Chairman: Sir Ronald Cohen

Chief Executive: Peter Englander

Year end	Turnover	Pre-tax profit
31/03/2008	£188,294,000	£109,379,000

Nature of company business
Apax Partners is an independent global private equity advisory firm.

UK employees: 45

Charitable donations

2008: £2,800,000

Membership: BitC

Community involvement

Established in 2006, The Apax Foundation (Charity Commission no. 1112845) is the formal channel for Apax Partners' charitable giving and receives a percentage of the firm's profits and carried interest.

'Apax Partners has a history of support for social enterprise and the firm is continuing this tradition with social enterprise chosen as the area on which the Apax Foundation will mainly focus. This encompasses charities working for the relief of financial hardship and the advancement of education in the United Kingdom and overseas.

'One of the primary goals of the foundation is to support the range and diversity of the personal charitable efforts of the Apax Partners team. The Apax Foundation supports their endeavours by making grants to all of the charitable organisations that benefit from the active involvement of a member of the Apax Partners team.'

Applications
In writing to the correspondent.

Corporate giving

In 2007/08, the firm donated £2.8 million to the Apax Foundation which in turn made grants totalling £808,931. This was broken down as follows:

- advancement of education (£670,000)
- relief of financial hardship £90,000)
- other charitable purposes (£48,931).

Beneficiaries included: Bridges Community Ventures; The Prince's Trust; and Private Equity Foundation. The largest single donation went to the Kennedy Memorial Trust, which provides scholarships to enable British postgraduates to study at Harvard University.

The foundation's 2007 report states that appeals from charities outside its main two areas of focus were largely turned down, and that the £48,931 given under 'other charitable purposes' mainly went to organisations working in the area of healthcare.

Employee-led support
The foundation supports the fundraising and volunteering activities of Apax Partners staff.

ARAMARK Ltd

Company registration number 983951

Millbank Tower, 21–24 Millbank, London SW1P 1QP

020 7963 0000; Fax: 0207963 0500

Website: www.aramark.co.uk

Correspondent: Hannah Martin, UK Communications Manager

Chief Executive: Andrew Main

Year end	Turnover	Pre-tax profit
28/09/2007	£364,286,000	£6,461,000

Nature of company business
The management and provision of a range of food, vending and refreshment services to industry and commerce.

Main locations: Leeds, Aberdeen

UK employees: 11,885

Charitable donations

Membership: BitC

Community involvement

The following information was taken from the company's website:

'Community activity is led by our Star Teams, which work in conjunction with Business in the Community. Star Teams provide the framework for ARAMARK employees to make a real difference to their local area with its goal to make a positive impact on the communities in which the organisation operates.

'ARAMARK also encourages teams and individuals to take part in their own choice of activities and these are publicised both internally, in our employee magazine, The Mark, and externally, often through the local press.'

Charity of the year: ARAMARK also supports nominated charities across the company. At present these are Outward Bound Trust, Hospitality Action and via the Pennies from Heaven scheme.

Applications
In writing to the correspondent.

Corporate giving

From the information that is available, it appears that most of the company's support is in kind in nature and/or directed through its employees. Unfortunately, we were unable to obtain a community contributions figure for 2007, whilst no cash donations were declared in the annual report and accounts for that year.

Nevertheless, as an active member of Business in the Community, we feel the company warrants its place herein.

Employee-led support

Payroll giving: Through the 'Pennies from Heaven' scheme employees are able to donate to the company's chosen charities by giving the odd pennies from their monthly pay.

Archant

Company registration number 4126997

Prospect House, Rouen Road, Norwich NR1 1RE

01603 628311

Website: www.archant.co.uk

Correspondent: John Ellison, Company Secretary
Email: john.ellison@archant.co.uk

Chairman: Richard Jewson

Chief Executive: John Fry

Year end	Turnover	Pre-tax profit
31/12/2007	£193,783,000	(£8,116,000)

Nature of company business
Publisher of local, regional and national magazines, newspapers and websites.

Main locations: Barnstaple, Ilford, Dereham, Diss, Exeter, Ely, Felixstowe, Harlow, Hitchin, Huntingdon, Ipswich, Sudbury, Weston-super-Mare, Welwyn Garden City, Buryt St Edmunds, Colchester, Cheltenham, Cromer, Maidstone, Lowestoft, London, Norwich, Wimbledon, Preston, Reigate, St Albans, Southampton

UK employees: 2,377

Charitable donations

2007: £102,000
2005: £103,000
2003: £73,000

Membership: BitC

Community involvement

The company provides grants in the areas in which it operates, which is across most of England and parts of Scotland. Consideration will be given to appeals from organisations concerned with: the arts, children/youth, education, enterprise/training, the environment, heritage, and sickness/disability. There is a preference for charities local to the company's operations.

Exclusions

No support for: advertising in charity brochures; appeals from individuals; fundraising events; overseas projects; political appeals; or, religious appeals.

Applications

In writing to the correspondent.

Corporate giving

In 2007, charitable donations by the company totalled £102,000. No further information was available.

In kind support

The group's magazines and newspapers help raise funds through highlighting local appeals in their pages.

Employee-led support

The Archant Gold Scheme matches the fundraising efforts of employees to a maximum of £3,000 each, and to a maximum of £40,000 in total for all employees.

Payroll giving: The company is part of the CAF payroll giving scheme and matches up to 50% of the donations, up to a maximum of £40,000 in total for all employees.

Commercially-led support

Sponsorship: A wide variety of good causes and arts projects are sponsored by the group.

Arla Foods Ltd

Company registration number 2143253

Arla House, 4 Savannah Way, Leeds Valley Park, Leeds LS10 1AB

0113 382 7000; Fax: 0113 382 7030

Website: www.arlafoodsuk.com

Correspondent: Public Relations Department

Year end	Turnover	Pre-tax profit
31/12/2007	£1,575,884,000	£46,080,000

Nature of company business
Arla Foods UK plc, through its subsidiary companies, is a leading supplier of milk and dairy products in the UK market. The group supplies liquid milk, cream, butter, spreads, cheeses, fresh dairy products, yoghurts and desserts to the major supermarkets.

Subsidiaries include: Claymore Dairies Ltd, Blakes Chilled Distribution Ltd

Main locations: Manchester, Naim, Norhallerton, Newcastle, Oakthorpe, Ruislip, Sheffield, Settle, Hatfield Peverel, Leeds, Ashby de la Zouch

UK employees: 2,776

Charitable donations

2007: £24,160
2006: £33,679
2005: £100,000
2004: £100,000
2003: £100,000

Community involvement

The company has produced a corporate social responsibility leaflet in which it outlines its policy regarding community/charitable support. The following is an extract from that leaflet.

'The company wants to contribute to the communities in which it operates. We also recognise our wider responsibility as corporate citizens to enable others to benefit from the prosperity of our business, when this is appropriate.

'We encourage and support employee and franchisee involvement in projects that have a direct impact on the local community.

'We will offer financial support to projects, within the areas in which we operate, that are supported by our employees and franchisees.'

Financial support is available in two forms only, both of which relate to the fundraising and volunteering activities of Arla employees, i.e. matched funding and projects in which employees/franchisees already provide non-fundraising help.

Exclusions

The following will not normally be supported: animal welfare; individuals; medical research charities; sport; heritage appeals; science and technology; charitable advertising; political or religious organisations; or pressure groups.

Applications

In writing to the correspondent.

Corporate giving

In 2006/07, the company made cash donations to charitable organisations of £24,160 (2005/06: £33,679).

Although we have no details of the beneficiaries, we do know that the company has pledged a donation to the Outward Bound charity to help send under-privileged children from across the UK on outdoor training schemes to develop their team working and social skills.

In kind support

Education: Employees are encouraged to work within the local community, through, for example, the 'Right to Read' scheme in Leicestershire and 'Reading Matters' in Leeds. Both of these involve staff in supporting school children with their reading development.

Employees have also worked closely with Education Leeds, organising one-day school conferences.

The company donates Arla products to local charities and community events.

Employee-led support

The company provide matched funding of sums raised by its employees/franchisees. If a charity or community group requires other technical or professional skills, the local depot or area will endeavour to find someone from within the business with the appropriate skills.

Funding is also given to projects in which employees/ franchisees already provide non-fundraising help. To receive funding employees/franchisees must work a minimum of 10 community hours a month in the project.

Arriva plc

Company registration number 347103

Admiral Way, Doxford International Business Park, Sunderland SR3 3XP

0191 520 4000; Fax: 0191 520 4001

Website: www.arriva.co.uk

Correspondent: Community Relations Support

Email: corporateresponsibility@arriva.co.uk

Chairman: Sir Richard Broadbent

Chief Executive: David Martin

Year end	Turnover	Pre-tax profit
31/12/2007	£2,000,700,000	£115,800,000

Nature of company business
The principal activities of the group at 31 December 2007 comprised the operation of bus and train services in the UK and nine countries in mainland Europe.

Subsidiaries include: The Original London Sightseeing Tour Ltd, London Pride Sightseeing Tour Ltd, Londonlinks Buses Ltd, Stevensons of Uttoxeter Ltd

Main locations: Sunderland

UK employees: 20,387

Total employees: 35,183

Charitable donations

2007: £111,640
2006: £148,677
2005: £201,426
2004: £157,515
2003: £122,346

Membership: BitC

Community involvement

Arriva's current community relations policy is as follows:

'Arriva's Community Relations policy focuses on supporting the communities we serve. We will actively support local and national charities and projects that set out to achieve this vision.

'Examples of areas that are likely to meet this objective are listed below:

- assisting people with disabilities to make a positive contribution to their communities
- supporting the elderly
- encouraging the young to be involved in the community, including education projects
- improving the environment.'

Exclusions

Arriva will not support activities in the areas listed below:

- activity in support of specific political party
- activity in support of specific religious movements
- advertising in charity brochures
- research projects that are not directly associated with the needs of the business.

Applications

In writing to the correspondent at the above address, or via email to: corporateresponsibility@arriva.co.uk

If you do not receive a response within 28 working days, please assume that your request has not been successful.

Corporate giving

In 2007, the company made cash donations of £111,640 to charity. Previously, support has been given to Macmillan Cancer Relief, Business in the Community, RNIB, Foundation for Citizenship, Changing Faces and ENCAMS.

The Community Relation Committee has established partnerships with organisations including Age Concern and Age Concern Scotland, Common Purpose, the Foundation for Citizenship at Liverpool John Moores University and Leicester Racial Equality Council.

In kind support

Education: As part of Arriva's focus on young people and education, the company produced a school pack for teachers and 11 to 16 year-olds in the UK. It supports key areas of the curriculum including lesson plans for maths, sensible road use, how to catch a bus and planning a route to school.

Health: In Liverpool, Arriva's Healthy Schools Bus, in partnership with Everton Football Club, has given more than 11,000 pupils a fun focus on healthy eating and exercise. The initiative includes follow-up visits, monitoring pupils' progress in nutrition and fitness. Plans are being developed to replicate the success of the scheme over a wider area.

Wider local activities have included free transport for community groups and free advertising on buses for local organisations and charities.

Employee-led support

Arriva employees are encouraged to give their time to local community groups and projects. These efforts are recognised through the Arriva Community Action Awards initiative, which makes cash awards available to employees for their community organisations.

As part of its focus on young people and education, Arriva produced a school pack for teachers and 11 to 16-year-olds in the UK. It supports key areas of the curriculum including lesson plans for maths, sensible road use, how to catch a bus and planning a route to school.

Schools can download the pack from Arriva's dedicated Arriva Schools website at: www.arrivaschools.co.uk/

Commercially-led support

Sponsorship: *Sport* – In Wales, Arriva is main sponsor for the Wales Deaf Rugby Union team and supports women's and children's soccer teams with sponsored kit.

Arup Group Ltd

Company registration number 1312454

13 Fitzroy Street, London W1T 4BQ

020 7636 1531; Fax: 020 7580 3924

Website: www.arup.com

Correspondent: Peter Klhyn

Email: ovarfound@arup.com

Chairman: Terry Hill

Year end	Turnover	Pre-tax profit
31/03/2007	£572,381,000	£30,817,000

Nature of company business
The company and its subsidiaries practice in the field of consulting engineering services, in architecture and other related professional skills. The group has 18 offices in the UK in addition to its head office in London.

Main locations: Edinburgh, Dundee, Southampton, Glasgow, Bristol, Cardiff, Cambridge, Newcastle upon Tyne, Liverpool, London, Manchester, Nottingham, Leeds, Solihull, Sheffield, Wrexham, Winchester, Belfast

UK employees: 7,564

Charitable donations

2007: £65,630
2006: £36,426
2005: £40,000
2004: £33,550

Community involvement

Established to commemorate the life of the late Sir Ove Arup, The Ove Arup Foundation (Charity Commission no. 328138) is an educational trust supporting initiatives related to the built environment.

Endowed by the partnership for the first seven years of its existence (1989–1995) through an annual gift, the trustees decided in 2000 to provide further funding over the next five years and to increase the scope of the foundation internationally.

Around one-third of the foundation's funds are available each year for major projects. It gives grants for research and projects, including start-up and feasibility costs. Further information is available on the foundation's website (www.theovearupfoundation.org).

Applications

In writing to the correspondent, with brief supporting financial information. Trustees meet quarterly to consider applications (March, June, September and December).

Further information is available at the foundation's website: www.ovearupfoundation.org

Corporate giving

In 2006/07, the Arup Group Ltd declared worldwide charitable donations of £239,000 (2005/06: £245,000), of which £65,630 was donated in the UK to its associated trust (see below).

The Ove Arup Foundation

In 2006/07, the foundation had an income of £76,000. Grants were made to 18 organisations totalling £151,500.

The largest grants in the UK were for £30,000 each and went to Royal Academy of Engineering and John Doyle Construction – 'Constructionarium'.

Other recipients included: The Vassall Centre Trust (£5,000); London Architecture Biennale (£3,000); Architectural Association Foundation (£2,000); and Lighting Educational Trust (£1,000).

ASDA Stores Ltd

Company registration number 464777

ASDA House, Southbank, Great Wilson Street, Leeds LS11 5AD

0113 243 5435; Fax: 0113 241 8666

Website: www.asda.co.uk

Correspondent: Julie Ward, Foundation Administrator
0113 241 7253; Fax: 0113 241 8666

Chief Executive: Andy Bond

Year end	Turnover	Pre-tax profit
31/12/2006	£15,657,093,000	£388,082,000

Nature of company business

Principal activities: the operation of food, clothing, home and leisure superstores throughout Great Britain.

Subsidiaries include: Gazeley Holdings Ltd, The Burwood House Group plc, McLagan Investments Ltd, Gazeley Properties Ltd

Main locations: Leeds

UK employees: 153,580

Charitable donations

2006: £300,000
2005: £300,000
2004: £559,996

Membership: A & B, BitC

Community involvement

The company stated that it does not make 'head office' donations, but that donations are given through the ASDA Foundation (Charity Commission no. 800382). ASDA funds the foundation with profits from the mid-week National Lottery. These funds are donated to support individual colleague requests on behalf of local good causes and to those sustainable projects making a real long term difference to local communities.

Additional income is received from the sale of products and fundraising locally for the national charities, Tickled Pink (Breast Cancer Care and Breast Cancer Campaign), Tommy's and Children in Need.

At a local level, ASDA let each store and depot choose which local charities to support. Stores also act as collection points for local charities, with an average of two charity collections a month. ASDA colleagues also play an active part in the communities where they live and work through volunteering their time to local schools and good causes.

Exclusions

No response to circular appeals. No support for advertising in charity brochures, appeals from individuals, overseas projects, political appeals, or local appeals not in areas of company presence.

Applications
ASDA Foundation

Unfortunately, The ASDA Foundation can only support a limited number of requests received direct from registered charities and local community groups.

It is set up to support requests which have the direct support and involvement from ASDA colleagues locally. Please contact your local store or depot first to see if this is something they are able to support.

You may also write to the Foundation Manager, Julie Ward, directly. Please bear in mind, however, that many such requests are received each year. It is therefore in your own interests to provide as much information as possible on the application on how this will benefit the local community.

Once the trustees have made their decisions (based on the information you provided) you will be informed whether your application was successful.

Your donation will then be paid in the form of a cheque from the ASDA Foundation and we look forward to supporting you and the good causes in your community.

Corporate giving

In 2006, the company donated £300,000 to the ASDA Foundation. No value appears to be attributed to its in kind support for charities at a local level.

During the same period, the ASDA Foundation had a total income of £6.25 million and made grants totalling £6 million. Of the restricted funds, £4,162,288 (2005: £3,587,918) was raised by ASDA Stores colleagues for Breast Cancer Care, Everyman £195,340 (2005: nil) and £391,383 (2005: £842,384) for Children In Need. A donation of £150,000 was made to Fare Pack which helped support the people who had lost their money through this company for Christmas hampers.

Smaller donations (of £1,000 or more) included those to:Wakefield Hospice (£30,525); The Poppy Appeal (£10,000); Zoe's Place (£7,000); Gzone (£5,000); National Wild Flower Centre (£3,000); and Charity Check (£1,000).

ASDA Foundation

Funded primarily by profit made by ASDA Stores Ltd on its midweek lottery and funds raised at charitable events organised by colleagues (staff), it focuses on:

'The objectives of the charity are:

- to support local good causes our colleagues get behind. By local we mean local to stores, depots and George House and ASDA House
- support local sustainable projects agreed by the trustees
- administer all funds raised for 'Tickled Pink' (Breast Cancer Care and Breast Cancer Campaign),

'Tommy's and Children in Need, which are ASDA's national campaigns.'

'The ASDA Foundation's main objectives are to make donations to the local good causes that have the direct support and involvement from our colleagues. Colleagues raise funds for their local charities/communities and apply to the ASDA Foundation for further funding where the following guidelines are applied for a minimum of two trustees to approve:

'Foundation guidelines:

- teams of colleagues raising money for a good cause – donation depending on how much raised. We will make a reasonable donation depending on the number of colleagues involved, local good cause and amount you have raised
- one colleague raising money for a good cause – £100 maximum
- colleague teams raising money for an individual – £200 maximum
- charity expeditions, e.g. white water rafting, marathons – £50 per colleague
- sponsored activity, e.g. London marathon
- colleague teams raising money for close immediate family – £500 maximum – donations depending on how much raised.'

In kind support

Every store supports a number of local charities and voluntary groups which are given some space in-store to advertise the services they provide or to look for support by being allowed to fundraise in stores.

Employee-led support

Employees' volunteering/charitable activities are supported by the company financially, and by allowing staff time off to volunteer. In 2007, staff volunteered 75,000 hours of their time working with groups and individuals around the UK.

Commercially-led support

Sponsorship: *Sport* – ASDA sponsors the National Kwik Cricket competition aimed at children aged five to 11.

Cause-related marketing: The 'Go Green for Schools' scheme encourages ASDA customers to reuse any carrier bag whilst shopping at the supermarket. For this, they are awarded a voucher which they can donate to a local school to collect and redeem for 'green' educational prize.

Further information is available at: www.asda-gogreenforschools.co.uk/

Associated British Foods plc

Company registration number 293262

Weston Centre, 10 Grosvenor Street, London W1K 4QY

020 7399 6500; Fax: 020 7399 6580

Website: www.abfoods.com

Chairman: Martin G Adamson

Chief Executive: George Weston

Year end	Turnover	Pre-tax profit
15/09/2007	£6,800,000,000	£508,000,000

Nature of company business
The activities of the group principally concern the processing and manufacture of food worldwide and textile retailing in the UK and continental Europe. The ultimate holding company is Wittington Investments Ltd.

Subsidiaries include: Food Investments Ltd, The Ryvita Co. Ltd, British Sugar plc, Jacksons of Piccadilly Ltd, AB Agri Ltd, ABF Grain Products Ltd, Jordan's (NI) Ltd, R Twining & Co. Ltd, Mauri Products Ltd, Patak's Foods Ltd, Patak's Breads Ltd, The Billington Food Group Ltd, ABF Investments plc, Abitec Ltd, Cereform Ltd, Primark Stores Ltd, Nambarrie Tea Co. Ltd, G Costa and Co. Ltd, British Sugar (Overseas) Ltd

Main locations: London

UK employees: 29,102

Total employees: 84,636

Charitable donations
2007: £1,600,000
2006: £400,000
2005: £300,000
2004: £400,000
2003: £200,000

Community involvement

Although we have again been advised that the company does not of itself make charitable donations, we feel it appropriate to draw readers' attention to the following.

All charitable requests sent to Associated British Foods are passed on to the Garfield Weston Foundation which, although operated entirely independently of the company, is administered from the same address and receives its income from its almost 80% holding of Wittington Investments Ltd (the holding company of Associated British Foods plc).

As one of the largest grantmaking trusts in the UK, details of the work of the Garfield Weston Foundation can be found in *A Guide to the Major Trusts Volume 1*, published by the Directory of Social Change.

In addition to the above, the company states in its annual report and accounts, that it actively encourages its operating companies to 'engage with the local community in the areas of operation'. Examples of this include the community activities of British Sugar through the British Sugar Foundation (see the separate entry for this company).

Exclusions

Sponsorship is not undertaken.

Applications

Any appeals addressed to the UK head office are forwarded to Philippa Charles, the administrator of the Garfield Weston Foundation (Tel: 020 7399 6565; Fax: 020 7399 6584).

With regard to subsidiary companies, we have been unable to find out if they hold independent budgets for giving at a local level even though the declared donations figure seems to support this.

Corporate giving

The company declared worldwide charitable donations of £1.6 million in its 2006/07 accounts. No further information regarding this was available, although we suspect it may cover donations made by operating companies at a local level where giving policies are also determined.

Associated British Ports Holdings Ltd

Company registration number 1612178

150 Holborn, London EC1N 2LR

020 7430 1177; Fax: 020 7430 1384

Website: www.abports.co.uk

Correspondent: Corporate Communications Manager

Email: csr@abports.co.uk

Chairman: Chris Clark

Chief Executive: Peter Jones

Year end	Turnover	Pre-tax profit
31/12/2007	£462,900,000	(£50,000,000)

Nature of company business
The provision of port and transport-related services to ship and cargo owners, and the ownership and development of properties at port locations.

Subsidiaries include: Grosvenor Waterside (Holdings) Ltd, Grosvenor Waterside Investments Ltd, Amports Vehicle Terminals Ltd, Amports Cargo Services Ltd, Grosvenor Waterside Developments Ltd, Southampton Free Trade Zone Ltd, Northern Cargo Services Ltd, The Teighmouth Quay Co. Ltd, ABP Marine Environmental Research Ltd

Main locations: Barrow, Barry, Ayr, Swansea, Teignmouth, Troon, Southampton, Plymouth, Port Talbot, Silloth, Newport,

Lowestoft, Ipswich, King's Lynn, Immingham, Hull, Fleetwood, Garston, Grimsby, Goole, Cardiff

UK employees: 2,423

Charitable donations
2007: £91,000
2006: £40,000
2005: £123,000
2004: £74,000
2003: £78,000

Membership: BitC

Community involvement

The following policy information is taken from the company's website:

'Our policy is to encourage our port directors and managers to plan and oversee their own local programmes. Although we encourage contributions to all community causes as company policy, we generally feel it is most appropriate to direct the bulk of our contributions towards charities in the maritime, medical, medical-research and educational sectors. We also help where there is a need for our resources, facilities or man-hours and provide these, in many cases, free of charge.

'We recognise that port development can be a sensitive issue for our local communities and we seek to take into account the impact of our proposals on them. Clear and open communication between our ports and their surrounding communities is undertaken prior to, and during, any major development.

'We direct our ongoing community initiatives towards the following areas:
- education
- charities
- arts sponsorship
- land and local partnerships
- civic organisations
- use of facilities.'

Exclusions

There are no definite exclusions; instead the company will consider all appeals individually.

Applications

In writing to the correspondent. Applications are sorted and likely candidates referred to the Group Chief Executive.

Information available: The company produces a Corporate Social Responsibility report.

Corporate giving

In 2007, the group made charitable donations of £91,000 (2006: £40,000). Support is regularly given to the following charities: Against Breast Cancer; Age Concern; Cancer Research UK; Fishermen's Mission; NSPCC; Tyhafan; Help the Aged; King George's Fund for Sailors; Leonard Cheshire; Leukaemia Society; Macmillan Cancer Relief; Marine Conservation Society; Mildmay; The Association of Royal Navy Officers; The Mission to Seafarers; The Royal National Lifeboat Institution; and The Sick Children's Trust.

In kind support

To assist with the development of the local skills base, the company continues to concentrate a great deal of community-based projects on giving assistance to improve the educational facilities near their ports. As well as financial support, the company supports competitions and learning initiatives.

The company also hosts port visits and tours for local schoolchildren. A number of their ports also offer work experience to local schoolchildren and students, apprenticeships, work placements and graduate work experience programmes.

Employee-led support

The company will consider sponsoring employees in their fundraising activities and provides support through staff secondments.

ABP encourage staff to sit as school governors and/ or give talks and presentations on ports and the economy, the environment and careers in transport, general business advice and other advice on working life.

Donations made by staff through fundraising and giving are matched by the company.

Commercially-led support

Sponsorship: *The arts* – the company sponsorships include the Welsh National Opera, English National Ballet and the English National Opera.

AstraZeneca plc

Company registration number 2723534

15 Stanhope Gate, London W1K 1LN

020 7304 5000; Fax: 020 7304 5151

Website: www.astrazeneca.com

Correspondent: Justin Hoskins, Assistant Company Secretary, Charitable Appeals Department

Chairman: Louis Schweitzer

Chief Executive: David Brennan

Year end	Turnover	Pre–tax profit
31/12/2007	£14,779,500,000	£3,991,500,000

Nature of company business
The group's principal activities are the research, development and marketing of medicines for serious health conditions.

Main locations: Alderley Edge, Cambridge, Macclesfield, Loughborough, Luton, London, Stonehouse, Tytherington, Wilmslow, Chorlton-cum-Hardy, Brixham, Bristol, Edinburgh

Total employees: 67,900

Charitable donations
2007: £9,100,000

Total community contributions: £35,000,000

Membership: BitC

Community involvement

The following extract is taken from the In the Community section of the company's website: 'Our community activities focus on bringing sustainable benefit in ways that are consistent with our business of improving health and quality of life, and on promoting the value of science among young people.

'We have a dedicated community support database that gathers global information centrally, enabling the sharing of information and best practice across the organisation and supporting accurate financial reporting of our overall spend in this area. The database also helps us to ensure that our efforts are aligned with our commitment to bring benefit mainly through healthcare and science education initiatives.'

Support from the corporate office in London is only given to UK-based charities and charities local to the office or to manufacturing sites around the UK. Overseas aid is given by the overseas branches/companies.

Exclusions

No support for circulars, advertising in charity brochures, individuals, older people, fundraising events, political/discriminatory groups, religious appeals, sport, anything contrary to company business or, with very limited exceptions, capital projects.

Applications

In writing to the correspondent at the head office address.

Corporate giving

In 2007, AstraZeneca spent a total of $588 million (£294 million) on community sponsorships and charitable donations worldwide, including $518 million (£259 million) on product donations, valued at average wholesale prices. Charitable donations accounted for $70 million (£35 million) of this, but regrettably, no indication was given as to how much went to UK charities.

The group supports the work of the Brightside Trust, a charity that aims to help underprivileged young people to enter the medical and healthcare professions. Support included a two year secondment to the charity as well as an ongoing contribution in cash (around £100,000 over three years).

Through its 'Inspiring Science' programme, run in conjunction with the CREST awards scheme in the UK, a programme of project work relevant to the secondary education science curriculum is undertaken. Schools of the students judged to have delivered the best projects receive a cash prize.

Further information is available at: www.inspiringscience.co.uk

AstraZeneca Science Teaching Trust

The AstraZeneca Science Teaching Trust (Charity Commission no. 1064864), an independent charity with a total trust fund of $32 million (around £21 million) provided by the company, supports a programme of projects designed to help build the knowledge, skills and understanding required to lead and teach science effectively and confidently in primary schools. For further information on the trust, please go to http://www.azteachscience.co.uk/

The AstraZeneca Foundation

We were advised previously that the AstraZeneca Foundation (Charity Commission no. 1014774) was in the process of being wound down. However, the trust's record at the Charity Commission is still active, although no accounts have been provided since 2001.

In kind support

Education: AstraZeneca runs a UK-wide bursary scheme to help secure the future of chemistry. Launched in 2003, the programme includes awards of £1,000 up to 4 years to 50 students studying chemistry at 23 UK universities. The scheme aims to encourage 'A' level students to study chemistry and university and first year students to pursue a career in chemistry on graduation.

The group also supports a Diversity Mentoring programme managed between the University of Manchester and the UMIST Careers Service. Aimed at establishing links between black and Asian students and employers, staff from various departments within the company help students learn a variety of personal and professional skills. Staff also contribute to a number of employability workshops.

A Partnering Schools scheme links employees and staff from local community secondary schools on a one to one basis. The main focus is the support of industry/work related aspects of the school curriculum, particularly in science/technology.

Employee-led support

Employees are encouraged to become involved in community-based charitable activities through a matched funding scheme, whereby individuals' efforts in fundraising may be matched by a company donation.

AT&T (UK) Ltd

Company registration number 1765868

Highfield House, Headless Cross Drive, Redditch B97 5EQ

01527 518 181

Website: www.att.com

Correspondent: Phil Coathup, Media Relations Director

Vice President: LLoyd Salvage

Nature of company business
Telecommunications and networking company.

Main locations: London

Total employees: 70,000

Community involvement

Previously, we were advised that the company's UK donations were channelled through its US foundation. Whilst there has been evidence of this in the past on the foundation's website, this no longer appears to be the case. In fact, the website now has little in the way of financial or grant information (you used to be able to search by country) and makes no reference to a willingness to fund organisations outside of the USA.

Irrespective of this, the company has always taken a proactive approach when it comes to funding and we have no reason to believe this has changed. Areas of interest include education, underserved communities and arts and culture, especially where these are linked to broadening access to technology.

Exclusions

The foundation does not support the following categories:
- individuals
- organisations whose chief purpose is to influence legislation or to participate or intervene in political campaigns on behalf of or against any candidate for public office

- endowments or memorials
- construction or renovation projects
- sports teams or any sports-related activity or competition, even if it addresses the foundation's programme interests
- fundraising events or advertising.

Applications

In writing to the correspondent.

As far as the foundation is concerned, as there is no longer any encouragement or evidence of applications from outside of the USA being accepted directly, please refer to AT&T (UK) Ltd for the latest advice.

Corporate giving

The company are involved with The Prince's Trust Technology Leadership Group and raised funds for Cancer Research UK in 2006 through the 'Tee It Up with AT&T' Global Charity Golf Tour.

The last grant information we have concerning the AT&T Foundation relates to 2004, when the only grant paid in the UK was $50,000 to the Charities Aid Foundation (CAF also received support every year from 1999 to 2002). Other beneficiaries since the foundation was established in 1996 are Almeida Theatre Company, Edinburgh International Festival, Royal Court Theatre, Royal National Theatre and Tate Gallery.

W S Atkins plc

Company registration number 1885586

Woodcote Grove, Ashley Road, Epsom, Surrey KT18 5BW

01372 726140; Fax: 01372 740055

Website: www.atkinsglobal.com

Correspondent: Keith Clarke, Chief Executive

Chairman: Ed Wallis

Chief Executive: Keith Clarke

Year end	Turnover	Pre-tax profit
31/03/2008	£1,399,500,000	£91,900,000

Nature of company business
The group operates primarily as a multi-discipline design and engineering consultants with a focus on engineering and appropriate building design. The company's operations are based in over 70 offices throughout the UK.

Main locations: Epsom

Total employees: 17,278

Charitable donations

2008: £191,527
2007: £205,813
2006: £97,534
2005: £85,000
2004: £101,000

Membership: BitC

Community involvement

In November 2007, the company revised its charity policy as follows:

'Traditionally, we have written cheques to charities which have had little benefit to engaging either staff, shareholders or the charities we have supported. We will now move towards supporting communities in two ways:

- *being good neighbours and supporting communities* – by encouraging our employees around the world to get involved in fundraising events such as sponsored sporting events and other challenges, and through local charitable donations, volunteering activities and sports and social events. We also make it easy for employees to make charitable donations through payroll giving.
- *pro bono consultancy advice* – by providing pro bono (time for free) consultancy advice which can benefit international relief and aid organisations and by giving pro bono consultancy advice, rather than offering volunteers or cash donations, we contribute our skills and at the same time learn from our experiences.'

Exclusions
No support for appeals from individuals.

Applications
In writing to the correspondent.

Corporate giving

In 2008, the group donated £191,527 (2007: £205,813) to principally local charitable organisations in areas of company presence.

In kind support
Education: Atkins employees in the UK are providing mentoring to young people to help them plan for their futures. Many Epsom-based personnel have joined programmes at local schools and involvement has also spread to include schools in Farnham and Horley.

Staff volunteers from the Faithful+Gould London office also help 16 local school children with their literacy and numeracy skills. Volunteers attend weekly lunchtime sessions with the children, either reading with them or playing number-based games.

Employee-led support
Employees are encouraged to volunteer and fundraise on behalf of local good causes.

Payroll giving: A scheme is in operation.

Aviva plc

Company registration number 2468686

St Helen's, 1 Undershaft, London EC3P 3DQ

020 7283 2000; Fax: 020 7662 8182

Website: www.aviva.com

Correspondent: (see 'Applications')

Chairman: Lord Sharman of Redlynch

Chief Executive: Andrew Moss

Year end	Turnover	Pre-tax profit
31/12/2007	£40,645,000,000	£1,857,000,000

Nature of company business

The company transacts life assurance and long-term savings business, fund management, and all classes of general insurance through its subsidiaries, associates and branches in the UK, Continental Europe, North America, Asia, Australia and other countries throughout the world.

Subsidiaries include: Norwich Union Wealth Management Ltd, Norwich Union Trust Managers Ltd, CGU Bonus Ltd, Commercial Union Life Assurance Co. Ltd, Norwich Union Life Holdings Ltd, London & Edinburgh Insurance Group Ltd, Norwich Union Annuity Ltd, CGU Insurance plc, General Accident plc, Norwich Union Healthcare Ltd, CGU Underwriting Ltd, Norwich Union Life & Pensions Ltd, Morley Properties Ltd, Morley Fund Management Ltd, Morley Pooled Pensions Ltd, CGNU Life Assurance Ltd, Northern Assurance Co. Ltd, Norwich Union Insurance Ltd, CGU International Insurance Ltd, Norwich Union Portfolio Services Ltd, your-move.co.uk Ltd, Norwich Union Investment Funds Ltd, Norwich Union Linked Life Assurance Ltd

Main locations: Croydon, Bristol, Cheadle, Eastleigh, Exeter, Glasgow, York, Southampton, Sheffield, Romford, Stevenage, Norwich, Newcastle

UK employees: 33,686

Total employees: 57,011

Charitable donations

2007: £1,400,000
2006: £1,400,000
2005: £1,700,000
2004: £1,300,000
2003: £1,300,000

Total community contributions: £4,000,000

Membership: A & B, BitC

Community involvement

Aviva's community support in the UK is in the main carried out under the Norwich Union brand name.

The company's policy on charitable giving is to support local charities and community organisations, particularly in those areas where the company has a major presence. In addition, it provides a significant level of support to a small number of national charities.

Support is also available through Morley Fund Management, a wholly owned, independently managed asset management business of Aviva plc. This includes charitable activity/giving/staff volunteering/sponsorship/partnerships and match funding.

Both Norwich Union and Morley publish their own CSR reports and support a variety of causes. We suggest, therefore, that the Aviva website is visited as each company has its own 'community' section which gives fuller details of the policy and programmes.

Exclusions

At group level, Aviva will not normally consider supporting:

- individuals looking for sponsorship or charity fundraising donations either on their own behalf or that of a charity (staff excluded)
- political organisations
- extreme 'high risk' or 'free sports'
- organisations or issues already supported by Norwich Union in the UK
- charities already receiving long-term support around the world, either from Norwich Union or an Aviva company
- a staff charity of the year (on a separate basis)
- paid advertisements in charity brochures or events programmes.

Applications

Applications should be made in writing to: Debbie Bullock, Community Affairs Consultant, Norwich Union, Wellington Row, York YO90 1WR. Email: debbie.bullock@norwich-union.co.uk

Corporate giving

In 2007, the group made total community contributions of £6.8 million (2006: £6.3 million). Of this, £4 million (2006: £3.7 million) was invested in the UK. Of the latter, £1.4 million (2006: £1.4 million) was in direct donations to charitable causes.

Some of the charitable causes supported during the year included:

- Breakthrough Breast Cancer
- Wheelpower
- The Princess Royal Trust for Carers.

In addition, in support of its 'Forward Thinking' initiative the company has continued with the partnership of the Oxfam 365 Alliance which provides immediate humanitarian aid to disasters occurring throughout the world. The company has committed to support the Oxfam 365 Alliance for three years from 2006.

In kind support

Support is also given through the donation of items such as IT equipment, furniture, company branded materials and the use of office space free of charge.

Employee-led support

Staff are encouraged to take part in community-related projects through various initiatives, such as, staff volunteering, mentoring and fundraising activities, which the company matches.

Payroll giving: The Give As You Earn scheme is in operation.

Commercially-led support

Sponsorship: Each individual business in the group is responsible for its own sponsorship and community support programmes, developed to meet their local market needs. Aviva, for example, w ill consider sponsoring good causes, education, music and sport projects.

Further information about Aviva and other group company sponsorships is available on its website.

Avon Cosmetics Ltd

Company registration number 592235

Nunn Mills Road, Northampton NN1 5PA

01604 232425; Fax: 01604 232444

Website: www.avon.uk.com

Correspondent: 'Donations'

Year end	Turnover	Pre-tax profit
31/12/2006	£283,772,000	£9,928,000

Nature of company business
The principal activities of the company are the distribution and sale of beauty products and the sale and distribution of gift and decorative products.

Main locations: Northampton

UK employees: 1,734

Charitable donations

1998: £19,000

Membership: BitC

Community involvement

Avon Cosmetics has long been associated with the fight against breast cancer and is the world's largest corporate supporter of the cause. The Avon Breast Cancer Crusade was launched in the UK in 1992 to raise funds for and awareness of breast cancer. Since then Avon has worked in partnership with charities including Breakthrough Breast Cancer, Macmillan Cancer Support and Breast Cancer Care. Avon's activities have supported research, awareness raising, lobbying and care and support services.

Outside of this, support is limited to local causes, especially in Northamptonshire, and again with particular relevance to women's issues.

Exclusions

No support for advertising in charity brochures, animal welfare charities, appeals from individuals, the arts, overseas projects, political appeals, religious appeals, science/technology or sport.

Applications

In writing to the correspondent.

Corporate giving

Although Avon has not declared any charitable donations in its annual report and accounts, we believe its in kind support of the breast cancer crusade to be sufficient to warrant inclusion here. Regrettably, the company's website currently provides no up-to-date information regarding the amount raised by the crusade in 2007/08.

In 2005 £1.2 million was raised in the UK by staff and customers for the Avon Breast Cancer Crusade. Whilst it is clear that the company is heavily engaged in facilitating this fundraising.

Employee-led support

Support is also given to employees' volunteering/charitable activities through financial help, matching employee fundraising and giving, and allowing company time off to volunteer.

Payroll giving: Avon operates the Give As You Earn scheme.

Commercially-led support

Cause-related marketing: Avon Breast Cancer Crusade raises funds through the sale of promotional pin badges and jewellery.

Those wishing to get involved in fundraising for breast cancer research can do so by ordering online the Avon Breast Cancer Crusade Fundraising Pack.

Avon Rubber plc

Company registration number 32965

Hampton Park West, Melksham, Wiltshire SN12 6NB

01225 896800; Fax: 01225 896899

Website: www.avon-rubber.com

Correspondent: Peter Slabbert, Chief Executive
Email: enquiries@avon-rubber.com

Chairman: Rt Hon. Sir Richard Needham

Chief Executive: Peter Slabbert

Year end	Turnover	Pre-tax profit
30/09/2007	£66,715,000	£2,926,000

Nature of company business
The principal activities of the group are the design and manufacture of respiratory protection products for defence, police, fire and other emergency services, together with the design and manufacture of a range of polymer based products for the dairy, defence and aerosol industries.

Main locations: Westbury, Trowbridge, Melksham

UK employees: 915

Charitable donations

2007: £13,257
2006: £22,787
2005: £26,000
2004: £31,000

Community involvement

The group maintains a fund with the Community Foundation for Wiltshire and Swindon, a charity dedicated to strengthening local communities. The group director of human resources is a trustee of the foundation, which targets its grants to make a genuine difference to the lives of local people.

Exclusions

No support for animal welfare charities, circular appeals, appeals from individuals, local appeals not in areas of company presence, large national appeals or overseas projects.

Applications

All applications are dealt with by the Wiltshire and Swindon Community Foundation, 48 New Park Street, Devizes, Wiltshire SN10 1DS (Tel: 01380 729284. Fax: 01380 729772; website: www.wscf.org.uk; email: info@wscf.org.uk).

Further details of the foundation can be found in *A Guide to Local Trusts in the South of England* published by the Directory of Social Change.

Corporate giving

In 2007, the company made cash donations in the UK of £13,257 (2006: £22,787) consisting exclusively of small donations to charities. This year Avon's fund provided a grant to the West Wiltshire Portage Service which supports development education to children with severe learning disabilities.

BAA plc

Company registration number 1970855

130 Wilton Road, London SW1V 1LQ

020 8745 9800

Website: www.baa.co.uk

Correspondent: Caroline Nicholls, Director BAA Communities Trust
Email: caroline_nicholls@baa.com

Chairman: Sir Nigel Rudd

Chief Executive: Colin Matthews

Year end	Turnover	Pre-tax profit
31/12/2007	£2,247,000,000	£747,000,000

Nature of company business
BAA plc owns and operates seven UK airports: Heathrow, Gatwick, Stansted, Aberdeen, Edinburgh, Glasgow and Southampton. Each airport is run by a separate operating company.

Subsidiaries include: Aberdeen Airport Ltd, Edinburgh Airport Ltd, World Duty Free plc, Southampton International Airport Ltd, Heathrow Airport Ltd, Gatwick Airport Ltd, Glasgow Airport Ltd, Stanstead Airport Ltd

Main locations: Heathrow, Gatwick, Edinburgh, Glasgow, Southampton, Stansted, Aberdeen

UK employees: 10,000

Charitable donations

2007: £1,376,238
2006: £1,313,000
2005: £1,446,000
2004: £1,088,000
2003: £736,000

Membership: BitC, L B Group

Community involvement

The company has its own charitable trust, The BAA 21st Century Communities Trust: (Charity Commission no. 1058617). This provides grants in the areas surrounding its airports. Support is concentrated on projects which will be of community benefit in the areas of education, environment and economic regeneration. Applications should be made to the airport near the project.

There are also a couple of charitable trusts connected to Gatwick Airport. Gatwick Airport Community Trust (Charity Commission no. 1089683) which supports welfare causes, community facilities and development, the arts, cultural, sports and environmental and conservation schemes. Applications should be made to: The Trustees, PO Box 102, Crawley, West Sussex RH10 9WX (01892 826088).

Gatwick Airport Pantomime Society (Charity Commission no. 1090214) supports a wide range of causes in West Sussex, including help for people who are sick, have disabilities, need medical treatment or have housing difficulties, community

development and animal charities. Applications should be made to: Barry Charles Lloyd, 14 Lambourn Close, East Grinstead, West Sussex RH19 2DP (01342 315991).

Exclusions

No support is given to circular appeals, advertising in charity brochures, animal welfare, appeals from individuals, the arts, elderly people, fundraising events, heritage, medical research, overseas projects, political appeals, religious appeals, science/technology, sickness/disability, or sport.

Support for a 'Charity of the Year' is not considered.

Applications

Applicants are advised to contact the community relations manager at their local airport.

BAA Aberdeen: Aberdeen Airport, Dyce, Aberdeen AB21 7DU (0870 040 0006;

Fax: 01224 775845).

BAA Edinburgh: Edinburgh Airport, Scotland EH12 9DN (0870 040 0007; Fax: 0131 344 3470).

BAA Gatwick: Gatwick Airport, West Sussex RH6 ONP (0870 000 2468).

BAA Heathrow: Heathrow Airport, 234 Bath Road, Hayes, Middlesex UB3 5AP (0870 000 0123; Fax: 020 8745 4290).

BAA Southampton: Southampton Airport, Hampshire SO18 2NL (0870 040 0009; Fax: 023 8062 7193).

BAA Stansted: Stansted Airport, Enterprise House, Bassingbourne Road, Stansted, Essex CM24 1QW (0870 000 0303; Fax: 01279 662066).

Information available: Written guidance is provided in letter form in response to requests. The company also produces a social responsibility report.

Corporate giving

In 2007, cash contributions from the company totalled £1,376,238. Of this, 0.15% went to the BAA Communities Trust.

The BAA Communities Trust gave a total of £433,680 in grants in 2006 (nine months period). Grants were generally in the range of £5,000 to £10,000 each, although some of larger amounts were made. Recipients included: VSO Global Xchange programme £157,000 – for 06/07); Young Engineers (£51,750); Bedfont Community Centre (£25,000); Green Corridor – Heathrow (£20,000); Gatwick Environment Centre Community Education Office (£14,000); Bishops Strortford Community, The Mitcher Kirk Project, Elthorne Park High School – special status, Scottish Council Foundation, and Young People of the Year Volunteers Board (£10,000 each); Create Programme (£8,265); Thaxted Youth Club Development (£6,500); and HIT Scotland (£6,000).

Gatwick Airport Community Trust gave £145,900 in 141 grants in 2005. This was broken down as follows: Young people £27,700); Elderly (£3,100); Disabled/disadvantaged (£23,350); Community facilities/environment (£39,100); Sport and recreation (£27,000); Arts, theatre and music (£25,650).

According to the accounts for the Gatwick Airport Pantomime Society no donations have been made in the last two years (2004/2005).

Employee-led support

The company matches employee giving g on a pound for pound basis, and employee fundraising to a maximum of £250. Staff are also given time off to volunteer.

Payroll giving: The company operates the Payroll Giving in Action and the Give As You Earn schemes.

BAE Systems

Company registration number 1470151

Warwick House, PO Box 87, Farnborough Aerospace Centre, Farnborough, Hampshire GU14 6YU

01252 373232

Website: www.baesystems.com

Correspondent: Alison Miller, Subscriptions & Donations Committee

Chairman: Dick Olver

Chief Executive: Mike Turner

Year end	Turnover	Pre-tax profit
31/12/2007	£14,309,000,000	£1,235,000,000

Nature of company business
The main activity of the Group is Defence – comprising the design and manufacture of civil and military aircraft, surface ships, submarines, space systems, radar, avionics, communications, electronics and guided weapon systems.

Subsidiaries include: Spectrum Technologies plc, Future Naval Systems, IFS Defence Ltd, Innovation Partnerships Worldwide Ltd, Gripen International, RG Ammunition, Airbus UK, Avionics Group, AMS Integrated Systems

Main locations: Srathclyde, Prestwick, Somerset, London, Northamptonshire, Wiltshire, Yorkshire, Surrey, Cumbria, Cwymbran, County Durham, Cheshire, Buckinghamshire, Bristol, Cambridgeshire, Bridgend, Lancashire, Leicestershire, Kent, Isle of Wight, Hertfordshire, Hampshire, Greater Manchester, Gloucestershire, Glascoed, Glasgow, Essex, Edinburgh, Dunfermline, Dorset

Total employees: 34,000

Charitable donations

2007: £1,400,000
2005: £1,200,000
2004: £1,100,000

Total community contributions: £6,100,000

Membership: BitC, L B Group

Community involvement

'BAE Systems takes an active role in community and educational activities, supporting charities and working directly with those communities close to our facilities worldwide.' National and local charities may be supported.'

Applications

In writing to the correspondent. The committee meets quarterly. Local appeals are handled by the regional site managers. Letters should at least be 'topped and tailed'.

Information available: The company produce an annual social responsibility report.

Corporate giving

In 2007, total community investment worldwide was £6.1 million. This figure included cash and in kind donations to charity as well as direct support for education. £1.2 million was donated in cash for charitable purposes in the UK. A major beneficiary of this was Macmillan – cancer support.

Employee-led support

Charity Challenge was launched in 1989, to challenge young employees to invent imaginative ways of raising funds for charities. In response, BAE matches £ for £ up to a ceiling of £100,000 any monies raised.

A number of staff give time and energy to support local community programmes involving education and training (such as job shadowing/work experience and mentoring schemes), and the development of local business enterprise initiatives. Staff are also seconded to charities and enterprise projects, through the individual business units rather than head office. The company matches employee fundraising and has a matching scheme for hours spent by employees volunteering (up to an allocated amount).

Education: The company is involved in a range of projects to promote better understanding between industry and education at national and local level. It aims to strengthen its links with a number of schools, technology colleges and universities.

Payroll giving: Varying payroll deduction schemes are operated in some parts of the business.

Commercially-led support

Sponsorship: Arts and good-cause sponsorship are undertaken.

Contact: Kate Watcham.

Bain & Company Inc. UK

Company registration number FC014328

40 Strand, London WC2N 5RW

020 7969 6000; Fax: 020 7969 6666

Website: www.bain.com

Correspondent: Graham Elton, Partner 020 7969 6050; Fax: 020 7969 6666
Email: graham.elton@bain.com

UK Managing Partner: Paul Rodgers

Nature of company business
Bain & Company is one of the world's leading global strategy consulting firms, serving clients across six continents.

Main locations: London

UK employees: 328

Charitable donations

Membership: BitC

Community involvement

The following information is taken from the company's website. Bain's London office encourages and facilitates its employees to contribute their time and skills to community work through the Bain Cares community involvement programme. This has three key areas:

- education
- homelessness
- high impact volunteering.

Further significant in kind investment is made through pro bono consulting on important social issues. Over 70% of the employees in Bain's London office are included in the community programme.

Exclusions

Bain do not make grants. All support is given in kind.

Applications

In writing to the correspondent.

Corporate giving

Although Bain do not give grants, the level of in kind support is significant and warrants inclusion here.

In kind support

Education: This involves employees in a variety of programmes including in-depth mentoring of secondary students, and one-on-one reading programmes with primary schoolchildren and mentoring through the Prince's Trust.

Homelessness: The company has had an ongoing working relationship with Business Action on Homelessness for a number of years. A recent example of this involved small teams of Bain volunteers creating a website.

Capital Cares: Bain is a founder member of the organisation which aims 'to create a step change in quantity and quality of employee volunteering in the UK'. This initiative has enabled employees to volunteer to undertake activities such as cleaning up the Thames or gardening at homeless shelters.

Pro Bono Consulting: Bain aims to make a significant case team investment (on average every two years) on important social issues. Work has recently been carried out alongside Business Action on Homelessness, and the World Faiths Development Dialogue.

Bain also provides support – financial, marketing, advisory – to foundations such as Fulbright, the Voices Foundation and the Wellbeing Trust.

Employee-led support

An Employee Challenge Fund has been established to enable one-off activities to be sponsored through the participation of London 'Bainies' in team-based challenges.

Payroll giving: The firm operate a payroll giving scheme.

J C Bamford Excavators Ltd

Company registration number 561597

Lakeside Works, Denstone Road, Rocester, Uttoxeter, Staffordshire ST14 5JP

01889 590312

Website: www.jcb.com

Correspondent: Steve Owens, Administrator, Bamford Charitable Foundation

Chairman: Sir A P Bamford

Chief Executive: John Patterson

Year end	Turnover	Pre-tax profit
31/12/2006	£386,300,000	£11,200,000

Nature of company business
The company manufactures heavy construction and agricultural equipment.

Main locations: Wrexham, Uttoxeter, Stoke-on-Trent, Rocester, Rugeley

UK employees: 1,227

Charitable donations
2006: £200,000
2005: £200,000
2004: £200,000

Community involvement

Information previously received led us to believe that the company channelled its community support through the Bamford Charitable Foundation (Charity Commission no. 279848); this is incorrect. Although the trust was initially endowed with a sum by the JCB Group some years ago, it relies solely upon the annual income derived from its investments to fund its grant making.

Certain employees of the company are, however, used by the foundation for management and administrative purposes for which no charge is made. In addition all requests received by the company for charitable donations are always referred to the foundation.

Exclusions

No support for advertising in brochures, animal welfare charities, appeals from individuals, enterprise/training, overseas projects, political appeals, sport, small purely local appeals not in areas of company presence, larger national appeals, or circulars. The company does not welcome proposals for arts sponsorship.

Applications

In writing to the correspondent. A donations committee meets quarterly. Local branches do not have an independent grant-making policy and local appeals should be addressed to head office. The company welcomes relevant appeals from charities, but the guidelines above should be carefully considered, as appeal mail is becoming too large to handle.

Corporate giving

The Bamford Charitable Foundation

Grants are made to support welfare purposes within a 40-mile radius of Rocester. Beneficiaries have included schools, hospices, hospitals, language centres, medical welfare associations and catholic organisations.

In 2006/07, the foundation had an income of nearly £58,600 and made grants totalling £125,750. This overspend has been a feature of the trust's finances in recent year and is met from an expendable endowment, the initial amount of which was £2 million.

Major beneficiaries during the year were: Littleover Methodist Church (£50,000); UNICEF (£15,000); The Victory (Services) Association, Headway Tunbridge Wells & District and The Countryside Restoration trust (£10,000 each); and Alton Castle (£7,000).

Other smaller grants were paid to: The Falkland Islands War Memorial Chapel Trust (£2,500); The Asswin Project (£2,000); Children in Crisis (£1,500); and Save China's Tigers (UK), The National Memorial Arboretum and North of England Victims Association (£1,000 each).

In kind support

Education: JCB has close liaison with 40+ schools (primary, middle and secondary levels) from across Staffordshire, Stoke-on-Trent and Derbyshire. The company provides a range of cross-curricular activities across all ages and provision for work-related experience weeks for year 10 students.

Employee-led support

Preference is given to projects in which a member of staff is involved, for which the company will provide financial support and/or match the employee's fundraising. Currently (2008), JCB employees are fundraising on behalf of the NSPCC.

Commercially-led support

Sponsorship: *Education* – JCB is the main industrial sponsor of the JCB Academy which is due to open in September 2010 for students aged between 14 and 19 from Staffordshire, Stoke-on-Trent, Derbyshire and Derby City. These young people will have a keen interest in one or more of its main specialisms: engineering, manufacturing and global business.

Bank of England

Company registration number RC000042

Threadneedle Street, London EC2R 8AH

020 7601 4444

Website: www.bankofengland.co.uk

Correspondent: Mrs Linda Barnard, Community Relations Manager 020 7601 4239; Fax: 020 7601 4553 Email: charity@bankofengland.co.uk

Chairman: Mervyn King, Governor

Year end	Turnover
29/02/2008	£197,000,000

Nature of company business
The Bank of England is the central bank of the United Kingdom and aims to maintain a stable and efficient monetary and financial framework in pursuance of a healthy economy.

The bank is based in London and has agencies in Belfast, Birmingham, Bristol, Cambridge, Exeter, Glasgow, Leeds, Liverpool, Manchester, Newcastle, Nottingham, Southampton, and Greater London. It operates a printing works in Loughton, Essex, in addition to its Registrar's Department in Gloucester. Subsidiaries include companies purchased in the course of its function of regulating the financial markets such as Minories Finance (formerly Johnson Matthey Bankers) following the sale of that company's principal business).

Main locations: Belfast, Birmingham, Leeds, Cardiff, Cambridge, Bristol, Exeter, Gloucester, Glasgow, Southampton, Newcastle-on-Tyne, Loughton, Manchester, Liverpool, London, Nottingham

UK employees: 1,752

Charitable donations

2008: £343,000
2007: £410,000
2006: £389,000
2005: £409,000
2004: £521,000

Total community contributions: £587,000

Membership: BitC

Community involvement

The Bank of England's Community Involvement Policy 2008–2011

'The Bank of England aims to be a socially responsible employer through encouraging its staff to be involved in community initiatives and by recognising their involvement. We aim to achieve this by:

- encouraging staff to become involved in community initiatives both through their own efforts and through a range of programmes managed by the Bank
- focusing donations on organisations that are supported by staff (within the Bank's charitable giving criteria)
- supporting the local community links of the Bank's regional agencies
- providing benefits in kind to the voluntary sector where Bank resources allow
- reporting to 'Court' [of directors] on our work with the community annually and reviewing our community involvement policy every three years.'

Exclusions

No support is given towards: expeditions; holidays; orchestras; conferences; overseas work; organisations of a political nature; religious activities (unless they benefit the wider community); appeals from individuals; choirs; theatres; churches; animals; or third-party fundraising.

Applications

Donations can be made locally at the discretion of the branch agent and subject to a limited budget. Otherwise, appeals should be addressed to the correspondent.

Information available: The bank produces a social responsibility report.

Corporate giving

In 2007/08, the Bank contributed £587,000 in support of its community programme (2006/07: £680,000). Donations in cash totalled £343,000 (2006/07: £410,000), this included £15,000 via the Bank of England Court Awards through which donations are made to community organisations in recognition of outstanding volunteering commitment by members of staff; £5,000 for the David Sharp School Governor Awards; £52,000 to community organisations via the Staff Volunteering Award Scheme, and £32,000 matched funding under the payroll Give As You Earn scheme. The cost of other community contributions, including time spent by staff on community involvement, was £244,000 (2006/07: £270,000), and donations to academic research amounted to £93,000 (2006/07: £134,000).

Please note that the Bank has not included the donations made towards academic research (£93,000) in its total contributions figure.

In kind support

As part of the Bank's Education Business Partnership activities in Tower Hamlets and Hackney, work experience placements are arranged for local people, while staff are encouraged to take part in various school initiatives.

The Bank also donates gifts in kind of surplus goods, computers and furniture.

Employee-led support

The Bank supports employees' volunteering/charitable activities through giving time off to volunteer, financial support, matching employee fundraising to a maximum of £250, and matching employee giving pound for pound. Staff are also encouraged to take up community positions, such as trustees, board members and magistrates.

Bank of Ireland UK Financial Services

Company registration number 2124201

PO Box 27, Temple Quay, Bristol BS99 7AX

0117 943 7207

Website: www.boiukfs.co.uk

Correspondent: Kelly Manners, Corporate Responsibility Officer
Email: kelly.manners@boiukfs.co.uk

Chairman: Des Crowley

Nature of company business
The company provides a range of financial services.

Main locations: Bristol

UK employees: 3,450

Charitable donations

2007: £100,000

Membership: BitC

Community involvement

This entry replaces that for Bristol & West plc which is now a member of the Bank of Ireland Group. The Bank of Ireland provided us with the following information:

'In March 2007 Bank of Ireland Group introduced a new community initiative, which has changed the way they contribute to charitable organisations and community groups. The concept was developed following a detailed review of Bank of Ireland's community investment, where one of the main findings was that valuable work being done by employees could be enhanced if encouraged and supported by the bank.

'As a result, the bank decided to channel the community investment into facilitating and supporting employee activities through a new initiative called *Give Together*.

'The Give Together initiative was established to support employees who wish to volunteer their time and support causes which are important to them. It involves a commitment by the Bank of Ireland to give each employee one day's leave per year to volunteer their time to a cause of their choice. The bank has also put in place a fund to support these endeavours and which allows the Bank of Ireland to contribute to employees fundraising achievements

'Many of the bank's previous methods of corporate giving are now incorporated into the Give Together initiative.'

However, please note that requests for funding in the West Country can still be applied for through the Bank of Ireland UK Charitable Fund administered by the Quartet Community Foundation (see 'Applications').

Exclusions

Bank of Ireland UK Charitable Fund: No support is given to appeals from individuals, general appeals, religious appeals, overseas travel, arts and sports projects with no community or charitable element, or medical research, equipment or treatment.

Applications

In writing to the Bank of Ireland UK Charitable Fund, c/o The Quartet Community Foundation. Guidelines and an application form can be downloaded from the foundation's website, or you can apply online at www.quartetcf.org.uk

Please note that for this fund applicants must be based and working in Bristol, Bath & North East Somerset, North Somerset, or South Gloucestershire.

Corporate giving

Bank of Ireland UK Financial Services did not quantify its level of community support in either cash or in kind form. However, given that its subsidiary (Bristol & West plc) made cash donations of over £100,000 in 2006/07 it is likely to be well in excess of this.

As mentioned elsewhere in this entry, grants are available to West Country-based organisations through the Bank of Ireland UK Charitable Fund. Grants can be for up to a maximum of £1,000 under the criteria of 'Children and education'. Recently, support has been given for a variety of activities including: a history project; music therapy; an environmental project; after school music lessons; and the refurbishment of training workshops.

Employee-led support

The company has recently established an employee volunteering scheme ('Give Together') which provides employees with one day's leave a year to volunteer for a charity of their choice.

As part of the Give Together initiative, the bank is operating a database of organisations that are interested making volunteering opportunities known to Bank of Ireland employees. If you would like opportunities for your organisation to be included, please send the details by post to: The Give Together Initiative, Bank of Ireland Group, 5th Floor, Baggot Street, Dublin 2, or email to givetogether@boimail.com

The company also matches employee fundraising and employee giving to a maximum of £700 each, per individual.

Payroll giving: The Give As You Earn scheme is operated.

Commercially-led support

Sponsorship: Neither arts nor good-cause sponsorship are undertaken.

The Banks Group

Company registration number 2267400

West Cornforth, Ferryhill, Durham DL17 9EU

01740 658 500; Fax: 01740 658 520

Website: www.hjbanks.com

Correspondent: Christina Rackley, Grants and Development Manager
Email: christina@bankscommunityfund.org.uk

Year end	Turnover	Pre-tax profit
31/03/2008	£40,935,000	£5,011,000

Nature of company business
Opencast coal mining and the development of interests in land.

UK employees: 265

Charitable donations

2007: £22,000

Community involvement

The Banks Group supports local community groups, sports clubs and voluntary organisations, offering practical advice and assistance where possible. It also provides a range of educational opportunities to local schools, colleges and universities.

The Banks Group has a community team working within the communities closest to the company's sites. Part of its role is to identify community projects that may benefit from Banks' site specific community benefits funds.

In addition to the above, there is also the Banks Community Fund which supports local environmental and community improvement projects in the areas surrounding Banks Group's operations. Monies for this come via the landfill Communities Fund, wind farm developments and property developments.

Exclusions

No support for individuals, political or religious appeals.

Applications

In writing to the correspondent.

Further information is available at: www.bankscommunity fund.org.uk or by calling 0191 384 5460.

Please note that County Durham Foundation administers the Landfill Communities Fund on behalf of the Banks Community Fund.

Corporate giving

In 2007, the company made charitable donations of £22,000. Beneficiaries included Wolsingham Wayfarers (£13,300), Yorkshire Wildlife Trust (£10,500), Number 66 Youth Drop-In Centre (£9,000) and St Andrew's Church, Cambois (£5,300).

In kind support

Education: 'We work with local schools, colleges and universities in the vicinity of our sites and have developed education packs. Our projects often provide a valuable educational resource and our staff are able to take part in lessons, educational visits or research projects.

'We have also provided funding to educational establishments close to our sites supporting the provision of a variety of new facilities including IT suites, new sports pitches, environmental improvements, energy audits, play areas and funded postgraduate research.'

Barclays plc

Company registration number 48839

Community Affairs, 1 Churchill Place, Canary Wharf, London E14 5HP

020 7116 1000

Website: www.barclays.co.uk

Correspondent: Rachael Barber, Global Head of Community Investment
Email: rachael.barber@barclays.com

Chairman: Marcus Aggius

Chief Executive: John Varley

Year end	Turnover	Pre-tax profit
31/12/2007	£23,523,000,000	£7,107,000,000

Nature of company business
Barclays plc is a UK-based financial services group engaged primarily in the banking and investment banking businesses. In terms of assets employed, Barclays is one of the biggest financial service groups in the UK. The group also operates in many other countries around the world.

Subsidiaries include: FIRSTPLUS Financial Group plc, Charles Schwab Europe, Woolwich plc, Gerrard Management Services Ltd

Main locations: London

UK employees: 62,000

Total employees: 128,900

Charitable donations

2007: £30,400,000
2006: £35,200,000
2005: £16,700,000
2004: £11,200,000
2003: £9,900,000

Total community contributions: £38,932,000

Membership: A & B, BitC, L B Group

Community involvement

'Investing in the community is an important part of Barclays sustainability strategy. We believe our business will benefit from contributing to the development and sustainability of the communities where we operate.'

Barclays' work focuses on three areas:

Banking on brighter futures – This is Barclays' flagship programme and, quote: 'Allows us to use our financial skills and expertise to maximum effect to help people work towards financial independence and security. We're clear that by aligning our community investment to our core business, we can make the maximum positive impact. Not only are we giving money, but also bringing the power and capability of our organisation to tackle social issues. We're focusing our efforts on financial inclusion, entrepreneurship, education and helping people into employment.'

Looking after local communities – 'To enable us to fulfil our local responsibilities, Looking after local communities is about investing in the many neighbourhoods around the world where Barclays has a presence. Supporting causes that matter in local markets is one of the best ways that Barclays can meet specific needs and engage local stakeholders – be they customers, community representatives or colleagues.'

Charity begins at work – This is a vital component of Barclays' community investment programme. 'At its heart is the desire to engage and support our colleagues to get involved with causes they care most about. We want to harness their energy, time and skills because we know they have a huge amount to give – and gain – by being involved.'

Exclusions

Barclays will not support the following:

- political parties or bodies
- promotion of religious beliefs (we do consider projects led by religious organisations provided the whole community benefits
- sponsorship of individuals
- Rotary, Lion Clubs and other third-party giving organisations
- hospital costs for individuals
- medical treatment and medical research
- capital appeals (for example, for buildings)
- the arts (unless the donation provides direct support to a disadvantaged group)
- micro-finance loan fund capital (donations can be used to support the establishment and operation of community motivated micro-finance programmes, but cannot be used as capital for on-lending direct to clients).

Applications

Enquiries/appeals to head office should be sent to the correspondent named above. Local enquiries/appeals should be addressed to the relevant contact given below.

Central – Email: helen.jones@barclay.com or paula.shore marston@barclay.com; Tel: 02467 845111.

Eastern – Email: kate.kingshott@barclay.com; Tel: 020 7116 5061.

North East – Email: david.ratcliffe@barclay.com; Tel: 0113 381 4529.

North West – Email: gareth.lewis1@barclay.com; Tel: 07775 55 308.

South West – Email: david.bond1@barclay.com; Tel: 07766 361 446.

Wales and West – Email: jean.king@barclay.com; Tel: 029 2042 6751.

Corporate giving

In 2007, Barclays invested £52.4 million (2006: £46.5 million) in community projects around the world of which £38.9 million (2006: £39.6 million) went towards supporting UK-based organisations.

Barclays states that the cash element of its UK investment totalled £30.4 million (2006: £35.2 million) which represents nearly double the amount given in 2005 (£16.7 million).

Some of the projects/organisations to benefit from the bank's support were: Crisis – 'Changing Lives'; RNID – Job Clubs; Help the aged; Horizons; Groundwork (Luton and South Bedfordshire); and Passage.

In kind support

Community Placements: This scheme introduces former Barclays employees (who have recently left the bank either through retirement or a redundancy package) to voluntary organisations which would benefit from the individuals financial skills and knowledge, and which fit within the focus of the bank's community programme.

Employee-led support

Volunteers & fundraising: Barclays state that because of the wide range of organisations (national and local) its employees want to support, its approach has always been not to limit help to a single 'adopted' charity. Employees are therefore supported in their choices in a variety of ways.

Staff wishing to provide practical help to charities and community groups can apply for grants through its employee volunteering scheme. Additionally, the Volunteer 2day scheme allows staff at least two days of Barclays' time each year in which to volunteer.

Charities or community groups which think they would benefit from Barclays' volunteer support through the 'Make a Difference Day' are encouraged to email the bank's local community team. Contact details and a template to help you with applying are available on its website.

Employees fundraising efforts are matched up to a set maximum. Employees can apply for matched funding a maximum of three times a year.

During 2007, over 43,000 employees actively engaged in the bank's community programmes receiving support for fundraising, volunteering and giving.

Nearly 9,000 of these employees took part in fundraising events, collecting £12.8 million on behalf of charity, whilst donating a total of nearly 95,000 work hours and 70,000 of personal hours towards volunteering activities.

Payroll giving: Barclays operates the Pennies from Heaven payroll giving scheme. It also offers Give As You Earn for employees. In the UK (and South Africa) 12,145 employees gave £1.39 million through the schemes of which £846,000 was matched by Barclays.

Commercially-led support

Sponsorship: – Arts and good-cause sponsorship is only undertaken at regional level.

Sport – Barclays' Spaces for Sports scheme focuses on regeneration and sports, creating sustainable sports sites for people to engage in sport and physical activities in areas without such facilities (www.barclays.com/community/spacesforsports).

Barrett Developments plc

Company registration number 5688068

Barrett House, Cartwright Way, Forest Business Park, Baron Hill, Coalville, Leicestershire LE67 1HF

01530 278 278; Fax: 01530 278 279

Website: www.barrettdevelopments.co.uk

Correspondent: (see 'Applications')

Chairman: Bob Lawson

Chief Executive: Mark Clare

Year end	Turnover	Pre-tax profit
30/06/2008	£3,554,700,000	£137,300,000

Nature of company business
The group's principal activities comprise house building and commercial development.

UK employees: 6.407

Charitable donations
2008: £53,300
2007: £22,900

Membership: BitC

Community involvement

According to the company's 2008 Corporate Responsibility Report, a charitable giving charter has been established which:

- links charitable giving to major developments and nearby local charities
- supports employees who engage in charitable and voluntary work
- has embedded community activity in its graduate development programmes.

The charter will be reviewed annually.

Applications

National charities should contact the marketing department at: Barrett Developments plc, Kent House, 1st Floor, 14–17 Market Place, London W1W 8AJ. (Tel: 020 7299 4898).

Local charities should contact the nearest regional office.

Corporate giving

In 2007/08, the company made charitable donations of £53,300 (2006/07: £22,900). Of this, £7,000 went to the Smith

Institute, £5,000 to the National Autistic Society, £3,000 to Shelter and the remainder to local and good causes.

Employee-led support

The company encourages its employees to undertake charitable and voluntary work.

BASF plc

Company registration number 667980

PO Box 4, Earl Road, Cheadle Hulme, Cheshire SK8 6QG

0161 485 6222; Fax: 0161 486 0891

Website: www.basf.de/uk/

Correspondent: Director of Corporate Services

Managing Director: Torben Jensen

Year end	Turnover	Pre-tax profit
31/12/2007	£403,227,000	(£48,776,000)

Nature of company business
Chemicals, paints, plastics, pharmaceuticals.

Subsidiaries include: Basell UK Ltd, Elastogram UK Ltd, Hydrowingas Ltd, Basell Polyolefins UK Ltd, BTC Speciality Chemical Distribution Ltd, Frank Wright Ltd

Main locations: Wantage, Cheadle, Deeside, Manchester, Woolpit, Middlesbrough, Ruddington, Cinderford, London, Nottingham, Alfreton

UK employees: 414

Charitable donations
2007: £84,088
2006: £111,475

Community involvement

BASF declined our invitation to contribute updated information for our research and, as such, we have been unable to glean little about what they support in the UK. Previously, the company has stated a preference for supporting local charities in areas where it operates (mainly in the North West, North East and East Midlands) and for organisations working in the fields of: the arts and culture; education and training; employment promotion; and science/technology.

Exclusions

No grants for purely denominational (religious) appeals or local appeals not in areas of company presence.

Applications

In writing to the correspondent for national appeals. For local appeals contact the nearest relevant site.

Corporate giving

In 2007, BASF made charitable donations in the UK of £84,088 (2006: £111,475). We have no details of the beneficiaries.

Employee-led support

Most of BASF's sites work with local schools by providing school visits, work experience placements and practical help with school projects.

Commercially-led support

Sponsorship: *The arts* – The company continues to sponsor the Hallé Orchestra, having done so since 1970.

Science/technology – BASF currently sponsors 'The Science of Survival' and the Energy Gallery at the Science Museum in London.

Baxter Healthcare Ltd

Company registration number 461365

Wallington, Compton, Newbury, Berkshire RG20 7QW

01635 206000; Fax: 01635 206115

Website: www.baxterhealthcare.co.uk

Correspondent: Office Services (Sponsorship)
Email: cfob@baxter.com

Year end	Turnover	Pre-tax profit
31/12/2006	£211,680,000	£21,988,000

Nature of company business
Technologies related to the blood and circulatory system.

Main locations: Thetford, Stockport, Liverpool, Northampton, Newbury, Oxford

UK employees: 1,006

Charitable donations

2006: £19,193
2005: £41,000
2002: £68,775

Community involvement

This international group operates the Baxter International Foundation which supports the health and well-being of communities worldwide where Baxter employees live and work. Since 2002, the foundation has focused exclusively on increasing access to healthcare, particularly for the disadvantaged and underserved.

Support is only given to registered charities. Charities are sometimes nominated by a Baxter employee, especially if they operate in an area where there is a Baxter facility, or where a large number of Baxter employees live.

All grants awarded are health focused.

In the UK, assistance is only given in the areas where the company operates. Currently, these are Liverpool, Newbury, Northampton, Oxford, Stockport and Thetford.

Exclusions

No grants are made to: capital or endowment campaigns; disease-specific organisations; educational institutions (except for programmes that are providing increased direct health services in a Baxter community); hospitals; individuals; organisations which benefit a restricted part of the community, such as service or religious charities; or fundraising events.

Applications

To be considered for support from the foundation, registered charities must be nominated by a Baxter employee, not via unsolicited applications, and be eligible under the foundations guidelines. Details of the latter can be found at www.baxter.com

Any queries about the foundation, your organisation's eligibility and so on, can be addressed via email to: fdninfo@baxter.com

Applications are considered in April, June, September and December.

Corporate giving

In 2006, the company declared in its annual report and accounts charitable donations in the UK of just under £19,200. We are not sure exactly how this was distributed, but Baxter Healthcare advised that the following national charities are supported: Great Ormond Street Children's Charity; NSPCC; and Children in Need.

Baxter International Foundation

In 2006, the foundation awarded around US$3.1 million (£1.6 million) in grants to support the health and well-being of communities worldwide. The only UK beneficiary during the year was Changing Faces which received US$7,952 (£4,065) as the third and final payment of a US$74,828 (£38,230) grant.

So far, in 2008, the foundation has made one grant in the UK of US$36,360 (£18,000). This went to beat in Norwich to increase services to migrant families addressing eating disorders in Thetford.

In kind support

Product donations are made in support of disaster relief programmes, underdeveloped nations and countries in crisis.

Employee-led support

The UK company operates a 'matching gifts' programme for employees fundraising efforts and allow staff company time off in which to volunteer.

Baxters Food Group Ltd

Company registration number SC23572

Fochabers, Moray IV32 7LD

01343 820 393

Website: www.baxters.com

Correspondent: (see 'Applications')

Chairman: Audrey Baxter

Chief Executive: Audrey Baxter

Year end	Turnover	Pre-tax profit
02/07/2007	£113,942,000	£6,695,000

Nature of company business
The manufacture of high quality, ambient, chilled and frozen food, supply retail and foodservice customers in the UK and key overseas markets.

UK employees: 1,041

> **Charitable donations**
> 2007: £128,078
> 2006: £173,822

Community involvement

The majority of the company's charitable support is directed through The Baxters Foundation (Charity No. SC033432) which is based at the same address as the company.

The foundation's interests are in the relief of poverty, health, education, citizenship, community development, the arts, heritage, culture, science, sports and recreation, and the environment.

The foundation benefits children and young people, older people, and people with disabilities or health problems. Support is given to organisations and individuals.

Although support is primarily given in Scotland, other areas of the UK may be considered.

Applications

In writing to the trustees of The Baxters Foundation at the address given above.

Corporate giving

In 2007, the company made charitable donations of £128,078 of which £102,000 went to the foundation. We have no information regarding any grants made by the foundation during the year.

Bayer plc

Company registration number 935048

Bayer House, Strawberry Hill, Newbury, Berkshire RG14 1JA

01635 563000; Fax: 01635 563513

Website: www.bayer.co.uk

Correspondent: CSR Committee

Email: corporate.communications@bayer.co.uk

Chairman: Werner Wenning

Year end	Turnover	Pre-tax profit
31/12/2007	£290,775,000	£33,522,000

Nature of company business
The marketing of healthcare and polymer products manufactured by Bayer Group.

Subsidiaries include: H C Starck, W Hawley & son, pbi Home & Garden

Main locations: Newbury, Norwich, Cambridge

UK employees: 664

Total employees: 106,000

Community involvement

'[Bayer's] community support programme is overseen by a committee which aims to be professional, sympathetic, impartial and systematic. That must include a firm and clear statement of what we can and cannot support, subject to available funds and the balance of our existing community work.

'Bayer supports activities that are local to us and are:
- linked to our employees' own community activities
- linked to one of Bayer's 5,000 products or services
- specifically benefiting from Bayer's involvement
- beneficial to numbers or groups of people.

'We support activities which enhance local quality of life through:
- the environment,
- community care,
- culture and the arts,
- education,
- projects in line with our Mission Statement,
- projects benefiting groups and not individuals.

'While activities meeting the above criteria will be considered, they do not automatically qualify for support, as other factors (such as budget already committed) must be taken into account.'

Exclusions

Bayer are unable to support:
- individuals rather than group activities
- religious, political or racially aligned movements
- projects or activities bridging a gap in government or local authority funding
- sporting or recreational activities unless closely associated to Bayer
- entries in log books, year books or support advertising
- projects of a local nature which are outside key locations of Newbury, Cambridge, Norwich and Dublin
- conferences, lectures, trips, respite breaks or holidays
- national initiatives.

Applications

Given that you meet Bayer's criteria, you will then need to complete the 'CSR Rrequest Form' (available from their website). The information you provide will supply Bayer with the key details they require to make an informed decision regarding your proposal.

Please post your completed CSR Request Form and supporting materials to:

CSR Committee
Bayer plc
Bayer House
Strawberry Hill
Newbury
Berkshire
RG14 1JA

Alternativey, you can send it by email: corporate.communications@bayer.co.uk or by fax: 01635 563513.

Please note that Bayer only accept postal, email or faxed requests and are unable to take 'phone calls to discuss individual requests.

Bayer's committee reviews applications received on a monthly basis throughout the year. Bayer will contact you by email or letter to let you know if they are able to support you or not.

Corporate giving

All community support is given through the Bayer Foundation

In kind support

The company supports education, particularly science projects for young people.

Employee-led support

Employee fundraising is matched by the company.

Commercially-led support

Sponsorship: The company undertakes arts and good-cause sponsorship.

Bellway plc

Company registration number 1372603

Seaton Burn House, Dudley Lane, Seaton Burn, Newcastle upon Tyne NE13 6BE

0191 217 0717; Fax: 0191 236 6230

Website: www.bellway.co.uk

Correspondent: G K Wrightson, Group Company Secretary

Chairman: H C Dawe

Chief Executive: J K Watson

Year end	Turnover	Pre-tax profit
31/07/2007	£1,354,022,000	£234,850,000

Nature of company business
The company's main activity is house building.

Subsidiaries include: Litrose Investments Ltd, The Victoria Dock Company Ltd

Main locations: Bedworth, Altrincham, Wetherby, Tamworth, Uxbridge, Wakefield, Ringwood, Merstham, Newcastle upon Tyne, Glasgow, Eastcote, Chadderton, Chelmsford, Cardiff

UK employees: 2,476

Total employees: 2,476

Charitable donations

2007: £95,956
2006: £87,291
2005: £85,290
2004: £97,786
2003: £89,197

Community involvement

The company prefers to support local charities near to main office locations (but see below).

The company has established the Bellway Fund within the Community Foundation (Tyne & Wear/Northumberland) in order for it to support charitable initiatives outside of the sphere of its core operations.

Exclusions

No support for advertising in charity brochures, appeals from individuals, animal welfare, fundraising events, overseas projects, political appeals, or religious appeals.

Applications

In writing to the correspondent.

Corporate giving

In 2006/07, the company made cash donations to charitable causes totalling £95,956 (2005/06: £87,291). No further information on how this was distributed was available.

We do know, however, that the following organisations received support via the Bellway Fund: Fairbridge in Tyne & Wear (£500); Northumberland Wildlife Trust (£300); and Jesmond Dene Real Tennis Club and The Edward Lloyd Trust (£250 each).

Employee-led support

The company matches employees fundraising, but we do not know to what level.

Berkeley Group plc

Company registration number 1454064

Berkeley House, 19 Portsmouth Road, Cobham, Surrey KT11 1GD

01932 868555; Fax: 01932 868667

Website: www.berkeleygroup.com

Correspondent: Charity Committee

Chairman: Tony Pidgley

Managing Director: Tony Carey

Year end	Turnover	Pre-tax profit
30/04/2007	£918,410,000	£188,050,000

Nature of company business
Principal activity: residential house building and commercial property investment and development.

Subsidiaries include: St James Group Ltd, Exchange Place No. 2 Ltd, St John Homes Ltd, Thirlstone Homes Ltd, West Kent Cold Storage Ltd, St George plc, The Beaufort Home Development Group Ltd, St David Ltd

Main locations: Edgbaston, Twickenham, Cobham, Potters Bar, Portsmouth

UK employees: 865

Charitable donations

2007: £171,973
2006: £190,977
2004: £440,957
2003: £287,000

Community involvement

We were unable to obtain any information about the company's current support. The following is therefore a repeat of the last information the company provided. Berkeley continues to support a wide range of local and national charities as long as they are based near to offices of operation. Preferred areas of support are: children/youth, elderly people, environment/heritage and sickness/disability charities.

Exclusions

No support for: animal welfare; appeals from individuals; the arts; education; enterprise/training; fundraising events; local appeals not in areas of company presence; medical research; overseas projects; political appeals; religious appeals; science/technology; social welfare; or sport.

Applications

In writing to the correspondent. However, we understand the company has a charity committee which tends to plan its giving in advance.

Corporate giving

In 2007, the company's charitable donations totalled £171,973 (2006: £190,977). We have no details of the beneficiaries.

Organisations supported in the past have included: Princess Alice Hospice (Esher, Surrey), St John Ambulance (Surrey), Paishill Park (Cobham, Surrey) and various cancer charities and children's hospitals.

Bestway (Holdings) Ltd

Company registration number 1392861

Abbey Road, Park Royal, London NW10 7BW

020 8453 1234; Fax: 020 8965 0359

Website: www.bestway.co.uk

Correspondent: Mohammed Younus Sheikh, Secretary to the Bestway Foundation

Chairman: Sir Anwar Pervez

Group Chief Execturive: Z M Choudrey

Year end	Turnover	Pre-tax profit
30/06/2007	£1,422,507,000	£58,366,000

Nature of company business
The principal activity of the group is the operation of cash and carry warehouses in the UK supplying groceries, tobacco, wines and spirits, beers and other household goods, together with property investment.

Subsidiaries include: Icecross, Map (UK)

Main locations: Bolton, Birmingham, Oldbury, Luton, London, Liverpool, Manchester, Northampton, Newcastle-under-Lyme, Peterborough, Plymouth, Romford, Swansea, Croydon, Bristol, Cardiff, Gateshead, Exeter, Leicester, Leeds

UK employees: 4,095

Charitable donations

2007: £680,000
2006: £767,000
2005: £684,000
2004: £610,000

Community involvement

The group donates a percentage of its annual profits to the registered charity, The Bestway Foundation (Charity Commission no. 297178), established by the group in 1987. The Foundation's objects are:

> the advancement of education for the public benefit both in the UK and overseas by providing assistance by way of grants, endowments, scholarships, loans or otherwise

> the Bestway Foundation has continued to provide scholarships to students and sponsor the Government's Specialist Schools and Academies Programme. The foundation has also continued to fund the development of village schools and rural Basic Health Care Units in Pakistan.

In 2007, the group's annual charity fundraiser was held at Royal Ascot. The main beneficiary charity was Barnardos

Exclusions

No grants for trips or travel abroad.

Applications

In writing to the correspondent, enclosing an sae. Applications are considered in March/April. Telephone calls are not welcome.

Corporate giving

In 2006/07, the group's annual report and accounts declared charitable donations of £680,000 (2006: £767,000) to the Bestway Foundation.

The Bestway Foundation

In 2007 the foundation had an income of £931,000 and awarded grants totalling £561,000 (2006: £762,000). Donations were broken down as follows: Registered UK charities (£233,000); Non-registered UK charities (£32,000); and Foreign charities – individuals (£296,000).

UK organisations awarded grants included: Crimestoppers (£68,000); Central Mosque of Brent (£50,000); British EduTrust Foundation (£36,000); Duke of Edinburgh's Award (£15,000); and Gatwick Detainees' Welfare Group and Padstones (£2,000 each).

BHP Billiton plc

Company registration number 3196209

Neathouse Place, London SW1V 1BH

020 7802 7000; Fax: 020 7802 3177

Website: www.bhpbilliton.com

Correspondent: (see 'Applications')

Chairman: Don Argus

Chief Executive: Marius Kloppers

Year end	Turnover	Pre-tax profit
30/06/2008	£35,115,000,000	£15,883,000,000

Nature of company business
BHP Billiton plc operated solely as a holding company for the BHP Billiton Group plc. The principal activities of the group are mineral and hydrocarbon exploration and production, metals production, marketing, and research and development.

Main locations: Liverpool, London

Charitable donations

2008: £723,000
2007: £375,000
2006: £632,772
2005: £577,235

Membership: BitC

Community involvement

The following extract is taken from the Community Investment Strategy section of the company's website: 'Across the company our community programs operate at a local, provincial, regional and national level.

▶ local – The majority of our efforts occur at our operations, where our businesses implement programs to develop and support the local communities. At our operations, the asset manager or local community relations professionals are responsible for managing their community support programmes [How this is done differs from site to site]

▶ provincial, regional and national – The company also participates in community investment programmes on a provincial and national level in countries where we have a number of businesses and play a major role in the resources sector of that country – examples include South Africa, Australia and Chile. These programmes generally focus on a small number of larger-scale projects that are of interest to the broader community within the country of interest.'

Applications

Applications should be made in writing to the corrspondent, giving details of the amount required and the purpose for which it will be used.

Write to: Cerys Percival, External Affairs UK, BHP Billiton Petroleum Ltd, Llaneurgain House, Northop Country Park, Northop, Flintshire CH7 6WD (Tel: 01352 842200).

Corporate giving

In 2007/08, the company made worldwide community contributions (including management costs) of £141,009,613 (around £95 million).

Cash donations in the UK totalled $1,068,780 (around £723,000). We have no details of the beneficiaries.

However, the company's Liverpool Bay Asset (LBA) provides support in North Wales, through increased economic opportunities, environmental improvements and positive community initiatives. Grants are available through the Lennox First Oil Fund. Grants range from £500 to a maximum of £2,000 and total around £30,000 a year.

Employee-led support

BHP Billiton has established a Matched Giving Programme through which the company will match the community contributions made by employees. Every employee (including full and part time) is entitled each year to match their contributions to not-for-profit organisations that benefit the community. These contributions can be employee volunteering, fundraising or cash donations (including payroll donations).

Awards are also made to employees under the BHP Billiton HSEC [Health, Safety, Environment and Community] and Sustainability Awards scheme. Eight short listed finalists nominate a charity or not-for-profit organisation to share in their award. These organisations will receive a donation of US$10 000 (Excellence), US$5 000 (Highly Commended) or US$2 000 (Merit).

Birmingham International Airport Ltd

Company registration number 3312673

Birmingham B26 3QJ

0121 767 7448; Fax: 0121 767 7065

Website: www.bhx.co.uk

Correspondent: Andy Holding, Birmingham Airport Community Affairs and Environment Unit 0121 767 7448; Fax: 0121 767 7359
Email: andyh@bhx.co.uk

Chairman: J L Hudson

Managing Director: M J Kelly

Year end	Turnover	Pre-tax profit
31/03/2007	£109,129,000	£17,068,000

Nature of company business
The principal activity is the operation and management of Birmingham International Airport and the provision of associated facilities and services.

Main locations: Birmingham

UK employees: 626

Charitable donations

2007: £50,000
2006: £50,000
2005: £50,000
2004: £50,000
2003: £50,000

Membership: A & B, BitC

Community involvement

The company set up a trust to fund a wide range of community-based projects which will benefit the community and environment around Birmingham Airport. The Community Trust Fund (Charity Commission no. 1071176) receives £50,000 each year from the airport, topped up by fines imposed on airlines for exceeding the airport's noise violation levels. Geographically, the trust supports a very defined area which, broadly speaking, is that bounded by Grove End, Berkswell, Honiley and Washwood Heath. Projects outside of this region cannot be funded, even if the communities feel they are affected by the disruption caused by the airport. The trust acts independently of the airport management, with nine representatives of the following bodies making up the trustees: The Airport Consultative Committee (3), Birmingham City Council (2), Birmingham International Airport (2) and Solihull Council (2).

Areas of work the trust supports are:

▶ environment improvement and heritage conservation

▶ bringing the community closer together through facilities for sport, recreation and other leisure-time activities

▶ improving awareness of environmental issues or environmental education and training activities

▶ encouraging and protecting wildlife.

It describes the types of projects it wishes to support as including community centres, community groups, sports, playgroups, schools, youth clubs, scouts, gardens/parks, environment, music and churches. Work should benefit a substantial section of the community rather than less inclusive groups, although work with older people or people with special needs is positively encouraged.

The maximum grant made is for £3,000, and grants tend to go to community groups with low incomes; organisations with large turnovers are rarely supported. Grants may be for capital or revenue projects, although the trust will not commit to recurrent or running costs, such as salaries.

Exclusions

No grants to: individuals, sports kits, trips or projects resulting in short term benefit e.g. events, performances or visits, commercial organisations, or those working for profit, projects which have already been carried out or paid for; organisations which have statutory responsibilities such as hospitals or schools, unless the project is clearly not a statutory responsibility. Grants are not normally given towards the purchase of land or buildings or general repair and maintenance; requests for equipment, fixtures and fittings may be supported. Grants will also not normally be recurrent.

Support will not be considered for advertising in charity brochures, animal welfare, overseas projects, political or religious appeals, medical purposes, or science/technology.

Applications

On a form available from the correspondent. When the form is sent, applicants will be advised when the next grant allocation meeting is being held. The trust may want to visit the project. All applications will be acknowledged.

Applications can be submitted at any time, with grants awarded twice a year in April and October. Successful applicants are required to submit a progress report after six months, and again after 12 for longer projects.

Grants will not be awarded to the same organisation in consecutive years. Applicants must wait at least three years before applying for another grant.

Information Available: The company produces further information in its application guidelines.

Corporate giving

The company makes an annual contribution of £50,000 to the trust, with money from fines increasing the fund to over £160,000. In 2006/07 it had an income of £54,000 and made grants totalling £46,000 to 25 local community projects.

In kind support

In addition to cash donations made via the Community Trust, the company provides non-cash support through gifts in kind. The value of these has not been costed.

Employee-led support

The company has an employee volunteering scheme and provides support by allowing company time off in which to volunteer.

Commercially-led support

Sponsorship: The company undertakes good-cause sponsorship.

Biwater plc

Company registration number 929686

Biwater House, Station Approach, Dorking RH4 1TZ

01306 740740; Fax: 01306 885233

Website: www.biwater.com

Correspondent: Richard Bourton, Coordinator
Email: corporate.communications@biwater.com

Chairman: A E White

Year end	Turnover	Pre-tax profit
31/03/2007	£232,100,000	£5,200,000

Nature of company business
Principal activities: contracting, manufacturing and the provision of services to the water industry worldwide.

Main locations: Dorking, Heywood, Bournemouth

UK employees: 1,037

Total employees: 2,514

Charitable donations

2007: £55,425
2006: £51,926
2005: £36,568

Community involvement

The company supports mainly Dorking charities. This is all the information we have been able to confirm about the company's community involvement.

Exclusions

No support is given to individual appeals, or purely denominational (religious) appeals. No sponsorship or advertising in charity brochures is undertaken.

Applications

In writing to the correspondent.

Corporate giving

In 2006/07, the company and its subsidiary undertakings made donations for charitable purposes of £60,229 (2006: £58,090) of which £55,425 (2006: £51,926) was in the United Kingdom mainly for education, community support and medical purposes.

Employee-led support

Payroll giving: The company operates a scheme.

Bloomsbury Publishing plc

Company registration number 1984336

36 Soho Square, London W1D 3QY

020 7494 2111; Fax: 020 7434 0151

Website: www.bloomsbury.com

Correspondent: Ian Portal, Group Company Secretary

Chairman: Jeremy Wilson

Chief Executive: Nigel Newton

Year end	Turnover	Pre-tax profit
31/12/2007	£150,211,000	£17,856,000

Nature of company business
The principal activities of the group are the publication of books and the development of electronic reference databases.

UK employees: 313

Charitable donations

2007: £3,000
2006: £34,000
2005: £126,215
2004: £51,044

Community involvement

The company states that it 'is a strong supporter of, and participant in, various charities and initiatives'. Ongoing support is given to UNESCO's World Book Day and Book Aid International.

Exclusions

No support for individuals, religious or political appeals.

Applications

In writing to the correspondent.

Corporate giving

Although the level of charitable donations made by the company has tended to vary, it has never dropped to as low a level as at present.

During 2007 donations of only £3,000 were made by the group for charitable purposes (2006: £34,000). This may be a 'blip', but it is too early to be certain.

In addition, however, the group was able to support numerous schools, libraries and other organisations, including charities such as Barnardo's and Shelter, with significant donations of books. No figure concerning the value of this in kind support appears to have been calculated.

In kind support

Product donations: As a sponsor and partner, of UNESCO's World Book Day, the company contributed in 2007 one of its titles to the ten specially created £1 books offered by the World Book Day Organisation to children in the UK through their schools and pre-schools.

The company was also pleased to support Book Aid International, the registered charity working in developing countries to create reading and learning opportunities for people of all ages to help them realise their potential and alleviate poverty.

Equal opportunities: 'The company continues its work with the Arts Council in their Diversity in Publishing Positive Action Traineeship Scheme. Designed to encourage diversity in the publishing industry, the scheme gives a graduate from an ethnic minority background the opportunity over six months to gain experience in the publishing industry with three major UK publishers, of which Bloomsbury is one.'

BMW UK Ltd

Company registration number 1378137

Ellesfield Avenue, Bracknell, Berkshire RG12 8TA

01344 426565; Fax: 01344 480203

Website: www.bmw.co.uk

Correspondent: Rosemary Davies, Public Relations Manager
01344 480102; Fax: 01344 480306
Email: rosemary.davies@bmw.co.uk

Chief Executive: Klaus Kibsgaars

Year end	Turnover	Pre-tax profit
31/12/2006	£3,395,374,000	£236,186,000

Nature of company business
The principal activity is the importation, storage and distribution of BMW products in the UK.

Subsidiaries include: Park Lane Ltd, Rolls-Royce Ltd

Main locations: Birmingham, Swindon, Hook, Thorne, Coleshill, Oxford, Goodwood, Bracknell

UK employees: 8,000

Charitable donations

2006: £25,000
2005: £25,000

Total community contributions: £115,729

Community involvement

We were previously advised that major donations are given to two or three national charities selected by the company, preferably related to the motor industry (BEN is the favoured charity), children or a charity in which a member of staff has a particular interest.

Exclusions

No response to circular appeals.

Applications

The policy outlined above means that BMW UK are unable to respond positively to letters requesting support/sponsorship.

Corporate giving

In 2006, the company made total UK community contributions of nearly £116,000. We have no details regarding the cash element of this sum, but assume it to be of similar size to that for 2005.

Smaller donations are made to local charities through the Berkshire Community Foundation, which cites BMW as a 'major donor'. Grants to local organisations can range from £50 to £1,000.

In kind support

Education: 'BMW (UK) Ltd has a long established commitment to supporting education across the UK. Launched in the UK over 17 years ago as part of the company's corporate responsibility commitment, BMW education programme provides free, curricular-linked and award-winning educational resources. It is BMW's intention for its programmes to be not only informative and engaging but accessible to everyone at: www.bmweducation.co.uk'

Employee-led support

Payroll giving: The company operates the BEN scheme.

The Body Shop International plc

Company registration number 1284170

Watersmead, Littlehampton, West Sussex BN17 6LS

01903 731500; Fax: 01903 726250

Website: www.thebodyshopfoundation.org

Correspondent: Lisa Jackson, Principal – Body Shop Foundation
01903 844039; Fax: 01903 844202

Chairman: Peter Saunders

Chief Executive: Sophie Gasperment

Year end	Turnover	Pre-tax profit
29/12/2007	£329,500,000	£43,400,000

Nature of company business
The Body Shop is a multi-local, values-led, global retailer. The group sells skin and hair care products through its own shops and franchised outlets in 47 markets worldwide.

Subsidiaries include: Soapworks Ltd

Main locations: Glasgow, Littlehampton

UK employees: 2,917

Charitable donations

2007: £1,700,000
2006: £1,000,000
2005: £1,300,000
2004: £1,000,000
2003: £900,000

Membership: BitC

Community involvement

The Body Shop mission statement states that: 'We will operate our business with a strong commitment to the well being of our fellow humans and the preservation of the planet.

'The Body Shop Values Principles set out our commitments and the actions we will take to further these commitments. Charitable contributions in cash or kind must always support the aims of these principles, and no donations can be made to organisations or causes which conflict with these aims.

'The Body Shop International will channel all its central donations through our foundation and its regional grant making committees.'

The foundation deliberately seeks out innovative projects working for social and environmental change, driven by enthusiastic, energetic groups at grass roots level. People who, because of the pioneering nature of their work, would find it hard to get conventional funding elsewhere.

With respect to the above, The Body Shop Foundation (Charity commission no. 802757) is funded by annual donations from the company and through various fundraising initiatives. Its aim is to:

- support organisations at the forefront of social & environmental change
- support groups with little hope of conventional funding

- support projects working to increase public awareness.

The foundation is currently running the following grants programmes:

- global main grants programme
- regional funding panels: Asia Pacific; UK & Republic of Ireland; Europe, Middle East & Africa; and The Americas
- global small grants programme
- local community grants programme – Littlehampton and Southwark areas.

The UK & Republic of Ireland will fund projects in 2009 which:

'Support local initiatives in the community for the benefit of the whole community'

Groups must be either charities or non-profit making organisations with an annual turnover of not more than £1.5 million a year.

Nominations for potential projects will be referred to The Body Shop Foundation by The Body Shop network of employees and consultants.

The foundation does not, unfortunately, accept applications from any other networks.

30th April 2009 – cut off date for nominations

Exclusions

The foundation does not:

- sponsor individuals
- fund sporting activities or the arts
- sponsor or support fundraising events, receptions or conferences.

In addition, no donations can be made to promote religious causes or political campaign causes, although the foundation may work with religious or political organisations on partnership projects and fund raise with organisations that have a political or religious foundation for causes that support its values and principles.

No donations can be made to, nor funds raised for organisations linked to animal testing, organisations advocating violence or discrimination or in other ways promoting behaviour inconstant with the foundation's principles.

Applications

The Body Shop International and The Body Shop Foundation no longer accept unsolicited applications for funding.

However, in exceptional circumstances the company may respond to a humanitarian emergency and make a special donation to a public appeal, but such a donation must have the approval of the CEO.

Information available: The company produce a comprehensive annual report, as well as the twice yearly publication, *Charity Matters*.

Corporate giving

In 2007, the company made charitable donations in the UK of £1.7 million of which £700,000 went to the foundation. We have no information about which organisations benefited from the donations made directly by the company.

The Body Shop Foundation

The top ten grants made by the foundation in 2007 were as follows: BUAV and Navdanya (£60,000 each over two years); Body and Soul (£59,226 over three years); MicroLoan

Foundation (£55,000 over two years), Amazon Rain Forest Foundation (£50,000); Tropical Forest Trust (£40,000 over two years); Global Action Plan (£21,493); Africa Now, Bio - Regional Development Group and STOP – Trafficking UK (£20,000 each).

Regional grants were made In the UK and Ireland to 10 organisations and totalled £90,000.

Grants available through the local community programme totalled £35,000.

In kind support

Gifts in kind club: The club closed in 2008 following doubts about its future.

Employee-led support

Employees are encouraged to take an active role in their local communities. At the UK global head office, employees are entitled to six days of volunteer time, supporting local projects and causes as individuals and as business teams.

Bombardier Aerospace Europe Ltd

Company registration number 2403482

Airport Road, Belfast BT3 9DZ

028 9045 8444; Fax: 028 9073 3396

Website: www.bombardier.com

Correspondent: Alan McKnight, Corporate Community Involvement Manager 028 9073 3538

Year end	Turnover	Pre-tax profit
31/01/2008	£507,000,000	£65,540,000

Nature of company business
The principal activities of the company are the design, development and manufacture of aircraft components and the provision of related products and services.

Main locations: Belfast

Total employees: 5,033

Charitable donations

2008: £1,028,000
2007: £152,197
2005: £214,835

Membership: A & B, BitC

Community involvement

Donations are made through the Bombardier Aerospace (NI) Foundation which, as of 2008, received 2% (2007: 1%) of the company's pre-tax profits for distribution to charitable causes in Northern Ireland.

As an active participant in the economic, cultural and social development of the communities in which it operates, Bombardier Aerospace strives to:

- encourage and enable employees to become involved in volunteering and fundraising
- support cross-community, educational and other community investment initiatives

- match funding for donations from the Employees Charities Society.

Bombardier is a member of Business in the Community's Opportunity Now campaign and works to ensure inclusiveness and equality for women in the workplace.

As part of its community outreach, and as a direct result of the West Belfast/Greater Shankill Task Force recommendations, Bombardier plays a major role in the Employers' Forum, aimed at addressing long-term unemployment in those areas.

To date, the Employers' Forum, which is funded by the foundation, has helped over 200 formerly long-term unemployed individuals into employment across the Greater Belfast area.

Exclusions

No support for projects outside Northern Ireland, individuals, travel, sports, arts, well-funded national organisations, large medical charities, capital projects, projects normally funded by statutory bodies, third party fundraising, i.e. advertising in charity programmes or at charitable social events.

Applications

By completion of an application form which should be requested either by telephone or in writing to the correspondent.

Corporate giving

In 2007/08, the company made donations for charitable purposes totalling $2,055,321 (just over £1 million). This is a significant increase over the previous year (2007: £153,000) and is due to a doubling of its allocation of pre-tax profits to the foundation from 1–2%. We are not sure if this percentage increase will be permanent (although we hope so) as 2008 saw the company celebrate 100 years of aviation heritage.

In kind support

The company provides materials for employee led community projects.

Employee-led support

Bombardier employees and apprentices are actively encouraged to fundraise for charity and to take on volunteering projects. From running marathons to building playgrounds, thousands have benefited from donations and time given by employees.

Supported by the company, employee volunteers have organised a Charities Society in which deductions from salary for charitable donations can be made, where requested by an employee. The Employees' Charities Society meets quarterly to decide which registered charities to support through such contributions. The foundation matches £ for £ donations to charities approved by the society.

Commercially-led support

Sponsorship: The foundation has forged close links with all levels of education in Northern Ireland. Bombardier has sponsored a chair in aerospace engineering at Queen's University of Belfast and has supported other projects at local universities. The company has also undertaken good-cause sponsorship.

Robert Bosch Ltd

Company registration number SC013418

Communications (RBGB/COM), Broadwater Park, Denham, Uxbridge, Middlesex UB9 5HJ

01895 834 466

Website: www.bosch.co.uk

Correspondent: Corporate Communications

Director: A Willmott

Director: H Kaess

Director: R Meier

Year end	Turnover	Pre-tax profit
31/12/2007	£468,758,000	£19,928,000

Nature of company business
Bosch is a leading global manufacturer of automotive and industrial technology, consumer goods and building technology.

Main locations: Denham, St Neots, Worcester, Stowmarket, Milton Keynes

Total employees: 271,300

Charitable donations

2007: £12,830

Community involvement

The Bosch Group in the UK is a subsidiary of Robert Bosch GmbH. The group is made up of a number of organisations, each of which has a separate responsibility for supporting their local communities.

There is a charitable foundation in Germany – The Robert Bosch Foundation – which we were advised considers appropriate applications from the UK (www.bosch-stiftung.de).

Exclusions

No support for local appeals not in areas of company presence.

Applications

Due to the non-centralised nature of support, please refer to your nearest Bosch facility.

Corporate giving

The company stated that it regularly provides support to charitable projects and local community groups within its catchment area. Support can be either in the form of cash donations or in kind. Cash donations vary in size, with decisions made on merit. In 2007 charitable donations totalled £12,830.

In kind support

In kind support can include the provision of products, e.g. power tools, for raffle prizes.

Employee-led support

Employees are encouraged to undertake voluntary work and fundraising activities. The company matches employee fundraising up to a maximum of £100.

Boyer Allan Investment Investment Management LLP

Company registration number OC304444

12–18 Grosvenor Gardens, London SW1W 0DH

020 7881 8100; Fax: 020 7881 8200

Website: www.boyerallan.com

Correspondent: (see 'Applications')

Year end	Turnover	Pre-tax profit
30/03/2007	£21,616,719	£13,701,170

Nature of company business
Provision of fund management services.

UK employees: 9

Charitable donations

2007: £500,000
2006: £871,828

Community involvement

Boyer Allan Investment Management (BAIM) is a specialist manager of Asian equity absolute return funds. Its charitable support in the UK is chanelled through The Queen Anne's Gate Foundation (Charity Commission no. 1108903) of which BAIM is the sole benefactor.

Established in 2005, the foundation seeks to support projects and charities within the following broad criteria:

'It seeks to make a contribution that is meaningful in the context of the project/charitywith which it is working. It tries to focus in particular on projects which might be said to make potentially unproductive lives productive. This tends to mean a bias towards educational, medical and rehabilitative charitrues and those that work with under priviledged areas of society. There is an attempt to focus a significant proportion of donations on the UK and Asia, In principle and increasingly, there is a willingness to commit or soft commit funding for three years if it enables the chosen charity or project to plan more effectively. The foundation supports one off appropriate causes, as they become available'.

Interestingly, in 2007 the foundation used a research-based charity (New Philanthropy Capital) to help it identify five different UK-based charities which might best match its giving intentions, making a three year soft commitment of a fixed sum to each.

Applications

In writing to: The Trustees, The Queen Anne's Gate Foundation, Wilcox and Lewis, Lincoln House, 1 Berrycroft, Willingham, Cambridge CB4 5JX.

Corporate giving

In 2007, the company donated £500,000 (2006: £871,828) to The Queen Anne's Gate Foundation, which in turn made grants totalling £260,000.

Beneficiaries included: Hackney Music Development Trust and Merlin (£30,000 each); World Medical Fund (£28,000); and Policy Exchange (£20,000).

BP plc

Company registration number 102498

1 St James's Square, London SW1Y 4PD

020 7496 4000; Fax: 020 7496 4630

Website: www.bp.com

Correspondent: Manager of Social & Global Investment

Chairman: Peter D Sutherland

Chief Executive: Dr A B Hayward

Year end	Turnover	Pre-tax profit
31/12/2007	£135,000,000,000	£16,000,000,000

Nature of company business
The group's principal activities comprise of exploration and production of crude oil and natural gas; refining, marketing, supply and transportation; and the manufacturing and marketing of petrochemicals. BP has major operations in Europe, North and South America, Asia, Australasia and parts of Africa.

Subsidiaries include: Britoil, Burmah Castrol

Main locations: London

Total employees: 96,200

Charitable donations

2007: £350,000
2005: £439,700

Membership: A & B, BitC

Community involvement

BP provided the f following overview of its UK support:

UK community programme

'Our products and operations influence communities and society in many ways, from the impact of our operations on a particular locality to the impact of revenues on a country's finances.

'As well as managing our impacts, we seek to improve the quality of life where we operate by investing in a range of community programmes. [These are:]

'*Arts and culture* – BP recognises the role that arts and culture play in the economic and social fabric of the country. Our programme maintains a focus on excellence and includes long-term, highly visible partnerships with leading organisations. The UK programme supports our reputation and relationships with key audiences, whilst enabling a wide range of benefits for BP employees such as specially organised private views, workshops and family days.'

BP's current cultural partners are the British Museum, National Portrait Gallery, Royal Opera House, Tate Britain and Almeida Theatre.

'*Environment* – We continue to emphasise the importance of environment and sustainability, supporting programmes such as the Scottish Forest Alliance, the biggest corporate commitment to the environment in Scotland.

'*Matched funding* – Through the BP Foundation, our employees are able to access matching funds for time spent on charitable activities and for donations and gifts to good causes.'

UK education programme

BP supports an extensive range of educational activities which focus on areas key to its business – energy and environment, leadership and business skills. There are three main strands to the company's educational support: strategic partnerships with the Science Museum and the Natural History Museum; the BP Educational Service; and the Schools Links programme.

Enterprising science – Launched in 2007, this is an education outreach programme for secondary schools designed to inspire students and teachers. Working in partnership with the Science Museum, the programme is aims to reach over 400 schools and around 60,000 students across the UK each year.

BP Educational Services – Having worked closely with practising teachers for over 40 years, the BPES continues to produce and distribute educational resource packs about BP and its industry for students aged 5–19. In addition, it responds to educational enquiries about BP and the energy industry.

Contact details are given in the 'Applications' section. A separate BP Educational Services website can be accessed via a link on the company's main site under 'Education'.

UK Schools Link – Since 1968, has put members of staff into primary and secondary schools to support subjects such as energy, environment and leadership and business skills. Full area coordinator contact details are provided on the company's main website under 'Education'.

Applications

In writing to the correspondent.

BP Educational Services (BPES) can be contacted by writing to: PO Box 105, Rochester, Kent ME2 4BE (Email: bpes@bp.com; Tel: 0871 472 3020).

Corporate giving

In 2007, BP made total worldwide contributions of $135.8 million (around £68 million). This includes $0.7 million (around £350,000) contributed by BP to UK charities. Whilst it is clear from the comments below that BP are investing a large amount of time (and money) in education initiatives, no separate figure was available for the UK.

BP state that: 'The growing focus of this is on education, the development of local enterprise and providing access to energy in remote locations. In 2007, we spent $77.7 million (around £39 million) promoting education, with investment in three broad areas: energy and the environment; business leadership skills; and basic education in developing countries where we operate large projects.

Employee-led support

'We encourage our employees to become involved in community and charitable activities and we support their contributions through our BP Employee Matching Fund. As a result of this employee match-giving programme, charitable organisations in the UK benefited from more than £1.75 million and over 30,000 hours of volunteering time in 2006 [latest year available].'

Commercially-led support

Sponsorship: *The arts* – BP states that it focuses its support on providing 'Access to Arts & Culture', access to opportunities, performances, or art that would otherwise not be exhibited and thus reach new and wider audiences.

BP has a number of partnerships within the field of arts and culture including those with British Museum, Royal Opera House, National Portrait Gallery, Tate Britain, National Theatre, Almeida Theatre and The National Art Collections Fund.

Bradford & Bingley plc

Company registration number 2269202

PO Box 88, Croft Road, Crossflatts, Bingley BD16 2UA

01274 555555

Website: www.bbg.co.uk

Correspondent: Michael Hammond, Head of Corporate Social Responsibility 0121 633 8143; Fax: 0121 643 6396 Email: csr@bbg.co.uk

Chairman: Rod Kent

Chief Executive: Steven Crawshaw

Year end	Turnover	Pre-tax profit
31/12/2007	£572,300,000	£126,000,000

Nature of company business
Building society. Its main activities include: lending money towards residential and commercial property and offering a range of retail savings services; operating as an independent retailer of mortgage, investment, and insurance products; offering residential estate agency and selected other property related services.

Subsidiaries include: Mortgage Express, The MarketPlace

Main locations: Birmingham

Total employees: 3,120

Charitable donations

2007: £593,000
2005: £443,250
2004: £876,933
2003: £732,637

Total community contributions: £1,680,900
Management costs: £106,000
CRM figure: £150,000

Membership: A & B, BitC, L B Group

Community involvement

Bradford & Bingley believe it is important to have a community programme that is relevant to its business, and so, continue to have preventing and alleviating the causes of homelessness as its main corporate area of support. In 2007, it used the increase in its community programme to launch a number of schemes supporting personal finance education in schools and with parents as a second area of corporate support.

Bradford & Bingley invests heavily in the West Yorkshire region, specifically in Bradford and the Aire Valley, where its head office is based. We support a wider range of community projects in West Yorkshire, including a number of grass roots and community sports projects run by the major professional sports clubs in the area.

Supporting its staff is also seen as important. Two schemes (matched fundraising and matched payroll giving) are therefore available to its staff across the country to support their choice of charities.

Charity of the Year: Yorkshire Air Ambulance (2007 – head office).

Exclusions

No support for advertising in charity brochures, animal welfare, appeals from individuals, the arts, elderly people, fundraising events, heritage, medical research, overseas projects, political appeals, religious appeals, or science/technology.

Applications

In writing to the correspondent at: Bradford & Bingley plc, Community Affairs Department, 64 New Street, Birmingham B2 4DU.

Please ensure that your application falls into one of the areas Bradford & Bingley supports. Unfortunately, applications outside of those areas will not be considered. They are also unable to support individual requests for sponsorship even if the charity being fundraised for falls into its areas of support.

Applications are accepted by post or email, and Bradford & Bingley are happy to have an initial discussion on the telephone if you are uncertain if your project is eligible for an application.

Although there is no specific application form, please include in your proposal specific details of the project you are requesting support for, costings and any publicity opportunities associated with your project.

Please do not send valuable documents or any artwork with your initial application as they will request these at a later date, if Bradford & Bingley intend proceeding with your application. Applications are normally replied to within 28 days.

Corporate giving

During 2007, Bradford & Bingley made total community contributions of £1,680,900 of which £593,000 was in cash donations. Management costs stood at £106,000, whilst a cause-related marketing campaign raised over £150,000 on behalf of Wallace & Gromit's Children's Foundation. Other major beneficiaries of support included: Shelter; Business Action on Homelessness; national Debtline; and Care for the Family.

A number of case studies of organisations that have benefited from Bradford & Bingley can be viewed at: www.bbg.co.uk/bbg/csr/community/casestudies/

Employee-led support

All employees are able to apply for funds to match their fundraising efforts for charity in a scheme which matches the first £250 of funds raised per employee. 2007 saw an increase of 42% in matching, totalling £32,680 (2006: £23,084). The number of staff receiving matching also went up 36% to 144 staff (2006: 106). This increase was driven by increased internal promotion, including presentations to all new starters in the group's induction programme.

Payroll giving: Bradford & Bingley also matches employee donations through the payroll-giving programme, Give As You Earn. It continued to promote the scheme to new and existing employees via online and internal promotions. 7.8% of its workforce now donate via Give As You Earn (2006: 8.5%), but average monthly amounts donated rose to £26.90 (2006: £23.84). As a group, Bradford & Bingley matched £81,331 of employee donations (2006: £78,675).

Overall, the company's staff helped raise £140,242 in their fundraising efforts.

Overall, employee involvement rose to £528,076 (2006: £513,162) and this trend is set to continue in 2008.

Commercially-led support

Cause-related marketing: For every new FirstSave and SmartSave account opened, Bradford & Bingley made a £1 donation to the Wallace & Gromit's Children's Foundation.

Sponsorship: Support is given to the National Museum of Photography, Film & Television in Bradford. Community and grass roots support is given sports organisations including Bradford Bulls.

Bristol-Myers Squibb Pharmaceuticals Ltd

Company registration number 2487574

BMS House, Uxbridge Business Park, Sanderson Road, Uxbridge UB8 1DH

01895 5230000; Fax: 01895 523010

Website: www.b-ms.co.uk

Correspondent: Grants and Donations Adminstrator

General Manager: F Pasqualone

Year end	Turnover	Pre-tax profit
31/12/2007	£126,324,000	£25,213,000

Nature of company business
The selling, distribution and development of ethical pharmaceutical products.

Subsidiaries include: ConvaTec Ltd

Main locations: Moreton, Uxbridge, Chester

UK employees: 637

> **Charitable donations**
> 2007: £2,000
> 2006: £82,000

Community involvement

Bristol-Myers Squibb's grants and charitable contributions programme supports local and national organisations whose purposes are compatible with the principal activity of the company (see 'Nature of company business').

The company also funds innovative cardiovascular research in the UK through the Bristol-Myers Squibb Fellowship and, through the One Vision competition, contributes essential funds to community HIV and AIDS groups.

Locally, grants may also be given for community projects around the company's main sites, which are in Chester, Moreton (Wirral), and Uxbridge.

Exclusions

Bristol-Myers Squibb does not make grants in support of non-scientific or non-educational programmes.

No support for individuals, political appeals, religious appeals, local appeals not in areas of company presence, fundraising events or advertising in charity brochures

Applications

In writing to the correspondent.

Corporate giving

Bristol-Myers Squibb did not respond to our request for information about its community support. The latest 2007 annual report and accounts, however, show that donations in the UK amounted to £2,000 in total. This was down from £82,000 in 2006, itself a small sum given the global presence of the company.

It may be that further funding comes from the Bristol-Myers Squibb Foundation in America, but as no accounts or list of international grants were available online, this is speculation on our part.

In kind support

Products are generally only donated for disaster relief purposes.

Employee-led support

Employees are encouraged to support their local communities.

In 2008, the company introduced the 'Day of Giving' initiative, allowing every employee one day of paid leave a year to engage in some form of charitable activity.

Commercially-led support

Sponsorship: *Health education* – Bristol-Myers Squibb sponsors 'One' Vision', a European photographic competition which encourage new and positive ways of looking at the life of people with HIV and AIDS. Through this competition, Bristol-Myers Squibb also contributes essential funds to community HIV and AIDS groups, including UK organisations.

Brit Insurance Holdings plc

Company registration number 3121594

55 Bishopsgate, London EC2N 3AS

020 7984 8500; Fax: 020 7984 8501

Website: www.britinsurance.com

Correspondent: C Curgenven, The Brit Insurance Charitable Trust
Email: csr@britinsurance.com

Chairman: John Barton

Chief Executive: Dane Douetil

Year end	Turnover	Pre-tax profit
31/12/2007	£1,259,507,000	£191,153,000

Nature of company business
A major UK-domiciled general insurance and reinsurance group writing both UK and international business.

UK employees: 743

Charitable donations
2007: £911,320
2006: £35,719

Community involvement

Brit Insurance charitable giving and community involvement strategy is described as follows:

'Charitable giving and community projects are selected on three criteria:

- a project must not only be a good cause but also an area relevant to Brit Insurance
- we prefer opportunities where our financial involvement can be leveraged for the benefit of the good cause, such as sponsored charity cricket matches
- projects should, where possible offer alignment with the group's vision, such as promoting the Brit Insurance brand.'

'The Brit Insurance Charitable Fund

'To facilitate the firm's charitable giving, the Brit Insurance Charitable Fund (Charity Commission no. 1116567) was established in July 2006, demonstrating the group's ongoing commitment to the support of local and international communities. The group donates up to 0.5% of the group's pre-tax profit each year, capped at £1 million, to the fund.

'The fund's purpose is to facilitate a more structured approach to our charitable giving. It is used to:

- support our multi-year partnership with the British Red Cross
- provide humanitarian aid in instances of uninsured catastrophic loss
- match money raised by our staff for UK registered charities and
- build a reserve to support ongoing charitable giving in future years.'

Applications
In writing to the correspondent.

Corporate giving

In 2007, the firm made charitable donations of £911,320 (2006: £35,719), all of which was paid to the associated trust.

The Brit Insurance Charitable Fund

In 2007, Brit Insurance entered into a three-year partnership with the British Red Cross. The aim is to support the common objectives of helping the UK community to be better prepared for and cope with emergencies. The fund donated over £287,000 to the British Red Cross during the year. A further £107,575 was distributed by the fund and categorised as follows:

- education (£1,600)
- health (£8,103)
- relief of poverty (£8,247)
- sports)£14,100)
- other (£17,720)
- medical research (£57,805).

In kind support
Education: Brit Insurance currently has weekly staff volunteering schemes operating in several schools in the London borough of Tower Hamlets, where individuals help pupils during lunch hours develop their reading, numeracy, sports and science skills.

Employee-led support

The fund gave £21,400 (2006: £9,000) to various UK registered charities, matching amounts raised and donated by Brit Insurance staff.

The firm also gives its employees two additional days of paid leave per year to volunteer their time through schemes offered by its charity partners.

Commercially-led support

Sponsorship: *Education* – the firm maintained its sponsorship of the Birmingham Business School (part of Birmingham University) Lecturer in Insurance and Risk Management

Britannia Building Society

Company registration number 104879

Britannia House, Leek, Staffordshire ST13 5RG

01538 399399; Fax: 01538 393337

Website: www.britannia.co.uk

Correspondent: Melissa Sanigar, Mutal Responsibility (CSR Team)
Email: melissa.sanigar@britannia.co.uk

Chairman: Rodney Baker-Bates

Chief Executive: Neville Richardson

Year end	Pre-tax profit
31/12/2007	£71,700,000

Nature of company business
Building society.

Subsidiaries include: Mortgage Agency Services Ltd, Western Mortgage Services Ltd, Verso Ltd

Main locations: Leek

UK employees: 4,300

Charitable donations
2007: £509,841
2006: £461,441
2005: £392,624
2003: £500,000

Total community contributions: £670,000

Membership: BitC, L B Group

Community involvement

Britannia Building Society provided the following outline of its community involvement:

'Our approach to community involvement is derived from our values and mutual heritage, and provides us with a significant way of putting our values into practice and of contributing to the communities in which we live and work.

'Having talked to our members and our people we have changed our priority areas to focus on where we believe we can make the biggest difference and this is by supporting education, wherever possible promoting an improvement in numeracy and/or financial capability.

'[The majority of the society's support] to local charities and good causes [is] through the Britannia Building Society Foundation (Charity Commission no. 1069081) and our Community Fund.

'We also recognise the importance of providing practical support through our three education initiatives:

'*The Number Partners scheme* – This programme uses number-related activities as a means to develop children's number skills, and supports primary and middle schools in raising numeracy achievement

'*Fit4Finance* – Is an education programme we have developed, designed to improve financial capability. It is for use within the secondary school environment and introduces students to the basics of personal finance through a series of engaging and interactive workshops. The programme also supports the Financial Service Authority's National Strategy for Financial Capability.

'*Young Enterprise* – Young Enterprise is built on a principle of 'learning by doing' and Britannia volunteers work with students and teachers to develop students' enterprise capability, financial awareness, business understanding and citizenship.

'At last year's Annual General Meeting our members endorsed an increase in this investment to at least 1% of net profits.

'Every other year our people select a Corporate Charity to support. In 2006/2007, this was CLIC Sargent, the UK's leading children's cancer charity.'

Exclusions

A full list of exclusions for the Britannia Building Society Foundation and the community Fund can be found on the company's website www.britannia.co.uk

Applications

Applications to the foundation should be made on a form available via email, charitable.foundation@britannia.co.uk, or by calling 01538 391734. A copy of the foundation's policy can be found on the internet or through requesting a policy leaflet. There are two regional trustee committees, and each committee meets twice a year.

Applicants which have received a grant or donation in the last two years will only be considered under exceptional circumstances. For more information refer to the Brittania website.

Applications to the Community Fund can be made by submitting an online application available on the Britannia website.

Corporate giving

In 2006/07 the society made total UK community contributions of around £670,000 of which £509,841 comprised cash donations.

At last year's annual general meeting the society's members endorsed an increase in community investment to at least 1% of net profits.

Britannia Building Society Foundation

The foundation was set up by the society in 1997 and as of 1 January 2008 receives a cash donation from the society of £500,000 a year (previously £300,000 per annum). Grants range from £1,000 to £25,000, with preference for specific items/equipment. Capital expenditure and salary costs will be considered in some circumstances. Applications are welcome from registered charities and schools working within

education, specifically numeracy and/or – financial literacy, and national charities that can ring fence their activities to a local community where we have a high density of members.

The Community Fund

The Community Fund receives a cash donation from the society of £100,000 a year. The Community Fund offers a quick and simple application process to voluntary groups, charities and schools, working within education, specifically numeracy and/or – financial literacy, which require donations of up to £1,000. Britannia also support individual members with a donation of up to £100. For more information please refer to its website www.britannia.co.uk.

In kind support

Through the Numbers Partners scheme, the board games used are paid for by Britannia and donated to the school.

Employee-led support

Britannia is involved with two national volunteering schemes that bring together business volunteers and schools: Numbers Partners and Young Enterprise. The society has also designed its own programme Fit4Finance to improve financial capability, for use within the secondary school environment. For more information please refer to the society's website www.britannia.co.uk.

Payroll giving: The company operates a payroll giving scheme.

Commercially-led support

Sponsorship: *The arts* – The society supports the arts and has along-term agreement with the Regent Theatre in Hanley, Stoke-on-Trent.

British Airways plc

Company registration number 1777777

HBBG, Waterside, Harmondsworth, Middlesex UB7 0GB

0870 850 9850

Website: www.ba.com

Correspondent: Community Relations

Fax: 020 8738 9848

Email: community.branch@britishairways.com

Chairman: Martin Broughton

Chief Executive: Willie Walsh

Year end	Turnover	Pre-tax profit
31/03/2008	£8,753,000,000	£883,000,000

Nature of company business
Principal activities: the operation of international and domestic scheduled and charter air services for the carriage of passengers, freight and mail and the provision of ancillary airline and travel services.

Subsidiaries include: Air Miles Travel Promotions Ltd, CityFlyer Express Ltd, Travel Automation Services Ltd, The Plimsoll Line Ltd, Go Fly Ltd

Main locations: Harmondsworth

UK employees: 39,193

Total employees: 45,140

Charitable donations

2008: £398,000
2007: £1,200,000
2006: £898,081
2005: £830,000
2004: £396,398

Total community contributions: £5,700,000
Management costs: £100,000

Membership: A & B, BitC, L B Group

Community involvement

At Heathrow, Gatwick and around the other UK airports that British Airways flies into, the company gives support to registered charities working within the local communities. The company has set out a number of focus areas for its community work. These are:

- education and youth development
- supporting our employees
- sustainable tourism
- environment
- heritage.

Exclusions

No support for appeals from individuals, political appeals or religious appeals. Advertising in charity brochures is rarely undertaken.

Applications

All requests must be made in writing and sent on charity headed paper by fax to 020 8738 9848 or by post to the address given above.

Please note the following when applying:

- applications should be made in February to join the British Airways Communities and Conservation programme (BACC).
- projects are advised if they have been successful at the beginning of April.
- British Airways will only accept applications from registered charities.
- if an application is successful the project receives an allocation of complimentary flights which are subject to availability. Please note: passengers on this type of ticket may be put on standby and may not always travel as booked if a fare-paying passenger needs their seat on the day of departure.
- the allocation is for use during the financial year. Organisations must reapply each February.

Corporate giving

In 2007/08 the company's community contributions worldwide totalled £5.7 million (2006/07: £6.3 million) of which cash donations direct to charitable causes amounted to £398,000 (2006/07: £1.2 million). No breakdown showing figures for the UK was available.

Examples of beneficiaries include: Lancing House – a local care centre in Crawley which offers residential opportunities for children with severe disabilities; and Clapperboard Youth Project – a programme which encourages young people to produce short films about social issues like bullying, racism and drugs received £10,375.

In kind support

Education and youth development – British Airway's Community Learning Centre (close to its Waterside headquarters at Heathrow) has welcomed over 44,000 young people and adult learners since opening in 1999. Interactive, airline-focused programmes relevant to the school curriculum are delivered to local school pupils. Programmes include global education weeks delivered in partnership with the United Nations International Children's Emergency Fund (UNICEF).

Education – Through corporate partnership with the Natural History Museum, British Airways has developed programmes to provide opportunities for pupils from Heathrow schools to visit the museum, meet scientists and experience the work of the Darwin Centre.

British Airway's continues to support the UNICEF Change for Good programme and has raised £2.5 million in the year to March 31, 2008.

Employee-led support

Numerous charities are supported by employee fundraising, including causes run by the staff themselves, such as Happy Child and Dreamflight, for underprivileged and sick children. The company operates an employee volunteering scheme. Other support for staff involvement includes tickets to assist employees supporting overseas projects, merchandise for raffles and consultancy support to staff charities.

Over the past three years over £230,000 has been awarded to charities supported by staff in their volunteering activities through the 'Community Volunteering Awards',

Payroll giving: The British Airways Giving Scheme, launched in December 2003, enabled over 4,000 retired and current employees to donate over £600,000 directly from their payroll to their chosen charities during 2007/08.

British American Tobacco plc

Company registration number 3407696

Globe House, 4 Temple Place, London WC2R 2PG

020 7845 1000; Fax: 020 7240 0555

Website: www.bat.com

Correspondent: UK Social Reporting Mananger

Chairman: Jan du Plessis

Managing Director: Paul N Adams

Year end	Turnover	Pre-tax profit
31/12/2007	£10,018,000,000	£3,078,000,000

Nature of company business
Principal activities: the manufacture, market and sale of cigarettes and other tobacco products.

Subsidiaries include: Rothmans Finance plc, Tobacco Insurance Co. Ltd, Weston Investment Co. Ltd, Rothmans International Tobacco (UK) Ltd

Main locations: London, Southampton, Aylesbury

Total employees: 97,696

Community involvement

Generally speaking, the group's community and charitable contributions vary to address local needs and aspirations, largely involving the environment, employment and education, arts and cultural activities, disaster relief and primary healthcare.

Globally, British American Tobacco plc (BAT) also encourages group companies to focus their corporate social investment activities around three themes:

- sustainable agriculture
- civic life
- empowerment.

In the UK, the major activities currently supported by BAT are the British American Tobacco Biodiversity Partnership, the Eliminating Child Labour in Tobacco Growing Foundation and restoration work on important historic buildings in Russia and China by the World Monuments Fund.

Exclusions

No support for causes outside the company's areas of focus.

Applications

In writing to the correspondent.

Information available: The company produce a Social Responsibility Report which can be downloaded from its website.

Corporate giving

In 2007, total community contributions amounted to £16.1 million (2006: £17.6 million) worldwide. Charitable donations in the UK accounted for £2.2 million (2006: £3.0 million). One of the beneficiaries was the British American Tobacco Biodiversity Partnership, which for the five-year period 2006 to 2010 will receive £1.5 million each year.

British Energy Group plc

Company registration number SC270184

GSDO Business Park, East Kilbride G74 5PG

01355 846000; Fax: 01355 846001

Website: www.british-energy.com

Correspondent: See 'Applications'

Chairman: Adrian Montague

Chief Executive: Bill Coley

Year end	Turnover	Pre-tax profit
31/03/2008	£2,811,000,000	£538,000,000

Nature of company business
The group's principal activity is the generation and sale of electricity.

Main locations: Bridgwater, Leiston, Hunterston, Heysham, Hartlepool, Eggborough, East Kilbride, Dungeness, Torness, Barnwood

UK employees: 6,121

Community involvement

The company's annual report and accounts for 2008 states: 'Last year, British Energy added 'community' to its company values to demonstrate its commitment to the people who live and work around all our sites. We have also appointed site-based community liaison officers to progress community relations plans tailored to the needs of the different sites.'

Charity of the Year: Multiple Sclerosis Society (2008/09).

Exclusions

No support for circular appeals, fundraising events, appeals from individuals, purely denominational (religious) appeals or local appeals not in areas of company presence.

Applications

Applications should be addressed to: Julie Bennett, PR Services Manager, British Energy, Barnett Way, Barnwood, Gloucester GL4 3RS.

Charity of the Year

To be considered for British Energy's charity of the year, the criteria charities need to meet are that they are:

- a national charity with a strong presence in both Scotland and England
- a charity that contributes to community life and can work with the company at a local level
- a charity that has the creativity and enthusiasm to maintain fundraising
- a charity that celebrates the company's values of safety, openness, and respect and recognition.

Corporate giving

In 2007/08, the company made cash donations totalling £197,499 (2006/07: £195,485). The majority of this went to the 2006/07 'Charity of the Year' – Help the Hospices.

No further information was available.

In kind support

The company provides in kind support by, for example, using landfill tax credits to fund refurbishment of nature reserves within the vicinity of its power stations.

Employee-led support

The company has promised to match funds raised by staff on behalf of their chosen charity of the year up to a maximum of £100,000.

Payroll giving: The company operates a scheme.

Commercially-led support

Sponsorship: *Arts and good-cause sponsorship* – Past examples include Edinburgh's Christmas Lights, St Andrew's Ambulance organisation's mobile first-aid unit for major events, children's fire safety and library learning projects around the country, Suffolk Police's air support and traffic accident helicopter, the UK Scouts PR badge and Northern Ballet's innovative theatrical programme.

Science – The Cheltenham and Edinburgh Science Festivals are sponsored to help stimulate interest in science, technology, engineering and maths subjects.

British Land Company plc

Company registration number 621920

York House, 45 Seymour Street, London W1H 7LX

020 7486 4466; Fax: 020 7935 5552

Website: www.britishland.com

Correspondent: Sarah Cary

Chairman: Dr Chris Gibson-Smith

Chief Executive: Stephen Hester

Year end	Turnover	Pre-tax profit
31/03/2008	£645,000,000	(£1,609,000,000)

Nature of company business
Property investment and development, finance and investment.

Subsidiaries include: London & Henley Ltd, 135 Bishopsgate Financing, Union Property Corporation Ltd, Broadgate Property Holdings Ltd, Exchange House Holdings Ltd, Derby Investment Holdings Ltd, Sealhurst Properties Ltd, Peacocks Centre Ltd, Adamant Investment Corporation Ltd, MSC Funding Ltd, Meadowhall Shoping Centre Ltd

Main locations: London

UK employees: 732

Charitable donations

2008: £36,000
2007: £177,093
2006: £67,640
2005: £92,487
2004: £186,717

Total community contributions: £1,036,000

Membership: A & B, BitC

Community involvement

The company states that: 'British Land builds constructive relationships with the communities in which it operates. It does this by supporting selected local initiatives through staff volunteering, skills mentoring and financial assistance. Larger national programmes may also be supported where they benefit communities neighbouring British Land's investments'.

'British Land is strongly committed to investing in the future through education, the arts and sport, with particular emphasis on helping young people.'

The company is a member of Arts & Business, Business in the Community and the London Benchmarking Group

Exclusions

The company will not provide support for political purposes.

Applications

In writing to the correspondent.

Information available: The company's 2007/08 Corporate Social Responsibility Report is available online.

Corporate giving

In 2007/08, British Land made total community contributions in the UK of just over £1 million. This comprised £850,000 to good causes through sponsorship, nearly £30,000 in time, £120,000 in gifts in kind, and £36,000 in cash donations.

This benefited a range of organisations and people including:

- Youth projects – British Land Chess Challenge, Reading is Fundamental and the NSPCC
- Arts – the Royal Opera House, the Tate Gallery, the Royal Ballet School and the Museum of London
- Sports – Capital Kids Cricket, SnowsportGB and the Tennis and Raquets Association.

In kind support

Education – 'In 2007, the team at the Peacocks Centre worked with Surrey Education Business Partnership and local secondary schools on business games, foreign language workshops and town planning exercises. They mentored over 300 Year 10 and 11 students from Bishop David Brown, Winston Churchill and Jubilee High schools, providing an insight into the world of work and hosted mock interviews followed by constructive, personalised feedback.'

Training – 'In 2007, St Stephen's Shopping Centre in Kingston-upon-Hull became the first UK shopping centre to work with The Prince's Trust and a range of retailers to offer disadvantaged young people the chance to participate in the 'Get into Retail' job scheme. Seven St Stephen's retailers provided 16 work placements as part of The trust's intensive three week programme, which culminated in job interviews. All learners gained Level 2 Health and Safety qualifications and five learners went on to get jobs.'

Employee-led support

British Land offers all its employees volunteering opportunities and encourages the management teams at its properties around the UK to get involved in local initiatives.

In 2007, the company's head office team spent almost 400 hours volunteering, while 26% were involved in volunteering initiatives during 2007/08. Examples include: A team of British Land volunteers helped to dig, clear and prune shrubs in a meadow at Waterlow Park in Camden; Meadowhall Shopping Centre volunteers converted a storage room at local Phillimore Primary School into a comfortable room for staff to work with children and their families on social issues including low self esteem, behavioural issues and family problems.

Commercially-led support

Sponsorship: British Land undertakes extensive good cause sponsorship of organisations involved in arts, education and sport.

British Nuclear Fuels plc

Company registration number 1002607

1100 Daresbury Park, Daresbury, Warrington, Cheshire WA4 4GB

01925 832000

Website: www.bnfl.com

Correspondent: (see 'Applications')

Chairman: Gordon Campbell

Chief Executive: Michael Parker

Year end	Pre-tax profit
31/03/2007	£2,272,000,000

Nature of company business
The principal activity is expertise across the whole range of the nuclear fuel business.

Subsidiaries include: International Nuclear Fuels Ltd, Deva Manufacturing Services Ltd, Magnox Electric plc, Direct Rail Services Ltd

Main locations: Bradwell, Calder Hall, Berkeley, Trasfyndd, Maentwrog, London, Oldbury, Wylfa, Dungeness, Risley, Sizewell, Sellafield, Hinkley Point, Hunterston, Littlebrook, Capenhurst, Chapelcross, Daresbury

UK employees: 14,213

Charitable donations

2007: £10,000,000
2006: £2,900,000
2005: £3,100,000
2004: £3,300,000
2003: £3,200,000

Community involvement

The company previously stated on its website that: 'Our community programme aims to be mutually beneficial for the communities in which we operate and our employees. We support areas most in need of our help – taking action now to improve the quality of life in the future. Our initiatives cover environmental, economic and social issues such as:

- health, drugs, the elderly and the disabled
- social exclusion, crime prevention, the homeless and the disadvantaged
- environmental restoration
- regeneration
- arts, music and sport.'

'In line with our overall policy and the government's initiative to reduce social exclusion, our charitable support strategy is mainly centred on areas of deprivation and social exclusion.'

'BNFL are also committed to supporting and developing its education programme at local, national and international levels, actively encouraging an interest in science and technology at all ages.'

Community support is also given by two of BNFL's subsidiaries.

National Nuclear Laboratories have worked with the Smallpeice Trust – a charitable organisation that supports the training of young people in the engineering sector. Whilst Sellafield Ltd work with the NDA on its socio-economic plans

to encourage employee involvement in local activities, charitable donation schemes and inward investment.

Charity of the Year: Some of the company's sites choose a charity of the year for which to raise money.

Exclusions

No support for circular appeals, large national appeals (except North West based), small purely local appeals not in areas of company presence, advertising in charity brochures, animal welfare charities, medical research, overseas projects, political appeals, or religious appeals.

Applications

At the time of writing (December 2008) we were advised that the company was in a state of flux and that the previous contact had left and not been replaced.

We suggest, therefore, that initial enquiries be made to the general manager of the nearest factory.

Corporate giving

In 2007, charitable contributions amounted to £10 million (2006: £3 million) in support of the group's community involvement and economic regeneration initiatives. This included a significant donation (£1 million) from BNFL Enterprise to the West Cumbria Development Fund, a contribution of £3 million to the Nuclear Academy and the commitment of a further £2 million to the North Copeland Academy, both in Cumbria.

Employee-led support

Staff are encouraged to become volunteers in their own time. The company provides match funding for employee fundraising up to a maximum of £100 per employee.

Payroll giving: The Give As You Earn scheme is in operation.

Commercially-led support

Sponsorship: *The arts* – Appeals for arts sponsorship are welcomed.

British Sky Broadcasting Group plc

Company registration number 2247735

Grant Way, Isleworth, Middlesex TW7 5QD

020 7705 3000; Fax: 020 7705 3030

Website: corporate.sky.com

Correspondent: The Head of Corporate Responsibility

Email: corp.responsibility@bskyb.com

Chairman: James Murdoch

Chief Executive: Jeremy Darroch

Year end	Turnover	Pre-tax profit
30/06/2008	£4,952,000,000	£60,000,000

Nature of company business
The leading satellite pay television operator, BSkyB launched its digital television services in the UK on 1 October 1998 offering 300 channels including sport, news, films and general entertainment.

Subsidiaries include: BSkyB Finance Ltd, Sky Subscribers Services Ltd, Sky Ventures Ltd, Sky In-Home Service Ltd, Sky Television Ltd

Main locations: Leeds, Manchester, Harrogate, Livingstone, Dunfermline, Isleworth

UK employees: 15,000

Charitable donations

2008: £5,195,000
2006: £3,825,000
2004: £1,050,061

Total community contributions: £6,037,000
Management costs: £863,000

Membership: A & B, BitC, L B Group

Community involvement

Sky continues to align its community investment activities to the wider goals of the business and its customers and utilises its brand, platform and technology in community investment. Current initiatives include: Living for Sport; Make a Difference – the staff community involvement scheme; Sky Learning Explorer; and Sky Arts At partnership scheme.

Sky Youth Action Fund

Over a six-year period Sky invested over £500,000 in the above fund. However, to ensure Sky supports its local communities in a way that delivers the most impact and provides opportunities for its staff to get involved, it is refocusing its community investment activities.

At present the small grants programme has been suspended and is no longer accepting applications. If you have already applied to the fund, Sky says it will be communicating with you individually.

Sky's new plans will be communicated through 'The Bigger Picture' so please check the website for updates.

Comprehensive information about each of these initiatives and the new small grants programme can be found at: www.jointhebiggerpicture.com

Exclusions

No support for animal welfare charities, appeals from individuals, elderly people, environment/heritage, medical research, overseas projects, political or religious appeals.

Applications

All formal requests for support must be made in writing. Funding decisions are made in two ways: nationally, the Head of Corporate Affairs and the Community Affairs Manager meet regularly to discuss proposals and requests; locally, each site has its own committee which decides on funding for local projects.

The company endeavours to respond in writing to every written request within 21 days of receipt.

Corporate giving

In 2007/08, Sky made total community contributions in the UK of £6.9 million. This was broken down as follows (amount in brackets):

- cash 75.3% (£5,195,000)
- volunteering/in kind 12.2% (£842,000)
- management costs 12.5% (£863,000).

The following areas were supported:

- education and young people 41.5%
- art and culture 24.8%
- other 20.2%
- social welfare £11.0%
- environment 2.5%.

In kind support

Education: 'Sky Learning Explorer was relaunched in January 2008. This dynamic online resource recommends TV programmes linked to curriculum subjects and a variety of interests, from across hundreds of channels on our digital platform.'

Sport: Over 17,000 young people have benefited from Sky Sports Living for Sport, a grassroots sports initiative run by the Youth Sport Trust.

Employee-led support

Employees are encouraged to take part in fundraising activities and are allowed two days paid leave in which to do so. They can also apply for match funding

Payroll giving: Employees can participate in a Give As You Earn scheme.

Commercially-led support

Sponsorship: *The arts* – Sky has partnerships with the English National Opera, English National Ballet, and the Hay Festival.

Sport – Over 5,500 coaches have been trained through the England and Wales Cricket Board's Coach Education programme sponsored by Sky Sports.

British Sugar plc

Company registration number 315158

Sugar Way, Peterborough PE2 9AY

01733 563171; Fax: 01733 563068

Website: www.britishsugar.co.uk

Correspondent: Geoffrey Clark, Charity Coordinator

Managing Director: Gino De Jaegher

Year end	Turnover	Pre-tax profit
16/09/2007	£649,700,000	£73,200,000

Nature of company business
British Sugar is a wholly-owned subsidiary of Associated British Foods (see separate entry). It operates from locations in East Anglia and the East Midlands (Bury St Edmunds, Cantley, Newark, Peterborough, and Wissington).

Main locations: Wissington, Newark, Peterborough, Bury St Edmunds, Cantley

UK employees: 1,841

Charitable donations

2007: £100,000
2006: £100,000
2005: £55,000
2004: £85,450

Community involvement

We were again advised in 2008 that the company no longer makes charitable donations and, as such, should not be included in this resource.

However, we believe, its continued inclusion to be justified in order to help give a fuller picture of UK corporate community support, whilst accepting the need to make clear the restrictions that now exist for organisations seeking funding from the company/foundation.

Whilst it is true that the focus of the company's charitable support has changed, the fact remains that it still has a charity budget, the majority of which is administered by the British Sugar Foundation (Charity Commission no. 290966). (However, this appears set to change according to the company's 2007 annual report and accounts which states: 'The directors are considering winding up this separate company [the foundation] during the forthcoming year and administering the donations directly through British Sugar plc.')

Following a review of its charitable giving policy the company, allocates all of its charitable and sponsorship funds, including the cost of product donations, to its employee matching scheme, and gives the following guidelines:

- all funds are allocated to British Sugar's employee matching scheme, 'Money Match'
- the company does not provide funds for political or profit making organisations
- the company does not take charity advertising as this is not considered to be an efficient means of managing its budgets
- the company specifically excludes the support of individuals.

Exclusions

Previous information from the company indicated that general and national appeals are not supported. No support for circular appeals, advertising in charity brochures, animal welfare, appeals from individuals, the arts, enterprise/training, fundraising events, overseas projects, political appeals, religious appeals, science/technology or sport.

Applications

In writing to the correspondent. Please be aware, however, of the change of policy that may come in to effect in 2008, i.e. the winding down of the foundation.

Corporate giving

In British Sugar's 2006/07 annual report and accounts the company declared charitable donations of £100,000 (2006: £100,000). It was previously thought that all of the company's donations were made through its foundation, but this does not appear to be the case given that only £62,500 was donated to the foundation in 2006 (the latest year for which accounts were available).

Presumably, the balance in 2006 of £37,500 was allocated to its employee matching programme, but why does the foundation also support this scheme in addition to making 'normal' donations? Somewhat confusing, you may agree, and not helped by British Sugar's unwillingness to provide information.

British Sugar Foundation

The foundation is administered by trustees appointed from senior employees of British Sugar plc. Applications for funds are submitted to local charity co-ordinators appointed by the trustees. Each application is considered on its merits and compliance with the charity's objectives and policy and qualifying donations are accordingly approved by local co-ordinators.

In 2006, the foundation had a total income of £74,000 of which £62,500 came from the company and £1,800 from the employees' payroll giving scheme. Charitable donations made during the period amounted to just over £68,000 and was broken down as follows: Environment/community (£26,000); Education (£8,000); and Healthcare (£34,000). Nearly £64,000 of this went to the 'Money Match' scheme in support of fundraising by employees for a charity of their choice.

Beneficiaries included: east Anglian Children's Hospice and Ovarian Cancer Relief (£4,800 each); Mid-Norfolk Railway Preservation Trust and West Suffolk Riding for the Disabled Association (£2,000 each); Blofield Pre-school Playgroup (£1,970); and Cantley First School (£1,800).

In kind support

The company makes product donations.

Employee-led support

Through its charitable foundation, the company makes every effort to encourage participation in community fundraising projects among its employees. It operates a 'Money Match' scheme, which effectively doubles the amount of money reaching the nominated charitable organisation.

Payroll giving: An employee scheme is operation (for which the foundation is the approved charity agency). In 2006, £1,800 was received from employees under the scheme.

Brixton plc

Company registration number 202342

50 Berkeley Street, London W1J 8BX

020 7399 4500

Website: www.brixton.plc.uk

Correspondent: Richard Howell, Company Secretary

Chair: Louise A V C Patten

Chief Executive: Timothy C Wheeler

Year end	Turnover	Pre-tax profit
31/12/2007	£82,000,000	£58,200,000

Nature of company business
Principal activities: property investment and development and some property dealing.

Subsidiaries include: B-Serv Ltd, Equiton Management Ltd, Premier Greeford Management Ltd

Main locations: London

UK employees: 88

Charitable donations

2007: £79,000
2006: £95,000
2005: £65,000
2004: £55,000
2003: £60,000

Community involvement

Brixton describes its policy for supporting local communities as follows:

'Our Community Investment Policy sets out our commitment to support community organisations local to our property portfolio as well as homeless charities. We also allow employees to take one day off work per year for volunteering.

'We are working to establish a new community partnership project in 2008 with the charity Wooden Spoon which makes donations to support specific projects. Our donation will go towards funding physical training equipment (for strength and conditioning) at Oaklands School, a special school in Hounslow.'

Exclusions

Support for registered charities only. No support for individuals, students, fundraising events, local appeals not in areas of company presence, local branches of national charities and charities whose main aim is to support other charities. Brixton Estate undertakes no secondment or sponsorship of the arts.

Applications

In writing to the correspondent. Grant decisions are made by the board which meets six-monthly.

Corporate giving

In 2007, the company donated £79,000 (2006: £95,000) to charitable causes. Beneficiaries included: London Cyrenians Housing (£25,000 towards the refurbishment of accommodation for homeless people in Hounslow, including people with severe and enduring mental health problems); and Henshaws School for Blind People (£15,000 to fund Skill Step, a training course for visually impaired people to help them gain confidence and independence).

In kind support

At Christmas, the company donate money to the homeless charity Crisis, rather than sending Christmas cards.

Employee-led support

Staff are encouraged to get involved in community projects and are given time off work for volunteering (one day per year). In 2007, employees gave 34 work days in support of community projects.

The company matches funds they raise (up to an agreed maximum). In 2007, Brixton gave £7,000 in match funding to projects supported by employees.

Payroll giving: a scheme was established in 2006.

Broadland Properties Ltd

Company registration number 483844

137 Scalby Road, Scarborough, North Yorkshire YO12 6TB

01723 373461; Fax: 01723 500021

Correspondent: Tessa Hazlewood, PA to the Chairman

Chairman: John Guthrie

Managing Director: John Guthrie

Year end	Turnover	Pre-tax profit
30/09/2007	£29,487,000	£7,317,000

Nature of company business
Property dealers.

Main locations: Scarborough

UK employees: 306

Charitable donations
2007: £288,444
2006: £115,754

Community involvement

We were advised by the contact that as 'an extremely private company we have no wish to be part of the guide'. This statement may be due to the fact that the company is wholly owned by the chairman (either directly or through family trusts) and, as such, it is difficult to tell whether donations made under the company's name are in fact those of the individual.

Our policy, however, remains to include all relevant companies in this guide.

Although all applications are considered, there is a preference for certain causes, with support generally only being given to charities with a Scarborough postcode.

Exclusions

Generally no support for local appeals outside of the Scarborough area. No support for advertising in charity brochures, animal welfare, appeals from individuals, overseas projects, political appeals or religious appeals.

Applications

In writing to the correspondent.

Corporate giving

In 2007, charitable donations totalled £301,553 (2006: £115,754) of which £13,109 was given by subsidiary companies in Poland. According to the company's annual report and accounts, the beneficiaries included the following: Scarborough Rugby Club (£225,000); Pindar School Sports Development (£25,000); Sedbergh School (£20,200); Eden Court (£5,000); Scottish Countryside Alliance (£3,000); National Children's Orchestra (£2,000); and Crimebeat (£1,000). A further £1,442 was donated to various awards and promotions, and to smaller charities.

N Brown Group plc

Company registration number 814103

Griffin House, 40 Lever Street, Manchester M60 6ES

0161 236 8256; Fax: 0161 238 2662

Website: www.nbrown.co.uk

Correspondent: Steve Smith, Head of HR
Email: enquiries@nbrown.co.uk

Chairman: Lord Alliance of Manchester

Chief Executive: Alan White

Year end	Turnover	Pre-tax profit
01/03/2008	£610,900,000	£78,000,000

Nature of company business
Provider of direct home shopping.

Main locations: Manchester

UK employees: 3,059

Charitable donations

2008: £114,392
2007: £52,371
2005: £37,433
2004: £35,426

Community involvement

The company's website states:

'The board of directors of N Brown Group plc recognises the importance of supporting the community in which it operates and supports a number of local concerns, such as hospices, a hospital, children's trusts and charities for the elderly.

'The company also supports the fundraising activities of its own employees and considers requests for charitable donations or support on their individual merit.'

Exclusions

No support for local appeals not in area of company presence.

Applications

In writing to the correspondent.

Corporate giving

In 2007/08, cash donations more than doubled to £114,392 (2007: £52,371). Examples of beneficiaries were not available, but we understand that donations are made principally to local charities serving the communities in which the group operates.

In kind support

The company maintains close links with the Christie Hospital in Manchester and regularly assists in fundraising for that organisation.

The group has also recently started to donate redundant IT equipment to charities operating in developing countries.

Employee-led support

The company supports the fundraising activities of its own employees.

Bruntwood Ltd

Company registration number 2825044

City Tower, Piccadilly Plaza, Manchester M1 4BD

0161 236 1647

Website: www.bruntwood.co.uk

Correspondent: Jane Booth, Bruntwood Community Fund

Chairman: Mike Oglesby

Chief Executive: Chris Oglesby

Year end	Turnover	Pre-tax profit
30/09/2007	£76,342,000	£13,520,000

Nature of company business
Property investment company.

Main locations: Leeds, Liverpool

UK employees: 348

Charitable donations

2007: £500,000

Total community contributions: £1,000,000

Membership: A & B, BitC

Community involvement

Bruntwood states that it invests up to 10% of its profits in the arts, and community and charitable causes, using its core skills and expertise to the benefit of each.

Support is selective as the company believes it can make more of a difference 'by directing our efforts at fewer causes'.

This support takes various forms, from cash donations and good-cause sponsorship, to employee volunteering and fundraising.

Regarding the latter, the company's (read employees) fundraising is channelled through two mediums – The Bruntwood Community Fund, run in conjunction with the Community Foundation for Greater Manchester, and The Oglesby Charitable Trust (Charity Commission no. 1026669) which has a family connection with the business.

Applications

In writing to the correspondent.

Applications to the Oglesby Charitable Trust should be made using the form downloadable from the trust's website (www.oglesbycharitabletrust.co.uk) and returned to: The Oglesby Charitable Trust, PO Box 336, Altrincham, Cheshire WA14 3XD

Corporate giving

Each year Bruntwood donate over £1 million (including arts and good-cause sponsorship) to worthwhile causes throughout the regions in which it operates – Leeds, Liverpool and Manchester areas. Of this, over £630,000 is in cash donations comprising around £500,000 a year to the Oglesby Trust and £130,000 raised by staff on behalf of local charities. (Note: We have discounted the latter amount in the figures quoted at the beginning of this entry.)

The Oglesby Charitable Trust

The trust supports activities across a broad spectrum and generally makes grants of between £5,000 and £20,000. To date, the maximum grant to any one project has been £50,000. For the financial year September 2007 to September 2008, the trust was committed to spending £420,000.

Areas of activity are: artistic development; educational grants and building projects; environmental improvement projects; the life and welfare of the underprivileged; and medical aid and research.

Acorn Fund – This fund is set aside each year for smaller donations (£200 to £1,000) and is administered in conjunction with the local community foundation in Manchester.

Further information about the trust is published in *A Guide to the Major Trusts – Volume 1*, published by the Directory of Social Change.

In kind support

Fundraising: Employees in Leeds, Liverpool and Manchester nominate a local charity as the sole beneficiary of their fundraising efforts for which they set their own targets. In 2007, charities as diverse as Lineham Farm in Leeds which caters for disadvantaged children, Henshaws for the Blind in Liverpool and the New Children's Hospital in Manchester, shared over £120,000 in total.

These donations are run and managed by the Bruntwood Community Fund in partnership with the Community foundation for Greater Manchester.

Volunteering: Through the Bruntwood Cares programme, employees are entitled to take two days each year to work with local communities. In 2007, employees provided over 550 hours of volunteering, in diverse tasks ranging from job coaching the unemployed and tree planting in primary schools to literacy training and job interview practice.

Employee-led support

Education: Bruntwood staff have worked through The Prince's Trust to help mentor long-term unemployed in a new business venture and helped the homeless back into the job market.

Commercially-led support

Sponsorship: *The arts* – organisations supported across the North West include, the Royal Exchange, The Royal Northern college of Music, The Tate Gallery, The Lowry, The Bridgewater Hall, The Halle Orchestra, and the Everyman & Playhouse Theatres.

BT Group plc

Company registration number 1800000

BT Group Communications, 81 Newgate Street, London EC1A 7AJ

020 7356 5000; Fax: 020 7356 5520

Website: www.btplc.com

Correspondent: Steve Kelly, Corporate Responsibility Team 020 7356 6678

Chairman: Sir Michael Rake

Ian Livingston: Ben Verwaayen

Year end	Turnover	Pre-tax profit
31/03/2008	£20,704,000,000	£1,976,000,000

Nature of company business
The group's principal activity is the supply of communications services and equipment

Subsidiaries include: Cellnet Group Ltd, Martin Dawes Telecommunications Ltd, Telecom Securicor Cellular Radio Ltd

Main locations: London

UK employees: 91,300

Total employees: 111,900

Charitable donations

2008: £2,500,000
2007: £3,000,000
2006: £2,500,000
2004: £1,200,000

Total community contributions: £22,300,000

Membership: BitC, L B Group

Community involvement

As a reply to our request for information was not forthcoming, most of what follows summarises the information contained in the company's 2008 sustainability report. Readers are advised to visit the relevant part of BT's website if further details are required.

'We donate money, time and expertise to make a difference to the communities where we operate around the world. Our community investment (including charity donations, volunteering and in kind support) is focused on activities that inspire people to make a better world through the power of communication skills and technology. The majority of these activities focus on helping young people and supporting arts and culture.

'Campaigns and partnerships

'*Better World Campaign* – Our Better World Campaign gives disadvantaged young people the skills they need to succeed in life and to improve their world. The Campaign includes education programmes in the UK and internationally, such as projects run in partnership with children's charity UNICEF.

'Our employees also raise money for our fundraising partners UNICEF and ChildLine.

'*Charity partnerships* – BT supports charities, aligned closely to our business, where we can make a real difference and add value to the charity's activities. This is more than donating money as there are many ways we can help using our professional expertise.

'*Emergency disaster relief* – BT responds to calls for help when disaster strikes or humanitarian aid is needed. This has included sending engineering teams into disaster zones to provide essential communications for the relief effort, setting up temporary call centres for victims and their families, and providing the mechanisms for donations online or by phone, working with the Disaster Emergency Committee

'*Telethons* – In the 2008 financial year, we helped the Disasters Emergency Committee, Sport Relief and Children in Need run telethons which raised substantial amounts of money for each.

'Employee engagement

'Our employees are critical to the delivery of our programmes, providing valuable in kind support. This is good for the communities they support, and also gives our people new skills and experiences. There are presently five areas in which employees are engaged:

'*Employee volunteering* – We encourage our employees to volunteer their time to support good causes, primarily through the BT Volunteers programme.

'*Community Champions* – BT Community Champions recognises BT employees who volunteer in their local community during their spare time. The scheme allows BT employees world-wide to apply for grants or sports kit (for an under 18s football team or a disabled adult team) for the local community group, charity or school, where they volunteer.

'*Chairman's Awards* – The annual BT Chairman's Awards recognises employees who make an outstanding commitment to community organisations outside working hours.

'*Employee giving* – We run payroll giving schemes in the UK and Ireland. We encourage all our people to give to charity, employees can make donations to their charity of choice and the company will match their contribution, up to a set total.

'*Judging awards* – We involve our employees in projects we support, by asking them to judge awards. For example, our employees select winners from 7,000 nominations for The Teaching Awards.

'*Arts*

'*Arts for All* – BT's Arts for All programme has helped make one of the world's largest modern and contemporary art collections easily accessible through sponsorship of Tate Online, the UK's most visited visual arts website.'

Exclusions

No response to circular appeals. No denominational appeals, political appeals, appeals from individuals or brochure advertising.

Applications

Decisions on major grants are made at head office by the Board Community Support Committee which meets quarterly. Smaller grants can be made by staff of the relevant Community Unit at their discretion. Local appeals should be sent to the appropriate BT local office. (Each BT zone has its own community affairs staff operating a programme which reflects the needs of that area.)

Contacts: Voluntary Sector Programmes – Beth Courtier (023 8082 3340); Education and Employment Partnerships – Dave Hancock (0121 230 7855).

Corporate giving

In 2007/08, BT made total worldwide community contributions of £22.3 million, including £2.5 million in cash donations. No figures were available indicating how much of this was given in the UK.

In kind support

BT gives in kind support to ChildLine, such as strategic and technical advice. Its support has included the donation of premises for several years, large-scale promotions and staff fundraising initiatives, and sponsoring the annual BT ChildLine Awards for Services to Children.

Employee-led support

Employee involvement: In 2008, through the BT Community Champions scheme, 842 grants were made worth £200,000.

Through the BT Volunteers programme, employees have the chance to contribute to the company's Better World Campaign by teaching lessons on communication skills in schools and youth clubs. 3,000 current and former employees volunteer in over 150 clubs around the UK. In 2008 they delivered lessons on communication skills to over 146,000 young people.

Payroll giving: BT's commitment to Give As You Earn enables employees to donate to the charity of their choice.

In the UK, BT has one of the largest payroll giving schemes. In 2008 employees gave just under £2.4 million which was matched with an extra £1 million contribution from BT.

Commercially-led support

Sponsorship: *The arts* – Through a pioneering partnership with the UK's leading modern art gallery, Tate, BT sponsors its website Tate Online. Support is also given to the preservation of the UK's telecommunications heritage.

Bunzl plc

Company registration number 358948

York House, 45 Seymour Street, London W1H 7JT

020 7725 5000; Fax: 020 7725 5001

Website: www.bunzl.com

Correspondent: Julia Battyll, Independent Consultant

Chairman: A Habgood

Chief Executive: Michael Roney

Year end	Turnover	Pre-tax profit
31/12/2007	£3,581,900,000	£191,100,000

Nature of company business
Providing outsourcing solutions and customer service orientated distribution and light manufacture, primarily of plastic and paper based products.

Subsidiaries include: Filtrona United Kingdom Ltd

Main locations: London

UK employees: 5,500

Charitable donations

2007: £200,000
2005: £201,000
2004: £200,000
2003: £193,000

Membership: BitC

Community involvement

The Bunzl group described its corporate community support policy in 2008 as follows:

'Bunzl is committed to being a responsible corporate citizen through support for appropriate non-political and non-sectarian projects, organisations and charities.

'At the group level a cross section of projects within registered charities are sponsored predominantly in the fields of healthcare, disability, environment and education.

'Each business area, as part of considering its impact on the local community, is encouraged to develop their own local charitable giving programmes in line with the group guidelines but taking into account local company requirements including marketing initiatives and budgetary considerations.

'All employees are encouraged to act as responsible and responsive citizens of their communities and to support projects, organisations and services that work towards the common good and improvement of their community and society.'

Exclusions

The group will not support advertising in charity brochures, animal welfare, appeals from individuals, arts, fundraising events, heritage, political or religious appeals, science/ technology, or sport.

Applications

In writing to the correspondent. Subsidiaries have a donations budget independent of head office and should be contacted directly.

Other Information: The group produce a social responsibility report which is available within the annual report and accounts.

Corporate giving

In 2007, the company made cash donations totalling £200,000. The company's 2007, Corporate Social Responsibility Report gave the following information concerning its charitable activities:

'Bunzl is a member of Business in the Community in the UK and at group level has continued to support a cross section of projects with registered charities in the fields of healthcare, education, disability and environment. In 2007 Bunzl and its employees across the world made significant donations to various cancer research and cancer care charities including sponsorship of projects relating to leukaemia research undertaken by the Leukaemia Research Fund and donations and local fund raising for Macmillan Cancer Support and Marie Curie Cancer Care. Bunzl continued to support Queen Elizabeth's Training College in the UK to assist in funding a new customer service training course. Support was once again given to Leonard Cheshire, this year to support a new training programme on TV production to assist people in applying for media jobs. Funding was provided to the British Occupational Health Research Forum to support research on 'The Wellbeing of Mobile Personnel'.

'For the first time, Bunzl provided support to a number of environmental projects which included funding the London Remade Local Authority Network Meetings which discuss recycling activities as well as providing funding for a school and two educational centres to purchase wind turbines to provide them with renewable energy.

'Donations were also made to two UK benevolent associations, Hospitality Action and The Lighthouse Club who support workers from two of the key industry sectors that Bunzl serves. In addition, Group companies and individual employees worldwide continue to support local charitable initiatives. In the UK, fund raising activities took place for the Evelina Children's Hospital, the Red Cross and Jeans for Genes Day.'

In kind support

In addition to cash donations, the company provides support through gifts in kind.

Employee-led support

All employees are encouraged to support projects, organisations and services that work towards the improvement of their community.

Bunzl matches employee fundraising up to a maximum of £1,000.

Payroll Giving: The company operates the Charity Direct payroll giving scheme.

BUPA Ltd

Company registration number 2306135

BUPA House, 15–19 Bloomsbury Way, London WC1A 2BA

0800 600 500

Website: www.bupa.co.uk

Correspondent: (See 'Applications' below)

Chairman: Lord Leitch

Chief Executive: Ray King

Year end	Turnover	Pre-tax profit
31/12/2007	£4,531,100,000	£398,000,000

Nature of company business
Principal activities: operation of health insurance funds and the provision of healthcare facilities and services, including ownership and management of hospitals, care homes, children's nurseries, homecare health screening services and occupational health services.

Subsidiaries include: Care First Group plc

Main locations: London

Total employees: 35,678

Charitable donations

2007: £5,700,000
2006: £5,300,000
2005: £2,578,500
2003: £2,500,000

Membership: BitC, L B Group

Community involvement

BUPA's community support programme has three separate, but complementary strands, namely: The BUPA Foundation (Charity Commission no. 277598); BUPA Giving; and BUPA Community Connections.

Donations made through *The BUPA Foundation* are designated to prevent, relieve and cure, sickness, ill-health and infirmity and to safeguard health by way of research. The foundation aims to produce long-term benefits that will have an impact on health of both individuals and the whole country. Currently, applications are invited for medical research grants in the following areas:

- surgery: projects ranging from development of surgical practices to evaluating outcomes and identifying/teaching new techniques
- preventive health: projects covering all health environments (including the workplace) from epidemiology to health maintenance
- information and communication: projects designed to enhance the partnership between medical professionals and the public/patients.

Grants are also given for medical research on a specific named theme, along with foundation awards made annually in recognition of excellence in medical research and healthcare.

BUPA Giving was set up in 2006 to celebrate the healthcare provider's 60th anniversary. It has a clear focus on supporting compelling and current social issues within regions that BUPA Group operates, such as health education, long-term care and medicine.

During 2006/2007, BUPA Giving has focused on long-term care and health education. In 2007/2008, a greater focus will be given to its international businesses – projects recommended and promoted by them. There are currently projects under appraisal from Australia, Thailand and Spain.

BUPA Community Connections helps ensure that the group identify and address some of the health and wellbeing needs of the communities in which it operates. Although originally set up to assist and support BUPA staff in their voluntary community work in the UK, it is now increasingly gaining an international flavour, in line with BUPA's overseas expansion.

Exclusions

The company does not support appeals from individuals, political appeals or religious appeals.

Applications

BUPA Foundation: The foundation's website (www.bupafoundation.com) provides detailed information regarding applications, eligibility and closing dates for each of the three fields in which awards are made. Any initial enquiries should be addressed to Lee Saunders (Tel: 020 7656 2591; Fax: 020 7656 2708; email: bupafoundation@bupa.com).

BUPA Giving: To apply for BUPA Giving funding you will need to register your interest and then request and complete an application form for funding. Full details are available on the website at: www.bupagiving.co.uk Any initial enquiries should be addressed to Clair Norgate (Tel: 020 7656 2179; email: bupagiving@bupa.com).

BUPA Community Connections: Initial enquiries should be addressed to Nicole Humphries (Tel: 020 7656 2343; Fax: 020 7656 2705; email: comconnections@bupa.com

Corporate giving

During 2007, BUPA made charitable donations in the UK totalling £5.7 million. This included payments to The BUPA Foundation of £2.7 million (2006: £2.6 million) and £3 million (2006: £600,000) under the BUPA Giving initiative to registered charities. A further £300,000 (2006: £300,000) was paid to the Sanitas Foundation in Spain.

BUPA Foundation

In 2006, the foundation's income was £1.2 million, the vast majority of this (£1,048,000) was Gift Aid donation made by the company.

The BUPA Foundation supports a number of annual awards to recognise and promote excellence in healthcare. The foundation continued its policy of donating grants to relevant research bodies, and during 2006 granted £2.5 million to 21 different projects (2005: £3.1 million to 26 projects).

During 2007 specialist projects which received grants included a Sheffield University analysis of a software program designed to deliver rapid rehabilitation for brain injury communication problems, aphasia and apraxia.

Medical research projects covered the entire health spectrum, including such conditions as sickle cell disease, obesity, depression, osteoarthritis and chlamydia. Other projects included a Cambridge University programme to create a single data set from three European studies on dementia, allowing greater comparison and insight.

In November 2007 the foundation received a written commitment from the company stating that it will continue to make an annual Gift Aid payment of at least 32.6 million a year, up to and including 2010.

BUPA Giving

2007 was the first full year of the new BUPA Giving initiative through which the group aims to give up to £3 million each year to good causes with charitable status in education, medicine or health and care. During the year, BUPA committed £3 million to 16 programmes. Most of the projects focused on elderly care initiatives including palliative care for the terminally ill and health and care advice services for older people. Beneficiaries included charities, hospitals, research centres and NHS primary care trusts.

Details of current projects receiving support are given on the website: www.Bupagiving.com

In kind support
BUPA Community Connections

Set up to assist and support BUPA staff in their voluntary community work, help can range from the provision of manpower, training, publicity and supplies, to practical advice on fundraising and volunteering activities. Financial support may also be given.

Employee-led support
BUPA Community Connections

Through this initiative, staff have supported a range of causes from the RNIB's *See It Right* campaign to raising money for UNICEF in its fight against child exploitation.

Other employee volunteering schemes have focused on education, the environment, the elderly, community mediation and homelessness. Further details on each of these is given on the company's website. Volunteering by staff is actively encouraged through the provision of a wide range of volunteering opportunities in over ten specialist areas such as children and young people, education, homelessness, and older people.

Payroll giving: The company operates the Give As You Earn Scheme.

Commercially-led support

Sponsorship: *Health* – BUPA continues to support the Great Run series because of its relation to health issues.

C E Electric UK Ltd

Company registration number 3271033

Manor House, Station Road, New Penshaw, Houghton-le-Spring, DH4 7LA.

0800 668877

Website: www.ce-electricuk.com

Correspondent: Jon Bird, Director, External Affairs
0191 387 7310

Chairman: David Sokol

Chief Executive: Greg Abel

Year end	Turnover	Pre-tax profit
31/12/2006	£538,300,000	£209,500,000

Nature of company business
CE Electric UK is the parent company of Northern Electric Distribution and Yorkshire Electricity Distribution, the electricity distribution businesses for the North East, Yorkshire and North Lincolnshire.

Subsidiaries include: Yorkshire Power Group Ltd, Northern Electric plc, Integrated Utility Services

Main locations: Leeds, Newcastle upon Tyne

UK employees: 2,468

Charitable donations

2006: £57,147
2005: £54,568
2004: £91,625
2003: £38,000

Total community contributions: £87,791

Membership: BitC

Community involvement

The company has produced detailed and clear information on its community programme and policies. It states: 'As the monopoly distributor of electricity throughout the region, we recognise that our customers and the community in which they live are the same. Our community involvement is thus an extension of our customer service programme and is aimed at making a visible difference to the life of those communities.'

CE Electric UK advised that it has an ongoing community investment strategy. Decisions on expenditure are made on a one-off basis, usually in response to requests from outside the company. The criteria used are:

- will the expenditure benefit a locality as opposed to a national cause?
- is the location one where we are working with the community on quality of supply or other issues?
- will we be a sole funder as opposed to one of a large number?
- is the expenditure on one of our preferred areas (environment, young people, rural affairs)?
- is there a reasonable opportunity for gaining positive PR commensurate with the level of expenditure?

There is a preference for supporting local charities in the North East, Yorkshire and north Lincolnshire areas, especially those concerned with youth, education and the environment.

Exclusions

No support for circular appeals, advertising in national charity brochures, animal welfare, appeals from individuals, the arts, fundraising events, heritage, medical research, overseas projects, political or religious appeals, science/technology, sickness/disability, or a 'charity of the year'.

Applications

In writing to the correspondent.

Corporate giving

In 2006, the group made total community contributions of £87,791 of which cash donations accounted for £57,147. Support was principally given to local charities serving the communities in which the group operates. Details of the beneficiaries were not provided.

Looking towards the future and the London 2012 Olympics, CE Electric UK has launched a long-term initiative to find and develop local athletic talent within its operating area. The scheme will fund the employment of Community and Performance Sports Coaches to help work with local athletic stars of the future over the next five years and beyond. Run in conjunction with Sportsmatch and England Athletics, the programme will also support athletics clubs and 'untapped' talent at schools across Yorkshire. CE Electric UK and the Community Coaches will be visiting local schools in the Autumn to spread the word about healthy living and getting fit for the future.

The company also has money invested in the Community Foundations for the Tyne & Wear, County Durham and Tees Valley. The income from these investments goes to fund community projects in the respective areas.

In kind support

CE Electric undertakes an education programme in schools and via the web to educate children in the need to avoid contact with electrical wires and equipment

Employee-led support

Employees are encouraged to volunteer for community-based and charitable activities. The company matches employees fundraising efforts up to a maximum of £200 per employee.

Under the Global Days of Service programme operated by the company's parent company, MidAmerican Energy Holdings Company, organisations for which employees volunteer can gain a financial contribution depending on the number of hours volunteered.

CA plc

Company registration number 1282495

Ditton Park, Riding Court Road, Dachet, Slough, Berkshire SL3 9LL

01753 577733

Website: www.ca.com/community

Correspondent: Tina Leach, Community Relations Specialist
01753 242860; Fax: 01753 241160
Email: christina.leach@ca.com

Year end
31/03/2007

Nature of company business
The group is one of the world's largest management software companies, delivering software and services across operations, security, storage, and life cycle management for performance and reliability of IT environments.

Main locations: Edinburgh, Taunton, Nottingham, Datchet, London, Altrincham

UK employees: 900

Charitable donations

2006: £500,000
2005: £500,000
2004: £500,000

Community involvement

Formerly trading as Computer Associates plc, the company has a preference for UK-wide or European charities. It prefers to support charities concerned with children/youth, education, science/technology and health.

For more than three decades, the parent company in the America has supported communities where its employees live and work. Serving a global company with offices in more than 46 countries, CA's Corporate Community Affairs department supports communities through employee-giving programmes, CA Together Community grants, CA Together IT Program offerings and corporate contributions. However, it appears that all such support is initiated by the company.

Exclusions

The company does not provide support for individual appeals or charities concerned with any form of discrimination and will only review grants that apply as above under 'Community involvement'.

Applications

The company no longer appear to offer the facility to make grant applications online as the majority of grants are initiated by CA and do not stem from unsolicited proposals.

Corporate giving

We were previously advised by the company that it makes charitable donations totalling around £500,000 a year in the UK. We were unable to confirm if this is still the case.

The company continues as a partner of The Prince's Trust Technology Leadership Group. CA has contributed significantly to the group, which has raised £4 million and set up 1,800 young people in business so far.

Past beneficiaries have included: National Centre for Missing & Exploited Children, Starlight, National Space Centre, Young Enterprise, Education Business Partnership, The Outward Bound Trust, Staywise (Royal Berkshire Fire & Rescue Service), Marie Curie Cancer Care, Thames Hospice Care, Guide Dogs for the Blind, World Food Programme, Children in Need, and the National Children's Home.

In 2005, the company established the Digital Schoolhouse charity (Charity Commission no. 1107476) in order to 'advance education of the public in computer software and other technologies'. In practice, the charity helps prepare students of all ages – though primarily aimed at 10 to 12 year olds – for success in a digital world. A donation of £40,227 was made by the company towards the cost of two staff engaged in teaching IT.

In kind support

In addition to cash donations, the company provides support through gifts in kind and staff secondments.

Employee-led support

The company encourages staff to volunteer and recently offered each member three days of volunteering time to participate in The Prince's Trust Namibian Desert Challenge. It also 100% matched funding on personal donations.

Payroll Giving Scheme: The Give As You Earn payroll giving scheme is in operation.

Commercially-led support

Sponsorship: The company does not undertake any form of sponsorship.

Cable and Wireless plc

Company registration number 238525

3rd Floor, 25 Red Lion Square, London WC1R 4HQ

020 7315 4000

Website: www.cw.com

Correspondent: Paul James, Head of Public Affairs

Chairman: Richard Lapthorne

Chief Executive: Tony Rice

Year end	Turnover	Pre-tax profit
31/03/2008	£3,152,000,000	£267,000,000

Nature of company business
The group's principal activity is the provision of telecommunication services.

Main locations: Coventry, London, Swindon, Southampton, Wokingham, Birmingham, Bracknell

Total employees: 13,510

Charitable donations

2008: £1,500,000
2007: £1,400,000
2006: £200,000
2005: £1,700,000
2004: £1,100,000

Community involvement

We did not receive a reply from Cable & Wireless following our request for updated information, which is unfortunate given that its policy seems to have changed considerably.

From the limited amount of information the company has made available, we quote as follows:

'We've a colleague-driven community agenda which encourages positive interaction with our local communities. We support them by providing: top-up funding; internal fundraising activities; external programmes such as supporting community regeneration; secondment; and electronic community notice boards.'

Exclusions

The company only supports proposals that match its policy and does not offer support for advertising. No support for individuals other than employees. Proposals must relate to locations where the company does business or potentially has global scope. No support for political or religious causes or UK-centric projects.

Applications

In writing to the correspondent or email community@cw.com

Corporate giving

In 2008, the company made worldwide community contributions of £1.5 million. No indication was given as to how much of this went to UK charities/community organisations.

In kind support

In 2008, Cable & Wireless stated that: 'Our two major in kind support programmes benefit Children in Need and we provide

11–14 year old students with the opportunity to advance their technology skills in our Bracknell ICT Academy.'

Employee-led support

The company actively encourages employees to support the work of the charities or voluntary organisations in their own local community.

Previously, the above was supported through a matched giving scheme. This 'fixed pool of funds' is used to match money raised for charitable causes by UK employees up to a maximum of £1,000 per employee in any one financial year. We do not know if this continues to be the case.

Payroll giving: The company operates the Give As You Earn scheme.

Commercially-led support

Sponsorship: *Education* – The company sponsor the Porthcurno Telegraph Museum in Cornwall which tells the story of global communications from the first use of electricity to how we communicate today.

Cadbury plc

Company registration number 52457

25 Berkeley Square, London W1X 6HT

020 7409 1313; Fax: 020 7830 5200

Website: www.cadbury.com

Correspondent: Alexandra Law, Community Investment Officer

Chairman: Roger Carr

Chief Executive: Todd Stitzer

Year end	Turnover	Pre-tax profit
01/01/2007	£7,971,000,000	£670,000,000

Nature of company business
Principal activities: the manufacture and marketing of confectionery.

Subsidiaries include: Reading Scientific Services Ltd, Connaught Investments plc, Berkeley Square Investments Ltd, Trebor Bassett Ltd

Main locations: Bournville, Maple Cross, Hertfordshire

UK employees: 706

Total employees: 70,000

Charitable donations

2007: £750,000
2006: £750,000
2005: £750,000
2004: £700,000
2003: £650,000

Total community contributions: £9,378,600
Management costs: £595,000

Membership: BitC, L B Group

Community involvement

The company's beverage and confectionery businesses were demerged on 7 May 2008, marking the beginning of a new era for Cadbury plc.

Cadbury's investment can be a mixture of money, the time and skills of its people and/or gifts in kind. A wide range of resources can be given in kind. These include product donations, use of meeting rooms and other facilities, as well as access to training and other specialist materials.

As the needs of communities vary from region to region and country to county, Cadbury's investment is not prescriptive. Local business units decide how much money, time and skills or gifts in kind they will invest, using the *Growing Community value around the world* guidelines to measure and manage their community investments.

Most requests for charitable donations in the UK are channelled through the Cadbury Foundation (Charity Commission no. 1050482) – the company's charitable trust in the UK. This has no endowment but is funded by grants from the company each year.

Grants are given mainly in support of organisations working with education and enterprise, health, welfare or the environment. National charities and local groups around its sites (in Birmingham, Bristol, London (Hackney) and Sheffield) may be assisted.

Exclusions

In view of the policy of concentrating grants behind selected projects, most ad hoc appeals have to be declined and are therefore not encouraged.

The foundation does not support: requests for commercial sponsorship, help with funding of individuals' education and training programmes, purchase of advertising space, involvement in fundraising projects, travel or leisure projects, donation of gifts in kind (including company products), regional projects unless in the locality of company operations.

Normally support has not been given for projects outside the UK since it is policy to provide support through local businesses in the many countries around the world where Cadbury has operations.

Applications

As indicated above, appeals outside the criteria defined are not encouraged, as most grants are committed in advance on an ongoing basis.

However, if you are able to answer 'Yes' to all the below, then it may be possible for the foundation to consider your organisation for funding:

- is the project promoting education, enterprise or employability within a group or groups of people?
- would your client base be considered 'at risk' or 'socially excluded'?
- are you located in geographical proximity to one of Cadbury's major UK operations (e.g., Birmingham, Sheffield, Bristol, London (Hackney))?
- are some of Cadbury's employees already involved?

Please write to the correspondent at:

Cadbury Foundation
Cadbury House
Uxbridge Business Park
Uxbridge
Middlesex
UB8 1DH.

If you are seeking sponsorship, advertising, fundraising or requests for donations or gifts in kind (including Cadbury's products) please contact your local business.

Corporate giving

In 2007, global donations, in kind support and staff time totalled £9.4 million of which £5.1 million was in cash donations. Management costs stood at £575,000. As Cadbury do not publish separate figures for the UK, we cannot give an accurate estimate of its total community investment. However, we do know that it donated £750,000 to the Cadbury Foundation.

Cadbury Foundation

In 2006, the latest year for which accounts are available, the foundation received a donation of £750,000 from the company. The foundation in turn made grants totalling just over £800,000, with beneficiaries in the UK including The Prince's Trust, The Confectioners' Benevolent Fund, Earthwatch, Young Enterprise, The History of Advertising Trust, Birmingham Girls and Boys Union and Research Autism.

In kind support

Cadburybusinesses donate a wide range of resources in kind including:

- products
- materials and promotional items
- equipment or furniture.

Education: Regular links are maintained with schools through work experience, work shadowing, collaborative projects and provision of school packs. A number of schools are now assigned a 'Links Manager' in order that the business can support their work.

Employee-led support

The company seeks to increase employee participation in community activities. Team challenges are effectively team-building and personal development activities which are performed by staff for the benefit of good causes. Various opportunities have been offered for staff to get involved, including: mentoring individual pupils, coaching and organising team sports, providing business and management advice and support to head teachers and community managers.

Employees' fundraising efforts are acknowledged through a 'Cash-Match' scheme up to a usual limit of £100 for an individual and up to £200 for team events. Employees have been cash-matched for activities ranging from raffles to sponsored show jumping.

Payroll giving: The 'Pennies from Heaven' scheme is available to employees wishing to make tax-effective donations to a charity of their choice.

Commercially-led support

Sponsorship: Good-cause sponsorship may be considered.

Cadogan Group Ltd

Company registration number 2997375

18 Cadogan Gardens, London SW3 2RP

020 7730 4567; Fax: 020 7881 2300

Website: www.cadogan.co.uk

Correspondent: Gill Nunn, Personal Assistant to Lord Cadogan

Chairman: The Earl Cadogan D.L.

Chief Executive: Stuart Corbyn

Year end	Turnover	Pre-tax profit
31/12/2007	£73,247,000	£30,812,000

Nature of company business
The principal activity of the group is property investment. Subsidiaries are involved in the manufacture and distribution of menswear, upholstered furniture and protective workplace clothing, and the retailing of furniture.

Subsidiaries include: Multifabs Ltd, Chelsea Land Ltd, Holliday & Brown Ltd, Christy & Co. Ltd, Oakley Leisure Parks Ltd, Furniture Village plc, Oakley Investment Ltd, Michelsons Ltd

Main locations: London

UK employees: 68

Charitable donations

2007: £178,000
2006: £88,000
2005: £50,000

Community involvement

In the recent past some uncertainty has surrounded this company's charitable giving. Did it make all of its donations through the associated Cadogan Charity (Charity Commission no. 247773), or did it make donations in its own right?

Thanks to a statement in the 2007 annual report and accounts, it now appears that we have an answer – 'In addition, [to the group's charitable donations] the Cadogan Charity, a shareholder in the company, makes donations to a variety of local and national charities.'

Exclusions

No grants to individuals.

Applications

In writing to the correspondent.

Corporate giving

In 2007, the group made charitable donations of £178,000 (2006: £88,000). We have no details of the beneficiaries.

Caledonia Investments

Company registration number 3142560

Cayzer House, 30 Buckingham Gate, London SW1E 6NN

020 7802 8080; Fax: 020 7802 8090

Website: www.caledonia.com

Correspondent: Major M G Wyatt, Director
Email: enquiries@caledonia.com

Chairman: Peter N Buckley

Chief Executive: Tim Ingram

Year end	Pre-tax profit
31/03/2008	(£36,500,000)

Nature of company business
Caledonia is a UK investment trust company, listed on the London Stock Exchange.

Subsidiaries include: The Sloane Club Group Ltd, Edinmore Holdings Ltd, Edinburgh Crystal Glass Co. Ltd, Amber Industrial Holdings plc, St Lawrence Properties Ltd, Sterling Industries plc

Main locations: London

UK employees: 43

Charitable donations

2008: £110,000
2006: £110,000
2004: £102,000

Community involvement

The company has a preference for appeals relevant to company business and charities in which a member of company staff is involved. There is also a preference for education, environment/heritage, arts and enterprise/training.

Exclusions

No grants for fundraising events, advertising in charity brochures, religious appeals, local appeals not in areas of company presence, large national appeals, overseas projects or circular appeals, and absolutely no individual sponsorship of college/university students.

Applications

In writing to the correspondent.

Corporate giving

In 2007/08, the company donated a total of £110,000 to charities. Grants to national organisations have previously ranged from £200 to £2,000. We have no details of the beneficiaries.

Calor Gas Ltd

Company registration number 303703

Athena Drive, Tachbrook Park, Warwick CV34 6RL

01926 330088

Website: www.calor.co.uk

Correspondent: Suzanne Weir, Communications Manager
Email: sweir@calor.co.uk

Managing Director: Alex Davis

Year end	Turnover	Pre-tax profit
31/12/2007	£338,200,000	£28,300,000

Nature of company business
Part of the worldwide SHV group, the principal activity of the company is the processing, marketing and distribution of liquefied petroleum gas.

Main locations: Warwick

Charitable donations

2005: £50,000
Total community contributions: £300,000 (2007)
CRM figure: £65,000
Membership: BitC

Community involvement

Calor Gas supports a wide range of community initiatives from charity work to education, rural and environmental projects. The company's website now provides comprehensive information about its community work, as the following quote shows:

'Calor is committed to contributing to the communities we serve. We are focused on building long standing relationships with relevant organisations and providing real support to make a difference. Initiatives such as Calor Village of the Year and our work with BITC, Rural Revival, The Fairyland Trust and ChildLine, have boosted communities and local businesses and contributed hundreds of thousands of pounds to local projects.'

Calor have, however, advised us that its charity budget is employee led, NOT external request led.

Applications

In writing to the correspondent. However, in view of the company's charity budget being employee led, the chances of receiving support appear slim.

Corporate giving

The company did not declare any charitable donations in its 2007 annual report and accounts. They did, however, inform us that in kind support, mainly for long-term educational projects, totalled £300,000 for the year.

In kind support

Calor's support of the Fairyland Trust has provided the trust with a Mongolian Yurt that is used as a travelling 'Fairy Café' as well as publication of its annual report and help at numerous Fairy Fairs.

Employee-led support

Education: Calor operates a mentoring programme where staff are encouraged to support and guide students in their coursework at local schools during lunch breaks. The company also operates Business Days for local schools, designed to give students an insight into business areas such as advertising, marketing, customer care and production.

These programmes have so far involved over 300 students in over ten schools.

Commercially-led support

Sponsorship: The Calor Village of the Year competition for England, Wales and Scotland provides a national prize fund of over £40,000 with additional prizes being given in over 43 counties.

The company state that the competition is: 'Calor's way of supporting customers in rural communities and encouraging rural sustainability.

'The competition is not about pretty window boxes and the village green. It is based upon six major aspects of village life

– community, business, young people, older people, environment and information technology.'

To mark the 10th anniversary of the competition in 2006, a special 'best of the best' competition was held featuring past regional winners. The outcome was £20,000 being awarded to the winning village of St Neot's.

Cause-related marketing: In 2005, Calor launchedthe 'Gift of the Gas' campaign to benefit those who need support from ChildLine, the UK's free, 24-hour helpline for children in danger or distress. The company has pledged to contribute £5 to the charity for every redundant Calor cylinder returned to the company's local sites. By the end of 2006, over £65,000 had been raised from returned gas cylinders and fundraising barbecue events held during the summer season.

Camelot Group plc

Company registration number 2822203

Tolpits Lane, Watford, Herts WD18 9RN

01923 425000; Fax: 01923 425050

Website: www.camelotgroup.co.uk

Correspondent: Dianne Thompson, Chief Executive

Chairman: Sir Peter Middleton

Chief Executive: Dianne Thompson

Year end	Turnover	Pre-tax profit
31/03/2008	£4,966,300,000	£52,900,000

Nature of company business
The principal activity of the company is the operation and promotion of the National Lottery in the United Kingdom.

Main locations: London, Liverpool, Cardiff, Glasgow, Belfast

UK employees: 913

Charitable donations
2008: £1,900,000
2007: £3,100,000
2005: £2,000,000
2004: £2,500,000

Membership: BitC, L B Group

Community involvement

The company concentrates its community support on combating disadvantage in areas close to its business. There are four main themes: developing skills, creating new opportunities, enhancing communities and encouraging social responsibility in the industry. The company's community investment programme is built around three main elements: community partnerships, employee involvement and the Camelot Foundation.

The geographical areas given preference are near to the company's headquarters in Watford, its call centre in Aintree – Liverpool, Glasgow, Cardiff and Belfast.

Exclusions

Activity outside of the community involvement policy; overseas appeals/sponsorship; individuals; advertisements in charity brochures/programmes; general appeals.

Applications

In writing to the correspondent.

Corporate giving

In 2007/08, the group made charitable contributions of £1.9 million of which £1.1 million was paid to the Camelot Foundation (Charity Commission no. 1060606). The group made further direct donations to other community and charitable organisations during the year of £800,000.

Further, unspecified, in kind support was also made during the year.

The Camelot Foundation

The following statement has been released:

'After a decade of supporting young people's charities around the UK the Camelot Foundation will be closing on 31 March 2008. All of our grant programmes are now permanently closed, and therefore regrettably we cannot accept any new grant requests.

'As already stated existing commitments to beneficiaries will be met from funds already set aside for the purpose.'

The company

The 'Community Partnership' element of its support sees Camelot working closely with many charitable and commercial organisations to the benefit of the community. According to the company these include:

- supporting business/school partnerships
- offering business skills for practical or teaching purposes to tertiary colleges
- supporting programmes aimed at creating skills and opportunities for young, disadvantaged, unemployed people
- funding strategic initiatives that focus on the infrastructure of community development and citizenship
- supporting research, education, and treatment regarding gambling addiction and responsible gambling.

Organisations that Camelot has worked with include: Media Trust, Common Purpose, Education Extra and GamCare.

In kind support

This is provided through gifts in kind and staff secondments.

Employee-led support

Camelot Group employees are encouraged and assisted to support the causes they choose through match funding and volunteering. This is made possible through Camelot's Employee Community Involvement programme. Camelot has also made direct contributions to their communities with 7% of Camelot employees contributing nearly 1,000 volunteer hours to assist local projects.

Employees can apply for match funding for charitable activities and events that they are actively involved in, staff are encouraged to raise funds for charities large and small across the UK.

Camelot employees are also offered half a day a month for volunteering activities. To further encourage employees to give their professional skills to organisations as well as to fundraise for charities of their choice, the company developed a 'time-bank' for matched funding purposes with a common value of £16 per hour.

Canary Wharf Group plc

Company registration number 3114622

One Canada Square, Canary Wharf, London E14 5AB

020 7418 2000; Fax: 020 7418 2222

Website: www.canarywharf.com

Correspondent: Howard Dowter

Chairman: Sir Martin Jacomb

Chief Executive: George Lacobescu

Year end	Turnover	Pre-tax profit
31/12/2007	£559,400,000	£104,300,000

Nature of company business
Property development, investment, and management.

Subsidiaries include: CW Lending Ltd, CW Lending II plc, Heron Quays Properties Ltd

Main locations: London

UK employees: 869

Total employees: 869

Charitable donations

2007: £394,451
2006: £208,838
2005: £284,317
2004: £96,763

Membership: BitC

Community involvement

The company has 'a continued commitment to supporting the local community', i.e. Tower Hamlets and East London.

Exclusions

No support for advertising in charity brochures, animal welfare, appeals from individuals, local appeals not in areas of company presence or potential 'charity of the year' partners.

Applications

In writing to the correspondent.

Information available: The company produces a corporate responsibility report (available on its environmental website).

Corporate giving

In 2007, the company made charitable donations of £395,451 (2006: £208,838). We have no details of the beneficiaries.

Canon (UK) Ltd

Company registration number 1264300

Cockshot Hill, Woodhatch, Reigate, Surrey RH2 8BF

01737 220000; Fax: 01737 220022

Website: www.canon.co.uk

Correspondent: Lisa Attfield, Public Relations Corporate PR Executive
Email: lisa.attfield@cuk.canon.co.uk

Managing Director: Andy Vickers

Year end	Turnover	Pre-tax profit
31/12/2006	£306,357,000	£14,675,000

Nature of company business
The principal activity of the company is digital imaging.

Subsidiaries include: Joe Walker Ltd, Libra Business Services Ltd

Main locations: Reigate

UK employees: 1,862

Charitable donations

2006: £41,644
2005: £46,372
2004: £35,287
2003: £15,751

Community involvement

Canon state that in the course of an average week they receive around 60–80 proposals from charitable or community organisations requesting support in either cash, product donation or printing form.

Through its CARE scheme (Community Action Review Enterprise), Canon will consider supporting national and local charities operating and conducting their business in the UK, especially those connected with one of the following six categories:

- business & community – aimed at building relationships with local businesses thus encouraging job creation and community interaction
- education – designed to support schools, colleges and extra-curricular activity
- art & culture – to benefit creative events and programmes which encourage community interest and participation
- humanitarian – designed to provide assistance and support for a variety of health related causes
- environment – aimed at supporting community and environmental organisations to help improve their surroundings
- employee matching – matching of Canon employee charitable fundraising efforts.

Exclusions

No support for overseas projects, religious or political appeals.

Applications

In writing to the correspondent who is a member of the CARE Committee. The committee meets regularly to assess requests for support.

Corporate giving

In 2006, Canon made cash donations in the UK totaling £41,644 (2005: £46,372). We have no information regarding the beneficiaries.

In kind support

The company's main form of non-cash support is through gifts in kind, such as the donation of equipment/consumables and printing publicity material/annual reports.

Employee-led support

Canon have an employee volunteering scheme and match employee fundraising up to a maximum of £250.

Payroll giving: The company has a scheme in operation.

Commercially-led support

Cause-related marketing: Canon raised £27,205 for the British Red Cross from sales of the red Canon PowerShot A460 digital camera in selected Tesco stores during 2007. Selling over 5,000 units, Canon donated £5 from the sale of each camera to the charity to fund essential services in the UK.

In lending its support to the British Red Cross Tesco Charity of the Year 2007 partnership, Canon has helped raise £2 million to fund crisis care in local neighbourhoods across the UK. All the money raised through the partnership will be locally spent on first aid training, emergency equipment and care in the home services.

Caparo Group Ltd

Company registration number 1387694

Caparo House, 103 Baker Street, London W1U 6L

020 7486 1417; Fax: 020 7224 4109

Website: www.caparo.co.uk

Correspondent: The Lord Paul of Marylebone

Chairman: The Lord Paul of Marylebone

Chief Executive: The Hon Angad Paul

Year end	Turnover	Pre-tax profit
31/12/2006	£632,800,000	£58,700,000

Nature of company business
Specialists in the manufacture and supply of steel and engineering products.

Subsidiaries include: Nupac Ltd, Osborne Hotel Torquay Ltd

Main locations: London

UK employees: 3,332

Charitable donations

2006: £522,000
2005: £500,000
2004: £400,000
2003: £400,000

Community involvement

The company makes its charitable donations through the Ambika Paul Foundation (Charity Commission no. 276127). The trust continues to support the education and training of young people and to apply income for the benefit of any charitable organisation or purposes as the trustees consider appropriate.

Exclusions

No support for: advertising in charity brochures; animal welfare; appeals from individuals; elderly people; environment/heritage; fundraising events; overseas projects; political appeals; religious appeals or sickness/disability charities.

Applications

In writing to: Trustees of The Ambika Paul Foundation, at the above address.

Corporate giving

In 2006, the company made charitable donations of £522,000 of which £500,000 went to a connected foundation (see below).

Ambika Paul Foundation

In 2006, the foundation had a total income of £740,000 and made 25 grants to organisations totalling £1.2 million. Beneficiaries in 2007 included the Royal Albert Hall Trust and Diabetes UK.

Capita Group plc

Company registration number 2081330

71 Victoria Street, Westminster, London SW1H 0XA

020 7799 1525; Fax: 020 7799 1526

Website: www.capita.co.uk

Chairman: Eric Walters

Chief Executive: Paul Pindar

Year end	Turnover	Pre-tax profit
31/12/2007	£2,073,300,000	£228,700,000

Nature of company business
The group provides a range of white-collar integrated professional support services to clients in local and central government, education, and the private sector. Services include: administrative services; consultancy; IT and software services; and human resource provision.

Main locations: London

Total employees: 26,424

Charitable donations

2007: £500,000
2006: £500,000
2005: £400,000
2003: £200,000

Membership: BitC, L B Group

Community involvement

Capita provided the following information regarding its charitable support policy:

'Capita is a committed partner to the communities in which we work, using our business activities to make a positive social impact.

'We have a clear charitable policy set out by the board. This states that the group will focus its efforts on two key themes, directly linked to our wider CSR strategy.

'From a group level, we concentrate our support on:
- initiatives that address social exclusion, whether due to illness, disability, economic or social circumstances
- regeneration.'

'We implement our community programme through our:
- local community partnerships
- charitable initiatives.'

'Our charity and community programme is managed by a central charity team raising funds for our corporate charity, which is chosen and supported by staff (Our corporate charity partnership lasts for two years, and our new partnership with Macmillan Cancer Support will commence January in 2008).'

'The charity team also have responsibility for assessing all matched funding applications, leaving a clear audit trail.'

'All group-wide initiatives such as our volunteering scheme are organised centrally and the team are supported by a network of charity champions with responsibility for recording and reporting on initiatives.

'Capita also supports our employees in their individually chosen charity initiatives across the group, ensuring we invest in the local communities where we work.'

Charity of the year: Macmillan Cancer Support (2008).

Exclusions
No support outside that being given to Capita's chosen charities.

Applications
Corporate support appears limited to the charities already mentioned. Unsolicited applications are unlikely to succeed.

Corporate giving
In 2007, the company made charitable donations of £500,000 (2006: £500,000). At group level support was concentrated towards the NSPCC and The Prince's Trust – a partnership which directly raised £1.55 million and a further £1.7 million through sponsorship of the charities' events. Specific local projects were also supported.

Employee-led support
In 2008, the Capita Challenge, an outdoor activity race bringing together teams of Capita staff from across the UK, raised £67,000 for the group's corporate charity, Macmillan Cancer Support

Commercially-led support
Sponsorship: capita undertake good-cause sponsorship. Currently, this is directed towards supporting Macmillan Cancer Support.

Capital One Holdings Ltd

Company registration number 3808862

Trent House, Station Street, Nottingham NG2 3HX

Website: www.capitalone.co.uk

Correspondent: Community Relations

Chairman: Richard Fairbank

Managing Director: Srini Gopalan

Year end	Turnover	Pre-tax profit
31/12/2006	£669,450,000	(£37,571,000)

Nature of company business
The provision of a range of banking, financial and related services

Main locations: Nottingham, London
UK employees: 1,699

Charitable donations
2006: £159,000
2005: £125,000
Membership: BitC

Community involvement
The company's website states the following: 'Capital One's Community strategy is focused on supporting looked after, disabled or disadvantaged children within our local areas Through our community initiatives we aim to make a real difference to the life experiences, education and aspirations of children in our local communities in both the short and long term through financial education and sports partnerships.

'We take time to learn all we can about our communities and work proactively with the major public, private and voluntary organisations to identify the areas of greatest need and then develop and champion projects and partnerships to address that need.'

Partners with whom the company has worked include: Scope; Notts County Football in the Community; BBC Children In Need; Whizz Kidz and Young Enterprise.

Besides financial support, Capital One takes part in a programme of community team challenges and is especially keen to help organisations working with children and young people who are most at risk of getting into drugs and crime.

Exclusions
The company does not support individuals or advertise in publications.

Applications
In writing to the correspondent.

Please be aware, however, that each year most funding is already allocated and that consideration will only be given to requests that closely fit the company's strategy.

Corporate giving
In 2006, the company made charitable donations totalling £159,000 (2005: £125,000). We have no information regarding the beneficiaries. Similarly, we have been unable to obtain a figure for the company's in kind support.

In kind support
Examples of such support include painting and decorating at inner city schools, conservation work in Bestwood Country Park and painting murals in schools and community groups.

Employee-led support
All of the company's employees are entitled to take one day away from work each year to take part in a team community activity. Teams of between five and 20 employees can be seconded for a day to undertake a one-day community challenge.

Employees who volunteer for 50 hours or more in their own time can receive up to £250 for their organisation.

Commercially-led support

Sponsorship: Events are only sponsored which are concerned with children's causes and would raise at least three times the amount of money requested for the sponsorship.

Cargill plc

Company registration number 1387437

Knowle Hill Park, Fairmile Lane, Cobham, Surrey KT11 2PD

01932 861000; Fax: 01932 861200

Website: cargill.com

Correspondent: (see 'Applications')

Managing Director: Graham Secker

Year end	Turnover	Pre-tax profit
31/05/2007	£752,657,000	£17,163,000

Nature of company business
Cargill is an international provider of food, agricultural and risk management products and services.

Subsidiaries include: Cerestar, The Duckworth Group, First4Farming, Sun Valley

Main locations: London, Wolverhampton, York, Worksop, Tilbury, Runcorn, Manchester, Liverpool, Hereford, Hull, Cobham, Within St Hughes

UK employees: 2,800

Charitable donations

2007: £48,946
2006: £66,215

Community involvement

Following our request to the company for updated information regarding its charitable/community support, we were advised of the following: 'We have decided to not continue with our entry. Cargill is not structured in a way that invites national applications from voluntary organisations as each of our businesses operate autonomously in their own locations and work with local organisations relevant to their community focus.'

However, we believe that as Cargill recognises that it has some duty to the communities it serves and encourages applications at different levels, an entry is appropriate.

Local giving – Cargill states on its website that: 'To facilitate and promote local community involvement, Cargill locations worldwide in Asia, Africa, Europe, North and South America are forming employee-led *Cargill Cares* Councils. Through these councils, Cargill collectively contributes millions of charitable dollars and thousands of volunteer hours to our communities each year. These councils seek to partner with local non-profit and charitable organizations that meet their guidelines and that can engage their employees in community involvement'.

Note: Local community organisations must request funding from the Cargill Cares Council (if established) at their nearest facility.

National/global giving – At corporate level support is focused on the following three main areas: nutrition and health, education and environmental stewardship. Through the Cargill Citizenship Fund, strategic grants are provided to regional, national or global non-profit or non-governmental organisations that provide programmes and services to multiple Cargill communities. The company provides direct grants for regional, national and global partnerships and provides matching funds for selected local projects supported by its businesses.

In addition to the above, the company supports staff volunteerism.

Exclusions

Grants are not given to:
- organisations that do not serve communities where Cargill has a business presence
- individuals or groups seeking support for research, planning, personal needs or travel
- public service or political campaigns
- lobbying, political or fraternal activities
- benefit dinners, fundraising events or tickets to the same
- fundraising campaigns, walk-a-thons, or promotions to eliminate or control specific diseases
- athletic scholarships
- advertising sponsorships
- religious groups for religious purposes
- publications, audio-visual productions or special broadcasts
- endowment campaigns.

Applications

Local organisations seeking support must contact their nearest Cargill Cares Council, if established.

Regional, national or global non-profit or non-governmental organisations meeting Cargill's criteria for support should submit a 2–3 page letter of inquiry via mail, fax or email. The letter should include the following: name of organisation and mission; description of project for which funds are requested; how the project/programme fits within Cargill's focus areas; amount requested.

The mailing address is: Cargill Citizenship Committee, PO Box 5650, Minneapolis, MN 55440–5650, USA.

Cargill will review the letter of inquiry and determine whether the organisation will be invited to submit a complete proposal. All letters will receive a response. Those organisations invited to submit a proposal must complete the Cargill Citizenship Fund Guidelines and Application Form. Cargill may request additional information or a site visit. The committee reviews applications on an ongoing basis. Decisions concerning applications are generally made within 90 days of receipt.

Corporate giving

In 2007/08, Cargill plc declared cash donations in the UK of £48,946. Given the comments made by the company regarding its decentralised giving, this may not be the total figure. We have no information relating to the beneficiaries.

In kind support

The company's main area of non-cash support is gifts in kind.

Employee-led support

Cargill encourages all employees to share their time and talent to enrich its communities. Its corporate employee volunteerism policy allows employees to take up to two hours per month from work to participate in Cargill-sponsored community service or volunteer opportunities.

Carillion plc

Company registration number 3782379

24 Birch Street, Wolverhampton WV1 4HY

01902 422431; Fax: 01902 316165

Website: www.carillionplc.com

Correspondent: Richard Tapp, Director of Legal Services, Chairman to the Appeals Committee

Chairman: Philip Rogerson

Chief Executive: John McDonough

Year end	Turnover	Pre-tax profit
31/12/2007	£3,330,700,000	£94,400,000

Nature of company business
Providing expertise in commercial and industrial building, refurbishment, civil engineering, road and rail construction and maintenance, mechanical and electrical services, facilities management and PFI Solutions

Subsidiaries include: Asprea Ltd, Planned Maintenance Engineering Ltd, Sovereign Hospital Services Ltd

Main locations: Wolverhampton, Leeds, Manchester, Liverpool, London, Bristol, Brentford, Glasgow

UK employees: 23,434

Total employees: 30,746

> **Charitable donations**
> 2007: £150,000
> 2006: £145,000
> 2005: £84,000
> 2004: £76,000
> 2003: £67,000
>
> Total community contributions: £967,583
>
> Membership: BitC

Community involvement

Carillion's community involvement benefits one of the following groups:charities, not for profit organisations representing economically and socially disadvantaged groups, schools and youth organisations, environmental, development and cultural groups, organisations which aid social economic regeneration, campaigns addressing specific community needs and social enterprise.

Furthermore, the charitable objective should be close to or have some connection with the group and its objectives, whilst the subject matter should be tangible and be able to reflect the support given by the group, i.e. the group should receive some public recognition.

The value of investment includes staff time spent in community involvement activities or on full or part-time secondments, provision of professional services, gifts in kind, use of facilities and loan of assets as well as financial contributions such as cash donations and payments or sponsorships.

Applications

In writing to the correspondent.

Information available: The company produces a Social Responsibility Report. Its website contains comprehensive details of its community activities.

Corporate giving

In 2007, the company made total community contributions of £967,583 (2006: £830,158) of which cash donations comprised £150,000 (2006: £145,000). Main beneficiaries included: Business in the Community; CRASH; RedR; Age Concern; and Wildlife trusts.

In kind support

This can include staff time spent in community involvement activities or on full or part-time secondments, provision of professional services, gifts in kind, use of facilities and loan of assets.

Employee-led support

Carillion businesses work closely with schools on raising awareness of the dangers of construction sites; staff conduct tours for children around sites during construction phases, helping them in CV writing and providing school work placements.

Payroll giving: The company operate a scheme.

Commercially-led support

Sponsorship: The company undertake good-cause sponsorship. Please address any proposals to the correspondent.

The Carphone Warehouse Group plc

Company registration number 3253714

1 Portal Way, London W3 6RS

020 8896 5000; Fax: 020 8896 5005

Website: www.cpwplc.com

Correspondent: (see 'Applications')

Chairman: John Gildersleeve

Chief Executive: Charles Dunstone

Year end	Turnover	Pre-tax profit
28/03/2008	£4,474,400,000	£124,100,000

Nature of company business
Independent retailer of mobile phones and services.

UK employees: 21,380

> **Charitable donations**
> 2008: £220,000
> 2007: £117,000
>
> Membership: BitC

Community involvement

Carphone Warehouse's two operating divisions each have their own partner charity. The distribution business supports

'Get Connected', and the UK Fixed Line division (TalkTalk) supports 'TreeHouse'. The company choose to back small charities that both relate to communication, so they can help them not only with fundraising, but also with the more practical and technical support that is often harder for charities to come by.

Applications

The company selects its own charitable partners. Unsolicited appeals are unlikely to succeed.

However, through employees fundraising efforts it may possible to get additional support from The Carphone Warehouse Foundation.

Corporate giving

In 2007/08, the company made charitable donations of £220,000 (2006/07: £117,000) which were mainly directed to supporting its charity partners – Get Connected and TreeHouse.

'TalkTalk has pledged £500,000 to TreeHouse over the next five years and will be working closely with the charity on a joint project to launch an online service to guide and connect families affected by autism through the maze of practical and emotional information. TalkTalk also continues to donate 1p for every call made to our directory service 118111 to TreeHouse.

'In addition to this, TalkTalk has continued its commitment to make broadband internet access a right not a privilege, and this year launched the TalkTalk Innovation in the Community Awards to do just that. We believe that internet access can change lives for the better but there are still a lot of people who have never used a computer and do not have access to modern technology.

'Non-profit making organisations and charities in need of funding for an internet-related project were invited to put forward requests for cash for technology products and services. Thirty organisations were chosen to win £2,000 each to help fund their particular project, as well as receiving TalkTalk free broadband.

'The 2007 winners represented a cross section of the UK, from Dundee Women's Aid, a charity that plans to create podcasts for survivors of abuse to encourage other women to seek help, through to Northern Seams, a charity that wishes to use the internet to inspire textile artists with learning difficulties.'

In kind support

Get Connected: 'In addition to raising funds for Get Connected, The Carphone Warehouse also covers all overheads for the charity including providing accommodation, equipment and IT support, covering utility bills, covering the cost of phone lines, printing, mailings and internet connection and offering marketing support and training free of charge.'

The two organisations have also worked together on the issue of children bullied beyond the school gates as a result of 'cyber bullying'– intimidation via mobile phones, email and instant messaging – and compiled a Phonewise guide that among other important issues included advice for parents and children to combat cyber bullying. The guide is available on carphonewarehouse.com/safety

Handset recycling: 'As part of our commitment to recycling and re-use we are offering a service for customers to dispose of their old handsets and raise valuable funds for our charity partner Get Connected and The Carphone Warehouse Foundation at the same time.

'For every handset recycled we currently donate £10 to be split equally between the two charitable organisations mentioned above. In the past 12 months we have raised over £112,000 in this way. In December 2007 we also started sending out a recycle bag with every purchase made via our direct channels. This has seen an increase of over 400% in handsets being returned for recycling or re-use.'

Employee-led support

To support employees with their own fundraising initiatives, the company set up The Carphone Warehouse Foundation over four years ago. Small grants are awarded to charities nominated by employees, or where there is a large demand for the same charity (for example Children in Need), a larger grant will be made on behalf of the whole company.

Employees who commit to taking part in fundraising activities organised by the company are awarded extra days holiday.

Payroll giving: Employees are given the opportunity to sign up for Give as you Earn and have raised over £26,000 for charity since the service was launched in 2006.

Catlin Group Ltd

Company registration number 3114348

3 Minster Court, Mincing Lane, London EC3R 7DD

020 7626 0486; Fax: 020 7623 9101

Website: www.catlin.com

Correspondent: Stephen Catlin, Chief Executive

Chairman: Sir Graham Hearne

Chief Executive: Stephen Catlin

Year end
31/12/2007

Nature of company business
Catlin Group Ltd is an international specialist property and casualty insurer and reinsurer.

Main locations: Birmingham, Glasgow, Ipswich, Kent, Leeds

Charitable donations
2007: £116,565

Community involvement

The group makes charitable contributions and encourages employee involvement in community programmes. Catlin during 2007 established a group-wide charity committee to manage the group's charitable contributions and activities on a centralised basis.

For 2008 the group has selected two charity partners in the UK (see below) to which Catlin will make a significant financial donation during the year.

Charity of the year – Havens Hospice and Starlight Children's Foundation (2008).

Applications

In writing to the correspondent.

Corporate giving

In 2007, the group made charitable donations worldwide of around £116,565. We do not how much of this was given in the UK.

Historically, the group has provided support to the Sick Children's Trust of which Stephen Catlin is chairman.

Employee-led support

The group has instituted several programmes which encourage employee charitable giving and involvement. Through one of these programmes the group grants time off to employees participating in Catlin- or Lloyd's-approved community involvement projects.

Under another programme the group will match funds raised by an employee on behalf of a qualified charity up to an annual limit of US$1,000 (about £500).

Payroll giving: In the UK the Give As You Earn programme is in operation. Through this the group will match qualified employee charitable contributions up to a limit of £600 per year.

Cattles plc

Company registration number 543610

Kingston House, Centre 27 Business Park, Woodhead Road, Birstall, Batley WF17 9TD

01924 444466; Fax: 01924 448324

Website: www.cattles.co.uk

Correspondent: Community Investment Officer

Email: cr@cattles.co.uk

Chairman: Norman Broadhurst

Chief Executive: David Postings

Year end	Turnover	Pre-tax profit
31/12/2007	£822,200,000	£165,200,000

Nature of company business
Provision of financial services such as secured and unsecured personal loans, hire purchase credit facilities and merchandise.

Subsidiaries include: Dial 4 A Loan, Welcome Financial Services Ltd, Shopacheck Financial Services, The Lewis Group, Welcome Car Insurance

Main locations: Oxford, Manchester, Leeds, Hull, Glasgow, Nottingham, Cleckheaton, Birstall

UK employees: 4,719

Charitable donations

2007: £409,946
2006: £433,621
2005: £422,180
2004: £262,727
2003: £93,480

Total community contributions: £456,745
Management costs: £178,340

Membership: BitC

Community involvement

Cattles primarily targets its support towards three key areas:

- raising standards in financial education
- improving the welfare of young people
- addressing the issues of social disadvantage.

Community investment in these areas is achieved in three ways:

- developing partnerships with a small number of key charities or community organisations whose work relates to Cattles' business activities and which follows its key areas of activity
- involving employees in its community and charity work and favouring projects where its employees have a particular interest
- contributing to charitable initiatives, through cash donation and gifts in kind (including time and resources), which relate to the activities of the business and reflect the three elements of its community investment policy.

Cattles' community investment officer identifies and co-ordinates the company's community activities, particularly volunteering projects. A charity panel of senior managers, chaired by the company secretary, evaluates requests for financial donations over £5,000 against formal criteria in line with its community investment policy.

Donations under £5,000 are considered by the CR Manager and approved directly by the company secretary.

Exclusions

No support for general appeals, fundraising events or individuals.

Applications

In writing to the correspondent.

Corporate giving

In 2007, community contributions in the UK totalled £456,745 (2006: £518,319) which comprised cash donations (£409,946), gifts in kind and employee volunteering time. An additional £178,340 was expended on managing the company's community investments. We have no details of the grant beneficiaries.

Cattles continued its support for the promotion of financial education through financial assistance and collaborative projects with Credit Action and DebtCred.

In kind support

The company may occasionally provide support through gifts in kind.

Employee-led support

Employee volunteering: 'We promote colleague volunteering [through] 'Hands Up', our volunteering initiative, [which] encourages colleagues at all sites to make an impact in their local communities. We work closely with Business in the Community's national employee volunteering programme, Cares … .

'However, we are increasingly sourcing our activities through the 'Hands Up' committees at our main office locations, because they can develop closer links with local communities and better understand their needs.

'In 2007, our colleagues undertook 2,644 hours of volunteering – an increase of 28% on 2006.'

CashMatch: 'This initiative gives colleagues the opportunity to double their fundraising for charitable and community activities. We will contribute an equal amount, up to £500, provided certain criteria are met. In 2007, we 'CashMatched' 22 projects with contributions totalling £7,420.

'We continue to support the Leeds Project, brokered by Outward Bound. This gives schoolchildren from disadvantaged areas in Leeds the opportunity to participate in a five-day residential programme of activities to promote self-confidence and personal development.

'We have also participated in the Employability Programme for Young Learners in Nottingham. This is a pilot scheme to encourage young people to undertake vocational qualifications.'

Payroll giving: 'The Cattles 50/50 Club is a scheme is operated by the company.

'This is our Give As You Earn (GAYE) scheme. Colleagues' contributions are matched by the company and donated to five charities selected by colleagues' online votes on our intranet. Colleagues who participate are also entered into a monthly prize draw.

'In July 2007 we donated £10,600 to each charity: Macmillan Cancer Support, The Children's Variety Club, Promise Dreams, Mencap and Henshaws Society for the Blind. Over 700 people now participate in the scheme – 15% of all our colleagues.'

Caudwell Holdings Ltd

Company registration number 2679207

Minton Hollings, Shelton Old Road, Stoke-on-Trent, Staffordshire ST4 7RY

Website: www.caudwell.com

Correspondent: (see applications section)

Year end	Turnover	Pre-tax profit
31/12/2005	£2,120,999,000	£91,968,000

Nature of company business
Supply of communications products and services.

UK employees: 8,248

Community involvement

The Caudwell Group is perhaps better known through its high street presence in the form of 'phones 4 u'. The related Caudwell Charitable Trust (Charity Commission no. 1079770), has all its administration and management costs covered by the company. It is not clear however, whether it makes any direct cash donations to the trust.

The aims of the Caudwell Charitable Trust are:

- to make donations to specific child cases of sickness, specialised medical requirements and dying wish holidays, applicants must be under the age of 18
- to buy or build a property to aid children/children's charities
- to continue to fulfil its half a million pound pledge to the NSPCC Full Stop Campaign.

In September 2006, the Caudwell Group announced that it had completed the sale agreement with Doughty Hanson & Co. and Providence Equity Partners, under which the private equity firms have acquired the entire group for a total of £1.46 billion. It is uncertain what affect this will have on the company's giving policy.

Exclusions

The Charity does not give to other charities or trusts, with the exception of the NSPCC.

Funding currently unavailable for:
- building works or fixtures and fittings
- gardening, fencing or hard surfacing
- domestic appliances, decorating, clothing or bedding
- respite care/childcare/residential holidays
- dolphin therapy/faith healing
- PCs or laptops, unless specifically designed for those with special needs
- motor vehicle purchase/lease/adaptations/accessories
- equipment repair, maintenance or adaptations
- holidays (excluding holidays for terminally ill children)
- lifts (internal or external)
- play equipment (not including therapy tricycles).

Applications

All applications must be made on one of the charity's application forms. This can be downloaded from its website, along with full guidelines (www.caudwellcharity.co.uk). Alternatively send a request by email (charity@caudwell.com) or telephone 0845 3001348 and leave your name and address, spelling out any difficult words on the charity's answering machine.

Corporate giving

The Caudwell Charitable Trust

In 2005, grants to 954 children totalling £1,797,500 were made.

Employee-led support

The Caudwell Group's first fundraising campaign 'Raise the Roof' was funded by a weekly jeans day, where company employees donated £1 to come to work in their jeans every Friday.

Cazenove Group plc

Company registration number 4152491

20 Moorgate, London EC2R 6DA

020 7155 5000; Fax: 020 7155 9800

Website: www.cazenove.com

Correspondent: Bernard Cazenove, Trustee
Email: bernard.cazenove@cazenove.com

Chairman: David Mayhew

Chief Executive: Robert Pickering

Year end	Turnover	Pre-tax profit
31/12/2005	£66,500,000	£48,100,000

Nature of company business
Investment bank.

Main locations: Salisbury, London, Oxford, Chester

UK employees: 1,154

Community involvement

Following an announcement in late 2004 that Cazenove would combine its investment banking business with JPMorgan's to form a new jointly-owned company called JPMorgan Cazenove, and the subsequent demerger of Cazenove Capital Management, the situation regarding its future level of community support has become a little unclear.

In previous years, the closely associated Cazenove Charitable Trust (Charity Commission no. 1086899), has received a number of substantial donations from the Cazenove Group. A number of major projects identified during this period subsequently had the responsibility for the large grants they were to receive taken on by the Cazenove Group. As a result, the company did not provide the trust with any substantial donations for the period May 2004 to December 2005.

Until it becomes clearer as to how the relationship between the new joint venture and the charitable trust is to proceed, the information given here relates to the trust.

The main areas of its work are homelessness, unemployment and children who are disadvantaged, although any charities that Cazenove employees are involved in may also be eligible. It is likely that preference is given to organisations around its offices, which are in Chester, London (Southwark), Oxford and Salisbury.

Applications

Applications to the trust should be made in writing and sent to: Bernard Cazenove, Trustee, Cazenove Charitable Trust at the above address.

Corporate giving

Cazenove Group Ltd made no charitable donations during 2005.

Cazenove Charitable Trust

According to the Cazenove Group's annual report and accounts for the year, the trust made donations totalling £153,500. No details of the beneficiaries were available.

Employee-led support

Previously, staff were available for volunteering and secondments, with fundraising efforts of staff are matched to a maximum of £1,000. We do not know if this is still the case.

Payroll giving: The company is involved in the payroll giving scheme organised by CAF.

CEF Holdings Ltd

Company registration number 316018

141 Farmer Ward Road, Kenilworth, Warwickshire CV8 2SU

01926 514380

Website: www.cef.co.uk

Correspondent: M S Jacobs, Trustee

Managing Director: Roger Thorn

Year end	Turnover	Pre-tax profit
30/04/2007	£592,000,000	£11,669,000

Nature of company business
Principal activity: electrical wholesalers and manufacturers.

Subsidiaries include: Dennis Vanguard International Ltd, City Electrical Factors Ltd

Main locations: Kenilworth

UK employees: 4,534

Community involvement

Historically, the company covenants its donations to the Janet Nash Charitable Trust (Charity Commission no. 326880), with the company and trust having a common director and trustee – Mr M S Jacobs.

The trust usually prefers to support a number of the same organisations each year, particularly children's and sickness/disability charities. In previous years some preference has been shown for causes in the West Midlands and Warwickshire where the company is based.

Exclusions

No support for advertising in charity brochures, animal welfare, appeals from individuals, fundraising events, overseas projects, political appeals, religious appeals or local appeals not in areas of company presence.

Applications

We have recently been informed by The Janet Nash Charitable Trust that: 'The charity does not, repeat not, ever, consider any applications for benefit from the public'.

All potential beneficiaries are identified personally by the trustees. Unsolicited applications are not, therefore, acknowledged.

Corporate giving

In 2006/07, the company made charitable donations of £438,000 (2006: £353,000) of which, we believe, some £375,000 was donated to the trust. We have no information regarding the beneficiaries of the balance of £65,000.

The Janet Nash Charitable Trust

In 2006/07, the trust had an income of £376,383 and made grants totalling £411,469. Of this, £122,340 was donated to organisations and £289,129 to individuals.

Benefiting organisations included: Martha Trust – Hereford (£55,000); The Royal Air Force Museum (£25,000); Dyslexia Institute (£6,000); and SENSE (£5,000).

In kind support

The company has given gifts in kind and rewired charities' properties on certain occasions.

Celtic Energy Ltd

Company registration number 2997376

Heol Ty Aberaman, Aberdare, Rhondda Cynon Taff CF44 6RF

01685 874201; Fax: 01685 878105

Website: www.coal.com

Correspondent: Richard Walters, Managing Director

Managing Director: Richard Walters

Year end	Turnover	Pre-tax profit
31/03/2007	£50,781,000	£1,614,000

Nature of company business
The main activities are opencast coal mining, land redevelopment and associated activities.

Main locations: Aberdare

UK employees: 268

Total employees: 268

> ### Charitable donations
> 2007: £24,470
> 2006: £26,000

Community involvement

Celtic Energy Ltd is the successor in South Wales to the former British Coal Corporation that was privatised by the government in 1994 and was responsible for all of British Coal's opencast mining activities in South Wales. Celtic Energy's community programme is mainly focused on the local communities around the company's sites.

Previous information provided suggested that support is given in three ways (see below). For all three categories, the company tends to support local schools, youth groups and disability organisations. National charities are only ever supported where they are working specifically in the area of the company's sites.

The three categories supported are:

- encouraging communication and education
- setting up site liaison committees to ensure community involvement
- Providing support to local schools, charities, sporting groups and local organisation.

Exclusions

No support for political or religious appeals. Local appeals not in areas of company presence.

Applications

In writing to the correspondent.

Corporate giving

In 2007, the company made cash donations in Wales of £24,470 (2006: £26,000). We have no details of the beneficiaries.

Previously, we were advised that each site has a local liaison fund which distributes money in support of local voluntary organisations. There also existed a central community budget. Donations from this were used to support organisations that fell outside the remit of the local liaison funds, but we are unsure if this still exists.

In kind support

The company has an educational programme, distributing information packs to schools on opencast mining, and encourages pupils to visit its operations. Support is also given through gifts in kind.

CEMEX UK Operations

Company registration number 249776

CEMEX House, Coldharbour Lane, Thorpe, Egham, Surrey TW20 8TD

01932 568833; Fax: 01932 568933

Website: www.cemex.co.uk

Correspondent: Chief Administrator for Charities

Chairman: Lorenzo Zambrano

Year end	Turnover	Pre-tax profit
31/12/2006	£1,031,987,000	(£45,102,000)

Nature of company business
Principal activities: production and supply of materials for use in the construction industry.

Main locations: Rugby, Barrington, South Ferriby, Rochester, Egham

UK employees: 5,709

> ### Charitable donations
> 2006: £14,567
> 2005: £37,000
> 2003: £186,000
> 2002: £215,000

Community involvement

Formerly RMC Group plc the company was taken over by CEMEX UK in 2005.

To facilitate the company's charitable community support it established the CEMEX UK Foundation in 2006 (Note: This is not a registered charity).

CEMEX UK Foundation

The activities of the foundation cover a number of key areas including the company's charity of the year, supporting employees volunteering and matched funding of employees fundraising efforts.

The foundation will also consider applications for financial and in kind support for community activities in the vicinity of company operations (there are over 450 locations in the UK).

However, these small scale donations still require approval by the foundation.

Grants are also available under the Landfill Tax Credit scheme through the CEMEX Community Fund. Further support for environmental projects is available via the Rugby Group Benevolent Fund.

In addition to the above CEMEX's website provides community news relating to its major sites at Rugby, Barrington, Rochester and South Ferriby. The emphasis appears to be on supporting local causes/projects along with nationwide support for initiatives involving community safety.

Charity of the Year: Butterfly Conservation (2007).

Exclusions

No support for circular appeals, animal welfare, appeals from individuals or advertising in charity brochures.

Applications

In writing to the correspondent. All appeals are considered by a monthly committee which decides what to support.

For further information about applications to the Rugby Benevolent Fund, please contact Ian Southcott, UK Community Affairs Manager at CEMEX House in Rugby.

Corporate giving

The latest 2006 annual report and accounts for CEMEX UK Operations declared a charitable donations figure for the year of £14,567 (2005: £37,000). This seems on the low side considering the 'substantial support' given to the charity of the year and the matched funding of employees fundraising efforts. However, as CEMEX chose not to reply to our request for information, this figure must remain along with the omission of any value concerning in kind support.

The company's website does, however, provide quite comprehensive details of some of the projects it has been involved in. For example:

Rehabilitating offenders – During 2007 CEMEX UK worked with a leading environmental regeneration charity, Groundwork, to support former offenders. To help them back to work, the former offenders assisted with a restoration project and learnt woodland management skills at Stanwell Quarry. The project aimed to provide the social and employment skills necessary for offenders to join or re-enter the workplace following a prison sentence.

Educational projects – Again in partnership with Groundwork (Hertfordshire), CEMEX UK supported educational projects, such as one with Green Lanes Primary School in Hatfield, where pupils studied quarrying, and learnt how the industry has influenced the local and wider environment.

Conservation issues – For 14 years CEMEX UK has published an annual conservation book with leading not-for-profit organisations to highlight conservation issues and support fundraising programmes. In 2007, it signed a memorandum of Understanding and published 'Birds & People' with BirdLife international. Through this book CEMEX UK hope to raise awareness amongst the public of the importance of bird conservation, and of the fact that declining bird populations are primarily due to habitat loss, something it is working to redress in the UK as part of its quarry restoration programmes.

The CEMEX Community Fund

The fund operates under the Landfill Communities Fund, to provide funding for community projects within 3 miles of a CEMEX quarry or landfill with grants. Support is available to a small number of projects with grants ranging from £1,000 to £15,000.

Under the Landfill Tax Credit scheme donations totalling £180,000 were made in 2006/07. Details of the beneficiaries and how to apply are available at: www.cemexcf.org.uk

Rugby Group Benevolent Fund

Projects seeking support must conform to a number of criteria before consideration can be given. For example, projects should be located in communities close to existing or former Rugby Cement sites and applicant organisations have charitable status. Projects benefiting current or former employees and their relatives will support an application.

Recent support includes: £500,000 to Myton Hospice; £125,000 to Church Lawford Village Hall; £22,000 to Rugby Volunteer Centre for a minibus; and £13,500 to Barrington Village Hall for roof repairs.

In kind support

Environment: CEMEX has worked with the Wildlife Trust and Suffolk Wildlife Trust in restoring quarry sites it is no longer extracting aggregates from. These provide both nature reserves and leisure facilities for the local community.

Employee-led support

The company foundation not only supports employees in their volunteering activities on behalf of the charity of the year, but also, to a lesser extent, where employees are giving their own time on behalf of a local community or charitable organisation.

For appropriate activities and charities matched funding may also be given up to a maximum of £250 per employee.

Centrica plc

Company registration number 3033654

Millstream, Maidenhead Road, Windsor, Berkshire SL4 5GD

01753 494000; Fax: 01753 494001

Website: www.centrica.com

Correspondent: Community Relations

Email: community@centrica.com

Chairman: Roger Carr

Chief Executive: Sam Laidlaw

Year end	Turnover	Pre-tax profit
31/12/2007	£16,300,000,000	£1,949,000,000

Nature of company business
Centrica's principal activities are the provision of gas electricity and energy related products and services. The group also operates gas fields and power stations and provides roadside assistance and other motoring services.

Subsidiaries include: British Gas Trading Ltd, Dyno Holdings Ltd, Accord Energy Ltd, British Gas Services Ltd, GB Gas Holdings Ltd, Hydrocarbon Resources Ltd

Main locations: Windsor

UK employees: 28,849

Total employees: 35,410

Charitable donations

2007: £4,065,000
2005: £6,700,000
2004: £5,800,000

Total community contributions: £4,485,000
Management costs: £678,000

Membership: BitC, L B Group

Community involvement

'Over and above the impact of our day-to-day operations, we seek to address issues of wider social concern that are relevant to our business. We focus our resources where we can make an effective contribution and enable our employees to get involved in community activities. To make a real difference, we must focus on those social issues that are most closely aligned with our business.

'Our approach is characterised by:

- systematic management based on clearly identified objectives
- long-term partnerships with community organisations and charities
- ongoing evaluation of our contributions and the impacts they achieve.'

Exclusions

Since Centrica focuses its investments in areas aligned with its business and strives to avoid any conflicts of interest, it does not offer support to individuals, animal welfare organisations, building projects, political or denominational groups, arts bodies or sports groups.

Applications

In writing to the correspondent.

Corporate giving

In 2007 the company made community contributions of £4.5 million in the UK, including £4.1 million in cash donations. Beneficiaries during the year included: British Gas Energy Trust (£1.1 million); Help the Aged; Save the Children; Scope; and RNIB.

In kind support

Centrica provides in kind support from computers and IT equipment to office furniture and stationary.

Centrica works with a range of charities and community organisations to support vulnerable customers and tackle fuel poverty. It is also involved in educational initiatives to raise awareness of energy efficiency and work with partners to support skills development.

Employee-led support

Employees are encouraged and enabled to 'make a positive impact' on their local communities. In 2007 staff were involved in more than 10,000 hours of volunteering activities. This equated to around £194,000 in cash terms.

Employee fundraising is matched to a maximum of £150 per employee per year.

Payroll giving: A scheme is in operation.

Commercially-led support

Sponsorship: This form of support is only considered if it forms part of a specific project with which the company is already involved.

Charter plc

Company registration number 2794949

322 High Hollborn, London WC1V 7PB

020 3206 0800; Fax: 020 7242 9149

Website: www.charterplc.com

Correspondent: James Deeley, Company Secretary

Chairman: Lars Emilson

Chief Executive: Michael Foster

Year end	Turnover	Pre-tax profit
31/12/2007	£1,451,100,000	£178,100,000

Nature of company business
The company is an international engineering company. The group's activities are concerned with welding and cutting, air and gas handling and specialised engineering. Products are manufactured internationally to meet customer requirements across a wide range of industries around the world.

Subsidiaries include: Howden Compressors Ltd, ESAB, Howden Sirocco Ltd

Main locations: London

UK employees: 11,240

Charitable donations

2007: £90,000
2006: £58,000
2005: £84,000
2004: £50,000
2003: £100,000

Community involvement

The company, through its subsidiaries, is 'involved in number of social, community and sponsoring activities. Individual businesses may contribute to specific activities in their location.

Exclusions

No support for circular appeals, advertising in charity brochures, appeals from individuals or local appeals not in areas of company presence.

Applications

In writing to the correspondent. Many more applications are received than can be supported, and applicants are advised to consider if there is any particular reason why their appeal should be supported by the company. All applications will be answered.

Corporate giving

In 2007, the company and its subsidiaries donated £90,000 (2006: £58,000) to charities. However, only £8,581 (2006: £8,000) was donated to charities in the United Kingdom. Within the United Kingdom, donations were made in the year to support charities working in education (£500), medical research/support (£4,806) and community support (£3,275).

Chelsea Building Society

Company registration number 102B

Thirlestaine Hall, Thirlestaine Road, Cheltenham, Gloucestershire GL53 7AL

01242 271526; Fax: 01242 271222

Website: www.thechelsea.co.uk

Correspondent: Sally Davies, CR & Community Support Consultant
Email: sally.davies@thechelsea.co.uk

Chairman: T Harrison

Chief Executive: R Hornbrook

Year end	Pre-tax profit
31/12/2007	£63,000,000

Nature of company business
Building society providing low cost retail savings and mortgages.

Main locations: Bournemouth, Reading, Worthing, London, Maidstone, Oxford, Paignton, Norwich, Chatham, Cheltenham, Brighton, Bristol, Watford, Ipswich, Leicester, Guildford, Birmingham, Exeter, Plymouth, Southampton

UK employees: 1,018

Charitable donations

2007: £141,835
2006: £173,370
2005: £73,000
2004: £75,000
2003: £50,000

Membership: A & B

Community involvement

The society has recently given just under half of its total contributions to charity through the Chelsea Building Society Charitable Foundation (Charity Commission no. 1079292). However, as of October 2008, the foundation was reviewing its donations policy and the following is subject to change.

The primary focus of the foundation is to help relieve suffering and disadvantage and to benefit local communities. The foundation's priorities for the allocation of funds are:

- homelessness
- the disadvantaged, vulnerable or socially excluded
- all forms of disability
- health – self help and voluntary groups
- encouraging prudent money management for example money advice services
- security and community safety.

Charity of the year (staff): Winston's Wish (2008).

Exclusions

Prior to the foundation's review of its donations policy, the following applied: The trustees will not usually consider grants for the following:

- activities which are mainly/usually the statutory responsibility of central or local government, or some other responsible body (except proposals for added support service)
- schools, universities and colleges (except for projects which will specifically benefit disabled students and are additional to statutory responsibilities)
- hospitals, medical centres, medical treatment research (except projects extra to statutory responsibilities)
- collecting funds for later distribution to other charities or individuals
- political or pressure groups
- profit distributing organisations
- individuals or individual fundraising efforts, including expeditions or overseas travel
- general fundraising events, activities or appeals
- fabric appeals for places of worship and the promotion of religion
- animal welfare or wildlife
- charities which have substantial reserves (in excess of 12 months expenditure) or in serious deficit
- the purchase of minibuses or other vehicles
- the acquisition, renovation and refurbishment of buildings.

No support for applications from outside of the society's areas of operation within the UK.

Applications
Chelsea Building Society Foundation

NB. As of October 2008, the following message was posted on the foundation's website: The Charitable Foundation's donation policy is currently being reviewed. Please do not submit an application, until further notice.

Previously, the following applied: Applications can only be considered if made in writing on the foundation's application form, which can be obtained on the website or by request from Linda Van Delden on 01242 271520 or linda.vandelden@thechelsea.co.uk

The completed application form should be forwarded together with any supporting or background material together with a copy of the signed financial reports and accounts to the correspondent. All applications will be acknowledged and applicants will be notified of the result of their application as soon as possible, although this could take up to six months.

The trustees meet twice a year in May and November to consider donations. current details of the foundation's priorities and exclusions can be found at: www.thechelsea-charitable-foundation.co.uk

Normally only applications from registered charities will be considered. Exceptionally, applications from self-help groups, voluntary organisations, projects with charitable aims/for charitable activities will be considered if the application is supported by a registered charity.

Chelsea Building Society

Further information about the society's community support programme can be obtained from the correspondent.

Information available: The society's 2008 Corporate Responsibility Report is available online.

Corporate giving

In 2006/07 the society made charitable donations totalling £141,835 (2005/06: £173,370) of which £60,075 (2005/06: £83,649) was paid to the foundation.

During the year the foundation made grants totalling £75,000. These ranged between £250 and £5,000 and were distributed to a variety of organisations, including the following: The Heart of Kent Hospice and People First (£2,000 each); Bromley Mencap (£1,575); Family Space in Hesters Way (£1,025); and Go Terrace Club, City Gate Community Projects, Walsall Disability Centre, TRAX – The Oxfordshire Motor Project, Pathway Workshop and Cruse Bereavement Care (£1,000 each).

In kind support

The society continues to support community projects through the provision of advice and expertise to charities and local community groups which enables them to raise funds for themselves.

Employee-led support

In recent years the Chelsea staff charity has also benefited from matched funding by the foundation on a £ for £ basis. Last year's (2007) staff charity, the British Heart Foundation received an additional £2,049 on this basis, which matched the sum raised by the staff's individual fundraising events.

The society also encourages its staff to volunteer, examples of which include:

Lynworth School – Every Thursday lunchtime volunteers visit Lynworth Primary School in Cheltenham and help the children with their reading. Since November 2007, a team of 13 have been giving up their lunch hours to do this.

Soup Kitchen – Every week two Chelsea volunteers help at the Cornerstone Community Centre's lunchtime soup kitchen in Whaddon, providing a valuable service to disadvantaged people.

Cheshire Building Society

Company registration number 103B

Castle Street, Macclesfield, Cheshire SK11 6AF

01625 613612; Fax: 01625 617246

Website: www.thecheshire.co.uk

Correspondent: Maria Mathieson, CSR & Sponsorships Manager

Chairman: Robert E Hough

Chief Executive: Karen McCormick

Year end	Turnover	Pre-tax profit
31/03/2007	£45,000,000	£7,200,000

Nature of company business
Building society provider of competitive investments, mortgages, and complementary financial services.

Main locations: Bolton, Maccelesfield, Mold, Wigan, Stockport, Warrington, Chester, Crewe, Buxton, Accrington

UK employees: 792

Charitable donations

2007: £196,000
2005: £268,000
2004: £700,000

CRM figure: £70,151

Membership: BitC

Community involvement

The society requested that we remove its entry 'with immediate effect'. However, we maintain our policy of including all relevant companies in our research findings.

The following information is taken from the society's website and annual report for 2007.

The Cheshire established a community support programme in 1997 which has benefited many local charities and community groups in the North West. The focus for this has been the Cheshire Foundation through which the society seeks to improve the way it offers support to the local community, making it more transparent and sustainable and easier for charities to apply.

The foundation makes decisions on funding applications through a board of foundation members made up of staff, members and people from the local community. The application form is simple and aims to make it easy to apply and for people to see exactly how it fits with the society's policy.

The foundation meets quarterly to consider applications for funding for larger sums and, for smaller projects, has introduced a new Community Contribution Award which enables local branch managers to support projects in their area.

The society's support falls into five areas:

Educational projects – Working together with organisations to develop understanding and value of education at all levels. The society will look at projects that are linked to the national curriculum and are also interested in innovative ways of bringing education to life for everyone.

Community support – This can encompass a wide range of activities, except those listed under 'Exclusions'.

Social inclusion – Support will be considered for projects that aim to ensure everyone, regardless of their background, experience and circumstances, can gain access to the services and facilities they need to achieve their own potential in life.

Grass roots sport – Consideration will be given to funding projects that will motivate young people into becoming active and so improve their physical, mental well being and their social awareness.

Financial education – As part of its responsibility as a lender, the society may offer support to projects that encourage financial awareness and also those that aim to alleviate the problems associated with debt.

Exclusions

No support for political, religious or military organisations, overseas charities, appeals from individuals, third-party funding or NHS funding

Applications

For the Cheshire Foundation you can download an application form and guidance notes from the society's website.

The foundation/society adheres to a strict policy of funding only registered charities that are either based in the North West, or that have a project or event taking place in its branch operating region.

The foundation meets on a quarterly basis in January, April, July and October. No funding decisions will be made outside these dates so take this into consideration when applying.

For the Community Contribution Award, your organisation must still fall into one of the categories supported by the society, but it is not necessary for your organisation to be a registered charity.

You can download an application form as above, or pick one up from your local branch.

If you require any further information about either of the above, please contact the society's corporate social responsibility team on 01625 652466, who will be happy to provide you with advice and guidance.

Corporate giving

In 2007, the society donated £196,000 to the development of its CSR agenda, which in turn helped to generate extra revenue of just under £75,000 for the organisations concerned. The Cheshire Foundation provided funding for 64 projects, including: Cerebral Palsy Sport – Boccia training weekend; The Anthony Nolan Trust; Children's Adventure Farm Trust; and Careline.

Financial education – In 2007, the society continued to work in conjunction with other organisations to develop and deliver educational programmes, which encourage young people to act responsibly when dealing with their finances both now and in the future.

Employee-led support

Staff members raised over £13,000 for their chosen charity partners – the Children's Adventure Farm Trust, Scope North West, Guide Dogs for the Blind, Barnardo's North West and the Donna Louise Trust.

Commercially-led support

Sponsorship: *Charity* – the society sponsors Barnardo's Business Breakfasts in the North West.

Cause-related marketing: *Affinity cards* -thesociety operates several affinity account schemes with, for example, NCH (previously the National Children's Home) and 21 hospices in the region. Each year the Cheshire donates from its own funds, 1% of the average balance of the accounts back to the affinity partner. From active accounts in 2007, these partners received cheques totalling £70,151.

Chevron Ltd

Company registration number 145197

1 Westferry Circus, Canary Wharf, London E14 4HA

020 7719 3000

Website: www.chevron.com

Correspondent: Public Affairs (Sponsorship)

Managing Director: R B Brown

Year end	Turnover	Pre-tax profit
31/12/2006	£6,262,300,000	£44,900,000

Nature of company business
Principal activities of the company are the refining, distribution, transport and marketing of petroleum products.

Subsidiaries include: Gulf Oil Refining Ltd, Gulf Oil Ltd, Pelmans Petrolium Ltd, Telegraph Service Stations Ltd, De La Pena Lubricants Ltd, Gulf Service Stations Ltd, Curran Petrolium Ltd

Main locations: Pembroke, Aberdeen

UK employees: 1,150

Charitable donations
2006: £400,000
2005: £300,000

Community involvement

The following information is taken from Chevron's United Kingdom Fact Sheet: 'In the United Kingdom, Chevron seeks to build partnerships that support the economic and social fabric of the communities where we work [Aberdeen, Pembroke, Swindon and East London]. We sponsor projects that support education, the environment, the arts and social enhancement'.

Exclusions

No support for circular appeals, individuals, local appeals not in areas of company presence, large national appeals or overseas projects.

Applications

In writing to the correspondent. Normally a decision will be made within 3 weeks of receiving an application. Decisions cannot be discussed over the telephone.

Corporate giving

Chevron Ltd made charitable donations in the UK in 2006 of £400,000 (2005: £300,000). Although we don't have details of the beneficiaries, we do know that Chevron's donations to NCH have topped £1 million (admittedly with funds raised thanks to the support of employees and customers).

In addition to the above, a further £212,000 (2005: £159,000) was donated Chevron North Sea Ltd in its area of operation.

Commercially-led support

Sponsorship: *The arts* – Chevron sponsors the Texaco Young Musician of Wales competition – a biennial competition open to children up to 18 years of age. It also sponsor programmes with the Royal Scottish Academy of Music and Drama.

Education – Chevron support education programmes in east London and supply science activity packs for Welsh schoolchildren. Chevron has supported Youth Action Northern Ireland for the last 17 years, helping children through a series of developmental programmes.

Environment – 'Focus Environment', an environmental photography competition for Scottish secondary schools is sponsored by the company.

The Pembroke refinery has expanded its community outreach by sponsoring environmental education in local schools.

Chrysalis Group plc

Company registration number 946978

The Chrysalis Building, Bramley Road, London W10 6SP

020 7221 2213; Fax: 020 7221 6455

Website: www.chrysalis.com

Correspondent: Jeremy Lascelles, Group Chief Executive
Email: enquiries@chrysalis.com

Chairman: Chris Wright

Chief Executive: Peter Lassman

Group Chief Executive: Jeremy Lascelles

Year end	Turnover	Pre-tax profit
31/08/2007	£56,375,000	(£5,971,000)

Nature of company business
Music publishing; the production and international marketing of records, CDs and music-related videos; the ownership and exploitation of sound recording masters; the wholesale distribution of CDs, DVDs, videos, books, magazines and other music-related products.

UK employees: 193

Charitable donations

2007: £21,786

Community involvement

Chrysalis's website contains the following statement regarding its community support in the UK: 'We recognise the benefit we can bring to the communities where we operate and to the wider world through charitable activities. We will make a positive contribution to the lives of the people around us, and facilitate our staff in contributing to worthwhile causes.'

Unfortunately, no information regarding what these benefits might be, or for whom, was available.

Exclusions

No support for religious or political activities.

Applications

In writing to the correspondent.

Corporate giving

In 2007, the group made charitable donations of £21,786 (2006: £15,246). No details of the beneficiaries were available.

In its annual report and accounts for the year, the group stated that: 'The Chrysalis Radio stations carried out many community-focused activities over the year and have contributed to many local charitable causes, assisting them in raising considerable sums of money.

'Both the Galaxy and Heart Networks ran a number of campaigns during the year, focusing on important social, community and cultural issues.'

Please note, however, that the group has since disposed of its radio station interests.

Employee-led support

The group appear to be active in encouraging its employees to volunteer and fundraise on behalf of worthwhile charitable causes, e.g. 'The Music Industry has initiated many charitable projects throughout the world and our music division staff both in the UK and overseas have devoted time to these worthwhile causes.'

Ciba UK plc

Company registration number 3249009

Charter Way, Macclesfield, Cheshire SK10 2NX

01625 421933; Fax: 01625 619637

Website: www.cibasc.com

Correspondent: Patrick Gorman, Head of Communications Northern Europe

Year end	Turnover	Pre-tax profit
31/12/2007	£403,943,000	£21,425,000

Nature of company business
Ciba is a global speciality chemicals company developing and supplying materials and processes that provide colour, care, durability and performance for a wide range of consumer and industrial products.

Main locations: Grimsby, Blackburn, Leatherhead, Paisley, Macclesfield, Clayton, Bradford

UK employees: 1,588

Charitable donations

2007: £146,500

Community involvement

Support is given to local communities in the areas in which the company is located. Its approach is to adapt community relations programmes so that they meet local neighbourhood needs. Initiatives include the encouragement of dialogue with its local communities through local community newspapers and the provision of feedback to enable the creation of appropriate activities. Charitable focus is placed upon issues including science and technology, and the environment.

Exclusions

Past information provided suggested that there is no support available for appeals from areas that are not located near to a Ciba UK plc site. No support for political or religious appeals or requests for individual aid/sponsorship.

Applications

In writing to the correspondent.

Corporate giving

In 2007, the company made cash donations in the UK of £146,500. This was broken down as £22,500 for charitable purposes and £124,000 for scientific, educational, research and welfare purposes. No other information was available.

In kind support

Science and Education: 'Ciba Specialty Chemicals is especially interested in programmes that help children, young people and families and that foster understanding and respect between community members. In particular, activities and programmes that improve science education will not only contribute to the creation of new generations of innovative scientists but will also improve the broader public understanding of our products and our industry.'

Environmental Excellence: The company website states 'The nature of our business means that responsible behaviour in all aspects of environment, health and safety (EHS) is essential.

Ciba Specialty Chemicals seeks to use its expertise in this area and reinforce its reputation by supporting community initiatives that improve the natural environment and that encourage efficient use of resources'.

Employee-led support

'Ciba UK plc encourages employee outreach, fundraising and involvement in local communities and recognizes the benefits for the individual, for the community and for the company. We will continue to support our employees in endeavours that improve the quality of life where they live and work.'

Some past examples of this have involved employees volunteering to help local causes including creating and maintaining a garden for The Harbourne Resource Centre, a specialist residential unit and day care centre for people with Alzheimer's disease and functional mental health needs; funding Netherlands Special School Christmas party and organising community challenges at Woodlands Cricket Club and Netherlands Scout Hut.

CIBC World Markets plc

Company registration number 2733036

Cottons Centre, Cottons Lane, London SE1 2QL

020 7234 6000; Fax: 020 7234 6691

Website: www.cibcwm.com

Correspondent: Angela Carter, Children's Miracle Selection Committee
Email: angela.carter@cibc.co.uk

Year end
31/10/2007

Nature of company business
Investment bank.

Main locations: London

Charitable donations
2007: £125,336
2006: £213,067
2005: £192,500

Management costs: £98,091

Community involvement

The company's charitable fundraising is mainly focused on 'Miracle Day', which occurs on the first Wednesday of December each year. All commission generated on that day is donated to children's charities via the CIBC World Markets Children's Miracle Foundation (Charity Commission no. 1105094). Further funds are raised at a number of events hosted by CIBC World Markets for clients and staff.

The key objectives of Miracle Day include:
- to raise the quality of life for children in the communities served by CIBC World Markets
- to demonstrate CIBC's dedication in helping to prepare children for future success
- to encourage volunteerism and foster community involvement on the part of CIBC's employees.

To be eligible to apply for funds groups must be UK/European registered charities which are well-administered, with a record of achievement and the potential for success which will bring a tangible benefit to children in the communities where they live within Europe.

Funding is also available under the CIBC World Markets Children's Foundation Arts Grant initiative. The grant is available to UK registered charities working with disadvantaged, disabled or sick children up to the age of 19. It will encompass a variety of charities whose innovative work stimulate children and encourage their creative participation, interaction and self-expression, through the performing arts and entertainment or the provision of therapy through the mediums of art or music.

For further information on the Arts Grant, please contact the correspondent.

Future plans

The following quote is taken from the foundation's 2006/07 annual report and accounts: 'As a result of the CIBC-Oppenheimer transaction, and the resultant sale of a key Miracle Day fundraising division of CIBD, the activities of the foundation are likely to be scaled back in the medium to long term.'

Exclusions

No grants are made to individuals, political or advocacy groups, private schools, endowment funds, grant making trusts or groups that limit their activities to a specified ethnic or religious group. Grants are for one year only and cannot be recurrent. Organisations which have applied unsuccessfully in each of the three previous years may not apply (although these prior applications do not affect any applications made after the one year break).

Applications

In the first instance, eligible charities should apply using the online application form.

The selection process begins in January with a review of the charities that have been nominated by clients, suppliers, professional affiliates or CIBC World Markets' employees. Charities who have applied independently via the Children's Miracle website are also considered. Any charities that do not comply with the specific Eligibility Guidelines are discarded. Charities that have been declined for more than three concurrent years are also removed, but can reapply a year later. The remaining charities are then invited to submit a proposal to the Children's Miracle Selection Committee, detailing their support for children's needs and their specific donation requests.

Full details of how to complete this stage of the application are given on the company's Children's Miracle Day website at: www.cibcwmmiracleday.com

Up to 14 charities may be selected to receive a donation from the forthcoming year's fundraising efforts. The selection process is usually completed by mid-May.

Corporate giving

CIBC World Markets Children's Miracle Foundation

In 2006/07, the foundation had an income of £286,709 of which £125,336 came from fees and commission earned by employees on Miracle Day (2006) and £57,751 from other donations and fundraising events. Operating and event costs of £98,091 (2006: £80,000) were covered by the company.

Grants totalling £203,500 (2006: £285,700) were made during the year, including those to the following nine charities chosen by the selection committee: CHICKS (£27,500); Children Action (£18,500); Children Heart Federation (£20,500); The Eveline Children's Hospital Appeal (£25,000); Hope (£22,500); Naomi House Children's Hospice (£25,000); Rainbow Trust (£24,000); SNAP (£24,000); and The Promise (£17,500).

The foundation's annual report and accounts usefully gives information on the background of each of the nine selected beneficiaries, the projects supported and the impact of the funding.

The foundation made additional donations to Junior League of London (£5,000), The Prince's Trust (£2,500) and Burnaby Blue Foundation (£1,500).

Arts Grant – Due to difficult market conditions and consequently lower fundraising levels, no arts grant was awarded for year end 2007.

In kind support

CIBC World Markets recognise that there are many essential regulatory requirements that charities are now expected to fulfil. To assist those charities it already works with via the foundation, in kind support is given in helping them deal with the practicalities of, for example:

- risk and health and safety assessments
- IT security policies
- business recovery planning
- money laundering.

CIBC has also provided meeting and training facilities and associated catering for meetings and seminars held by the chosen charities at its offices.

Employee-led support

In addition to the donation of commissions, staff are encouraged to take part in sponsored activities, which have included runs, bungee jumps and slimming programmes.

Citibank International plc

Company registration number 1088249

Citigroup Centre, 33 Canada Street, Canary Wharf, London E14 5LB

020 7986 4000; Fax: 020 7986 2266

Website: www.citigroup.com

Correspondent: See 'Applications'

Chairman & Chief Executive: Wiliam J Mills

Year end	Turnover	Pre-tax profit
31/12/2007	£1,154,000,000	£283,000,000

Nature of company business
Provider of financial services.

Main locations: London

UK employees: 4,798

Charitable donations

2007: £1,177,607
2005: £964,000
2004: £895,000
2003: £880,000

Membership: BitC, L B Group

Community involvement

Part of the Citi group, the company has three areas of giving:

- financial education – such as educational projects, encouraging improved consumer habits and the creation of wealth in a community
- educating the next generation – such as literacy development, technology-based curriculum resources, career and education preparation activities, teacher training and access to arts and culture
- building communities and entrepreneurs – such as affordable housing, economic development, welfare-to-work schemes, community infrastructure, sustainable development, disaster appeals and community-based health and welfare services.

Citi Foundation

The Citi Foundation reviews proposals by invitation only from organisations with demonstrated successes in its outlined focus areas. It has sharply focused its grant making to satisfy ongoing commitments in these areas throughout the world.

The focus areas are:

- microfinance and micro entrepreneurship
- small and growing businesses
- education
- financial education
- environment – sustainable enterprise.

Fuller information on each of these is available on the company's website.

Exclusions

The Citi Foundation does not provide funding related to:

- advertising, special events, dinners, telethons, benefits, or fundraising activities
- religious, veteran or fraternal organisations (unless they are engaged in a project benefiting an entire community)
- individuals
- political causes, campaigns, or candidates
- memorials
- private foundations
- requests deemed as 'pass-through' funding
- matched funds.

Applications

Please note that the foundation will not review any unsolicited letters of inquiry or proposals.

Corporate giving

In 2007, the company declared UK charitable donations of £82,607 (2006: £77,662). We have no details of the beneficiaries. However, in addition to this localised giving, the company, through the Citi Foundation, makes substantial grants to UK-based organisations (see below).

Citi Foundation

In 2007, over 2,500 grants were made totalling more than US$72 million (around £36 million). Of this, US$2.2 million (£1.1 million) was given in the UK in 28 grants. Major beneficiaries included: Charities Aid Foundation America (11 grants totalling US$865,000/£433,000); Young Enterprise East Midlands, London and Scotland (four grants totalling US$253,000/£127,000); Friends of the Prince's Trust Inc. (US$275,000); and Habitat for Humanity Great Britain (US$200,000/£100,000).

Please note that the grants to the Charities Aid Foundation were on behalf of the following: African Caribbean Diversity, Business in the Community, Bygrove Primary School, Create Arts Ltd, Greenwich and Lewisham Roots and Wings, Specialist Schools an Academies Trust, Speakers Trust, Teach First, Tower Hamlets Education Business Partnership, Toynbee Hall, UK Career Academy Foundation.

Employee-led support

The Citigroup Volunteer Incentive Programme is designed to recognise employees who devote their personal time to community service and to support the organisations for which they volunteer. To qualify for a grant, employees must complete 50 hours of service with an approved organisation during a 12-month period or less. The Citigroup Foundation will award a US$500 grant to the organisation that benefits from the employee's service. Individual employees may only request one grant per calendar year.

If you wish your group to be added to the approved list of recognised organisations, it is necessary for at least five or more Citigroup employees to put your name forward.

Citroën UK Ltd

Company registration number 191579

221 Bath Road, Slough SL1 4BA

0870 606 9000

Website: www.citroen.co.uk

Correspondent: Kay Jackson, Human Resources

Year end	Turnover	Pre-tax profit
31/12/2006	£1,030,623,000	£12,964,000

Nature of company business
The main activity of the company is the importing and the sale of Citroën cars, vans and replacement parts.

Main locations: Slough

UK employees: 552

Charitable donations
2006: £71,000

Community involvement

We have been unable to obtain any useful information from the company regarding its community support. Nevertheless, having spoken to the relevant department, it does appear to deal with any applications received on an ad hoc basis.

Previously, we were advised that, as general rule, it is better to apply for support through the individual dealerships.

Exclusions
No support for individuals.

Applications
In writing to the correspondent.

Corporate giving

In 2006, the company made contributions for charitable purposes of £71,000 (2005: £69,000) to BEN, the motor trade benevolent fund.

Clariant UK Ltd

Company registration number 172280

Calverley Lane, Horsforth, Leeds LS18 4RP

0113 258 4646; Fax: 0113 239 8473

Website: www.clariant.co.uk

Correspondent: Company Secretary

Chairman: J H B Ketteley

Year end	Turnover	Pre-tax profit
31/03/1999	£374,200,000	£100,000,000

Nature of company business
The principal activities are the manufacture and distribution of speciality chemical products and the manufacture, assembly and distribution of technical safety systems.

Subsidiaries include: Lancaster Synthesis Ltd, A P Chemicals Ltd

Main locations: Aberdeen, Ruabon, Leeds, North Allerton, Pontypridd, Wigan, Selby

Total employees: 2,963

Charitable donations
1999: £46,147
1998: £60,255

Community involvement

Formerly BTP plc, the company was taken over in March 2000 by Swiss-based Clariant. As it is 'not company policy to complete questionnaires', we have been unable to update the information we hold. We therefore repeat the information previously published

Donations are given to local charities in areas of company presence.

Exclusions

No support for advertising in charity brochures, animal welfare, appeals from individuals, overseas projects, political appeals, religious appeals or local appeals not in areas of company presence.

Applications

Appeals should be addressed to the appropriate company or branch manager.

Corporate giving

In 1999, the company donated £46,000 to charity. No further information was provided.

Clinton Cards plc

Company registration number 985739

The Crystal Building, Langston Road, Loughton, Essex IG10 3TH

020 8502 3711; Fax: 020 8502 0395

Website: www.clintoncards.co.uk

Correspondent: Secretary to the Chairman

Chairman: Don Lewin

Chief Executive: Don Lewin

Managing Director: Clinton Lewin

Year end	Turnover	Pre-tax profit
29/07/2007	£539,800,000	£15,124,000

Nature of company business
The main activity is the specialist retailing of greeting cards and associated products. The group has 730 stores nationwide.

Subsidiaries include: Strand Cards Ltd, The Greeting Store Group Ltd, Macnoll Ltd, Papertree Ltd, Plumbell Ltd, GSG Holdings Ltd

Main locations: Loughton

UK employees: 5,810

Charitable donations

2007: £309,000
2006: £360,000
2005: £300,719
2004: £188,670

Community involvement

Donations are principally made to national charities, with numerous smaller payments made to other charities.

Applications

In writing to the correspondent.

Corporate giving

Since 2005, the company's charitable donations have remained fairly consistent and in 2007 stood at £309,000 (2006: £360,000). The main beneficiaries were: Marie Curie Cancer Care, Barnardos; British Heart Foundation; The Grown Up Congenital Heart patients association; and RSPCA.

Close Brothers Group plc

Company registration number 520241

10 Crown Place, London EC2A 4FT

020 7655 3100; Fax: 020 7655 8917

Website: www.closebrothers.co.uk

Correspondent: R D Sellers, Company Secretary

Chief Executive: Colin D Keogh

Group Managing Director: Stephen Hodges

Year end	Pre-tax profit
31/07/2007	£190,192,000

Nature of company business
Close Brothers is the parent company of a group of companies involved in merchant banking.

Subsidiaries include: Air & General Finance Ltd, Reabourne Technology Investment Management Ltd, Kingston Asset Finance Ltd, OLIM Ltd, Braemar Finance Ltd, Eidos Partners, Winterflood Investment Trust, Surrey Asset Finance Ltd, Armed Services Finance Ltd, Winterflood Securities Ltd, Commercial Finance Credit Ltd, Mortgage Intelligence Ltd

Main locations: London

UK employees: 2,571

Charitable donations

2007: £187,000
2006: £147,000
2005: £323,000
2004: £46,000

Membership: BitC

Community involvement

We were advised that the company does not participate in surveys. We understand from its annual report, however, that it provides two types of charitable donation. Firstly, group companies contribute to recognised charities where significant humanitarian or environmental incidents have occurred. Also staff may have their own charitable fundraising endeavours matched by the group; the group continue to look to improve staff awareness of this to encourage participation.

Exclusions

No support for appeals from individuals.

Applications

In writing, in the first instance, to the correspondent.

Corporate giving

In 2007, the company's charitable donations amounted to £187,000. Unfortunately, we have no details of the beneficiaries.

Employee-led support

Payroll giving: The Give As You Earn scheme is in operation.

Clydesdale Bank plc

Company registration number SC001111

30 St Vincent Place, Glasgow G1 2HL

0141 248 7070; Fax: 0141 204 0828

Website: www.cbonline.co.uk

Correspondent: (see 'Applications')

Chairman: Malcolm Williamson

Chief Executive: Lynne Peacock

Year end	Turnover	Pre-tax profit
30/09/2007	£1,209,000,000	£404,000,000

Nature of company business
The company is a wholly owned subsidiary of National Australia Bank Ltd. It offers a full range of banking services through 230

branches in Scotland, England and the Isle of Man. In addition to general banking business, these services include investment management, executor and trustee work, insurance broking, debtor finance, corporate finance, corporate trusteeship, registration and global custody.

Subsidiaries include: Edinburgh

Main locations: Glasgow

UK employees: 5,700

Charitable donations

2007: £280,000
2006: £221,000
2001: £81,000
2003: £100,000

Membership: A & B

Community involvement

In 1987, Clydesdale Bank plc in Glasgow became a member of National Australia Bank Group. In October 2004, the entire business and undertakings of Yorkshire Bank plc (also a member of the National Australia Bank Group) were transferred to the Clydesdale.

Clydesdale Bank takes active steps to support external organisations and promote improvement in areas where its business has an impact. Its community activities operate on four complementary platforms: charitable donations; community partnerships; charity partner; staff involvement.

Charitable donations – In July 2008, the bank launched the Yorkshire and Clydesdale Bank Foundation (not a registered charity) to formalise its tradition of supporting people and their local communities. The foundation will provide support to registered charities, not-for-profit organisations, community and other voluntary organisations. In terms of financial support four key areas of focus have been selected at this time:

» the advancement of environmental protection or improvement
» the advancement of citizenship through initiatives that support and promote volunteering
» the advancement of financial education including initiatives that promote accessibility to both financial education and financial services
» the advancement of community development through initiatives that build and strengthen the communities in which we operate.

Wherever possible, applications from registered charities or not-for-profit organisations, community and voluntary sector organisations will take priority over applications from individuals, political or religious organisations.

Activities should take place inside the bank's 'beneficial area' (areas covered by branches of the bank, financial solutions centres, and HQ locations).

Project expenses will be prioritised rather than direct salary expenses.

Charity partnerships – Through its community partnership programme, the bank works with a select number of groups to address shared issues of concern. Its current community investment priorities are numeracy and financial capability. These are supported through two flagship programmes – Count Me In and Count and Grow – details of each are available on the bank's website.

As well as proactively seeking suitable community partners, Clydesdale Bank also welcomes approaches from charities or not-for-profit organisations that can demonstrate their ability to manage a community project and evaluate its success objectively. Details of what you need to do are given in the Application section.

Charity partner – In February 2008, Clydesdale and Yorkshire Banks announced the launch of a brand-new charity partnership initiative with Help the Hospices. An initial donation was made by the bank along with a commitment to match pound for pound any money raised on behalf of the charity by the bank's staff.

The bank is a member of Scottish Business in the Community.

Exclusions

No response to circular appeal. No support for advertising in charity brochures, animal welfare, appeals from individuals, overseas projects, political appeals, religious appeals, capital projects or salary expenses, or local appeals not in areas of company presence.

Please note that due to the volume of partnership proposals received the company is unable to discuss these by telephone, or to meet with organisations prior to receiving a written proposal.

Applications
Charitable donations

To apply to the foundation for funding, you will need to print off the Yorkshire & Clydesdale Bank Foundation application form from the bank's website. Complete the application and post it to, Yorkshire & Clydesdale Bank Foundation, 20 Merrion Way, Leeds LS2 8NZ together with relevant supporting information.

The foundation shall respond to all applications it receives. It may take up to four months to process an application, so please be aware of this before contacting the foundation for a decision.

Successful grant recipients may be contacted for the purposes of assessing the impact of the donation.

Charitable partnerships

If your organisation satisfies these criteria and would like to consider a partnership there is no application form to complete. All we ask is that you send us a proposal setting out the following:

» a brief history of your organisation
» confirmation of charitable or not-for-profit status
» how your organisation is funded, including details of any other corporate partners
» a copy of your annual report/review and accounts
» the sponsorship fee and project costs
» benefits to Clydesdale Bank as sponsor and an outline of how you plan to acknowledge support from the bank
» supporting PR/Communications plan (outline only) – you may wish to include press cuttings of previous projects or partnerships
» details on how you plan to evaluate the impact of your project.

Completed proposals should be sent to: Irene Swankie, Community Affairs Manager, Clydesdale Bank Exchange, Level 7, 20 Waterloo Street, GLASGOW G2 6DB.

Please note that in view of the volume of proposals received, the bank is unable to enter into discussion by telephone or to meet with organisations prior to receiving a written proposal.

Corporate giving

In 2006/07, Clydesdale Bank made charitable donations of £280,000 (2005/06: £221,000). Previously, national grants ranged from £100 to £10,000. Local grants ranged from £50 to £500.

Major grant recipients in 2006/07 included: The British Heart Foundation and the group's new charity partner, Help the Hospices which received a grant of £10,000.

The group also helped younger generations through two dedicated programmes:

- Count Me In – is a children's numeracy programme in 148 libraries across Scotland and England. More than 1,200 canvas bags of numeracy materials have been provided to date, along with story time sessions, to teach children as young as one the value of learning to count. This programme plans to double its reach next year
- Count and Grow – has been rolled out to 305 primary schools across Scotland and England's West Midlands, to help children improve their mathematics skills.

Employee-led support

The bank actively promotes volunteering opportunities for its staff that allow them to volunteer during bank hours rather than in their own personal time. In recognition of the latter, however, a Staff Volunteer Grant programme rewards staff that do so by providing grants to charitable organisations which they work with in their own time. Grants of up to £500 are awarded quarterly.

Payroll giving: The Give As You Earn scheme is operated by the company. To date over 12% of the bank's staff are donating to charities and because of this.

Commercially-led support

Sponsorship: The bank sponsors the arts, sport and business-related organisations/events. Full details of the bank's sponsorship requirements are given on its website. The contact is:

Helen Everett, Brand & Sponsorships, 3rd Floor, 20 Merrion Way, Leeds, LS2 8NZ (Tel. 0113 247 2400).

Coats plc

Company registration number 104998

1 The Square, Stockley Park, Uxbridge, Middlesex UB11 1TD

020 8210 5000; Fax: 020 8210 5025

Website: www.coats.com

Correspondent: Jeannie Welch, PA to the Company Secretary

Chairman: Gary Weiss

Chief Executive: Michael Smithyman

Year end	Turnover	Pre-tax profit
31/12/2007	£840,600,000	£67,450,000

Nature of company business
Principal activities: manufacture, processing and distribution of sewing thread for industrial and domestic use, homewares and fashionwares.

Subsidiaries include: William Hollins & Co. Ltd, Jaeger Holdings Ltd, The British Van Heusen Co. Ltd, CV Home Furnishings Ltd, Hicking Pentecost Ltd, The Jaeger Co. Ltd, Pasolds Ltd, The Jaeger Company's Shops Ltd, Tootal Group Ltd, Tootal Thread Ltd

Main locations: Uxbridge, Glasgow

UK employees: 277

Total employees: 22,151

Charitable donations
2007: £14,000
2006: £16,000
2005: £11,000
2004: £66,055
2003: £38,500

Community involvement

Previous information suggested charities which the appeals committee would ordinarily support come under the following headings: education, the community, the arts, medical research and healthcare, and the environment. Beneficiaries are almost invariably closely associated with the company and its associates.

Applications
In writing to the correspondent.

Corporate giving

In 2007, the company made charitable donations of around £14,000 (2006: £16,000). We have no details of the beneficiaries.

The Coats Foundation Trust

We previously understood that the above foundation (Charity Commission no. 268735) received an annual donation from the company. This is not the case. Although historically associated with the company, the foundation's income is derived from investments.

However, the Coats Trustee Company Ltd, which administers the trust, includes directors from the. company. Educational awards in textile-related areas and for those with no previous educational degree are considered as priorities, as are individuals with long-term futures in the UK. The directors will consider applications from organisations which have a textile-related background and which could have a greater impact in this area. For example, the trust has established a 'Coats Doctoral Scholarship' with Nottingham Trent University which supports a PhD student in a textile-related discipline. In addition, the trust has supported a three-year North London Education Programme at Copthall School which is focused on developing needlecraft, hand knitting and textiles within the curriculum. This is due to expire in 2008. Post year-end, the board also agreed to support a three-year PhD placement at Leeds University's Colour Imaging Team.

In 2006/07 the foundation made grants totalling £165,545.

Employee-led support

Previous information stated monies raised by employee fundraising are matched by the company for certain selected charities. It is unknown whether this is still the case.

Commercially-led support
Sponsorship: *Education* – The company supports several academic appointments in a number of educational centres.

Cobham plc

Company registration number 30470

Brook Road, Wimborne, Dorset BH21 2BJ

01202 882020; Fax: 01202 840523

Website: www.cobham.com

Correspondent: James Streater, Director – CR & Sustainability
Email: james.streater@cobham.com

Chairman: G F Page

Chief Executive: A E Cook

Year end	Turnover	Pre-tax profit
31/12/2007	£1,061,100,000	£173,500,000

Nature of company business
Design and manufacture of equipment, specialised systems and components used primarily in the aerospace, defence, energy and electronics industries and the operation and maintenance of aircraft, particularly in relation to special mission flight operations.

Subsidiaries include: FR Aviation Group Ltd, European Antennas, Precision Antennas, Chelton (Electrostatics) Ltd, Flight Precision Ltd, Micromill Electronics Ltd, Flight Refuelling Ltd, Chelton Radomes, Wallop Defence Systems, Chelton Ltd, Slingsby Aviation Ltd, Racal Antennas, FR Aviation Services Ltd, Chelto Radomes Whitney, Slingsby Engineering Ltd, ERA Technology, FR Aviation Ltd

Main locations: Almondbank, Bournemouth, Southampton, Nottingham, Wimbourne, Teeside, Kinloss

UK employees: 2,426

Total employees: 8,990

Charitable donations
2007: £67,744
2006: £77,846
2005: £51,469
2003: £36,324

Community involvement

The company restricts its charitable support to causes in the Dorset area where it is based and to business-related national organisations. Within this area it will consider charities in the fields of children/youth, education, enterprise/training, fundraising events, medical research, science/technology and sickness/disability. Advertising in charity brochures will also be considered, again if Dorset-based.

Exclusions
No support for animal welfare, individuals, the arts, elderly people, environment/heritage, overseas projects, political appeals, religious appeals, social welfare or sport.

Applications
In writing to the correspondent.

Corporate giving

In 2007, the company made charitable donations totalling £67,744 (2006: £77,846). The following breakdown was provided in relation to donations in excess of £200 each:

- business enterprise charities £11,203
- armed services £10,100
- health charities £2,450
- local interest charities £1,482
- rescue service charities £1,155.

We have no details of the individual organisations receiving support. However, the 2007 annual report and accounts does state: 'Throughout 2007, Cobham continued to be a corporate sponsor and partner of the following organisations: Soldiers, Sailors, Airmen and Families Association (SSAFA); The Science Museum; and Young Engineers'.

In kind support
In kind support can be provided to local initiatives in the form of the free use of meeting rooms and premises, the donation of surplus computer equipment and furniture, and the offer of places on in-house training courses.

Coca-Cola Great Britain

Company registration number 1724995

1 Queen Caroline Street, Hammersmith, London W6 9HQ

020 8237 3000; Fax: 020 8237 3700

Website: www.coca-cola.co.uk/citizenship

Correspondent: The Secretary, The Consumer Information Centre
Email: corporateresponsibility@eur.ko.com

Chairman: S Guha (President)

Year end	Turnover	Pre-tax profit
31/12/2007	£131,338,000	£17,153,000

Nature of company business
Principal activity: production of soft drinks.

Main locations: East Kilbride, Aberdeen, Peterlee, Wakefield, Warrington, Nottingham, Coventry, Peterborough, Northampton, Milton Keynes, Bristol, Cardiff, Uxbridge, London

UK employees: 4,600

Charitable donations
2006: £1,405,000
2005: £937,000
2004: £851,000

Total community contributions: £1,615,000
Management costs: £285,000

Membership: A & B, BitC

Community involvement

Unless otherwise stated, the community investment information given here refers as whole to Coca-Cola Great Britain (CCGB) which effectively comprises Coca-Cola Holdings (United Kingdom) Ltd and Coca-Cola Enterprises Ltd (CCE).

Each year Coca-Cola contribute to the local communities in which it operates, both through its own community investment activities and through local community sponsorships, charitable donations, employee volunteering and the provision of in kind donations. Each year since 2004,

CCGB's community contribution has represented at least 1% of annual pre-tax profits

Support is also available through the Coca-Cola Youth Foundation and, to a lesser extent, from The Coca-Cola Foundation based in the United States.

Applications

In writing to the Consumer Information Centre at the above address.

Corporate giving

In 2007, Coca-Cola Holdings (United Kingdom) Ltd declared charitable contributions of £453,000 comprising: Community (£10,000); Sports and recreation (£111,000); and Environmental awareness (£332,000). However, as we were unable to obtain a figure for Coca-Cola Enterprises, we include below the combined figures for the two divisions (CCGB and CCE) for 2006 as quoted on the company's website.

(Please note that the financial information given for 2007 refers to Coca-Cola Holdings (United Kingdom) Ltd ONLY).

During 2006, Coca Cola's total community contribution was valued at £1.9 million. This comprised £1,405,000 in cash, £210,000 in time/in kind support and £285,000 in management costs.

Community programmes

Coca-Cola invests in programmes at each of its sites for the benefit of local communities. The focus is on helping young people achieve their best. This in two ways – supporting them through education and encouraging them to take part in physical activity. Examples are given below:

- supporting young people through education – education centres
- supporting young people through education – with Business Dynamics
- encouraging active lifestyles
- Coca-Cola Youth Foundation
- business mentoring
- Mission Antarctica
- Ronald McDonald House Charities.

Fuller information is available about each of the above on Coca-Cola's website.

Coca-Cola Youth Foundation

'The 'Coca-Cola' Youth Foundation (CCYF) was established in 1995 to make a positive contribution to the development of young people in Great Britain. Under the terms of its constitution, it is empowered to make donations to such charitable institutions as chosen by the trustees, but particularly to those that help young people fulfil their potential through education or sports. Since its inception, the Foundation has donated in excess of £1 million to numerous good causes in Great Britain, from small, local charities to nationwide appeals.'

In 2007, the 'Coca-Cola' Youth Foundation chose to support three projects: Groundwork; Special Olympics; and Action for South Africa.

The Coca-Cola Foundation

A grant of $200,000 (around £100,000) was donated to the University of Edinburgh in 2007 to provide continued support for the 'Scholarships Change Lives' programme.

Employee-led support

Coca-Cola Great Britain works in active partnership with the London Borough of Hammersmith & Fulham Education Business Partnership (LBHFEBP) to support a programme of business mentoring to young people from schools local to its offices in Hammersmith.

Payroll giving: A scheme is operated by the company.

Commercially-led support

Much of Coca-Cola's community support is classified under 'cause-related marketing' and thus does not feature in any donations account.

Colgate-Palmolive (UK) Ltd

Company registration number 178909

Guildford Business Park, Middleton Road, Guildford GU2 8JZ

01483 302222; Fax: 01483 303003

Website: www.colgate.co.uk

Correspondent: PA to the VP & General Manager

VP & General Manager: Christopher Pedersen

Year end	Turnover	Pre-tax profit
31/12/2006	£192,136,000	£3,989,000

Nature of company business
Producer of toothpastes, soaps, toiletries, detergents and similar products.

Main locations: Guildford

UK employees: 143

Charitable donations

2006: £4,202
2005: £33,267
2003: £44,000

Community involvement

Despite requests for information about what the UK arm of the company is doing to support charitable and community organisations here, no information was forthcoming.

The parent company in the United States supports children's causes across the world concerned with promoting the importance of oral health through education and prevention. The primary focus is to reach children in schools through videos, storybooks, songs, CD-ROMs and interactive activities.

Applications

In writing to the correspondent.

The global grants programme address is:

Colgate-Palmolive Company
Contributions Department
300 Park Avenue
New York, NY 10022
USA

Corporate giving

In its 2006 annual report and accounts, Colgate-Palmolive UK Ltd declared charitable donations of £4,200 (2005: £33,267). No details of the beneficiaries were available.

Although this latest donation figure is below the threshold for inclusion in our research, it may be a one-off given previous donations made by the company. We are therefore leaving details of the company available for the time being.

However, given the agreed closure of the Salford manufacturing plant in mid-2008, the imperative to continue giving any meaningful level of support to organisations in the IUK may well cease to exist.

Communisis plc

Company registration number 173691

Wakefield Road, Leeds LS10 1DU

0113 277 0202; Fax: 0113 271 3503

Website: www.communisis.com

Correspondent: Martin Young, Company Secretary

Chairman: Peter Hickson

Chief Executive: Steve Vaughan

Year end	Turnover	Pre-tax profit
31/12/2007	£290,590,000	£7,871,000

Nature of company business
The principal activities of the group are the manufacture of printed products for direct marketing, forms, stationery and critical transactional products (such as statements and cheques) and the provision of print sourcing services.

Subsidiaries include: Waddington Labels Ltd

Main locations: Liverpool, Leicester, Newcastle-upon-Tyne, London, Bath, Crewe, Manchester, Lisburn, Rickmansworth, Leeds

UK employees: 2,016

Charitable donations
2007: £32,191
2006: £31,125
2005: £34,250
2003: £24,245

Community involvement

Communisis provides support for various local charities sited all over the UK; however it does give preference to those in areas of company presence.

It did, however, make the following statement in its 2007 annual report: 'We recognise, however, that at a time when profits and dividends have been under pressure we must be sensitive in the area of corporate giving, and we continue to monitor carefully our charitable donations'.

Previously, we were advised that the company prefers to support charities concerned with animal welfare, children/youth, education, the elderly, enterprise/training, environment/heritage, fundraising events, medical research,

overseas projects, science/technology, sickness/disability, social welfare and sport.

Exclusions
Sports sponsorship for individuals.

Applications
The company does not provide support for advertising in charity brochures, the arts and political or religious appeals. No support is given towards appeals from individuals.

Information Available: The company produces a Social Responsibility Report which is contained within its Annual Report.

Corporate giving

In 2007, the company made cash donations totalling £32,191 (2006 £31,215). We have no details of the beneficiaries.

Employee-led support
Company support for employees' volunteering/charitable activities is determined on each individual case.

Compass Group plc

Company registration number 4083914

Rivermead, Oxford Road, Denham, Uxbridge UB9 4BF

01895 554554; Fax: 01895 554555

Website: www.compass-group.com

Correspondent: Carol Wilkinson, Corporate Affairs

Chairman: Sir Roy Gardner

Chief Executive: Richard Cousins

Year end	Turnover	Pre-tax profit
30/09/2007	£10,268,000,000	£436,000,000

Nature of company business
The principal activity is the provision of contract food services to business and industrial organisations around the world.

Subsidiaries include: Eurest, Select Service Partner Ltd, National Leisure Catering Ltd, Payne & Gunter Ltd, Select Service Partner Airport Restaurants Ltd, Letheby & Christopher Ltd

Main locations: Uxbridge

UK employees: 66,105

Total employees: 361,327

Charitable donations
2007: £1,162,000
2006: £1,556,000
2005: £1,340,000
2003: £1,157,000

Management costs: £710,000

Membership: BitC

Community involvement

Compass states on its website that: 'We are proud of the strong track record we have in community engagement. Since 1996 the Compass in the Community programme has recognised the best community-based initiatives run by our businesses and teams across the world, focused on tackling social exclusion, improving employability and promoting sustainability and diversity. The programme rewards those initiatives that have the greatest impact by providing additional funding.'

Exclusions

The company does not support advertising in charity brochures, animal welfare, individuals, the arts, elderly people, heritage, medical research, overseas projects, political or religious appeals and science/technology.

Applications

In writing to the correspondent.

Corporate giving

In 2006/07, the company made worldwide community contributions of £1,162,000. We do not know what proportion of this was given in the UK, but some of the beneficiaries are listed below.

Programmes recognised by Compass in the Community in the last year have included:

- All Leisure's project to support Zoe's Place, a hospice for babies at Alder Hey Hospital, Liverpool
- the Eurest team at Stirling Management Centre, Stirling University, Scotland have run the 'Hospitality Profession Promotion Programme' for the past three years. More than 300 pupils from three local schools have passed through the on work placements, with some attending one day a week and others progressing to Scottish Vocational Qualifications.
- the ESS team initiative for the rehabilitation of female prisoners provides training and support, including the chance to gain National Vocational Qualification catering qualifications, training in customer service, health and safety and basic food preparation.

In kind support

Compass have been working with the charity Training for Life which assists people from a socially excluded or long term unemployed background re-establish their self-esteem.

The company has also support the Hoxton Apprentice in London's Shoreditch. At the 100-seater Restaurant for Life, a team of apprentices, who were previously unemployed or homeless are trained and mentored by a complement of professionally qualified and experienced personnel over a six-month period. Following this, many move onto work placements or full-time employment with companies such as Whitbread or Compass.

Employee-led support

Employees undertaking voluntary work in the community are recognised by the company through the presentation of awards and donations to their nominated charities.

Payroll giving: this has generated more than £140,000, supporting over 87 different charities during 2007.

Congregational & General Insurance plc

Company registration number 93688

Currer House, Currer Street, Bradford BD1 5BA

01274 700700; Fax: 01274 370 754

Website: www.congregational.co.uk

Correspondent: Margaret Slater, Marketing Manager

Fax: 01274 700 767
Email: marketing@cgins.co.uk

Chairman: David Collett

Managing Director: Carlo Cavaliere

Year end	Turnover	Pre-tax profit
31/03/2007	£24,467,000	£496,000

Nature of company business
The transaction of general insurance business, in the form of the insurance for fire and other damage to property.

Main locations: Bradford

UK employees: 50

Charitable donations

2007: £102,000
2006: £3,330,000
2005: £260,000
2004: £120,000

Total community contributions: £11,500

Community involvement

The company is a wholly-owned subsidiary of The Congregational & General Charitable Trust (Charity Commission no. 297013). The trust was established to 'promote the Christian religion and in particular United Reformed Church and Congregational denominations and other churches which are of the protestant tradition'. It supports a wide range of churches, educational establishments, charitable organisations and community projects.

The trust regularly receives a proportion of company profits from the insurance company. A council of members are responsible for the administartion and management of the trust and all grants are made entirely on merit.

Exclusions

The company does not make political donations.

Applications

Applications to the associated trust should be made in writing to: David Collett, Secretary to the Trustees, Currer House, Currer Street, Bradford, West Yorkshire, BD1 5BA.

The closing dates for applications to be considered are 31 January and 31 July each year.

Corporate giving

The company make an annual Gift Aid contribution to the trust. In 2007, this amounted to £102,000.

Congregational & General Charitable Trust

In 2006/07, the trust had assets of £12.7 million, an income of £386,000 and made 58 grants totalling £204,000. Grants (with number in brackets) were broken down as follows:

- churches and other religious organisations £171,000 (49)
- other charities £17,000 (6)
- religious bursary payments £15,000 (2)
- colleges and schools £1,000 (1).

Employee-led support

Employees have supported various charities during the past 12 months via fundraising.

Commercially-led support

Sponsorship: The company undertake good-cause sponsorship.

Thomas Cook Group plc

Company registration number 742748

The Thomas Cook Business Park, Coningsby Road, Peterborough PE3 8SB

01733 417100

Website: www.thomascookgroup.com

Correspondent: (See 'Applications')

Chairman: Thomas Middelhof

Chief Executive: Manny Fontela-Novoa

Year end	Turnover	Pre-tax profit
30/12/2007	£6,607,510,000	£199,010,000

Nature of company business
The principal activity is the operation of leisure travel industry businesses in the UK, Ireland, mainland Europe, Scandinavia, Australia, Canada, Mexico and the USA. The group distributes through a range of retail outlets, telephone and e-commerce channels; operates tours for a range of customers to destinations worldwide; has its own fleet of aircraft and cruise ships; and operates a portfolio of hotels and other resort properties.

Subsidiaries include: Going Place Leisure Travel Ltd, Late Escapes Ltd, The BTN Finance Company, Carousel Holidays Ltd, Sun International (UK) Ltd, Blue Sea Overseas Investments Ltd, The Travelworld Group Ltd, Blue Sea Investments Ltd, UKLG Ltd

Main locations: Rochdale

UK employees: 11.953

Total employees: 22,101

Charitable donations
2005: £15,000
2003: £76,000
2002: £637,795

Community involvement

In June 2007, My Travel Group plc and Thomas Cook AG merged to form Thomas Cook Group plc. As a consequence of this the new group's community support policy is only beginning to take shape. The following explanation is taken from the group's website:

'We firmly believe we should play an active part in the communities where most of our people live and work. Thomas Cook has a tradition of charitable donations, and of supporting voluntary activity and fundraising by employees.

'Historically, much of this work has been driven by employees themselves and supported by Thomas Cook or MyTravel. Partly as a consequence, the levels and nature of activity have been broadly spread and somewhat patchy. Going forward, we aim to develop a more co-ordinated policy, and to channel our support through a more coherent framework. We are currently discussing proposals to establish an independent Thomas Cook Foundation as the primary vehicle for the Group's corporate giving and for our support of employee volunteering and fundraising.

'The following targets have been established for 2008:

- maintain our partnership fundraising for organisations such as the Travel Foundation, who are an important part of our strategy on the environment and social issues in our destinations, working with local non-governmental organisations
- launch the Thomas Cook Foundation as a charitable foundation with an independent board of trustees. This will be the primary vehicle for the Thomas Cook Group's own corporate giving and for our support of employee volunteering and fund raising [NB. This is in fact a renaming of the MyTravel Charitable Trust – Charity Commission no. 1091673]
- focus our giving for 2008 on children, education and the environment.'

Exclusions

Generally, no support for projects outside of children, education and the environment.

Applications

All requests for charitable support within the stated guidelines should be addressed to: Benjamin Janes, The Thomas Cook Foundation, 6 Trull Farm Buildings, Tetbury, Gloucestershire GL8 8SQ. Email: tct@thetrustpartnership.com; Telephone: 01285 841902.

Corporate giving

The company's latest 2007 annual report and accounts do not give a charitable donations figure. It does, however, state the following: 'During the past year the business, our customers and our employees raised more than £1.2 million for charitable causes including local community projects, the Travel Foundation and the new Thomas Cook Children's Critical Care Unit at King's College Hospital'.

In kind support
This takes the form of gifts in kind.

Cookson Group plc

Company registration number 251977

165 Fleet Street, London EC4A 2AE

020 7822 0000; Fax: 020 7822 0100

Website: www.cooksongroup.co.uk

Correspondent: Mrs Pat Dowton, Appeals Administrator

Chairman: Robert Beeston

Chief Executive: Nick Salmon

Year end	Turnover	Pre-tax profit
31/12/2007	£1,620,000,000	£151,400,000

Nature of company business
The Cookson Group is a holding company for an internationally-based group of companies principally engaged in the manufacture of specialist industrial materials, equipment, processes and services for use in industry. The group is divided into three divisions: electronics, ceramics and precious metals.

The group is located mainly in the UK, North America and Western Europe.

Subsidiaries include: Wilkes Lucas Ltd

Main locations: London

Total employees: 13,390

Charitable donations

2007: £100,000
2006: £100,000
2005: £100,000
2004: £100,000
2003: £300,000

Community involvement

The company supports both national and local charities, with a preference for those based in the City or its environs. Preferred areas of support include: homelessness (especially regarding young people), advertising in charity brochures, animal welfare charities, children/youth, education, elderly people, environment/heritage, medical research, overseas projects, and sickness/disability charities.

Exclusions

No support for appeals from individuals; the arts; enterprise/training; fundraising events; political appeals; religious appeals; science/technology; social welfare; or sport.

Applications

In writing to the correspondent. Telephone approaches are not welcomed.

Corporate giving

In 2007, cash donations to UK charities totalled £100,000. We have no details of the beneficiaries, although previously, support has been given to Sight Savers International, The Bede Foundation, CBI Education Foundation, Council for Industry & Higher Education and Crisis.

Cooper Gay (Holdings) Ltd

Company registration number 998625

52 Leadenhall Street, London EC3A 2EB

020 7480 7322; Fax: 020 7481 4695

Website: www.coopergay.com

Correspondent: A A Mason, Secretary to the Cooper Gay Charitable Trust

Chairman: Frank Witthun

Chief Executive: Toby Esser

Year end	Turnover	Pre-tax profit
31/12/2007	£68,120,000	£10,933,000

Nature of company business
Insurance and reinsurance brokers.

Subsidiaries include: James Steele Insurance

Main locations: London

UK employees: 487

Charitable donations

2006: £78,197
2005: £229,092
2004: £215,177

Community involvement

Donations are made by deed of covenant to the Cooper Gay Charitable Trust (Charity Commission no. 327514). This trust has the following objects:

- to make grants/donations for provision or maintenance of facilities in hospitals, homes or other bodies/organisations
- to promote research and results of research to the public.

The trust also encourages staff of the company and its subsidiaries to submit applications for charities in which they have a particular interest.

Exclusions

Only registered charities are supported. No support for students.

Applications

In writing to the correspondent. Applications are considered twice a year.

Corporate giving

Although no donations were made in 2007 (2006: £78,197) by the company to the trust, we think this is a one-off occurrence.

Cooper Gay Charitable Trust

In 2006/07, the trust made grants totalling £105,575. These ranged between £250 and £2,500 each. Examples of beneficiaries include: Camp Rising Sun Charitable Foundation (£2,500); The Petersfield Society for Special Needs (£2,000); The Orchid Cancer Appeal, Arundel Castle Cricket Foundation, British Polio Fellowship and National Ankylosing Spondylitis Society (£1,000 each); Fire Service National Benevolent Fund, Life of Your Own and St Baldricks Foundation (£500 each); and Tuberous Sclerosis Society (£250).

The Co-operative Group

Company registration number 11761R

8th Floor, New Century House, Corporation Street, Manchester M60 4ES

0161 834 1212; Fax: 0161 833 1383

Website: www.co-operative.coop/corporate/

Correspondent: Sarah Kleuter, Senior Community Manager
0161 827 5950; Fax: 0161 827 6230
Email: sarah.kleuter@co-operative.coop

Chairman: Len Wardle

Chief Executive: David Anderson

Chief Executive: Peter Marks

Year end	Turnover	Pre-tax profit
12/01/2008	£9,075,500,000	£149,900,000

Nature of company business
The major activities of the Co-operative Group include food retailing, funerals, travel agents, pharmacies and farming. It is the parent organisation of Co-operative Financial Services, whose operating subsidiaries, the Co-operative Bank plc, smile and Co-operative Insurance Society, provide an extensive range of banking and insurance products. Within these financial statements, results are allocated into three key segments – Trading, Banking and Insurance.

Subsidiaries include: CIS Mortgage Maker Ltd, Millgate Insurance Brokers Ltd, Syncro Ltd, Farmcare Ltd, Hornby Road Investments Ltd, Goliath Footwear Ltd, CIS Policyholder Services Ltd, CRS (Properties) Ltd, Herbert Robinson Ltd, CIS Unit Managers Ltd

Main locations: Manchester

UK employees: 81,385

Charitable donations

2007: £8,300,000
2005: £4,400,000
2004: £3,900,000
2003: £1,350,000

Total community contributions: £10,000,000
Management costs: £400,000

Membership: BitC, L B Group

Community involvement

In general, the group's community investment strategy targets support at co-operative, self-help and community groups in the areas in which it trades. This support is measured using the London Benchmarking Group model, which includes both cash and in kind donations. The figure quoted includes all Co-operative Group units across the UK, but excludes commercial and arts sponsorship with direct commercial benefits as well as support for the wider co-operative movement (unless this has clear charitable purposes).

Charity of the Year: The Children's Society and DiabetesUK (2007)

Exclusions

Generally, no grants are made towards: projects which are in conflict with the group's ethical policy; funding political parties; religious appeals; the costs of individuals or groups to travel overseas for charitable purposes or fundraising; funding for individuals, including school fees; sports and arts initiatives (unless it is a project which benefits disadvantaged groups and sports or arts is a means to these ends); equipment for hospitals and schools which would normally be funded by statutory sources, and salaries or running costs.

Applications

Further information can be had by contacting the correspondent, or by visiting the websites mentioned herein.

Application forms and details on applying to the Community Dividend Fund can be found at: www.co-operative.coop/en/community-fund/

Corporate giving

In 2007, the group made total community contributions of nearly £10 million (2006: £5.2 million) in the UK of which £8.3 million was in cash donations (2006: £4.4 million). This was broken down as follows:

Financial support £8,300,000

Employee time £1,500,000

Gifts in Kind £200,000

Management costs £400,000.

The ten largest contributions made by the group (comprising 50% of the total) were as follows: The Co-operative Foundation (£1.86 million); Customers Who Care – climate change (£560,000); Green Energy for Schools (£480,000); RSPB affinity card (£470,000); The Community Fund (£335,000); Oxfam affinity card (£310,000); Membership work with schools and young people (£300,000); From Farm to Fork (£300,000); Consumer Credit Counselling Service (£280,000); and Amnesty International affinity card (£260,000).

Co-operative Foundation

'The Co-operative Foundation is a charitable trust that was set up in 2000 and is solely funded by The Co-operative Group – United Region. The foundation awards grants of £500 to £30,000 and seeks to support locally-led groups that can demonstrate evidence of living the co-operative values and principles of self-help, equality, democracy and concern for the community. Additionally, projects attracting funding must fall within the United Region trading area and benefit disadvantaged groups or communities.'

In 2007, the foundation made grant totalling £895,000.

The Co-operative Community Fund

The key objective of the community fund is to support self-help voluntary and community groups. The fund is overseen by a group of trustees, with the group's 45 area committees having responsibility for allocating community fund awards and assessing applications within their areas. Applicants must demonstrate that their project benefits a local community in which at least one Co-operative Group business trades, has a charitable purpose, and is aligned to the group's values and principles.

In 2007, out of a total disbursed of just over £1 million, 20% of funding went to 'arts and culture' projects, including drama, craftwork, music and local history projects, alongside cultural festivals. Citizenship projects – those that meet primarily for the purpose of enhancing community well-being – attracted another 20% of awards.

In kind support

In kind donations are made by the group, but we have no further details regarding this.

Employee-led support

Volunteering – Staff within the group are actively encouraged to volunteer – donating their time, expertise, energy and enthusiasm to their local communities.

Three categories of volunteering activities are available to staff: team challenges, individual volunteering (e.g. victim support volunteers, mentoring, reading or numeracy volunteering in schools) and specialist volunteering (e.g. Prince's Trust Business Mentoring, interview technique training for prisoners, financial education training).

Matched giving – The 'Charity Booster' scheme enables staff who fundraise for charity to apply for a boost to increase the amount of money they raise, and subject to certain conditions, individuals can apply for a £100 boost, and teams up to £400.

Payroll giving: Staff are able to contribute to their chosen charity through the provision of a payroll giving scheme.

Commercially-led support

Cause-related marketing: *Affinity cards* – The bank has an affinity partnership, with partners receiving a donation for each new branded card and a margin on its use. Partners include: RSPB, Oxfam, Amnesty International UK, Greenpeace, Tearfund, Save the Children, Help the Hospices, WaterAid, ActionAid, Barnardos, Help the Aged, Children's Aid Direct, Christian Aid and Ramblers Association.

'Customers Who Care' – This scheme donates 1.25 pence for every £100 spent on credit and debit cards. Cumulatively, this fund has given over £4 million in donations to over 80 charities and organisations since its launch in 1994.

Cooper-Parry LLP

Company registration number OC301728

3 Centro Place, Pride Park, Derby DE24 8RF

01332 295 544; Fax: 01332 295 600

Website: www.cooperparry.com

Correspondent: Human Resources Department 01332 295544
Email: thought@cooperparry.com

Chairman: Colin Shaw

Chief Executive: Jeremy Bowler

Year end	Turnover	Pre-tax profit
31/12/2007	£15,250,734	£3,511,842

Nature of company business
Accountants and business advisors.

Main locations: Nottingham, Nottingham, Leicester

UK employees: 235

Charitable donations

Total community contributions: £100,000

Membership: BitC

Community involvement

Cooper-Parry's community support is mainly given in the form of employees' time. A wide variety of community activities have been supported, ranging from charities dispensing relief to the needy to those providing help for the deaf, local arts and music groups, and schools and universities. Each year a charity is nominated to raise funds for through various events.

Charity of the year: The Stroke Association (2008).

Exclusions

No cash donations are made in support of charitable causes. No support for local appeals outside of Nottingham, Leicester and Derby, where the firm has offices.

Applications

In writing to the correspondent.

Corporate giving

The firm's community support, although in kind, has previously been valued at around £100,000 during one year.

The company also hosts the Cooper Parry Corporate Challenge, a half marathon which raises money for designated charities each year. In 2007, over £40,000 was raised for the nominated charities.

In kind support

As a founder member of the local ProHelp Group, a regular and substantial commitment to larger community enterprises is made.

Time is normally provided free of charge, particularly to smaller groups and organisations, but more substantial bodies may be asked to contribute toward the costs involved.

Employee-led support

Cooper-Parry encourages its employees to volunteer and provides paid time off to its people through its volunteering policy, flexible working patterns and career breaks.

Corus Group plc

Company registration number 2280000

30 Millbank, London SW1P 4WY

020 7717 4444; Fax: 020 7717 4455

Website: www.corusgroup.com

Correspondent: Ms Allison Scandrett, Company Secretary 020 7717 4444; Fax: 020 7717 4455

Chairman: Jim Leng

Chief Executive: Philippe Varin

Year end	Turnover	Pre-tax profit
30/12/2006	£9,733,000,000	£313,000,000

Nature of company business
The manufacture and sale of steel and aluminium. Major manufacturing businesses are located in Port Talbot and Llanwern in South Wales, Scunthorpe and Teesside, Rotherham, Scunthorpe, Deeside and Ebbw Vale, with distribution outlets throughout the UK and Europe.

Subsidiaries include: Orb Electrical Steels Ltd, Cogent Power Ltd

Main locations: Halesowen, Deeside, York, Wolverhampton, Saltburn-by-the-Sea, Scunthorpe, Rotherham, Port Talbot, Newport

UK employees: 23,800

Total employees: 41,900

Charitable donations

2006: £272,605
2005: £394,019
2004: £340,358
2003: £283,341
2002: £472,635

Community involvement

Corus promotes and encourages economic, environmental, social and educational development where possible. Many Corus businesses have strong links to their neighbouring towns and surrounding regions and give support to cultural, social, educational and sporting activities that contribute to the well-being of residents, both in the immediate vicinity of Corus' plants and elsewhere.

The company also supports its employees' involvement in local initiatives.

Exclusions

No support for purely denominational appeals, small purely local appeals not in areas of company presence, appeals from individuals, fundraising events or circulars.

Applications

Applications (including sponsorships) should be made in writing to the correspondent, although local appeals should be made through local offices of Corus.

Corporate giving

In 2006, Corus made charitable donations in the UK totalling £272,605 (2005: £394,019). We have no details of the beneficiaries.

However, the company's website included the following information: 'During 2007/08, over 20 organisations benefited from the Community Awards of Corus Strip Products UK, South Wales. These included All Souls Church Community Youth Club, the Lymphoma Cancer Unit, Morriston Hospital, Neath and District Sea Cadets, Swan Rescue Wales and the Victims of Chernobyl Trust Fund.

'Teesside Cast Products donated £10,000 as a founder member of the Corporate Partnership scheme set-up by Nature's World, the Middlesbrough-based charity that runs a 25-acre environmental park.

'Corus Engineering Steels, Corus Construction & Industrial, Teesside Cast Products and Corus Tubes donated several thousand pounds for the benefit of local schools, hospitals and charities. Beneficiaries of their donations included:

- Billingham Dance Festival (which brought a Mexican dance troupe to Dormanstown)
- Adrenaline Alley (we contributed towards a community skate park programme in Corby)
- Corby Town and Hartlepool United (through our sponsorship of the clubs' youth policies)
- Grange Lane Junior School, Scunthorpe (where we supported the library refurbishment)
- Wingfield Comprehensive School, Rotherham (which we assisted in achieving Business and Enterprise Specialist School.'

In kind support

Education: In addition to monetary donations, Corus also support the educational development of the communities of which they are a part. The primary purpose is to encourage interest in, and enthusiasm for, the study of materials science and its application in engineering, manufacturing and technology-based industries.

In the UK, Corus sponsor teachers as well as student prizes in material science subject areas in association with various institutes and universities.

Many of the company's sites have educational liaison programmes. Corus employees and Multiserv contractors at Teesside Cast Products lent their support to Banksfield School, Middlesbrough, to provide education on good environmental practices. The visit included a nature field trip to Coatham Marsh Site of Special Scientific Interest, which neighbours the steelworks.

Employee-led support

The company encourages its staff to volunteer and fundraise on behalf of local charities, as the following examples show:

Volunteers from Corus Colors, Shotton, joined other Flintshire businesses, voluntary and community groups, together with renowned environmentalist David Bellamy in the Big Dee Day; an initiative to clean up litter along a 30 mile stretch of the River Dee.

Employees at Corus Tubes, Hartlepool, raised £10,000 for a local cancer research charity in support of a colleague.

Eight volunteers from Corus Engineering Steels, Rotherham, developed a sensory garden at Robert Ogden School, Thurnscoe, to create an enjoyable environment for pupils with autistic spectrum disorder. The business also donated outdoor seating from the new Sheffield branch of the Emmaus charity for their garden.

Commercially-led support

Sponsorship: *Sport* – Corus is the premier sponsor for British Triathlon. This involves a number of community based initiatives including Corus Kids of Steel. This is a UK wide series of events designed to give school age children the chance to try the sport in a safe, fun and non-competitive environment whilst encouraging activity and learning about healthy lifestyles.

Costain Group plc

Costain House, Vanwall Business Park, Maidenhead SL5 4JB

01628 842444; Fax: 01628 674477

Website: www.costain.com

Correspondent: Tracey Wood, HR and Legal Director
Email: corporate.responsibility@costain.com

Chairman: David P Allvey

Chief Executive: Andrew Wyllie

Year end	Turnover	Pre-tax profit
31/12/2007	£747,600,000	£19,800,000

UK employees: 3,622

Charitable donations

2007: £35,533
2006: £13,129
2005: £21,121

Membership: BitC

Community involvement

The company's community involvement policy states: 'Costain Group's efforts within the community concentrate on three closely related areas:

- education and training
- enterprise and urban regeneration
- the built environment.

'These will be driven primarily through joint project work, work placements, secondments, gifts in kind, joint training and other schemes. [As such,] the community involvement policy emphasises and favours active participation rather than purely financial support.

'However, there may be occasions where, in addition to involvement, some modest financial support is required to enable projects to get off the ground, or maintain momentum. To cater for this, the group operates the Costain Community Chest – a scheme on which employees (or outside organisations in which they are involved) can draw for small amounts of money.

'The Costain Community Chest is administered through a small committee in the head office. Details can be obtained from the correspondent.'

Exclusions

No support for local appeals not in areas of company presence.

Applications

In writing to the correspondent setting out briefly why your application should be eligible for a donation.

Donations are normally for very small sums of money and are made to registered charities only.

Corporate giving

In 2007, the group made cash donations in the UK of £35,533 (2006: £13,129). Support has recently been given to: St Edmund's Girls' Football Team; Help a South Wales Child; and West Yorkshire Rotary Clubs Technology Tournament.

In kind support

At divisional level the group has undertaken refurbishment projects. For example, in updating a sixth form centre for pupils at Altwood School in Maidenhead, and refurbishing a derelict building on behalf of the Gatehouse scheme in London, to provide sales space for products produced by the mentally disabled.

At head office, staff have been involved in a lunchtime reading scheme with a local primary school. Whilst accounting and public relations expertise is provided to the local parish church for their 'Breakaway' project for homeless people. The church has also had its roof replaced at cost.

Employee-led support

Staff are encouraged to become involved in local community projects and may receive financial support on behalf of their chosen project through the 'Community Chest' fund.

Coutts & Co

Company registration number 36695

440 Strand, London WC2R 0QS

020 7753 1000; Fax: 020 7753 1028

Website: www.coutts.com

Correspondent: Mrs C L Attwater, Administrator, The Coutts Charitable Trust

Chairman: The Earl of Home

Year end	Turnover	Pre-tax profit
31/12/2006	£357,911,000	£163,768,000

Nature of company business
Banking and allied financial services. Coutts is the private banking arm of the Royal Bank of Scotland Group. The bank's main location is London, but there are 17 regional offices.

Main locations: Liverpool, Manchester, Newcastle upon Tyne, Oxford, Nottingham, Winchester, Tunbridge Wells, Bristol, Cardiff, Cambridge, Isle of Man, Jersey, Leeds, Eton, Guildford, Bath, Birmingham, Bournemouth

UK employees: 1,362

Charitable donations

2006: £832,956
2005: £522,088
2004: £405,195
2002: £226,000

Community involvement

The Coutts Charitable Trust (Charity Commission no. 1000135) was set up in 1987 to formalise Coutts's charitable giving and makes a large number of small donations to a wide range of charities each year. A portion of the charitable budget is, however, used for larger donations.

The trust's main source of funding is derived from the covenant income calculated at 0.5% of profits chargeable to corporation tax of Coutts s & Co. for the preceding year.

Grants are given by the trust to UK organisations only and it prefers to support organisations in areas where the bank has a presence, mainly London. Charities supported include those involved with helping the homeless, rehabilitation and teaching self help (drug; alcohol; young offenders), disadvantaged adults and children, youth organisations, the elderly, medical research, heritage, education and the relief of poverty.

'Many applications are supported by key clients and, in these circumstances, the criteria may be relaxed. Staff and pensioners of Coutts & Company, involved with charities in a personal capacity, are encouraged to apply to the trust and support is also given to members of staff who give their time voluntarily to raise funds for charities of their choice.'

Exclusions

No response to circular appeals. No support for appeals from individuals or overseas projects.

Applications

Applications to the Coutts Charitable Trust should be addressed to the correspondent above, at any time. Applications should include clear details of the purpose for which the grant is required. Grants are made regularly where amounts of £500 or less are felt to be appropriate. The trustees meet quarterly to consider larger donations.

Corporate giving

Coutts Charitable Trust

According to the 2006 accounts (the latest available for the company), Coutts donated £832,956 (2005: £552,088) to the trust which made grants ranging from £500 to £750 to UK registered charities "where a few hundred pounds can make a great difference'. Some larger donations of £2,000 or more were also made.

In the year 2007, approximately 1,600 applications (2006: 1,400) for assistance were received by the trust and the trustees identified and made donations totalling £617,663 (2006: £363,187) to 866 charitable organisations (2006: 724). The largest donations were to: Children in Crisis (£5,000); Amber Foundation (£3,200); Cancer Research Campaign (£2,550); Lymphoma Association and The Samaritans (£2,500 each); and Bowel Cancer UK (£2,000).

Beneficiaries receiving under £1,000 each were not individually named, but broken down into categories, with the six largest being as follows:

- social welfare (£71,733
- religious (£68,250)
- education (£51,580)
- physically disabled (£42,922)
- children (£39,380)
- homeless (£31,450).

Employee-led support

Payroll giving: The company operates the Give As You Earn scheme.

Commercially-led support

Sponsorship: *The arts* – support has been given to the Almeida Theatre, the Design Museum and the Royal Opera House, amongst others.

Coventry Building Society

Company registration number 3662832

Oakfield House, PO Box 600, Binley Business Park, Coventry CV3 9YR

0845 7665522

Website: www.thecoventry.co.uk

Correspondent: Ms Anna Cuskin, Coventry Building Society Foundation

Chairman: David Harding

Chief Executive: David Stewart

Year end	Turnover	Pre-tax profit
31/12/2007	£131,900,000	£66,800,000

Nature of company business
Building society.

Main locations: Coventry

UK employees: 890

Charitable donations

2007: £111,644
2006: £77,973
2005: £54,044
2004: £50,000
2003: £54,758

Membership: BitC

Community involvement

The society has two methods of supporting the community. Firstly, support is channelled through the Coventry Building Society Charitable Foundation (Charity Commission no. 1072244) which receives an annual donation from the society.

The society only makes donations to registered charities that are based or active within the region covered by Coventry Building Society's branch network. Its priority is to give to groups, or activities, aimed at improving the quality of life and opportunity among groups who are disadvantaged or deprived, the consequence of which may lead to social exclusion.

They welcome applications that focus on:

- young people, particularly those who are disadvantaged
- vulnerable groups such as the frail and the elderly, people with physical disability, people with learning disabilities or those who are mentally ill
- small neighbourhood groups in areas where they are experiencing the greatest disadvantage
- supporting communities and voluntary organisations through assisting them in the achievement of social and community development.

Secondly, the society has a 'TLC in the Community' programme, the aim of which is to support and enhance the work of the charitable foundation.

The TLC in the Community Programme will support initiatives and activities:

- that actively involve Society staff who volunteer their support or raise funds to benefit charities or causes within the community
- that aim to improve the quality of life and opportunity amongst those who are disadvantaged
- that benefit the community by improving local services or facilities
- by organising and/or supporting charitable promotions/events within the local community area served by the Society's branch network.

The TLC programme will support national charities, but wherever possible, would prefer to benefit to be for local projects within the branch operating area. An organisation does not need to be registered to receive support from TLC.

Charity of the year: Royal National Institute of Blind People (2007).

Exclusions

The society will not consider grants for the following:

- large charities which enjoy national coverage
- charities with no base within the branch area
- charities with an annual donated income in excess of £250,000
- charities with assets over £500,000
- projects requiring an ongoing commitment
- large capital projects
- maintenance or building works for buildings, gardens or playgrounds
- major fundraising
- projects which are normally the responsibility of other organisations (such as the NHS, Education Department and local authorities)
- sponsorship of individuals
- requests from individuals
- replacing funds that were the responsibility of another body
- educational institutions unless for the relief of disadvantage
- sporting clubs or organisations unless for the relief of disadvantage
- medical research and equipment
- more than one donation for the same organisation in any one year – further applications will be considered after three years
- animal welfare
- promotion of religious political or military causes.

Applications

To apply for a grant print off and fill in the application form from the company website listed below. Send the completed application form accompanied with a copy of recent report and accounts to the correspondent.

In some circumstances the society may request further information before considering the application. The trustees meet in February, May, August and November.

The society states: 'it may not be always be possible to support all applications even if they fully meet the foundation's criteria. We reserve the right to support those charities we believe to be worthy of our support'.

Information available: Further information regarding the application form and policy guidelines is available at the society's website: www.thecoventry.co.uk

Corporate giving

In 2007, the society made cash donations of £111,644 of which £50,000 went to its charitable foundation.

Coventry Building Society Charitable Foundation

As the foundation wishes to support as many good causes as possible the maximum single donation will normally be £3,000. As a general rule, donations are normally between £500 and £2,000.

In 2007, the foundation made 48 donations totalling £75,200 to charitable causes, of which 45 were for sums of £1,000 or over. Beneficiaries included: The Albrighton Trust and Dream Maker's Children's Charity (£3,000 each); House on the Corner Community Project and Laurence-Moon-Bardet-Biedi Society (£2,000 each); Sport 4 Life UK and Birmingham Centre for Arts Therapies (£1,500 each); and No Panic and Oesophageal Patients Association (£1,000 each).

In kind support

The society provides fundraising assistance to a number of major charitable appeals by allowing the use of its branches as collection points for public donations.

TLC provides in kind support by donating gifts and prizes for fundraising events which include items such as balloons, goodie bags, teddy bears, clocks, book tokens, champagne and books. They will also place community advertisements in programmes for local fundraising events such as fetes, carnivals and concerts. TLC also provides large publicity cheques to anyone who wishes to publicise the amount they have raised for a charity or other organisation.

Employee-led support

The society encourages staff to take part in community activities. In 2007 it launched a new policy in which a day's paid leave is given to every member of staff to work for the charitable or community initiative of their choice.

A staff matching initiative means that the society also matches funds raised by staff members for charitable causes.

In addition, through various educational partnerships, 30 staff members volunteered to work in local schools, whether facilitating business games or providing valuable interview practice.

Credit Suisse

Company registration number 891554

One Cabot Square, London EC14 4QJ

020 7888 8888; Fax: 020 7888 1600

Website: www.credit-suisse.com/uk

Correspondent: Vice President Corporate Social Responsibility

Chairman: Eric Varvel

Year end	Pre-tax profit
31/12/2007	£4,000,000

Nature of company business
Global investment bank.

Main locations: London

Community involvement

Obtaining details of Credit Suisse's UK community support has, in the main, proved difficult. We, therefore, repeat the last information provided by the company.

Support is given to towards the education of inner-city youth, such as after-school educational programmes and arts, music and sports groups. Other types of beneficiaries have included older people's homes, schools, public parks and homelessness causes. Much of the UK support is centred around its head office in Tower Hamlets. It has a transatlantic partnership with Habitat for Humanity, involving itself with building houses in Southwark, Tower Hamlets and New York.

Previously listed as members of Business in the Community and the London Benckmarking Group, this no longer appears to be the case.

Charity of the year: The Place2Be (2008).

Applications

In writing to the correspondent. All European donations are processed centrally from London.

Corporate giving

In 2007, the group made donations in Europe of US$887,000 (around £443,000). We do not know what proportion of this was given in the UK or to whom. The exceptions to this are the Isle of Dogs Community Foundation which the company regularly supports and the nominated charity of the year.

Employee-led support

Staff are encouraged to take part and establish fundraising events for the charity of the year.

Commercially-led support

Sponsorship: *The arts* – Numerous sponsorships are undertaken by the firm relating to art, music and film.

Crest Nicholson plc

Company registration number 1040616

Crest House, Rycroft Road, Chertsey, Surrey KT16 9GN

01932 580555; Fax: 0870 336 3990

Website: www.crestnicholson.com

Correspondent: Margaret Brown, Secretary to the Company Secretary

Fax: 0870 243 8395
Email: info@crestnicholson.com

Chairman: David Shearer

Chief Executive: S Stone

Year end	Turnover	Pre-tax profit
31/10/2006	£690,700,000	£80,100,000

Nature of company business
Property developer.

Main locations: Cardiff, Brentwood, Bristol, Hemel Hempstead, Weybridge, Tamworth, Westerham

UK employees: 790

Total employees: 790

> ## Charitable donations
>
> 2006: £46,000
> 2005: £48,000
> 2004: £36,000
> 2003: £15,000
> 2002: £22,000

Community involvement

Following a three-year partnership with Shelter which ended in 2005, the company has embarked upon a two-year fundraising partnership with the Variety Club. It supplements this financial commitment with in kind support for a number of environmental/conservation initiatives.

Applications

In writing to the correspondent.

The company produces a *Social Responsibility Report.*

Corporate giving

In 2005/06, the company made cash donations in the UK totalling £46,000. We assume this was mainly given in support of The Variety Club, its current charity partner. So far, the company has raised over £180,000 on the charity's behalf.

In kind support

The company has worked in partnership with the Surrey Wildlife Trust and The Woodland Trust to raise public awareness about important conservation issues and to protect rural habitats.

Employee-led support

Employees are encouraged to take part in fundraising activities and participate in sponsored events on behalf of the company's nominated charity partner.

Cummins Ltd

Company registration number 573951

Yarm Road, Darlington DL1 4PW

01325 556000; Fax: 01325 368040

Website: www.cummins.com

Correspondent: Human Resources Department

Chairman: Tim Solso

Chief Executive: Tim Solso

Year end	Turnover	Pre-tax profit
31/12/2006	£790,624,000	£40,132,000

Nature of company business
The principal activity is the manufacture, sale, distribution and servicing of diesel engines and components. The company is a subsidiary of Cummins Inc (US).

Subsidiaries include: Holset Engineering Co. Ltd, Newage International Ltd

Main locations: Ramsgate, Huddersfield, Daventry, Darlington, Stamford, Hinckley, Wellingborough, Cumbernauld, Stockton-on-Tees, Peterborough

UK employees: 2,468

> ## Charitable donations
>
> 2006: £49,947
> 2005: £38,389

Community involvement

Previously, we were advised that within the UK, the company prefers to support projects local to its manufacturing plants and offices. Organisations concerned with youth, education, the environment, and disadvantaged people are favoured.

Exclusions

No support for appeals from individuals, or local appeals not in areas of company presence.

Applications

In writing to the correspondent.

Corporate giving

In 2006, the company declared cash donations to charity of just under £50,000 (2005: £38,389). We have no information regarding the beneficiaries.

In kind support

The main areas of non-cash support are secondments, gifts in kinds and training schemes.

Employee-led support

To encourage employee volunteering and involvement, each plant has a Community Involvement Team which coordinates community activities based on local needs. These can include mentoring schemes with local schools and fundraising events on behalf of local good causes. The latter may receive additional money from the Cummins Foundation.

Recently, employees at the Darlington site have supported Young Enterprise North East (YENE), part of the UK business-education charity Young Enterprise.

P Z Cussons plc

Company registration number 19457

PZ Cussons House, Bird Hall Lane, Stockport SK3 0XN

0161 491 8000; Fax: 0161 491 8191

Website: www.cussons.com

Correspondent: The Secretary

Chairman: A J Green

Chief Executive: G A Kanellis

Year end	Turnover	Pre-tax profit
31/05/2007	£577,900,000	£67,900,000

Nature of company business
Principal activities: manufacture and distribution of soaps, toiletries, cleaning agents, pharmaceuticals, refrigerators and air conditioners.

Subsidiaries include: Cussons Group Ltd, Cussons (UK) Ltd, PC Products (1001) Ltd, Cussons (International) Ltd, Parnon Ltd, Fragrance Chemicals Ltd

Main locations: Stockport

Total employees: 9,877

Charitable donations

2007: £50,000
2006: £50,000
2005: £53,000
2004: £50,000

Community involvement

Within the corporate social responsibility section of its Annual Report and Accounts, the company states: 'We support a range of charitable causes, both in the UK and overseas, mainly through a UK-based shareholding trust (The Zochonis Charitable Trust, Charity Commission no. 274769) and additional contributions made through staff time and gifts in kind.'

Past information has suggested the company has a preference for local charities in areas of company presence, particularly projects involving children and youth, social welfare, medical, education, recreation and people with disabilities.

Exclusions

The company will not make any form of political contribution.

Past information has suggested that generally, the company will give no support for circular appeals, fundraising events, advertising in charity brochures, individuals, denominational appeals, large national appeals or overseas projects.

Applications

The charities committee only meets once a year in May. Appeals should be addressed to the correspondent at head office.

Corporate giving

The company donates around £50,000 each year to charities. We have no details of the beneficiaries.

Despite encouraging staff volunteering and providing gifts in kind, it does not appear to calculate the value of these forms of support to the community.

The associated Zochonis Charitable Trust made grants of £1.9 million in 2006/07, for general charitable purposes. Its income is derived almost exclusively from share holdings in the company, but acts independently.

In kind support

In addition to cash donations the company provides support by providing gifts in kind.

Employee-led support

The company allows employees time off to volunteer.

Daejan Holdings plc

Company registration number 305105

Freshwater House, 158–162 Shaftesbury Avenue, London WC2H 8HR

020 7836 1555; Fax: 020 7497 8941

Website: www.daejanholdings.com

Correspondent: B Freshwater, Chairman

Chairman: B S E Freshwater

Year end	Turnover	Pre-tax profit
31/03/2008	£86,952,000	£47,067,000

Nature of company business
Property investment and trading, with some development. The major part of the group's property portfolio comprises commercial, industrial and residential premises throughout the UK and in the US.

Subsidiaries include: Astral Estates (London) Ltd, The Cromlech Property Co. Ltd, Bampton Holdings Ltd, St Leonards Properties Ltd, InputStripe Ltd, The Halliard Property Co. Ltd, City and Country Properties (Midlands) Ltd, Hampstead Way Investments Ltd, Seaglen Investments Ltd, Pegasus Investment Co. Ltd, Brickfield Properties Ltd, Limebridge Co. Ltd, Rosebel Holdings Ltd, City and Country Properties (Camberley) Ltd, Bampton

(B&B) Ltd, Inputstock Ltd, Bampton (Redbridge) Ltd, City and Country Properties (Birmingham) Ltd, The Bampton Property Group Ltd

Main locations: London

UK employees: 137

Charitable donations
2008: £120,000
2007: £120,000
2006: £120,000
2005: £120,000

Community involvement

Part of The Freshwater Group of companies, Daejan mainly supports orthodox Jewish charities, especially in the educational and medical fields, in the USA, Britain and Israel. Support is also given to organisations concerned with the relief of poverty. The company channels its giving through the Charities Aid Foundation.

The Freshwater Group is also associated with two or three other substantial private charitable companies, whose policy is similar to that of Daejan Holdings.

Exclusions
Organisations dealing with professional fundraisers, large overhead expenses and expensive fundraising campaigns are avoided. Support is not given to the arts, enterprise or conservation.

Applications
In writing to the correspondent (who is also the correspondent for the payroll giving scheme). There is no donations committee.

Corporate giving

The company maintained its level of charitable support at £120,000 in 2008. No further information was available.

Employee-led support
Payroll giving: The company operates the Give As You Earn Scheme.

Daily Mail and General Trust plc

Company registration number 184594

Northcliffe House, 2 Derry Street, London W8 5TT

020 7938 6349; Fax: 020 7937 4625

Website: www.dmgt.co.uk

Correspondent: Charities Committee

Chairman: Rt Hon. Viscount Rothermere

Chief Executive: C J F Sinclair

Year end	Turnover	Pre-tax profit
30/09/2007	£2,138,000,000	£253,400,000

Nature of company business
Principal activity: publication and printing of newspapers and periodicals.

Subsidiaries include: Staffordshire Sentinel Newspapers Ltd, DMG Pinnacle Ltd, Northcliffe New Media Holdings plc, Euromoney Publications plc, The Publishing Co. Ltd, Hull Daily Mail Publications Ltd, W.H.Y Publications limited, Northcliffe Newspapers Group Ltd, Cornwall & Devon Media Ltd, Herald Express Ltd, Derby Daily Telegraph Ltd, Harmsworth Quays Printing Ltd, Leicester Mercury Group Ltd, DMG Trinity Ltd, The Journal Co. Ltd, Aberdeen Journals Ltd, DMG Home Interest Magazines Ltd, DMG Angex Ltd, Lincolnshire Publishing Co. Ltd, Bristol United Press plc, Armdag Newspapers Ltd, Northcliffe Retail Ltd, Gloucestershire Newspapers Ltd, Nottingham Post Group Ltd, Essex Chronicle Series Ltd, Metropress Ltd, Harmsworth Quays Ltd, DMG Exhibition Group Ltd, The Western Morning News Co. Ltd, Express & Echo Publications Ltd, Alderton Ltd, DMG Business Media Ltd, Arts and Entertainment Programming Ltd, Grimsy & Scunthorpe Newspaper Ltd, Associated Newspapers Ltd, South West Wales Publications Ltd, New Era Television Ltd, DMG Antique Fairs Ltd, Central Independent Newspapers Ltd, Teletex Ltd, British Pathe plc, DMG Radio Ltd, Westcountry Publications Ltd, The Cheltenham Newspaper Co. Ltd, DMG Regional Radio Pty Ltd, The Printworks Ltd, The Courier Printing & Publishing Co. Ltd, Publications Ltd

Main locations: London

Total employees: 16,839

Charitable donations
2007: £866,000
2006: £809,000
2005: £880,000
2003: £548,000

Community involvement

Daily Mail & General Trust's (DMGT) charitable donations are allocated by a charities committee at DMGT, as well as being made on a smaller scale by divisional and local managements. The committee prefers to make donations to media and local charities where there is an employee representative who will sponsor and report back on the impact the allocation has had.

In addition to the above, the group runs numerous fundraising campaigns through its newspapers, media subsidiaries and events.

Charity of the year: Cancer Research UK (2007 – Metro).

Exclusions
No support for circular appeals, appeals from individuals, older people, enterprise/training, environment/heritage, fundraising events, overseas projects, political/religious appeals, sickness/disability charities, social welfare, or sport.

Applications
In writing to the correspondent.

Corporate giving

In 2006/7, the company donated a total of £866,000 (2005/06: £806,000). Beneficiaries included: Demelza House Children's Hospice; Surrey Docks Farm; and Kate's Kids for a Cure. Comprehensive information regarding the group's charitable and community support throughout the UK is available on DMGT's corporate website under 'DMGT in the Community'.

In kind support

Items left over from reader promotions have been donated to community groups. A children's library in an inner city housing estate Glasgow was set up and has now tripled in size because of its popularity. It is stocked with classic novels, encyclopaedia and cartoon DVDs and provides these items free to local youngsters.

Employee-led support

Payroll giving: Associated Newspapers operates an on-line payroll giving scheme, working in partnership with Workplace Giving UK, which enables staff members to make more tax-efficient personal donations to their preferred charities.

Commercially-led support

Sponsorship: *The arts* – the company undertakes arts sponsorship (local to company headquarters).

Sport – Now in its 18th year The Daily Mail Schools Rugby is the largest schools rugby tournament in the world, with an entry of 986 schools in 2007.

Data Connection Ltd

Company registration number 1578918

100 Church Street, Enfield, Middlesex EN2 6BQ

020 8366 1177; Fax: 020 8363 1468

Website: www.dataconnections.com

Correspondent: Doreen Willis, Charitable Appeals
Email: info@dataconnections.com

Year end	Turnover	Pre-tax profit
31/08/2007	£51,922,000	£250,000

Nature of company business
Providers of communication and telephony software and hardware technology to major parts of the world's computer industry, to service providers and to large enterprises.

Main locations: Enfield

UK employees: 400

Charitable donations
2007: £92,710
2006: £90,654
2005: £18,124
2004: £7,573
2003: £258,360

Community involvement

As an IT company based in Enfield, we understood that around 90% of its donations budget is allocated to causes in the borough, the remaining 10% being spent on national programmes. We have been unable to confirm if this is still the case.

There is a preference for causes supported by employees (offices are currently in Enfield, Edinburgh and Chester).

Applications

In writing to the correspondent.

Corporate giving

In 2007, the company made charitable donations of £92,710 (2006: £90,654). Unfortunately, we have no information as to the organisations benefiting from this

DDB UK Ltd

Company registration number 933578

12 Bishops Bridge Road, London W2 6AA

020 7258 3979; Fax: 020 7402 4871

Website: www.ddblondon.com

Correspondent: Mrs Fiona Shafran, Head of Human Resources

Chairman: Stephen Woodford

Chief Executive: Stephen Woodford

Year end	Turnover	Pre-tax profit
31/12/2006	£107,007,000	£5,011,000

Nature of company business
The principal activity of the company is advertising and marketing services.

Subsidiaries include: Smythe Dorward Lambert Ltd, Alcone Marketing Group Ltd, Omnicom Finance Ltd, The Computing Group Ltd, Scope Ketchum Sponsorship Ltd, Market Access Ltd, Markforce Associates Ltd, Paling Walters Targis Ltd, Premier Magazines Ltd, Prism International Ltd, TBWA Simons Palmer Ltd, Omnicom UK Ltd, Solutions in Media Ltd, TISSA Ltd, Countrywide Communications Ltd, The Anvil Consultancy Ltd, WWAV Rapp Collins Group Ltd, Colour Solutions Ltd, First City/BBDO Ltd, Gavin Anderson Ltd, Macmillan Davies Hodes Consultants Ltd, Scope Communications Group Ltd, Doremus & Co. Ltd, Specialist Publications Ltd, Alcone/Europe Ltd, Floral Street Holdings Ltd, Porter Novelli Ltd, Medi Cine International plc, WWAV Rapp Collins Ltd, Macmillan Davies Hodes Advertising Ltd, DAS Financial Services Ltd, Interbrand UK Ltd, Ketchum Public Relations plc, BMP Countrywide Ltd, Griffin Bacal Ltd, Billco Ltd, CPM International Group Ltd, Genesis Digital Creation Ltd, Countrywide Porter Novelli Ltd, Perception Design Ltd, Interbrand Group Ltd, BBDO Europe Ltd, BMP DDB Ltd, Data Warehouse Ltd

Main locations: London

UK employees: 406

Charitable donations
2006: £43,000
2005: £29,000
2004: £40,000
2002: £44,000

Community involvement

DDB London is one of the companies in the Omnicom Group and is the trading name of DDB UK Ltd.

We were advised that the company supports national and international charities with direct donations. It normally supports the arts, children/youth, education, the elderly, enterprise/training, environment/heritage, fundraising events, medical research, political and religious appeals, science/technology, sickness/disability, social welfare, sport and advertising in charity brochures.

The company's charity of the year is chosen through staff nomination of a charity which is directly involved with any of the issues stated above.

Applications

In writing to the correspondent.

Corporate giving

In 2006, cash donations to charity totalled £43,000 (2005: £29,000). Beneficiaries included: World Wildlife Fund; NABS; History of Advertising Trust; and Brain Tumour UK.

Employee-led support

the company has an employee volunteering scheme.

Payroll giving: The Give As You Earn and NABS schemes are in operation.

De Beers

Company registration number 2054170

17 Charterhouse Street, London EC1N 6RA

020 7404 4444; Fax: 020 7430 1821

Website: www.debeersgroup.com

Correspondent: Mr Robert Barltrop, Secretary to the Oppenheimer Charitable Trust

Chairman: Nicky F Oppenheimer

Managing Director: Varda Shine

Year end	Turnover	Pre-tax profit
31/10/2007	£6,836,000,000	£1,375,000,000

Nature of company business
Principal activities: mining of gem and industrial diamonds; marketing through the Central Selling Organisation of diamonds produced by the group and other producers; manufacture and marketing of synthetic diamond and related hard materials for use in industry; management of a portfolio of international investments in mining, industrial and finance companies.

Main locations: London

UK employees: 574

Charitable donations

2007: £60,000
2006: £60,000
2005: £60,000
2003: £69,753

Management costs: £7,500

Membership: BitC, L B Group

Community involvement

In 1961, the Oppenheimer Charitable Trust (Charity Commission no. 200395) was established to channel some of the donations of the Diamond Trading Companies of the De Beers Group. De Beers Consolidated Mines Ltd, which does not operate in this country, channels its donations through the De Beers Fund. The Fund makes grants predominantly in South Africa, Botswana and Namibia, where the company has large mining interests, although help is also given worldwide.

Social investment is focused on projects initiated and driven by communities, with key requirements being sustainability and impact.

Exclusions

The company does not provide support for appeals from individuals, animal welfare, overseas projects, fundraising events or political appeals.

Applications

Grants are made in three ways: by application to the trustees; by recommendation to the trustees; and on the initiative of the trustees themselves.

Corporate giving

In 2007 the Oppenheimer Charitable Trust made grants in the UK totalling £87,050. In the main, grants were of a very small amount, the majority being for £750. Full details of the recipient organisations are listed in the Trustees Annual Report for the year ending 31 October 2007. Some examples include: Royal Opera House Foundation (£7,800); Macmillan Cancer Support (£1,500); Victoria and Albert Museum (£1,000); Combat Stress and Hackney Quest (£750 each); and Let's Face It and Wheel Power (£500 each).

Employee-led support

The company supports employees' volunteering/charitable activities by allowing them company time off and by providing financial support.

De La Rue plc

Company registration number 3834125

De La Rue House, Jays Close, Viables, Basingstoke, Hampshire RG22 4BS

01256 605000; Fax: 01256 605004

Website: www.delarue.com

Correspondent: Mrs Teresa Kerr, PA to Chair and Chief Executive

Chairman: Nicholas Brookes

Chief Executive: Leo Quinn

Year end	Turnover	Pre-tax profit
25/03/2008	£753,600,000	£126,700,000

Nature of company business
The company is a commercial security printer and papermaker, involved in the production of over 150 national currencies and a wide range of security documents. The company is also a leading provider of cash handling equipment and solutions to banks and retailers as well as a range of identity systems to governments worldwide.

Subsidiaries include: Royal Mint Services Ltd, Camelot Group plc, Portals Group, Portals Property Ltd

Main locations: Byfleet, Knutsford, Lisburn, Peterborough, Portsmouth, Dunstable, Gateshhead, Loughton, Overton, Westhoughton, Bath, Basingstoke

UK employees: 2,327

Total employees: 6,274

Charitable donations

2008: £79,000
2007: £110,587
2006: £97,000
2005: £205,000

Community involvement

In addition to charitable donations made by the company, support is also provided by the De La Rue Charitable Trust (Charity Commission no. 274052). The trust is reliant on investment income as it doesn't receive any donations from the company.

Unfortunately, we have no information concerning the type of project the company is likely to support. We do know, however, that the trust aims to direct funds to causes around the world in countries where De La Rue operates.

Emphasis is given to educational projects which promote relevant skills, international understanding and bring relief from suffering.

Exclusions

Generally no support for circular appeals, fundraising events, brochure advertising, individuals, purely denominational (religious) or political appeals, local appeals not in areas of company presence or large national appeals. No telephoned applications can be considered.

Applications that do not fall within the above categories will not be considered unless there are extenuating or emergency circumstances. Grant applications made by individuals either in the UK or abroad cannot be considered.

All circular appeals will be rejected.

Applications

In writing to the correspondent. Registered charities only can apply.

Applications are considered at trustees meetings held in February and July.

Corporate giving

In 2007/08, cash donations by the company totalled £79,000 (2006/07: £110,587). We have no details of the beneficiaries.

The De La Rue Charitable Trust

The trusts income is generated from dividends received from investment fund holdings. In 2005/06, this amounted to £53,399 of which £44,430 was paid out in grants. Besides matching De La Rue employee donations, the trust also helped Deafway.

Funds are allocated to charitable and good causes that fall within policy categories, for example, education, international understanding, relief of suffering, the hospice movement and for special community projects and institutions close to De La Rue locations and within its national and international markets.

Employee-led support

The charitable trust matches employee fundraising. Each company location is encouraged to sponsor a different local cause on an annual basis with employees donating time and commitment as well as funds.

Payroll giving: The company operates the Give As You Earn scheme.

De Vere Group plc

Company registration number 14504

179 Great Portland Street, London W1W 5LS

Website: www.devere.co.uk/

Correspondent: The Company Secretary

Year end	Turnover	Pre-tax profit
25/09/2005	£312,031,000	£58,958,000

Nature of company business
The main activity is the operation of hotels and leisure facilities.

Main locations: Warrington, Leeds, Blackpool, Chester, Norwich, Cambridge, London, Loch Lomond

Total employees: 6,379

Charitable donations

2004: £50,000
2003: £77,100
2002: £98,700
2001: £99,100
2000: £104,000

Community involvement

Despite contacting the company several times we have been unable to obtain any up to date information regarding its community support policy. We therefore repeat the last information published.

As of 7 September 2006, the company was delisted from the London Stock Exchange following its acquisition by AHG Venice Ltd. At this stage we do not know how, if at all, this may affect the company's current community support policy detailed herein.

According to the company's 2005 annual report, due to the multiplicity of locations from which it operates the group's strategy is to encourage each business unit to develop its own social responsibility policies. As a result of this, the hotel and fitness club division, for example, supports over 30 national and international charities as well as local charities, hospices and hospitals.

In addition to this the group provides in kind support and encourages its employees to become involved in local charity and community events.

Exclusions

No support for local appeals not in areas of company presence.

Applications

In writing to the correspondent. Alternatively, contact the nearest De Vere Group company.

Corporate giving

In 2004/05, the company's charitable donations in the UK totalled £55,000 (2004: £50,000). Small donations of around £10 or a bottle for a fundraising event are distributed regularly. Larger donations are considered by a charitable appeals committee two/three times a year. Donations can be for £100 to £10,000 and may be given by deed of covenant.

Examples of national charities supported during the year include Macmillan Nurses, British Heart Foundation and Save the Children.

In kind support

Many of the hotels and fitness clubs within the group provide free access to their facilities by, for example, allowing the use of swimming pools to teach under-privileged children to swim, or, by allowing the use of kitchens to teach teenagers from local youth centres how to prepare healthy food.

The company also provides training and work experience under several recognised programmes.

Employee-led support

Employees provide career talks for teenagers who are about to leave school/college, whilst some hotels and clubs run schemes to allow qualifying employees paid time off to support chosen charities and community events.

Payroll giving: The Give As You Earn scheme is in operation.

Deloitte

Company registration number 2400371

Stonecutter Court, 1 Stonecutter Street, London EC4A 4TR

020 7936 3000; Fax: 020 7583 1198

Website: www.deloitte.co.uk

Correspondent: Richard Stone, Director of Community Investment
Email: richardstone@deloitte.co.uk

Chief Executive: John Connolly

Year end	Turnover	Pre-tax profit
31/05/2007	£1,802,000,000	£564,000,000

Nature of company business
Audit, tax, corporate finance and management consultancy services.

Main locations: Bristol, Cardiff, Leeds, Southampton, Reading, London

UK employees: 11,250

Charitable donations

2007: £1,139,908
2006: £1,000,000
2005: £400,000
2004: £400,000
2003: £250,000

Total community contributions: £6,051,898
Management costs: £532,511

Membership: A & B, BitC, L B Group

Community involvement

The Deloitte Foundation supports a wide variety of charities, with a particular focus on causes supporting children and young people, health and the community. A significant portion of the foundation's budget is used to provide matched funding for staff contributions, to payroll giving and charity fundraising.

Deloitte commits in excess of 1% of UK pre-tax profit towards its community involvement. It is committed to supporting the community at a national and local level through its network of 20 offices throughout the UK.

Charity of the Year: Cancer Research UK and NSPCC (2008/09).

Exclusions

No support for advertising in charity brochures, appeals from individuals, the arts, overseas projects or political/religious appeals.

Applications

In writing to the Deloitte Charity Committee. However, few ad hoc or unsolicited requests for funding are approved by the committee.

Corporate giving

In 2006/07 Deloitte made charitable donations in the UK totalling £1.14 million. In addition to this, more than £3.4 million in professional services has been given to the community and £1.5 million of employee time through volunteering projects involving over 2,000 staff.

Disability sport

Deloitte has launched a £3.4 million programme to develop disability sport in the UK, between now and 2012. The initiative is 50% funded by government.

In addition, the firm are creating a Deloitte Disability Sports Institute, to be run by the British Paralympic Association. This will build a bigger grass roots community of active competitors in disability sport, and help identify the champions of the future.

Deloitte is also doubling the financial support available to disabled competitors, through the Sports Aid national Talented Athlete Scholarship Scheme, assisting 500 disabled athletes to progress to world class performance.

Youth employment

Deloitte is making a £2.5 million investment over the next five years to develop a new generation of employability skills trainers in FE Colleges across the country. Over the course of the programme, the Deloitte initiative will train up to 800 new trainers. These trainers will teach employability skills classes to students on vocational courses, helping them to develop the skills, attitudes and behaviours that they need to secure and sustain employment.

In kind support

In kind support is given through the provision of pro bono professional services. 15,000 hours of professional time is given through business mentoring and school mentoring projects across the UK.

Deloitte also operate a 'Computers for Charity' scheme, whereby each Christmas staff are invited to apply for a fully reconditioned laptop on behalf of any UK charity or community organisation that they currently support. Up to 100 laptops each year are provided, with more than 500 having been given away since the scheme began.

Employee-led support

Employee fundraising is matched by the company up to a maximum of £500 per person. Whilst employee giving is matched up to a maximum of £100 per person, per month.

Employees can also receive up to half-a-day per month off to volunteer for approved community projects.

Payroll giving: The Give As You Earn scheme is in operation. The charitable fund also matches the contributions made by the staff fund through this. In 2007 a total of £700,000 was raised through payroll giving, including £125,000 matching from Deloitte.

Commercially-led support

Sponsorship: Deloitte has a broad range of sponsorship programmes that include supporting the arts, culture and sport. A key partnership has been made with the Royal Opera House. Deloitte is also a second tier sponsor of the 2012 Olympic and Paralympic Games.

Derbyshire Building Society

Company registration number 165B

PO Box 1, Duffield Hall, Duffield, Derby DE56 1AG

08456 004005

Website: www.thederbyshire.co.uk

Correspondent: Mrs Chris Butler, Community Develoment Manager 01332 844340
Email: community@thederbyshire.co.uk

Chairman: Alan Woods

Chief Executive: Graham Picken

Year end	Pre-tax profit
31/12/2007	£9,600,000

Nature of company business
Core business activities are focused on: mortgage lending, personal savings and investment products, life and general insurance business, and personal financial advice.

Main locations: Derby

UK employees: 740

Charitable donations
2007: £5,274
2006: £6,941
2005: £3,688
2003: £20,846

Membership: BitC

Community involvement

Derbyshire Building Society's website states:

'We are committed to making a positive difference to the quality of life in the communities in which we serve.

'We embrace the principle that corporate citizenship is vital to the long-term success of the Society and play an active role in tackling a whole range of issues – crime reduction, drug addiction, economic regeneration, social inclusion and breaking down the barriers of disability and discrimination.

'Although we provide financial support to community projects and charities every year, our work is not just about money. It's also about investing time, imagination, effort and expertise to support projects and stimulate new initiatives.

'Everyone at The Derbyshire is encouraged to take part in community and charity events and each year.'

Exclusions

No support for advertising in charity brochures, animal welfare, appeals from individuals, overseas projects or political or religious appeals.

Applications

In writing to the correspondent.

Corporate giving

Derbyshire Building Society's declared cash donations in 2007 amounted to £5,274. Its in kind support, however, appears to be quite significant given the following information provided on its website:

'With a dedicated Community Development Team, the support of our customers and enthusiasm from our employees, Derbyshire Building Society was able to provide help to over 200 charities, community groups, organisations and good causes in 2007.

'Derbyshire Building Society is very committed to supporting groups in our local area and our Community Strategy for 2008 includes several ways in which we hope we can offer this support.

'Our Community Development Strategy for 2008 focuses on three key areas:

'Sport in the Community

'Through our key sporting relationships with Derby County Football Club and our other football affinity relationships (Grimsby Town, Mansfield Town and Sheffield Wednesday) plus those with Sporting Futures and Derbyshire Sport, we support and promote initiatives that aim to improve the health of people in the communities in which we operate. We are proud to be key supporters of Sporting Futures and the Derbyshire Building Society 10K Run and Fun Run for the 6th year in 2008.

'Financial Education

'We at the Derbyshire Building Society are committed to helping deliver a vital strategy, working with the Financial Services Authority, who is leading the National Strategy for Financial Capability, to improve the nation's knowledge and understanding of personal finance. We have designated much time and effort into creating an appropriate, interactive and engaging resource for learning that we hope will become an essential part of financial education in our region. Our branch staff will deliver this package to schools and businesses across the network.

'Corporate Social Responsibility

'Corporate Social Responsibility is much more than addressing environmental issues. For us at the Derbyshire, it gives us an opportunity to demonstrate to our communities that they are as important to us as we are to them. Our members have expressed a desire to want to make a difference within their communities and it is our intention to support that.'

Unfortunately, Derbyshire Building Society does not appear to calculate the value of this support, but we believe it to be of a sufficiently high level to warrant inclusion.

In kind support

Employees' expertise is sometimes provided to support projects and stimulate new initiatives.

Employee-led support

Many branches of Derbyshire Building Society have adopted Rainbows Children Hospice as their charity of the year. Staff participate in fundraising activities on its behalf, facilitate public giving, for example, by inviting members of the public to contribute to Rainbows 'Light of Hope Appeal' by purchasing a light in celebration of the life of someone special.

To help co-ordinate this and other, though not all, community initiatives supported by staff, a Community Development Team was established in 2000.

Commercially-led support

Sponsorship: *Environment* – East Midlands in Bloom

'This annual competition, sponsored by Derbyshire Building Society, offers cities, towns and villages throughout the East Midlands the opportunity to showcase their commitment by improving and maintaining their immediate environment.'

Sport – Derbyshire Building Society 10k and Fun Run, Derby

'Held in conjunction with Sporting Futures a Derby based charity that uses sport as a catalyst to engage with young people enabling them to build meaningful relationships with family, friends and the wider community in which they live.'

Deutsche Bank

Company registration number 1032332

Winchester House, 1 Great Winchester Street, London EC2N 2DB

020 7545 8000

Website: www.db.com/unitedkingdom

Correspondent: Kate Cavelle, Director, Deutsche Bank CSR UK
Email: kate.cavelle@db.com

Chairman: The Lord Aldington

Year end
31/12/2007

Nature of company business
Deutsche Bank is the holding company of a group providing international merchant banking and investment management services.

Subsidiaries include: Morgan Grenfell

Main locations: Edinburgh, London

UK employees: 8,000

Charitable donations

2007: £4,800,000
2006: £3,000,000
2005: £4,500,000
2004: £3,500,000
2003: £3,400,000

Total community contributions: £5,175,000
Management costs: £160,000

Membership: A & B, BitC, L B Group

Community involvement

As one of the largest employers in the City of London, Deutsche Bank feels it is important to build strong relationships between the bank, its employees and its community partners. Each year, Deutsche Bank London invests in its local neighbourhoods, running programmes geared towards increasing access to and enhancing the quality of education, improving employability skills, supporting entrepreneurship, identifying opportunities to actively engage in the community and widening access to arts and culture.

As part of its support for community development, the bank focuses on the following three key global themes:

▸ education – by funding programmes that support retention, achievement and progression

▸ community development – focusing on disadvantaged communities in London and prioritising neighbouring boroughs through community sport, educational outreach, employment and employability, homelessness and neighbourhood renewal

▸ the arts – nurturing artistic talent.

Within the above themes, projects supported must have characteristics as outlined on www.communityuk.db.com/guidelines.php

In addition, Deutsche Bank is committed to working with young people to raise aspirations, build confidence, provide opportunities and break down barriers.

In 2007 Deutsche Bank began its first community development finance partnership – investing money in charities rather than just providing grants. This is an area of activity it plans to expand in 2008.

Charities of the Year: Throughout 2008 the bank has supported supporting three charities. These are: The Angus Lawson Memorial Trust; CHICKS; and Teenage Cancer Trust.

Note: Deutsche Bank's charities committee has decided to extend the current partnerships until December 2009.

Exclusions

As a bank, support is not given to the following, although this does not prevent us from supporting individual employee efforts in respect of such donations including matched giving:

▸ animal welfare projects

▸ capital projects

▸ drugs related projects

▸ heritage projects

▸ individual sponsorship

▸ medical/medical research charities

▸ charities or initiatives with religious/political objectives

▸ sponsorship of events/tables for projects not associated with our core community development activities.

Applications

Community development support: Deutsche Bank builds its community investment programmes around three key global themes – education, community development and art. The funding guidelines for each are laid out in detail. Funding applications are approved by the bank's UK charities committee, which comprises of representatives from the various business areas. The committee generally meets on a monthly basis.

All proposals and queries from prospective and successful applicants must be submitted by email to:

Kerry Ortuzar – Community Development Manager
Direct line: 020 7547 6092
Fax: 0113 336 1890
Email: kerry.ortuzar@db.com

Harriet King – Community Development Co-ordinator
Direct line: 020 7545 3310
Email: harriet.king@db.com

Once you have submitted your proposal, please be patient – the bank receives many requests for funding and endeavours to fully consider each application. You will be notified of the decision – successful or not – as soon as possible.

Charities of the Year 2010: The selection process for Charities of the Year 2010 is likely to begin in June 2009. Please revisit the corporate social responsibility section of the bank's website at that time for further information.

Information available: The bank publishes an annual UK social responsibility report.

Corporate giving

In 2007, the bank made total community contributions in the UK of £5,175,000 of which £4.8 million was in cash donations. This was broken down as follows:

- education £1,390,000
- social investment £1,260,000
- art £330,000
- employee programmes:
  - 'Initiative Plus'/'Community Awards' £130,000
  - Charity of the year £30,000
  - Matched giving £1,000,000
  - Community challenges £10,000
  - Franchise funding £390,000
  - Donations direct from business areas £260,000.

Employee volunteering in working hours was valued at £350,000 and Gifts in kind at £25,000. Management/administration costs were a remarkably low £160,000 – other companies please note!

In kind support

Initiative Plus: The bank, through a major employee volunteering programme called Initiative Plus, encourages its staff to provide their time, skills and energy on a voluntary basis to local education projects. Staff can apply for a grant of up to £300 from the bank to donate to the organisation with which they volunteer.

Gifts in Kind: In 2007 Deutsche Bank gave in excess of £15,000 worth of gifts to over 20 charitable organisations and schools.

Recycling: Deutsche Bank is now working with Green-Works for disposal of all our redundant furniture.

Employee-led support

The bank's matched giving scheme matches employee charitable donations like for like, (up to £3,000 per person per year), no matter whether they donate through GAYE, a one-off donation or through sponsorship. For the latter, there is no limit on how much an employee can fundraise within the bank!

Community Awards: Deutsche Bank values the time employees spend supporting their preferred causes and charities. Community awards have been devised to recognise commitment of time by employees to these good causes, 'out of hours'. The awards are between £100 and £1,000 each to the benefiting cause. Each year there is also a 'Community Award of the Year', selected from all the year's community

awards. This award is worth up to £5,000 to the benefiting cause. In 2007, the bank granted 57 community awards.

Payroll giving: The bank offers its employees the Give As You Earn scheme and automatically matches employee donations.

Commercially-led support

Sponsorship: *Sport* – Athletics and other sporting activities have been sponsored by the bank.

Dhamecha Group Ltd

Company registration number 4386546

Wembley Stadium Industrial Estate, First Way, Wembley, Middlesex HA9 0TU

020 8903 8181; Fax: 020 8902 4420

Website: www.dhamecha.com

Correspondent: P K Dhamecha, Trustee

Year end	Turnover	Pre-tax profit
31/03/2007	£327,976,000	£5,854,000

Nature of company business
The principal activities are wholesale food cash and carry, property dealings and the manufacture and sale of paper disposable products.

Subsidiaries include: London Paper Products Ltd

Main locations: Wembley, Barking, Croydon, Enfield, Watford

UK employees: 344

Charitable donations
2007: £225,000
2006: £200,000
2005: £200,000
2004: £200,000
2003: £180,000

Community involvement

The company makes an annual charitable donation to the closely-linked Laduma Dhamecha Charitable Trust (Charity Commission no. 328678). The trust supports general charitable purposes in the UK and abroad, but primarily seeks to provide the following:

- relief for sickness by provision of medical equipment and/or establishing or improving the facilities at hospitals as the trustees determine
- to provide for the advancement of education and/or educational establishment in rural areas so as to make children self sufficient in the longer term.

Only organisations can benefit.

Applications

In writing to the correspondent, who is a trustee of the Laduma Dhamecha Charitable Trust.

Corporate giving

In 2006/07, the company made charitable donations of £225,000 of which £200,000 went to the Laduma Dhamecha Charitable Trust.

During the year the trust made charitable donations of £56,000. No list of beneficiaries was available.

Diageo plc

Company registration number 23307

8 Henrietta Place, London W1M 9AG

020 7927 5200; Fax: 020 7927 4600

Website: www.diageo.com

Correspondent: Will Peskett, Head of Corporate Citizenship
Email: corporatecitizenship@diageo.com

Chairman: Dr Franz Humer

Chief Executive: P S Walsh

Year end	Turnover	Pre-tax profit
30/06/2008	£10,643,000,000	£2,093,000,000

Nature of company business
The group's principal activity is the manufacture and distribution of spirits, wines and beer.

Subsidiaries include: United Distillers & Vintners (HP) Ltd, Guinness Ltd, United Distillers & Vintners (ER) Ltd

Main locations: London

Total employees: 24,373

Charitable donations

2008: £10,700,000
2007: £10,600,000
2006: £11,800,000
2005: £14,400,000
2004: £7,300,000

Membership: BitC, L B Group

Community involvement

As well as the support given through the Diageo Foundation (Charity Commission no. 1014681), the company makes its own contributions to assist charitable and community activities in the communities it serves. Currently, besides its primary focus on responsible drinking, Diageo's other community activities fall into three further focus areas, chosen to reflect where it's businesses have the greatest impact and where the company can make the most difference. These are:

- skills for life – working with unemployed or disadvantage young adults to become accepted, active citizens of their community
- water of life – projects that protect the environment or improve access to safe drinking water in developing countries
- local citizens – supporting Diageo's employees in actively engaging in the community, by assessing community needs, harnessing employees' skills, and encouraging volunteering and fundraising
- disaster relief – the provision of humanitarian aid in the form of emergency relief and supporting longer-term reparation projects whilst facilitating employee-led fundraising.

The Diageo Foundation

The Diageo Foundation's aim is to create positive, long-term change in the community. It focuses on areas of humanitarian need, primarily in developing countries in Africa, Latin America, Asia and Eastern Europe, where it can make the most difference. The foundation provides kick-start funding and expertise in establishing local projects, some of which are run in partnership with local businesses.

The foundation makes charitable donations, matches employee fundraising in the UK and provides longer-term social investment in areas where we can make the most difference.

To be eligible for funding from the Diageo Foundation, projects must fall within one of the four key focus areas listed above. They must also demonstrate the following:

- addressing a community/social need, in particular excluded and disadvantaged people who, with support, can help themselves to transform their own lives
- building partnerships with community groups and NGOs
- helping build the skills-base of individuals or communities
- maximising grants to make them as effective as possible
- building the economic prosperity of a community
- planning a clear exit strategy and appropriate mechanisms to ensure that the benefits derived from the project are sustainable
- having clear, well-defined objectives in place, including planned outcomes, desired impact, measurement and evaluation
- enhancing the project, if appropriate, by working in partnership with a local Diageo business.

There is normally a three-year limit to any funding commitment

The maximum funding available for any one project is £50,000. Payments are made normally over a maximum period of three years.

The Diageo Foundation encourages projects which obtain additional funding from external sources as this can lead to sustainability.

Exclusions

The following are outside the foundation's guidelines:

- organisations which are not registered charities
- individuals
- loans or business finance
- medical charities or hospitals
- promotion of religion
- animal welfare
- expeditions or overseas travel
- political organisations
- advertising
- product donations
- capital projects (e.g. buildings).

Applications

Applications to the Diageo Foundation should be addressed to the Administrator at the above address (Tel: 020 7927 5417; Email: diageofoundation@diageo.com).

Please write providing details of the project, how it relates to the Diageo Foundation's focus areas and the amount of funding required – on no more than two sides of a sheet of paper. The foundation will contact you if it requires further details.

You will normally receive written notification of whether your application has been successful or not within 6–8 weeks.

Corporate giving

The company commits approximately 1% of annual worldwide trading profit to support community activities – about £23.9 million in total in 2007/08. During the year, UK group companies made donations of £10.7 million to charitable organisations, including £1 million to the Diageo Foundation and £7.1 million to the Thalidomide Trust. Group companies in the rest of the world made donations totalling £13.2 million.

The range of projects supported by Diageo is wide, from education and the environment to employability and homelessness. Its website provides a comprehensive list and outline of the organisations and people it has helped, an example of which are given below.

Employment: Tomorrow's People Trust was set up by Diageo nearly 20 years ago (although it is now legally independent of the company) and has become a specialist national charitable organisation helping people and communities.

With a commitment to invest in Tomorrow's People for a further five years, Diageo is currently working with the trust to explore a responsible drinking programme, with the aim of helping to combat alcohol abuse in our communities.

In kind support

The company acknowledges that whilst financial contributions are important, the giving of time and skill by its staff or surplus products and other in kind donations can often achieve more.

Employee-led support

Employee fundraising/giving receives match funding.

Payroll giving: The company operate the Give As You Earn scheme.

Commercially-led support

Sponsorship: The company undertakes good-cause sponsorship.

Dow Chemical Company Ltd

Company registration number 537161

Estuary Road, King's Lynn, Norfolk PE30 2JD

01553 692100; Fax: 01553 694559

Website: www.dow.com

Correspondent: Carol Allen, UK Communications

Year end	Turnover	Pre-tax profit
31/12/2006	£432,905,000	£14,541,000

Nature of company business
The company is a worldwide manufacturer and supplier of chemicals and performance products, plastics, hydrocarbons and energy, and consumer specialities including agricultural products, and consumer products.

Main locations: King's Lynn, Wilton, Sandbach, Seal Sands, Staines, Middlesbrough, Mirfield, Nuneaton, Billingham

UK employees: 310

Charitable donations
2006: £30,495
2005: £39,571

Community involvement

Dow states on its global website that: 'The challenge of becoming more transparent lies in part in the ability to provide information relevant to a wide variety of stakeholders. The communities in which we operate are an important stakeholder for Dow. In an effort to increase the relevancy of our public reporting efforts for this particular stakeholder, Dow – in addition to its global report website – will publish to the Internet key data for its 20 major manufacturing locations.'

Whilst we whole heartedly commend Dow's efforts in this respect, it is unfortunate from a UK point of view that their facilities here do not rank amongst the top 20. The scant information we did receive only arrived after contacting their US office to point out the unwillingness of its UK subsidiary to cooperate with us.

The following information was provided by the UK Communication's at Dow Chemical: 'Our corporate donation policy is to support the communities in which we have a significant presence, which for us in the UK is primarily King's Lynn, Mirfield and the Teeside area.

'Specifically, we aim to support social needs, scientific education, or projects that improve the environment. In addition, projects should bring a real benefit and be supported by organisations in the local community.'

Exclusions

No response to circular appeals. No support for advertising in charity brochures, appeals from individuals, local appeals not in areas of company presence, enterprise/training, overseas projects, political appeals, religious appeals or sport.

Applications

According to Dow's Corporate Giving leaflet, 'Sharing Our Success', preferential consideration is given to requests for donations recommended by employees. Unsolicited applications/blanket appeal letters are not therefore considered.

Corporate giving

In 2006, Dow made charitable donations in the UK of £30,495 (2005: £39,571). No further information was available.

Employee-led support

Employees' volunteering/charitable activities are supported by the company. We were previously advised that Dow match employees' fundraising and giving to a maximum of £500 each, although we do not know if this is still so.

Dow Corning Ltd

Company registration number 486170

Cardiff Road, Barry, Vale of Glamorgan CF63 2YL

01446 732350; Fax: 01446 747944

Website: www.dowcorning.com/barry

Correspondent: Community Relations Co-ordinator
01446 732350; Fax: 01446 747944

Year end	Turnover	Pre-tax profit
31/12/2006	£378,234,000	£20,754,000

Nature of company business
International provider of innovative silicone and silicon-based products, technologies, and services.

Main locations: Barry

UK employees: 662

Community involvement

Each year Dow Corning receives many requests for support for local projects with help being given through donations of equipment, sponsorship or practical support from employees. The company stressed that though happy to listen to new requests for support, funds are limited. Moreover, in considering applications it looks at a number of factors.

A small team of employees meet monthly to discuss all the requests. Priority is given to requests from local groups and the team tries to make sure that any Dow Corning donation helps as many people as possible and has a long-term benefit.

Consideration is given to requests that meet the following criteria:

- projects that are local to the Barry, South Wales site and benefit people locally. Preference is given in order to Barry and Sully areas then Vale of Glamorgan. Requests from further a field cannot be considered
- activities that will help young people learn more about science, maths and technology, or skills that they will need in their future careers
- ideas that will help organisations or communities to improve safety or the local environment and that lead to better community vitality
- projects that promote good citizenship.

The company appears to take its responsibility towards the local community very seriously. Besides providing assistance in the forms mentioned above, regular communication with local people takes place through a number of channels. These include: the publication of a regular community newsletter – 'Dow Corning News'; the provision of a helpline for those concerned about environmental and health and safety issues; open house 'Forums for Neighbours'; and a monthly Community Advisory Panel consisting of representatives from the Barry area.

Exclusions

No support for raffle prizes, for individuals (such as sponsorship for overseas travel or individual fundraising), donations to central funds of charities, political or religious groups, one-off events such as fetes, parades, shows, tournaments, concerts, group travel expenses for excursions or overseas adventures, medical research, general fundraising appeals where Dow Corning funding is not used on specific projects or purchases, uniforms or sports strips for sports teams, national or international appeals, or advertising.

Applications

In writing to the correspondent. Only written appeals will be considered.

Corporate giving

The company were unwilling to disclose the value of its charitable donations in the UK, or details of beneficiaries.

Generally, however, support is given to schools, local charity groups and a local science museum. For those interested, the company's website gives some specific examples of groups supported. These can be found within the pages of its community newsletter.

Previously, the company has stated: 'Occasionally, Dow Corning receives requests to help support large-scale projects. These are often multi-thousand dollar requests and are way beyond the site's own donations budget. A separate funding avenue has been set up whereby local organisations can apply for a corporate grant. Grant requests can be received from across Europe and are reviewed by European site managers. They are awarded once annually.'

In kind support

The company may occasionally make donations of equipment.

Environment: The company has recently completed building a 'green' nature centre at Cadoxton Ponds, next its site. Built from sustainable resources, the building features solar panels, rainwater harvesting, and ground-sourced heating. Opened in spring 2007, the building is used, amongst other things, as a classroom for visiting school parties.

Employee-led support

Employees are encouraged to become involved in supporting their local communities through practical help. A major part of this is the active programme the company has in supporting students and teachers in local schools with science, maths and technology.

Employee fundraising is matched by the company up to a maximum of £250.

Dresdner Kleinwort Ltd

Company registration number 551334

PO Box 52715, 30 Gresham Street, London EC2P 3XY

020 7623 8000; Fax: 020 7623 4069

Website: www.dresdnerkleinwort.com

Correspondent: Bruce Taylor, Corporate Social Responsibility Team

Chairman: A C D Yarrow

Year end	Turnover	Pre-tax profit
31/12/2007	£860,793,000	£104,251,000

Nature of company business
Investment banking.

Main locations: London

Charitable donations
2007: £74,018
2006: £29,997

Community involvement

The company concentrates its support on promoting regeneration in East London, supporting local charities, and local projects of national charities, which:

- encourage and promote new and young businesses

enhance the skills and broaden the horizons of young people

meet specific community needs.

Projects should be one-off or have the potential to become financially sustainable in future years. Preference is given to work which encourages collaboration between private, voluntary and public sector organisations, attract additional resources and seek to share best practice and experiences to a wider audience.

Charity of the year: Richard House (2008).

Applications

In writing to the correspondent. Applications for funding must be submitted by June each year.

Corporate giving

Having obtained up-to-date financial information on the company, it appears that the level of cash support is some what lower than we believed. Furthermore, as we did not receive a reply to our request for information, we have no figure for Dresdner's in kind support.

In 2007, the company made charitable donations of £74,018 (2006: £29,997) 'to a trust, which is used for charitable purposes.' Unfortunately, we have been unable to identify this trust, but it appears not to be one of the Kleinwort family trusts.

In kind support

Since the late 1990s, Dresdner, through staff volunteers, has supported Reading and Number Partner schemes at a primary school in Tower Hamlets. The aims of the scheme are to help improve pupils' communication and literacy or numeracy skills, confidence and motivation, as well as developing employees' personal and professional skills and building the sense of community within the bank.

Employee-led support

The company has a matching funds scheme for employee fundraising. Employees are also encouraged to volunteer.

Payroll giving: The company operates the Give As You Earn scheme

Commercially-led support

Sponsorship: *The arts* – Sponsorship is mainly of events in the City of London, such as the City of London Festival and the Spitalfields Festival. A number of major arts organisations have also been supported. However, sponsorship is usually an exception rather than the norm.

DSG International plc

Company registration number 333031

Maylands Avenue, Hemel Hempstead, Hertfordshire HP2 7TG

0870 850 3333

Website: www.dsgiplc.com

Correspondent: Community Relations Manager 0870 850 3333 Email: communityrelations@dixons.co.uk

Chairman: Sir John Collins

Chief Executive: John Browett

Year end	Turnover	Pre-tax profit
03/05/2008	£7,929,700,000	(£192,800,000)

Nature of company business
The company's main activity is the retailing of high technology consumer electronics, personal computers, domestic appliances, photographic equipment, communication products and related financial and after sales services.

Subsidiaries include: DSG Retail Ltd, PC World, Curry's, Coverplan Insurance Services Ltd, The Link, Partmaster, Mastercare Service and Distribution Ltd, PC World Business

Main locations: Nottingham, Sheffield, Bury, Hemel Hempstead

Total employees: 40,730

Charitable donations
2008: £400,000
2007: £875,000
2006: £875,000
2005: £875,000
2004: £875,000
Membership: BitC

Community involvement

DSG International has funded charities and communities for many years through its registered charity DSG International Foundation (Charity Commission no. 1053215). Since the foundation was set up in 1996 it has funded many projects in the areas of education and health, with a preference for those with employee's involvement. More recently, the foundation has supported 'Switched on Communities', DSG's community involvement programme.

Switched on Communities

Launched in June 2006, the programme aims to provide technology and training to those who need it most. As part of the programme DSG has four partners: Foyer Foundation; Eco-Schools; e-Learning Foundation; and AbilityNet.

DSG 's community programme currently focuses on its four charity partners and in supporting the charitable work of its employees. As a result, it is unable to process requests from other charities and groups. The current 'Switched on Communities' initiative will run until July 2009. DSG anticipate reviewing the programme in early 2009, so please check their website for further developments.

Please check this website for further developments.

Exclusions

No grants are made towards: third party fundraising activities; political or religious organisations; projects that should be funded from statutory sources, overseas appeals; community sponsorship of any kind; or animal charities.

Applications

DSG's community programme currently focuses on its four charity partners and in supporting the charitable work of its employees. As a result, it is unable to process requests from other charities and groups. The current 'Switched on Communities' initiative will run until July 2009. DSG anticipate reviewing the programme in early 2009, so please check their website for further developments.

Corporate giving

In 2007/08, the group made total community contributions of £1,228,000 (2006/07: £1,141,000). Of this, £400,000 (2006/07: £875,000) was donated to the DSG International Foundation which made grants totalling £1,043,000.

DSG International Foundation

The latest accounts available for the foundation cover 2006/07 when grants were made totalling £849,000.

Beneficiaries included: AbilityNet (£202,500); Foyer Federation (£177,095); Encams (£101,998); e-Learning Foundation (£94,400); Dixons City Academy (£25,000); Institute of Economic Affairs (£12,000); St Joseph's RC High School (£10,000); Reform Research Trust (£7,500); Jubilee Sailing Trust (£5,000); and Refugee Housing Trust (£2,400).

Grants tend to range from £100 to £10,000. Donations below £1,000 are often made in the form of gift vouchers to support the purchase of specific items of equipment.

In kind support

The company also gives assistance through seconding staff to enterprise initiatives and gifts in kind.

Employee-led support

Wherever they are based, many of the group's employees give up their time and skills to help support local community activities. In recognition of this commitment, the group provides employees (as individuals, or at a store level) with grants to support their fundraising and volunteering.

'Many employees are given the opportunity to take part in team challenges, from decorating a local charity office to supporting Young Enterprise schemes at schools. If you have an idea for a suitable challenge, please email corporate.affairs@dsgiplc.com

'Employees are also offered community-related training options for personal and management development including volunteering, mentoring and skills-transfer opportunities ranging from partnering head teachers to working with young offenders.'

In 2006/07, the foundation supported 300 smaller charities and gave out 200 employee grants.

Payroll giving: The Give As You Earn scheme is operated.

Commercially-led support

Sponsorship: We were previously advised that the company's sponsorship programmes all come from the marketing, rather than community, budget, and decisions are made for purely commercial reasons. However, charitable programmes have been run in the past and will be considered for the benefits they can bring the company.

Du Pont (UK) Ltd

Company registration number 4556216

Wedgwood Way, Stevenage, Hertfordshire SG1 4QN

01438 734000; Fax: 01438 734836

Website: www2.dupont.com/Social_Commitment

Year end	Turnover	Pre-tax profit
31/12/2007	£352,689,000	£23,753,000

Nature of company business
The group's principal business is the manufacture, sale and distribution of chemical products (fibres, polymers, chemicals and specialities, and electronics).

Main locations: Londonderry, East Kilbride, Maydown, Ruabon, Corby, Stevenage, Sudbury, Bristol, Darlington, Romiley

UK employees: 867

Community involvement

The company's website states that: 'DuPont is committed to improving the quality of life and enhancing the vitality of communities in which it operates throughout the world. Through financial contribution and the volunteer efforts of its employees, DuPont supports programmes that address social progress, economic success and environmental excellence – all vital components of community sustainability.

'Each year, DuPont contributes to numerous efforts that meet the needs of various groups and global communities where the company operates. Areas of support include:

- educational programmes
- culture and the arts
- environmental initiatives
- human and health service organisations
- civic and community activities'.

Within these criteria support may be available from three sources. Firstly, from the individual DuPont business units in the UK. Secondly, from the Corporate Contributions Office in the USA. Thirdly, from the DuPont Centre for Collaborative Research and Education, also in the USA.

Exclusions

No grants are made to: non-registered charities; disease-specific organisations; endowment funds; service organisations; individuals; political causes; sectarian groups whose work is only available to members of one religious community; or organisations without good equal opportunity processes.

Applications

As each DuPont site in the UK is responsible for its own community contributions, please contact the most appropriate one.

Applications are also considered centrally by its head office in the USA. The DuPont Contributions and Membership Team are responsible for non education-related monetary contributions. Most corporate grants involve programmes in the DuPont headquarters community of Wilmington, Delaware, and other communities where the company has a major presence.

Applications must be submitted in writing on a one to two-page letter defining who your organisation is, the project which requires funding and how this meets the aims of the company's corporate responsibility programme. An email address should also be included, if possible. Applications are generally considered around May and September.

For non-education related appeals, the address is:

Corporate Contributions Office
DuPont Public Affairs
1007 Market Street
Wilmington, DE 19898
USA.

For educational appeals, the address is:

DuPont Center for Collaborative Research and Education
PO BOX 80030/1370
Wilmington, DE 19880–0030
USA.

Corporate giving

As each DuPont site in the UK is responsible for its own community contributions, no community contributions figure was available. However, we believe the company's stated commitment to supporting community sustainability warrants its inclusion here.

DuPont Community Fund

Since 1990, over 400 projects worldwide have received support from the fund. Company sites can nominate projects that enhance local community life for awards on an annual basis. The fund matches $ for $ up to $10,000 (around £6,000) any donation made to the project by the local DuPont site.

DuPont Centre for Collaborative Research and Education

Unlike the above fund, it does not appear to be necessary for projects to be nominated by a DuPont site (although support from such may add weight to your application). However, in applying, it must be clearly shown how the project relates to DuPont's mission, operating philosophy, and areas of support of the company's community involvement programme. Grants are geared towards primary, secondary and higher education institutions and programmes.

In kind support

The company website suggests that in kind support, e.g. the donation of land to a conservation group, may be made in cases where the organisations programmes and activities relate to the company's goals.

Employee-led support

Through the DuPont Volunteer Recognition awards, the time and effort given by employees in support of their favoured charity or local community is acknowledged by the company. In addition to this, grants of $1,000 (around £600) are given to the organisation benefiting from the volunteering employees.

Dwr Cymru Welsh Water

Company registration number 2366777

Pentwyn Road, Nelson, Treharris CF46 6LY

01443 452300; Fax: 01443 452323

Website: www.dwrcymru.com

Chairman: Lord Burns

Managing Director: Nigel Annett

Year end	Turnover	Pre-tax profit
31/03/2007	£578,000,000	£47,500,000

Nature of company business
Provision of water services.

Main locations: Treharris

Charitable donations
2007: £32,874
2006: £33,395
2005: £22,394
2004: £24,570
Membership: BitC

Community involvement

Glas Cymru is a single purpose company formed to own, finance and manage Welsh Water (Dwr Cymru). It is a 'company limited by guarantee' and because it has no shareholders, any financial surpluses are retained for the benefit of Welsh Water's customers.

The company has previously stated the following with regards to its community support policy: 'When Glas Cymru acquired Welsh Water, the board decided not to engage in major corporate sponsorship and donations, but to focus our effort on community engagement around the traditional strengths of Welsh water in the fields of education, conservation and recreation centred on the assets of the company'. This primarily takes the form of in kind support.'

Applications
Note: As a not-for-profit company operating for the benefit of its customers, any donations that are made by Welsh Water are done so in support of employees fundraising efforts. Applications outside of this are not, therefore, accepted or acknowledged.

Corporate giving

In 2006/07, the company made charitable cash donations totalling nearly £33,000. Major beneficiaries included: Water Aid (£17,900); Keep Wales Tidy (£10,000); Mike Paines Bursary Memorial (£2,278); and Ty Hafan (£1,500).

Although no figure for community contributions was available, this could be quite substantial based on the examples given under 'In kind support'.

In kind support
Education: Welsh Water has developed a programme of activities to educate children about their environment through, for example, the *Living and Learning with Water* interactive website. It also operates four education centres located across Wales staffed by full-time seconded teachers or environmental rangers and to which visits are free of charge. Finally, in partnership with the Welsh Assembly's Healthy Schools Initiative, *Think Water – Dewis Dwr*, it has supported the provision of water coolers to nearly 400 schools based in 'Communities First' areas across Wales.

Recreation: The company encourages visitors to share in the resources offered by its reservoirs. Facilities include fishing, sailing, canoeing, windsurfing and diving. Larger sites offer visitor centres, bird watching hides, picnic areas and marked pathways and nature trails.

Community involvement: *Crimestoppers* – Welsh Water works with the four Welsh Police Forces to prevent distraction burglaries often in the form of bogus callers. Customers concerned about the latter can register for the company's password scheme. This enables them to identify genuine company representatives by use of an agreed word or phrase.

Employee-led support

The company stated that: 'We have continued to promote our community investment scheme to assist employees who wish to become involved in charitable or other projects within their local communities'. In other words, any donations the company makes are to support (match) the fundraising efforts of its employees.

In 2006/07, employees participated in the 'World of Work' scheme in support of local schools and fundraised throughout the year on behalf of WaterAid raising over £100,000.

Dyson Ltd

Company registration number 2627406

Tetbury Hill, Malmesbury, Wiltshire NS16 0RP

01666 827200

Website: www.dyson.co.uk

Correspondent: The James Dyson Foundation

Email: jamesdysonfoundation@dyson.com

Chairman: Sir James Dyson

Year end	Turnover	Pre-tax profit
31/12/2006	£135,788,000	(£124,804,000)

Nature of company business
Manufacture of domestic appliances.

Charitable donations

2006: £2,140,000
2005: £2,885,000
2004: £150,000

Community involvement

The company's support is channelled through the James Dyson Foundation (Charity Commission no. 1099709). Established in 2002, the foundation promotes charitable giving, especially to charities working in the fields of science, engineering, medicine and education. With a committee to manage giving, and registered charity status, it is intended that the James Dyson Foundation will assist educational institutions working in the field of design, technology and engineering, as well as charities carrying out medical or scientific research. Locally, the foundation seeks to support charitable projects in or nearby Malmesbury, the town where Dyson is based.

Dyson's own employees also contribute to the foundation and are encouraged to take an active role in selecting projects and fundraising, especially for Dyson's charity partnerships (CLIC – Cancer and Leukaemia in Childhood, Meningitis Research Foundation and Breakthrough Breastcancer).

Dyson state that: 'We occasionally donate small grants to charitable projects that share our philosophies and objectives. Due to our [large] commitment to the Dyson School of Design Innovation, we're not currently donating large grants'.

Exclusions

The foundation does not provide support for political purposes and local appeals not in areas of company presence.

Applications

If your fundraising falls within the foundation's objectives, please fill in the online application form at: www.jamesdysonfoundation.com/jdf/application.asp

A response within two weeks is promised.

Corporate giving

The James Dyson Foundation

The foundation relies principally on funds received from Dyson Ltd which, in 2006, donated £2,140,000. During the year 2006/07, the foundation made grants totalling £916,194 which was broken down as follows: Education and training (£874,159); Social and community welfare (£29,887); and Science and medical research (£12,148).

Beneficiaries included:

- *Education* – Bath Technology Centre (£666,297), Royal College of Art (£112,000), Upper Street Events Design Show (£11,684) and Amba Ras School (£5,000)
- *Science* – Royal Marsden Cancer Campaign (£5,000), CLIC (£4,157) and Children in Need (£1,276)
- *Social* – Claymills Pumping engine Trust (£13,296), Dorothy House Hospice (£5,000) and Malmesbury & Tetbury District Round Table (£3,000).

In kind support

Design engineers from Dyson host workshops at schools and universities throughout the country and the foundation provides free resources to Design and Technology teachers throughout the UK.

The company provide an information pack for teachers and lecturers which can be used in conjunction with the Dyson Education Box and both are free of charge.

Each year, the company donate a number of Dyson vacuum cleaners to charitable causes within the James Dyson Foundation's objectives.

Employee-led support

Dyson workers in Malmesbury, Wiltshire, also contribute to the foundation and are encouraged to take an active role in selecting projects and fundraising, especially for Dyson's charity partnerships.

E.ON UK plc

Company registration number 2366970

Westwood Way, Westwood Business Park, Coventry CV4 8LG

024 7642 4000; Fax: 024 7642 5432

Website: www.eon-uk.com

Correspondent: The Corporate Responsibility Manager

Chairman: Dr Paul Golby

Chief Executive: Dr Paul Golby

Year end	Turnover	Pre-tax profit
31/12/2007	£8,609,000,000	£744,000,000

Nature of company business
Principal activities are electricity generation, distribution, and energy trading and retailing.

Subsidiaries include: Ergon Insurance Ltd, Kinetica Ltd, East Midlands Electricity, Wavedriver Ltd, DR Investments

Main locations: Nottingham, Coventry

UK employees: 16,800

Charitable donations

2007: £130,055
2006: £28,943
2005: £74,673

Total community contributions: £2,500,000

Membership: BitC, L B Group

Community involvement

E.ON UK's community support is focused on areas relevant to the company's business activities – where it is based and where its employees live and work, i.e. predominantly in and around its offices, call centres and power station sites.

As well as a regional focus, community activities are targeted on areas relevant to the business and where maximum benefit can be brought. Community investment strategy is based on two main themes – the company aims to develop projects that fit into one of these: Education through Energy and Community Energy Solutions.

Exclusions

No support for: advertising in charity brochures; animal welfare; appeals from individuals; enterprise/training; fundraising events; medical research; political appeals; religious appeals; or sickness/disability charities.

Applications

In writing to the correspondent.

Corporate giving

In 2007, donations to charitable organisations amounted to £130,055 (2006: £28,943). We have no details of the beneficiaries.

In kind support

E.ON UK has worked in partnership with Age Concern England for nine years, delivering 'We Test You Rest', an electric blanket testing and replacement service for older people.

Employee-led support

The company encourages its people to get involved in its employee volunteering programme – over 1,700 participated in 2005.

The company match funds employees fundraising efforts.

Payroll giving: The company has established an employee payroll giving scheme.

Other initiatives exist to support employee fundraising activities, such as providing maths and IT support for schoolchildren.

eaga plc

Company registration number 3858865

Partnership House, City West Business Park, Scotswood Road, Newcastle upon Tyne NE4 7DF

0191 245 8501; Fax: 0191 245 8560

Website: www.eaga.com

Correspondent: Sam Robinson

Email: sam.robinson@eaga.com

Chairman: Charles Berry

Chief Executive: John Clough

Year end	Turnover	Pre-tax profit
31/05/2008	£638,960,000	£28,365,000

Nature of company business
The group is a 'green support services company' engaged in the provision of outsourced services and products that address a wide range of environmental and social challenges.

Main locations: Cardiff, Birmingham, Belfast, Birkenhead, Knowsley

UK employees: 4,150

Charitable donations

2008: £135,000
2007: £250,000

Membership: BitC

Community involvement

The company primarily supports charitable causes through the eaga Partnership Charitable Trust (Charity Commission no. 1088361). In 2007, however, it also established an eaga Community Fund to support community organisations as they seek to tackle, at a local level, the social and environmental issues that are aligned with the company's own business interests.

'The fund supports projects that educate, raise awareness and demonstrate engagement in addressing environmental issues at a grass roots level. Applications that also offer opportunities for participation and direct involvement for eaga staff are particularly welcome, as we feel we have a role to play in encouraging our employees to become engaged and contribute positively to their local communities.

'The fund is currently active in regions where eaga has substantial areas of operations: namely, North East England; South Yorkshire; Wales; Scotland; and Northern Ireland. Looking forward our objective is to significantly increase the size of this fund and number and range of projects funded and develop a volunteering scheme running alongside it to provide practical help and support'.

Applications

Applications to the community fund should be made in writing to the correspondent.

For the eaga Partnership Charitable Trust, applicants are requested to complete an application form. All applications that are completed in full and fulfil the main aims of the trust will be assessed at a formal meeting of trustees. Meetings are held three times a year. The trustees review applications against specific criteria and objectives.

Completed applications should be returned to: Dr Naomi Brown, eaga Partnership Charitable Trust, 23 Macadam Gardens, Penrith CA11 9HS (Tel: 01768 210 220; email: eagact@aol.com).

Corporate giving

In 2007/08, the company made charitable donations of £135,000 (2007: £250,000). This was mainly in support of the associated trust which gives grants for action and research projects into the causes of fuel poverty and its impact on health.

Through the newly established eaga Community Fund, the most recent round of funding saw support being given to a total of 33 local projects across the five funding regions, representing a huge array of activity from renewables demonstration kits and historic woodland management to supporting community farms and community clean-ups.

For example, as part of a local environmental scheme to demonstrate how much energy is used to 'feed' electrical appliances, children at Newcastle's Byker-based community project – Kids Kabin – use their pent-up energy to power household gadgets. The centre, which provides activities for children aged between 8 and 16, was successful in applying to the eaga Community Fund and awarded £4,000 to further develop their scheme.

In kind support

eaga in partnership with Computer Aid International has donated over 500 laptops, PCs and monitors, all of which have been refurbished and are now in use in developing countries. In addition, eag has supplied Computer Aid with printers, scanners, cables and telephony equipment.

Employee-led support

eaga encourages its staff to participate in projects of value to their local community.

East Midlands Airport

Company registration number 5150652

Building 34, Nottingham East Midlands Airport, Castle Donnington, Derby DE74 2SA

01332 852801; Fax: 01332 852959

Website: www.eastmidlandsairport.com

Correspondent: Community Fund Administrator 0845 1088 544 Email: community@eastmidlandsairport.com

Managing Director: Penny Coates

Year end
31/03/2008

Nature of company business
Principal activity: Airport operator.

Main locations: Derby

UK employees: 250

Charitable donations

2007: £50,000
2006: £50,000
2005: £40,000
2004: £40,000
2003: £40,000

Membership: BitC

Community involvement

East Midlands Airport (EMA) supports local communities within a 10-mile radius of the airport, although in practice, those benefiting appear mainly to be within a 5-mile radius. Donations are made through the East Midlands Airport Community Fund which is funded by an annual donation from the company and the surcharges it levies on those airlines generating too much noise during night flights. The airport's community programme is focused on six key topics:

- education
- environment
- community engagement
- employee engagement
- sport
- arts and culture.

Exclusions

No support for local appeals not within 10 miles of the airport boundary.

Applications

Guidance notes and a Community Fund application form are downloadable from EMA's website. Completed applications should be returned to the correspondent.

Due to the increased level of applications the meetings for 2008 will be held bi-monthly.

Corporate giving

East Midlands Airport Community Fund receives around £50,000 a year from the company which, together with the money received from noise pollution fines, enabled it to make grants totalling £85,500 in 2007/08. Successful applications were up 17.8% on last year with 99 projects receiving a grant. Geographically, these were spread as follows (number of grants in brackets): Derbyshire (37); Leicestershire (40); Nottinghamshire (20); and Staffordshire (2).

Beneficiaries included: *Derbyshire* – Melbourne Scout and Guide HQ (£2,000) and Friends of Chellaston Brickworks Nature Reserve (£1,000); *Leicestershire* – Hathern Horticultural Society (£1,000) and East Leake Methodist Church (£500); *Nottinghamshire* – Rev and Go (£1,000) and Bumps and Beyond (£550); and *Staffordshire* – Rolleston Cricket Club (£1,400) and Burton upon Trent Civic Society (£1,000).

In kind support

Environment: EMA will continue to maintain and enhance the six-mile 'trail' it has established around the airport's perimeter fence.

Education: 'Education runs through many of the programmes that the airport supports.' Some of these include: work experience; a skills academy; Year in Industry placements; and; ethics workshops.

Sport: 'The airport works with sporting partners that offer inclusive sport for all as well as those with an exceptional talent. We recognise the need to encourage young people into sporting activity and a healthier lifestyle.'

Support has been given to the Leicester-Shire and Rutland and Nottinghamshire Youth Games, English Federation of Disability Sport, and the Derbyshire Talented Athlete Fund.

Employee-led support

The airport continues to encourage staff to get involved in local charity work by volunteering their time. [In 2007/08], airport staff once again supported the BBC's Children in Need event with the live show, hosted from the terminal building.

A formal volunteer scheme is due to be launched shortly.

Commercially-led support

Sponsorship: *The arts* – 'EMA's sponsorship programme seeks to engage both children and adults within the wider community through active participation, creative thinking and hands-on development. It also aims to widen the opportunities for individuals and groups to engage with the arts by choosing our partners carefully to improve access to the arts for all.'

Current partnerships include those with Dance4, Viva and New Perspectives. Support has also been given to The Spark Children's Arts Festival and Travelling by Tuba.

Ecclesiastical Insurance Group plc

Company registration number 1718196

Beaufort House, Brunswick Road, Gloucester GL1 1JZ

01452 528533; Fax: 01452 423557

Website: www.ecclesiastical.co.uk

Correspondent: Mrs R J Hall, Allchurches Trust Ltd

Chairman: B J E Sealy

Chief Executive: M H Tripp

Managing Director: S A Wood

Year end	Turnover	Pre-tax profit
31/12/2007	£362,402,000	£35,798,000

Nature of company business
Principal activity: general and long-term insurance.

Subsidiaries include: Ecclesiastical Insurance Office Ltd, Crusade Services Ltd, Ansvar Insurance Co. Ltd, Gerling Global London Market Ltd, Ansvar Conference Services Ltd, Hinton & Wild (Home Plans) Ltd, The Churches Purchasing Scheme Ltd, Blaisdon Properties Ltd, Ansvar Pensions Ltd, Allchurches Investment Management Services Ltd, Eccint Ltd, Allchurches Life Assurance Ltd

Main locations: Gloucester

UK employees: 853

Total employees: 1,056

Charitable donations

2007: £14,100,000
2006: £10,700,000
2005: £5,350,000
2003: £4,300,000

Community involvement

The company is owned by the Allchurches Trust (Charity Commission no. 263960) to which all charitable grants made by the company are given. The object of the trust is to promote the Christian religion and to contribute to the funds of any charitable institutions, associations, funds or objects and to carry out any charitable purpose.

The trust has adopted the following priorities:

- supporting the mission and work of the dioceses and cathedrals of the Church of England by the distribution of annual grants
- supporting requests for financial assistance from Anglican churches, Churches of other Denominations and Christian communities and organisations in accordance with its grant making policy
- maintaining a special project fund to support substantial projects which may have a broad impact on the Christian community in the UK
- establishing an overseas project fund to support the church and Christian community overseas in accordance with its grant making policy.

There is a preference for charities working within Gloucestershire.

The trustees regularly review the grant making policy of the trust 'to ensure it remains appropriate to the strategic direction of the charity and its objects'. A copy of the grant making policy is available from the company secretary at the registered office.

Applicants are advised to visit the website: www.allchurches.co.uk

In addition to the above, the group has partnerships 'with a number of organisations that share our social conscience and values' and to which it gives support. Staff are also encouraged to volunteer for local community-minded charities.

Exclusions

The trustees do not make grants to charities with political associations. Support is not normally given for advertising in charity brochures, animal welfare charities, individuals, the arts, fundraising events, medical research, or sport.

Applications

Applications are not considered by the company. Instead, applications should be submitted in writing in the form prescribed, detailing charity number, the objectives of the charity, the appeal target, how the funds are to be utilised, funds raised to date and previous support received from the trust. If available, the application should be accompanied by supporting literature and annual report.

Further details about the work of Allchurches Trust Ltd or advice on how to apply for financial assistance can be obtained by contacting the Company Secretary, Beaufort House, Brunswick Road, Gloucester, GL1 1JZ or email: atl@eigmail.com

Corporate giving

In 2007, the company made charitable donations totalling £14.1 million. Of this, £12.7 million was donated to Allchurches Trust (see below) and included an expendable capital endowment of £5.0 million and a special grant of £500,000.

Allchurches Trust

During 2007, the trust allocated charitable distributions amounting to £5,753,000. A breakdown of these grants is as follows (number of grants in brackets): Dioceses £4.7 million (110); Parishes and other charities £554,000 (748); and Cathedrals £469,000 (111). Some of the named beneficiaries inclded: St Jude's Church – Southsea; Launde Abbey Trust – East Norton; St Madoc Christian Youth Camp – Swansea; Formby Methodist Church – Liverpool; Louth & District Hospice; and University of Gloucestershire (towards curricular development in the Mission through Sport programme at the university).

In addition to the above the group also supported a number of partnerships, including those with English Heritage, The Children's Society, and the National Association of Decorative and Fine Arts Society.

Employee-led support

Employees supported local community-minded charities including The Greenbelt Christian Festival at Cheltenham, Gloucester Youth Housing Association, Headway, The Family Haven and Milestone School.

Commercially-led support

Cause-related marketing: The company has launched an ISA charitable giving scheme; or the 'nicer ISA' as they have termed it!

Under the scheme, every Ecclesiastical ISA investor has the opportunity to select a charity from a carefully chosen list. If this option is taken up, the equivalent of 0.25% of an individual's savings will be donated to their selected charity on an annual basis.

Economist Newspaper Ltd

Company registration number 236383

25 St James's Street, London SW1A 1HG

020 7830 7000; Fax: 020 7839 2968/9

Website: www.economist.com

Correspondent: Georgina Saad, Charities Liaison Officer

Chairman: Sir Robert Wilson

Group Chief Exectuive: Helen Alexander

Year end	Turnover	Pre-tax profit
31/03/2008	£266,399,000	£47,089,000

Nature of company business
Principal activities: publication of The Economist and specialist publications including European Voice and, in the United States, CFO, Journal of Commerce, and Roll Call; supply of business information (Economist Intelligence Unit).

Main locations: London

UK employees: 1,157

Charitable donations

2008: £151,184
2007: £124,597
2006: £88,070
2005: £105,000
2004: £200,000

Total community contributions: £302,043

Community involvement

Cash donations are largely made through The Economist Charitable Trust (Charity Commission no. 293709). The principal activity of the trust is the disbursement of monies received from The Economist Newspaper Ltd to various charities. 50–60% of the trust's donations go to charities in the fields of communication, education, literacy and retraining for individuals and groups who are disadvantaged in some way.

A match funding scheme is in operation for individual staff members' fundraising efforts. Between 30% and 40% of the trust's donations are given towards this.

Exclusions

The Economist Charitable Trust does not support appeals from non-charities, circular appeals, applications of a chain-letter type, gala charity events, advertising in charity brochures, appeals from individuals, larger national appeals, church restoration appeals, politically sensitive organisations, organisations of a religious or denominational nature, single service (among forces) charities, arts sponsorship (see above) or appeals from ordinary educational establishments (e.g. schools, university building funds). *Special schools or projects for disabled students are the exception to this rule.*

Animal welfare appeals are supported via staff matching only. Fundraising events are only supported by gifts in kind, and these are usually bought from other (e.g. disabled) voluntary organisations. Sport appeals are only supported if for the disabled.

Applications

Applications to the trust should be addressed to: Georgina Saad, The Economist Group, 26 Red Lion Square, London WC1R 4HQ.

A simple letter plus latest report & accounts is preferred – a telephone call to clarify specific queries is welcomed (ring: 020 7576 8061). The Economist Charitable Trust is run by a small team of staff volunteers. Applications can be made at any time.

Advice to applicants: The company states that multiple approaches are wasteful and counter-productive, particularly when they are addressed to directors who retired some time ago, indicating use of out-of-date lists. A few applications each year are rejected simply because they are badly presented. Many more fail because their deadlines for events are far too close when they apply. Applicants are also advised that if they are asked for additional information, this is a sign of interest in the project and not the opposite.

Unsigned, circular appeals will not receive a response.

Corporate giving

In 2007/08, the group made total community contributions of £302,043 (2006/07: £225,250). Of this, £151,184 (2006/07: £124,597) was donated to the associated trust.

During the year, the trust made grants totalling £110,226 with the average donation being £730 (2006/07: £986). We have no details of the beneficiaries.

In kind support

The company's main area of non-cash support is gifts in kind. For example, the Economist supports the visual arts by allowing its premises to be used for exhibitions. There are frequent events throughout the year, allowing up and coming artists to display their work to the general public.

Employee-led support

A wide range of causes are supported via staff matched fundraising.

Payroll giving: The company operates the Give As You Earn scheme.

Commercially-led support

Sponsorship: Arts sponsorship may be undertaken.

EDF Energy plc

Company registration number 2622406

40 Grosvenor Place, Victoria, London SW1X 7EN

020 7242 9050

Website: www.edfenergy.com

Correspondent: Community Involvement Team

Email: corporate.responsibility@edfenergy.com

Chairman: Daniel Camus

Chief Executive: Vincent de Rivaz

Year end	Turnover	Pre-tax profit
31/12/2007	£5,759,600,000	£336,900,000

Nature of company business
Operators of coal fired power stations. Suppliers of gas and electricity.

Main locations: Sunderland, London

UK employees: 13,035

Charitable donations

2007: £2,724,824
2006: £2,370,505
2005: £2,270,000
2003: £1,655,431

Membership: A & B, BitC, L B Group

Community involvement

The company is interested in causes concerned with education, youth, community development, environment and sport Support is given in the area the company operates which covers London, the south east and the south west of England, as well as around its customer services centre in Sunderland. It has entered into a special partnership with Mencap, which it encourages its entire staff to make monthly contributions to.

The company has an associated charitable trust – EDF Energy Trust (Charity Commission no. 1099446). The trust aims to relieve fuel poverty in the UK and mostly supports customers of group companies. In other words, it donates a sum of money to individuals in order for them to be able to pay their domestic bills. Effectively, this is a tax-efficient way for the group to recover funds owed to it from non-payers without adding to the financial burden of the individuals involved.

Since 2007, however, the trust has provided grants to organisations in the groups operating area which provide money advice to individuals. Although grants for the next three years funding (2007–2010) have been allocated, the trustees may make further awards next year (2009) and this will be announced on the trust's web site.

Grants are also available for community-based renewable energy projects through the Green Energy Fund (see 'Commercially-led support' for details).

Charity of the year: Mencap.

Applications

Organisations wishing to apply to the trust should address their letter to: EDF Energy Trust, 3rd Floor, Midgate House, Midgate, Peterborough PE1 1TN (Tel: 01733 421021; email: edfet@charisgrants.org.uk).

Further information about the trust is available at: www.edfenergytrust.org.uk

Corporate giving

In 2007, the company made total cash donations in the UK of £2,724,824. This included a grant of £2.45 million to the EDF Energy Trust and around £300,000 in matched funding to its charity partner, Mencap.

In kind support

Education: EDF support education through its 'Crucial Crew' and 'Junior Citizen' programmes. A team of six advisers, supported by volunteers, works in schools and at public events (often in partnership with the police, fire service, ambulance service and rail operators) to educate children about the dangers of playing in high risk areas such as substations or rail networks. At its West Burton Discovery Centre, EDF offer free environmental education to schools.

Employee-led support

The company has a 'Helping Hands' scheme which allows all employees to spend two days performing voluntary work on normal pay if they match these two days of work in their own time.

EDF contribute up to £100,000 in matched funding to its charity partner Mencap every year; it also matches funds raised by any employee up to a maximum of £100 a year. The company received 431 applications for personal matched funding in 2007.

Payroll giving: Over 900 EDF Energy employees make regular charitable donations through a payroll giving scheme, supporting mover than 156 charities.

Commercially-led support

Cause-related marketing: EDF Green Tariff customers pay an additional 0.42 pence per kWh (inc. VAT) on top of standard rates. This amount is matched by the company and placed into a Green Energy Fund which is used to support the installation of renewable generation equipment for community-based and educational projects.

Sponsorship: *Sport –* 'Since its launch in January 2007, more than 40,000 children have been given the chance to learn and play 'tag rugby' through the EDF Energy National Schools Rugby Programme.'

Egg Ltd

Company registration number 2448340

Riverside Road, Derby DE99 3GG

01332 335236

Website: www.egg.com

Correspondent: Community Relations

Email: community@egg.com

Chairman: Nick Prettejohn

Chief Executive: Mark Nancarrow

Year end	Turnover	Pre-tax profit
31/12/2005	£497,600,000	£106,700,000

Nature of company business
Online financial institution.

Main locations: Derby

UK employees: 2,100

Charitable donations

2005: £250,000
2004: £250,000
2003: £250,000

Total community contributions: £500,000

Membership: L B Group

Community involvement

Since May 2007 Egg has been part of Citigroup. The intention is to bring together their community programmes in order to have a bigger impact on the communities around where they work. However, at the time of conducting our research (2008), Egg was uncertain whether a single entry or two separate ones would be more appropriate.

Having promised to check with their colleagues at Citibank, no clarification has been forthcoming, so for the present, we are continuing with entries for both Egg (without updated figures) and Citibank.

The company's support is given through its Local Talent Fund, which aims to support local causes committed to developing local talent. The beneficial area is within 25 miles of any of its offices, which are in Derby, Dudley and London. Projects must involve Egg employees, either before an application is made or providing opportunities for staff to get involved. Areas of support are:

- Education – 'from primary all the way up to post graduate'
- Sport – 'table tennis to mountaineering, whatever your game is'
- The arts – 'including visual and performing arts'
- Regeneration – 'anything from fixing the local scout hut roof to painting a narrow boat'.

Applications

'Before applying for a share of Egg's developing local talent fund, please check your scheme meets our requirements. And keep in mind it's not just about money, you could ask for a bit of elbow grease from our people too.

'The guidelines state that:

- your scheme must be located within 25 miles of one of Egg's sites based in Derby, Dudley or London
- the purpose of your scheme must be the development of local talent
- your scheme must fall into one of the four key areas – education, sport, the arts or regeneration
- your request must involve the use of people who work for Egg.'

'If you think your scheme fits in with the theme we've outlined, now's the time to apply.

'You can write to us at:

Egg Banking
Citigroup
Community Relations
Riverside Road
Pride Park
Derby
DE99 3GG.

'Or simply drop us an email to community@egg.com telling us how we can use our talent to develop yours.'

Corporate giving

In 2005, Egg gave £250,000 in cash grants. It appears that this is roughly the same each year. It also allowed staff to volunteer during work time, at a cost of the equivalent of £250,000 to the company. Beneficiaries included Derby County Football Club to launch a football skills challenge in a number of local schools, Derby Rugby Football Club to launch a rugby development programme, Derbyshire Community Foundation for a music competition and Derbyshire Local Education Authority for a creative thinking project with primary school head teachers.

Since becoming part of the Citigroup, '[Egg] has joined forces with Create Arts to bring the Count the Beats initiative to local primary schools. Professional musicians teach the children to explore the link between maths and music and how this relates to common mathematical questions they face such as percentages, fractions and numerical patterns.

'Workshops encourage children to write their own piece of music which is then performed on the final day to the entire school. Funded through the Citi Foundation we are currently working with Create Arts in Derby, London and Manchester.'

In kind support

Mentoring: 'Our people have started going into local schools to mentor young people. This ranges from helping students through our financial education programme, gaining a solid foundation of knowledge in everything from saving and investment to managing debt and planning for the future. We also have sporting mentors who offer their support through the power of sport. We have volunteers from all five Citi and Egg sites, currently working in local schools in Derby, Sunderland, Dudley, London and Manchester.'

Employee-led support

All employees are encouraged to be active within the communities, which can take place during working hours. The guidelines state 'keep in mind it's not just about money, you could ask for a bit of elbow grease from our people too'.

Payroll giving: The company participates in the GAYE scheme.

Electronic Data Systems Ltd

Company registration number 53419

4 Roundwood Avenue, Stockley Park, Uxbridge, Middlesex UB11 1BQ

020 8848 8989; Fax: 020 8756 0130

Website: www.eds.com

Correspondent: Bianca Slatter

Email: bianca.slatter@eds.com

Executive Vice President: Bill Thomas

Managing Director: Swean Finnan

Year end	Turnover	Pre-tax profit
31/12/2006	£2,403,173,000	£208,062,000

Nature of company business
A leading technology services company delivering a broad portfolio of information technology and business outsourcing services.

Subsidiaries include: Electronic Data Systems

Main locations: London, Luton, Uxbridge

UK employees: 15,303

Charitable donations
2006: £37,732
2005: £67,924
2004: £49,805
2003: £54,540

Community involvement

Although Electronic Data Systems (EDS) in the UK previously advised us that it no longer had a policy of making cash donations to charity, it has consistently declared such donations in its annual report and accounts. Furthermore, although also advised that it favoured supporting charities suggested by employees, the provision of a contact name appears to indicate that other applications will be considered.

Outside of this the UK company also provides a variety of in kind support from education outreach programmes to employee volunteering opportunities.

Finally, there is the American-based EDS Foundation which support projects concerned with technology, arts and culture, education and health. Applications are accepted from outside the US as long as certain criteria are met. However, there is no recent evidence of the foundation having awarded grants in the UK. Whether this is purely down to a lack of applicants, or the quality of applications, we could not say.

Applications

Applications to the company in the UK should be sent to the correspondent. For those of you considering applying to the foundation in the US, we ask you to note the following:

▷ organisations outside the US must download and complete the Non-US Applications for Funding – 2008 form

▷ non-US applications require a minimum request of $10,000 USD and must be completed in English

▷ all programmes funded by the foundation must have a current EDS employee volunteer partnership.

For a full explanation of what is required we suggest you visit: www.eds.com/about/community/foundation/faq.aspx

Applications are considered three times a year and must be submitted before the specified closing dates. Details of these are available on the company's website.

Corporate giving

In 2006, the company made cash donations in the UK of £37,732 (2005: £67,924). We have no details of the beneficiaries.

The EDS Foundation

The EDS Foundation was created to support EDS' philanthropic efforts in communities where the company's employees live and work around the world. In 2007, the foundation awarded grants totalling nearly $900,000 (c. £450,000) of which about 46% went towards supporting education initiatives.

In kind support

The company has an Education Outreach programme which offers creative learning experiences to students. For example, 'EDS and England's Worthing High School joined in partnership to create a six-week initiative that helps prepare students for careers. As part of this initiative, EDS employees help students create their first CVs, write cover letters, and complete applications. Students also practice for job interviews and participate in mock interviews at EDS offices'.

The company also runs the EDS Technology Grant Programme, which 'helps teachers of children ages 6 through 18 purchase information technology products and services that will improve their students' ability to learn. Each year, EDS offices worldwide sponsor and award $1,500 grants to teachers through a competitive application process. The grants are awarded to teachers through their schools, and schools applying for a grant must be located within 50 miles of a sponsoring EDS account.

Grants must be used to pay for technology products, training and services. EDS encourages teachers to propose innovative classroom projects or student exercises. Teachers are asked to explain the innovative nature of their project, how they or their students will use the requested technology and how the technology will improve their students' ability to achieve curriculum objectives. Examples of qualified grant expenditures include computer software and hardware, multimedia equipment, Web-cams, CD-ROM libraries, scanners, modems, Internet access, technical training, specialize technology tools and equipment such as Robotics Kits and other classroom learning aides that are considered advanced in the area of technology'.

Employee-led support

EDS organises Global Volunteer Day (GVD) each October. The following is an extract from the company's website. 'Since its inception in 1993, EDS colleagues have worked on more than 4,000 community projects, contributed more than 500,000 hours and touched the lives of more than 1 billion people in 32 countries'.

EMI Group Ltd

Company registration number 229231

27 Wrights Lane, London W8 5SW

020 7795 7000; Fax: 020 7795 7296

Website: www.emigroup.com

Correspondent: (see 'Applications')

Chief Executive: Elio Leoni-Sceti

Year end	Turnover	Pre-tax profit
31/03/2007	£1,808,300,000	(£263,600,000)

Nature of company business
EMI covers all aspects of the music industry from music recording and publishing through to manufacture, marketing and distribution.

Subsidiaries include: Virgin Records Ltd, Virgin Music Group Ltd

Main locations: London

UK employees: 1,201

Total employees: 6,312

Charitable donations

2007: £200,000
2006: £300,000
2005: £300,000
2004: £300,000
2003: £400,000

Membership: BitC

Community involvement

In August 2007, the EMI group of companies was acquired by Maltby Capital Ltd. All references, financial or otherwise, refer to EMI Group plc prior to this change of ownership.

'EMI has an active and on-going community investment programme. Globally, the main causes we support are youth and education, arts and culture, and health and welfare. At group level, we focus on promoting music education and access to music. This ensures that our community investment activities are aligned with our core business; we believe it is also the way in which the business can best utilise its energy, creativity and expertise to deliver long-term benefits to the community.

'The company's flagship initiative is the EMI Music Sound Foundation (Charity Commission no. 1104027) which supports secondary schools seeking specialist performing arts or music status, provides grants to other schools, music teachers and music students, and offers a number of bursaries through colleges in the UK and Ireland.

'[However], as a result of a recent strategic review, EMI MSF decided to look for a way to make the same sort of impact on music education at a primary level as it had in the secondary sector through its specialist schools programme. The charity this year [2007] commissioned the Institute of Education to carry out research looking at the value and provision of music education in the UK during the early years of primary school.'

The EMI MSF supports the following:

- non-specialist schools to fund music education
- music students in full time education to fund instrument purchase
- music teachers to fund courses and training.

Exclusions

EMI Group will not fund secondments, individuals seeking sponsorship, expeditions, sporting activities or wildlife charities. No donations are made to political, sectarian, religious or racist organisations.

The EMI Music Sound Foundation will not support applications from outside the United Kingdom, non-school based community groups, music therapy centres, and so on, applications over £2,500

Applications

Applications to the EMI Music Foundation should be made using the form downloadable from its site (www.musicsoundfoundation.com). Guidance notes are provided with the form.

Completed applications should be returned to: Janie Orr, Chief Executive, EMI Music Sound Foundation, 27 Wrights Lane, London W8 5SW.

Corporate giving

In 2006/07, worldwide charitable cash donations were £800,000 of which £200,000 was given in the UK. This was complemented by additional community investment from participation in industry fundraising events around the world, arts sponsorship, staff time and gifts in kind. No figure for the latter was made available.

EMI Music Sound Foundation

EMI continues to cover virtually all of the foundation's administration costs, which enables the charity to spend close to 100% of its investment income on supporting schools, teachers and students in the UK and Ireland. To date, EMI MSF has granted awards in excess of £2.7 million, close to half of which has supported state secondary schools in their bids to become specialist performing arts or music colleges. The charity is the largest single sponsor in this sector.

The foundation continued to support music education in the Royal Borough of Kensington & Chelsea, where the group's headquarters are located, and to work with Teach First to recruit the most able graduates to teach music in under-resourced secondary schools across the UK.

Other key partnerships include London's Roundhouse and the London Sinfonietta.

In kind support

The royalties-free performance of songs that EMI owns the copyright to has been approved for benefit concerts. Benefit CDs have been released, with all profits generated going to a particular cause.

Employee-led support

The company aims to encourage and support the commitment, enthusiasm and participation of employees who are involved in voluntary activities within their local communities, and give consideration to projects which they put forward and in which they become involved. An employee-matching scheme exists for UK employees.

Commercially-led support

Sponsorship: *The arts* – The EMI Group is a corporate member of several arts organisations including the Roundhouse in London.

Ernst & Young LLP

Company registration number OC300001

1 More London Place, London SE1 2AF

020 7951 2000; Fax: 020 7951 1345

Website: www.ey.com/uk

Correspondent: Nicky Majors, Director of Corporate Responsibility
Email: nmajor@uk.ey.com

Chairman: Mark Otty

Year end	Turnover	Pre-tax profit
30/06/2007	£1,226,000,000	£326,000,000

Nature of company business
Financial and professional services provider.

Main locations: Reading, Southampton, Liverpool, London, Luton, Manchester, Newcastle, Nottingham, Cambridge, Bristol, Hull, Inverness, Leeds, Glasgow, Edinburgh, Exeter, Birmingham, Belfast, Aberdeen

UK employees: 8,723

Charitable donations

Total community contributions: £4,100,000

Membership: A & B, BitC, L B Group

Community involvement

The following statement was provided by the firm: 'The basis of our community investment programme is to support and encourage our people to make a difference in the communities in which they live and work, by giving them the opportunity to apply their time and talents to create positive change. To facilitate this, we support our people in contributing to charities and communities in a variety of ways: through providing paid volunteering leave, matched fundraising, payroll giving and making donations to charities in recognition of work our people do in their own time. Our people can use their community investment 'entitlement' to support charities and communities of their own choice or support the firm's community partners.

'The firm-organised opportunities we offer our people are focused around four key community partners. We do, however, also support a number of other charitable organisations which fit with our core approach, criteria and focus.

'As an organisation we also strive to make an impact in the areas of education and entrepreneurship, particularly amongst young people.'

Exclusions

The firm does not support its peoples' involvement with charitable organisations which are:

- politically focused or biased groups
- religious groups, but will support religious-based charities such as Oxfam
- small animal charities with a narrow geographic or subject focus, but will support recognised national charities such as the RSPCA, Guide Dogs for the Blind, the World Wildlife Fund and those protecting endangered species.

Applications

In writing to the correspondent or contact your nearest regional office.

Corporate giving

In 2007/08, the firm made an overall contribution to communities in the UK of £4.1 million (this covers cash, time and management costs).

Based on the LBG model, Ernst & Young's contribution for the financial year ending 30 June 2008, can be broken down into three categories of community involvement:

- **community investment** – long-term strategic involvement in community partnerships to address a limited range of social issues chosen by the company (£2,833,012)
- **charitable gifts** – intermittent support for a range of good causes in response to the needs and appeals of charitable and community organisations (£575,526)
- **commercial initiatives** – activities in the community, usually by commercial departments, to support directly the success of the company, promoting its corporate brand identities and other policies, in partnership with charities and community-based organisations (£694,796).

Unfortunately, the above figures do not separate out in kind support and management costs, as it is not the firms policy to make this publically available.

The four principal organisations benefiting from this were: The Prince's Trust; Education Partners; Action for Children; and Comic Relief/Sport Relief. Further details about the support given to each are available on the firm's website.

In addition to the above, support was given to a number of key community organisations, including: Mango; TaxAid; Crisis; SMart; Unicorn's Children's Theatre; StreetShine; CSV; and numerous local charities and community groups.

In kind support

The firm's commitment to supporting the non-profit sector saw the waiving of professional fees totalling over £800,000. This included the provision of accounting services to Comic Relief.

Employee-led support

Ernst & Young provided us with the following information:

- our people volunteered 29,000 hours in the community (2006/07: 20,000)
- 26% of our people volunteered for charity on work time (2006/07: 18%)
- our people raised £1 million for charitable causes (2006/07: £880,000)
- Ernst & Young contributed over £600,000 to charities in matched funding
- our volunteering had a positive impact on over 30,000 young people
- as the honorary account for Sport Relief we have counted over £2.3 million of public donations and provided pro bono accounting worth over £275,000
- our people donated over £200,000 to charity through our Give As You Earn scheme (2006/07: £176,000).

Commercially-led support

Sponsorship: *The arts* – the firm continued in 2008 with its long-term association with the Tate.

Esh Group

Company registration number 3724890

Bowburn North Industrial Estate, Bowburn,
County Durham DH6 5PF

0191 377 4570; Fax: 0191 377 4571

Website: www.eshgroup.co.uk

Correspondent: (see 'Applications')

Email: enquiries@eshcharitabletrust.org.uk

Chief Executive: Brian Manning

Year end	Turnover	Pre-tax profit
31/12/2007	£148,432,000	£10,217,000

Nature of company business
The principal activities of the group during the year were building, construction, civil engineering and property refurbishment.

UK employees: 1.158

Charitable donations

2007: £221,177
2006: £201,660

Membership: BitC

Community involvement

The group's cash support for charitable and community organisations is primarily made via the Esh Group Charitable Trust. (Note: The Charity Commission no. given for the trust is 1112040. However, this brings up the Esh Foundation, which appears not to be making grants and has not lodged any accounts.)

The trust aims mainly to help young people, the disadvantaged, the environment and communities within the North East of England.

The company encourages its staff to volunteer and fundraise on behalf of local charities, and has been heavily involved with the 'Fit for Employment' programme run in partnership with Durham Community Business College.

Exclusions

No support for applications that are not of benefit to the people and communities of the North East of England.

Applications

Further details of how to apply to the trust, eligibility criteria and so on, are available at: www.eshcharitabletrust.org.uk

Please note that you can only apply for one grant in each financial year. If you are unsuccessful in your application, you cannot re-apply for the same project at a later date.

Furthermore, 'Flagship' projects are chosen by the company's board of directors and unsolicited applications are not encouraged.

Corporate giving

In 2007, the company made charitable donations of £221,177 (2006: £201,660) most of which went to the associated charitable trust.

Esh Group Charitable Trust

'Set up with an initial donation from the company of £1 million, the shareholders have decided to support these activities for the foreseeable future across the group. The trust will, therefore, receive £200,000 every year for five years starting from 2006.

'This money will be used each year to achieve maximum benefit. Through the trust we will be able to support larger projects and it will provide a way by which all employees can lend a hand.

'We hope to find some 'flagship projects' which will merit substantial support of up to £100,000 as well as many smaller projects, such as those that staff have chosen in the past.'

The following extract on the trust's activities is taken from the group's 2007 annual report and accounts:

'Now its second year, the trust has paid out £136,925 in grants to 22 applicants throughout the region. We continue to work with Durham Community Foundation through our operational and executive trust boards to receive, assess and approve applications.

'In the year we launched a flagship project designed to instigate a wide range of positive outcomes using the focus of a horticultural project in schools across the region. Through 'Grow with Esh' £20,000 was distributed between twenty middle and secondary schools from Northumberland to Teesside and westward towards Hexham and Weardale and £5,000 prize money was shared between the four prize-winning schemes.

'In early 2008 the project was promoted to over 800 primary schools in the region. This year's cohort of 20 schools are based as far afield as Cornhill on Tweed in the North and Saltburn on Sea in the South.'

Employee-led support

Esh employees have recently taken part in a Coast 2 Coast bike ride and raised £1,600 on behalf of Cancer Research.

Esso UK Ltd

Company registration number 1589650

ExxonMobil House, Mailpoint 8, Ermyn Way, Leatherhead, Surrey KT22 8UX

01372 222000; Fax: 01372 223222

Website: www.esso.co.uk

Correspondent: Community Affairs Assistant, UK Public Affairs

Chairman: Rob Franklin

Year end	Turnover	Pre-tax profit
31/12/2007	£12,980,800,000	£1,339,000,000

Nature of company business
Principal activities: the exploration for, production, transportation and sale of crude oil, natural gas and natural gas liquids; the refining, distribution and marketing of petroleum products within the UK.

Subsidiaries include: Mainline Pipelines Ltd, Dart Oil Co. Ltd, Retail Petroleum Services Ltd, Cleveland Petroleum Co. Ltd, Comma Oil & Chemicals Ltd, ExxonMobil International Ltd, Redline Oil Services Ltd, Mode Wheel Property Ltd

Main locations: Leatherhead, Fawley, Fife, Aberdeen

UK employees: 7,464

Charitable donations

2007: £500,000
2006: £400,000
2005: £1,500,000

Total community contributions: £1,500,000

Membership: BitC

Community involvement

Although Esso UK Ltd (part of ExxonMobil) informed us that: 'We no longer find it appropriate to be included in your directory ... ', we maintain our policy of publishing information on all relevant companies.

The following information is, therefore, largely taken from the 'Corporate Responsibility' section of its website.

'It is ExxonMobil's policy to be a good corporate citizen wherever we do business. In the UK, we support the local communities around our key business locations. Our focus is on employee volunteering, education, environmental and neighbourhood projects.'

The company directs its support to the neighbourhoods around its key business locations. As a result its community programme is based on the needs and wants of the people in those areas. Emphasis is placed, therefore, on: education (particularly the teaching of science, technology, maths and environmental concerns), and the environment. ExxonMobil employees and their families are also encouraged to participate in community initiatives through the VIP (Volunteer Involvement Programme) scheme.

ExxonMobil proactively plans its programmes and likes to establish long-term working partnerships with the organisations it works with in the voluntary sector. Almost all funds are committed at the beginning of the year, therefore unsolicited requests are rarely supported. There is a preference for voluntary organisations working in the areas of Leatherhead, Fawley, Fife and Aberdeen.

Exclusions

No response to circular appeals. No grant support for advertising in charity brochures, animal welfare, appeals from individuals, medical research, overseas projects, political appeals, religious appeals, or sport.

Applications

The company responds to all appeals received, but in view of the policy outlined above unsolicited appeals are very rarely successful.

Corporate giving

In 2007, Esso invested £1.5 million in community projects and initiatives, of which £500,000 was in charitable donations.

According to company press releases, recent (2008) beneficiaries of support, included: New Hope Community Church (£1,520); Marchwood Infant School (£1,500); New Forest Disability Information Service (£1,000); Netley Sailing Club (£500); The Gateway Club (£500); and St Francis Pre-School.

In kind support

Education: 'The ExxonMobil Link Schools programme is now reaching out to about 35 schools around our key operating locations. This is delivered by organisations including Learning Through Landscapes who encourage schools to look at the potential their school grounds have for learning and enjoyment, and CREATE (Centre for Research, Education And Training in Energy) who are using their experience and expertise to help shape the programme and to offer schools a package of support including advice, materials and resources.'

Employee-led support

Volunteering: 'In 2006, we launched the ExxonMobil Energy Challenge, recruiting volunteers to provide practical advice to low-income householders on ways they can reduce their fuel costs. The volunteers visit vulnerable households and community venues, offering tips on ways to conserve energy and to keep homes warm. They also help people to apply for available grants and benefits. The initiative is being carried out in partnership with Community Service Volunteers (CSV), National Energy Action (NEA) and Energy Action Scotland (EAS).

'Through our Volunteer Involvement Programme (VIP) we encourage employees and their families to contribute their time, talent and energy to local charities and non-profit organisations. To assist and recognise their efforts, we provide contributions to the organisations that our employees and their families support'

Payroll giving: The company operates the Payroll Giving in Action scheme.

Euro Packaging Ltd

Company registration number 1328600

20 Brickfield Road, Yardley, Birmingham B25 8EH

0121 706 6181; Fax: 0121 706 6514

Website: www.europackaging.co.uk

Chairman: Bill Ronald

Chief Executive: Atilla Balogh

Year end	Turnover	Pre-tax profit
31/12/2007	£133,429,000	(£1,433,000)

Nature of company business
Manufacturer and consolidator of packaging products.

UK employees: 274

Charitable donations

2007: £0
2005: £5,550,000
2004: £2,301,000

Community involvement

The company makes its charitable donations through the Euro Charity Trust (Charity Commission no. 1058460). The objects of Euro Charity Trust are listed as 'the relief of poverty, to assist the vulnerable and to assist in the advancement of education in the UK and the rest of the world'. The trust receives all its income from the group headed by Euro Packaging Holdings Ltd. Donations are made to both organisations and individuals worldwide.

In November 2006, MidOcean Partners announced the acquisition of various companies comprising the Euro

Packaging Group. It was uncertain how, if at all, this would affect its giving policy.

Applications

In writing to the trustees at 118 Amington Road, Yardley, Birmingham B25 8JZ.

Corporate giving

In 2005, the trust had an income of £6.6 million of which £5.55 million (2004: £2.3 million) came from the company. Grants totalled £3.9 million. It is likely grants are made to organisations in the area local to Euro Packaging sites (Birmingham in the UK, and Malaysia) and Malawi, where the settlor is originally from.

Evans Property Group

Company registration number 4422612

Millshaw, Ring Road, Beeston, Leeds LS11 8EG

0113 271 1888; Fax: 0113 271 8487

Website: www.evanspropertygroup.com

Correspondent: Pauline Horsbrough

Chairman: M W Evans

Managing Director: J D Bell

Year end	Turnover	Pre-tax profit
31/03/2005	£38,528,000	£20,523,000

Nature of company business
Property investment and development.

Subsidiaries include: Marchington Properties, Millshaw Property Co. Ltd, White Rose Property Investments Ltd, Mulgate Investments Ltd, Lichfield Securities Ltd, Furnival Estates Ltd, Astra House Ltd

Main locations: Leeds

UK employees: 57

Charitable donations

2005: £123,605
2004: £188,272
2003: £58,013
2001: £42,487

Community involvement

Unfortunately, as we have been unable to update the information previously provided, it is repeated herewith. (Please note that the group's website is currently under reconstruction and may provide relevant information once it has been completed.)

Charitable support is given to both local and national charities. The group has supported various charities on a long term basis.

Exclusions

No support for local appeals not in areas of company presence, appeals from individuals, animal welfare, overseas projects, and political or religious appeals.

Applications

In writing to the correspondent.

Information available: The company produce a social responsibility report.

Corporate giving

In 2004/05, the group made cash donations totalling £123,605. During the year the group continued its support of a wide variety of local and national charities including the NSPCC, Gurkha Welfare Trust, the Variety Club, Barnardos, Yorkshire Cancer Research, and Yorkshire County Indoor Bowling.

In kind support

The company provides support through gifts in kind and joint promotions.

Employee-led support

An employee volunteering scheme is in operation and the company matches employee fundraising.

Commercially-led support

Sponsorship: The company undertake arts and good-cause sponsorship. Please contact Claire White for further information.

Execution Ltd

Company registration number 4058971

Block D, The Old Trueman Building, 91 Brick Lane, London E1 6QL

020 7456 9191; Fax: 020 7375 2007

Website: www.executionlimited.com

Correspondent: Jacky Joy, Trustee
Email: info@executionlimited.com

Chairman & Chief Executive: Nick Finegold

Nature of company business
Institutional stock broking firm.

Charitable donations

2007: £1,550,000
2006: £945,000

Community involvement

The firm states that: 'Execution Ltd has developed a philanthropic programme to tackle poverty and disadvantage in the UK. To achieve this, in July 2003 the firm formed the Execution Charitable Trust (ECT), Charity Commission no. 1099097. Funding for ECT is generated through Execution Ltd's annual charity trading days through which the gross commissions earned by Execution Ltd are given to ECT.

'The responsibility of ECT is to allocate and administer the charitable funds raised by Execution Ltd. This funding has been donated to local community organisations throughout the UK. The allocation of ECT funding to effective charities is undertaken with the advice of New Philanthropy Capital.'

The criteria by which NPC selects charities are determined by the trust which describes its aim as being 'an entrepreneurial and progressive funder of effective charities that tackle the causes and symptoms of poverty and disadvantage'. The criteria are listed below.

To tackle poverty and disadvantage, the ECT has chosen to support multi-purpose community organisations that:

- are based in deprived communities in the UK
- are led by passionate members of the local community
- provide a wide range of activities and opportunities for people of all ages and backgrounds
- enhance the social and economic well-being of the community
- enhance people's self-confidence, skills and employment prospects
- reduce feelings of loneliness and isolation
- strengthen citizen engagement in decision-making processes
- campaign for better government or corporate policies and public services.

ECT is willing to award unrestricted grants to the charities it supports. ECT believes that this type of funding gives effective charities the flexibility necessary to achieve their goals.

In addition to providing financial support, ECT can also provide other types of assistance to help strengthen and sustain the work of the charities it funds including consultancy support.

Applications

Charities are asked not to approach Execution Charitable Trust with funding proposals as the trust has appointed New Philanthropy Capital (NPC) to proactively identify effective organisations on its behalf. However, if you wish to alert NPC to the work of your charity, please complete the online form at www.executioncharitabletrust.org to submit basic information. This information will be added to NPC's database.

Corporate giving

On 18 October 2007, the firm's annual charity trading day raised over £1.5 million which brings the total raised in the last six years to more than £5.8 million.

The Execution Charitable Trust

Information regarding the beneficiaries of the 2007 charity trading day is currently unavailable. However, details should appear in time on the charity's informative website which includes a breakdown of beneficiaries since 2003 by geographical area.

The site also mentions that in June 2007 the trustees allocated grants totalling just under £400,000 to four new charities and two existing charities. The four new charities were: Charterhouse-in-Southwark – London; Greenhouse Schools Project – Wales; South Side Family Centre – Bath; and St Mark's Family Centre – Mitcham. The two existing charities were: London Citizens and New Avenues Youth and Community Project.

In 2006 the trust had assets of £1.35 million, an income of £960,000 (of which £945,000 came from the firm) and made 36 grants totalling £793,000. The major beneficiary was: ARK (Absolute Return for Kids) which received £219,000. Other beneficiaries included: Trinity Community Centre – London; London Citizens; Corner House Cross Community Family Centre – Belfast; Bryncynon Community Revival Strategy – North Wales; FARE – Glasgow; and The Warren – Kingston upon Hull.

In kind support

ECT can also provide other types of assistance to help strengthen and sustain the work of the charities it funds. Moreover, ECT undertakes a workshop every year for charities funded to facilitate the exchange of lessons learned. In 2005, the workshop focused on how charities track and articulate the results of their work.

F&C Asset Management plc

Company registration number SC073508

Exchange House, Primrose Street, London EC2A 2NY

020 7628 8000; Fax: 020 7628 8188

Website: fandc.com

Correspondent: The Charities Committee

Chairman: Robert Jenkins

Chief Executive: Alain Grisay

Year end	Turnover	Pre-tax profit
31/12/2007	£277,800,000	£25,900,000

Nature of company business
The group's business is asset management.

Main locations: London, Edinburgh

UK employees: 901

Charitable donations

2007: £117,000
2006: £94,000
2005: £75,000
2004: £85,000
2003: £58,000

Membership: BitC

Community involvement

The following extracts are taken from F&C's 'Policies on the Community':

'In line with good practice, F&C seeks to differentiate between community activities that are largely philanthropic in nature (charitable) and those that have a more direct business benefit (social investment and commercial initiatives in the community).

'In seeking to maximise its positive impact on society through active involvement with the communities in which it operates, F&C is committed to:

- focusing on activities which support and reinforce its social and environmental responsibility
- consulting key stakeholders about their expectations of F&C
- supporting selected charities
- encouraging employee involvement in community related initiatives
- encouraging employee donations and fundraising events by staff, and where appropriate, matching their contributions.

'F&C has a formally constituted Charities Committee, chaired by an executive director, which is responsible for the apportionment of donations within these policy guidelines'.

Following consultation with employees across the group at the end of 2007 a vote was taken to support a 'charity of the year'.

Applications

In writing to the correspondent.

Corporate giving

In 2007, the company made charitable donations of £117,000. (2006: £94,000). A beneficiary was UK Career Academy.

In kind support

Through UK Career Academy the company provide a number of trained mentors to work one-to-one with individual students.

For 2008, F&C has entered into a partnership with Camden EBP to establish a schools volunteering programme, for which all employees will be encouraged to participate.

Employee-led support

Payroll giving: The Give As You Earn (GAYE) scheme is in operation.

F&C has a policy of matching employee donations and has set a budget of £25,000 to match employee GAYE contributions.

Commercially-led support

Sponsorship: *The arts* – support has been given to the Royal Academy of Arts and in 2008 to the Chelsea Flower Show.

Family Assurance Friendly Society Ltd

Company registration number 110067

16–17 West Street, Brighton, East Sussex BN1 2RL

01273 725272; Fax: 01273 736958

Website: www.family.co.uk

Correspondent: Faye Russell, Community Programme Manager 01273 725272; Fax: 01273 776856 Email: frussell-communityprogramme@family.co.uk

Chairman: Robert Dolman

Chief Executive: John Reeve

Year end	Turnover	Pre-tax profit
31/12/2007	£152,000,000	£2,569,000,000

Nature of company business
Provision of financial services (life assurance, savings and protection schemes).

Main locations: Brighton

UK employees: 280

> ### Charitable donations
>
> 2007: £19,000
> 2005: £7,000
> 2003: £6,480
>
> Total community contributions: £30,000

Community involvement

There is a preference for charities local to Brighton & Hove and the East Sussex area, and for those in which a member of staff is involved.

Support is generally considered for organisations concerned with children/youth and for fundraising events.

Exclusions

The society does not normally support advertising in charity brochures, appeals from individuals, enterprise/training, heritage, overseas projects, political/religious appeals, science/technology or social welfare.

Applications

In writing to the correspondent. Further information and advice are available to applicants from the society.

Information available: The society comments on its social responsibilities with its annual report and accounts.

Corporate giving

In 2007, community contributions totalled £30,000 of which £19,000 was donated in cash to support local charities and the local activities of national charities.

In previous years support has been given to: Blatchington Mill School, Middle Street Primary School, Brighton and Hove City College and in cooperation with Brighton & Hove City Council, the provision of music workshops to 12 nurseries.

Employee-led support

Employees' volunteering/charitable activities are supported by the company. The society allows time off (four days a year) and matches employee fundraising up to a maximum of £250 per person a year.

Commercially-led support

Sponsorship: Neither arts nor good-cause sponsorship are undertaken.

Fenwick Ltd

Company registration number 52411

Elswick Court, 39 Northumberland Street, Newcastle upon Tyne NE99 1AR

0191 232 5100; Fax: 0191 239 6621

Website: www.fenwick.co.uk

Correspondent: Mrs A Moles, Secretary to the Company Secretary

Chairman: M A Fenwick

N A H Fenwick

Year end	Turnover	Pre-tax profit
26/01/2007	£280,325,015	£35,947,568

Nature of company business
Department stores.

Main locations: Canterbury, Brent Cross, Leicester, Kingston, Newcastle, London, York, Windsor, Tunbridge Wells

UK employees: 2,433

Charitable donations

2007: £116,000

Community involvement

Repeated requests for information regarding the company's community investment policy have gone unanswered. We believe, however, that the company is a corporate member of the Northumberland Wildlife Trust, The Migraine Trust, The Bobath Centre and the Commonwealth Youth Exchange Council.

Previously, we were advised that the company supports projects in areas where it has a presence (i.e. the North East, North Yorkshire, East Midlands and South East). There is a preference for: the arts; children/youth; education; elderly people; medical research; sickness/disability charities and social welfare.

Exclusions

No support for circular appeals, advertising in charity brochures, political appeals, overseas projects or small purely local appeals not in areas of company presence.

Applications

In writing to the correspondent. Local stores have an independent budget for appeals.

Corporate giving

In 2007, the company made cash donations of £116,000 to various charitable causes.

Past grant beneficiaries have included: St Oswald's Hospice, Canterbury Festival, Northumberland Wildlife Trust, St Edmund's School – Canterbury, and St Andrew's Hospital – Northampton.

In kind support

Main areas of non-cash support are: gifts in kind and training schemes.

Commercially-led support

Sponsorship: *The arts* – The company undertakes sponsorship. We have no information regarding current or past support.

Fiat Group Automobiles UK Ltd

Company registration number 201514

Fiat House, 240 Bath Road, Slough, Berkshire SL1 4DX

01753 786400; Fax: 01753 577710

Website: www.fiat.co.uk

Correspondent: Sydney Bryan, Fiat Charity Administrator 01753 519624

Year end	Turnover	Pre-tax profit
31/12/2006	£585,166,000	(£25,924,000)

Nature of company business
Principal activity: Fiat car distributors.

Main locations: Slough

UK employees: 152

Charitable donations

2006: £30,441
2005: £27,941
2004: £72,000

Community involvement

The company's donations are made through the Fiat Auto (UK) Charity (Charity Commission no. 1059498) which was established on 1 January 1993 to formalise the charitable activities of Fiat Auto (UK) Ltd and the Fiat Dealer Network. The charity's income comes from the following:

Fiat Dealers & Fiat Auto (UK) Ltd – each pay £1 for every new Fiat sold through the Fiat Dealer Network

Fiat Auto (UK) Ltd pays 35p for every:

(a) new Fiat vehicle sold other than through the Fiat Dealer Network

(b) new Alfa Romeo car sold through any sales channel.

Fiat Auto (UK) Ltd collects the monies from the Fiat Dealer Network and pays these, together with its own contributions, to a separate bank account which is managed by the trustees. All administrative expenses are borne by the company.

The trustees review their policy for making donations to take account of the wishes of Fiat Auto (UK) Ltd and the Fiat Dealer Network. Their policy is to make donations only to registered, or accepted charities, and, in particular, to concentrate their main charitable efforts towards those charities that benefit children.

Exclusions

Generally no support for circular appeals, appeals from individuals, purely denominational (religious) appeals, or political appeals.

Applications

In writing to the correspondent.

Corporate giving

Fiat Auto (UK) Charity

In 2005, (the latest accounts available), the charity had an income of £30,441 and made grants totalling £29,959. The beneficiaries were:

- Children's Society (£25,000)
- BEN – Motor Trade Benevolent Fund (£4,959).

Employee-led support

The company has an employee volunteering scheme.

Payroll giving: The company operates a payroll giving scheme which makes contributions to the trade charity BEN.

Commercially-led support

Sponsorship: Good-cause sponsorship is undertaken.

Cause-related marketing: Joint promotions are run on behalf of BEN.

Fidelity Investment Management Ltd

Company registration number 2349713

Oakhill House, 130 Tonbridge Road, Hildenborough, Kent TN11 9DZ

Website: www.fidelityukfoundation.org

Correspondent: Susan Platts-Martin, Fidelity UK Foundation 01732 777364

Year end	Turnover	Pre-tax profit
30/06/2007	£775,672,000	£23,806,000

Nature of company business
The management and distribution of unit trusts and the management of pension funds.

UK employees: 2,797

Charitable donations

2007: £11,758,593
2006: £11,209,528
2005: £13,738,000
2004: £10,220,000

Community involvement

Fidelity Investments community involvement and charitable giving falls into one of four categories:

- a community sponsorship programme (Fidelity Cares), which supports small fundraising and community events local to its offices. Full criteria are given on the company's website at: www.fidelity.co.uk
- employee activities, e.g. volunteering, charity days and a matched funding scheme
- educational initiatives – supporting initiatives linked to its business, such as financial capability and enterprise education.
- the Fidelity UK Foundation (Charity Commission no. 327899).

The foundation currently directs the majority of its grants to locations where the company has an office, i.e. Kent, Surrey and London. Support is focused on arts and culture, community development, education, and health.

With a view to those charities receiving grants achieving long-term self-sufficiency, support is usually for projects such as capital improvements, technology upgrades, organisational development and planning initiatives.

Exclusions

Fidelity (the company) will not support the following:

- religious, political and animal-support charities
- individuals
- individual schools
- events for exclusive audiences such as black tie events
- high-risk activities, such as parachute jumps, motor racing and abseiling.

In addition, it does not usually support sports events, clubs and teams, nor advertise in charity event programmes, diaries or directories.

The *Fidelity Foundation* applies the restrictions listed below.

Grants are not generally made to:

- start-up, sectarian, or political organisations
- private schools, and colleges or universities
- individuals.

Grants are not made for:

- sponsorships or benefit events
- scholarships
- corporate memberships
- advertising and promotional projects
- exhibitions.

Generally grants are not made for running costs, but may be considered on an individual basis through the foundation's small grant scheme.

Grants will not normally cover the entire cost of a project.

Grants will not normally be awarded to an organisation in successive years.

Applications

In writing to the correspondent, including a copy of the foundation's summary form, downloadable from www.fidelityukfoundation.org/apply.html

The site includes full details of the application requirements.

Each application is considered on an individual basis against the foundation's criteria. Telephone meetings and/or visits are made by foundation staff to establish a fuller understanding of the applicant and their needs.

Although there are no deadlines for submitting grant proposals, final decisions can take between three and six months, with an initial response being given to all applicants within three months.

Corporate giving

In 2007, the company made cash donations in the UK totalling £11,758,593 (2006: £11,209,528). Of this, £11,636,500 (2006: £11,106,938) went to the Fidelity UK Foundation. The balance of £122,093 (2006: £102,590) covered a substantial number of individual donations supporting local children's charities, schools and hospitals.

Fidelity UK Foundation

The foundation's assets in 2007 stood at £93 million. It had a total income of nearly £13 million and made grants totalling nearly £3.7 million. This figure was broken down as follows:

- arts and culture £1,436,000
- health £1,279,761
- community £668,123
- education £307,000.

Beneficiaries included: *Arts and Culture* – Handel House Trust (£500,000) and Strawberry Hill Trust (£100,000); *Health* – Institute of Neurology – UCL (£255,000) and Peninsula Medical School Foundation (£93,000); *Community* – White Lodge Centre (£150,000) and St Ethelburga's Centre (£24,000); and *Education* – The Gerwood Foundation (£75,000) and Chichester Festival Theatre (£25,000).

We have no information regarding the beneficiaries of the Fidelity Cares sponsorship programmes for small local fundraising and community events.

In kind support
Education

Fidelity aim to provide younger people with the skills and confidence they need to develop into responsible and individual corporate citizens, and help them make informed choices about their future.

Support is therefore given to initiatives that reflect the company's values and areas of expertise:

- financial education – projects that reflect its expertise, encouraging greater knowledge and understanding about longer term financial planning and investments
- enterprise education – projects that enable young people to have a greater knowledge and understanding about the world of business
- literacy – initiatives that aim to improve literacy levels. Fidelity works closely with local schools through its reading partner schemes
- arts and culture – through its outreach programme, Fidelity are committed to providing access for the local community to arts and culture, particularly for young people who might otherwise not have the opportunity.

Other areas of interest include projects that enhance young people's understanding of technology and support them in planning their careers and developing future aspirations.

Please note: Fidelity do not make cash donations to individual schools, instead preferring to fund projects that benefit several schools or to offer employees' time and skills.

Employee-led support

Fidelity supports and encourages its employees to be active members of their communities. They do this through the schemes listed below.

Grant matching: Through the employee grant-matching programme, funds raised for charitable or not for profit organisations are matched by the company.

Volunteering: Fidelity provides its employees with access to potential volunteering opportunities and some direct funding to cover costs.

Payroll giving: Through Give As You Earn, Fidelity facilitates regular giving by providing this scheme for all employees and covering all administration costs.

Filtronic plc

Company registration number 2891064

15 Parkview Court, St Paul's Road, Shipley, West Yorkshire BD18 3DZ

01274 535610; Fax: 01274 598263

Website: www.filtronic.co.uk

Correspondent: Human Resources Manager

Chairman: John Poulter

Chief Executive: Charles Hindson

Year end	Turnover	Pre-tax profit
31/05/2008	£54,651,000	(£14,862,000)

Nature of company business
The principal activity is the design and manufacture of microwave products for wireless telecommunications systems and defence applications.

Main locations: Newton Aycliffe, Shipley, East Kilbride, Wolverhampton

UK employees: 390

Charitable donations
2008: £6,000
2007: £6,000
2006: £27,000
2005: £26,000
2004: £25,000

Community involvement

Past information suggested the company has two main charities which it supports and which are also supported by employee fundraising events. Any other support given to charities is likely to be local and small-scale.

Exclusions

The company will not support any political purposes.

Applications

In writing to the correspondent.

Corporate giving

In 2008, the company made cash donations totalling £6,000 an amount indicative of the steady decline that has taken place since a high of £84,000 in 2000. We have no details of the beneficiaries.

Employee-led support

The company encourages its staff to actively take part in fundraising events.

Financial Services Authority

Company registration number 1920623

25 The North Colonnade, Canary Wharf, London E14 5HS

020 7066 5976; Fax: 020 7066 5977

Website: www.fsa.gov.uk

Correspondent: Linda Harris, Community Affairs
Email: linda.harris@fsa.gov.uk

Chairman: Sir Callum McCarthy

Chief Executive: Hector Sants

Year end	Turnover	Pre-tax profit
31/03/2007	£308,100,000	£18,400,000

Nature of company business
Regulator for the financial services industry.

Main locations: London, Edinburgh

UK employees: 2,720

> **Charitable donations**
>
> 2007: £18,138
> 2006: £200,000
> 2005: £100,000
>
> Total community contributions: £332,646
> Management costs: £90,797
>
> Membership: BitC, L B Group

Community involvement

The following is a summary of the FSA's Community Affairs Programme:

'As we are funded by a levy on the industry, it was decided that only staff volunteering and providing relevant in kind resources (such as computer equipment and offering the use of meeting rooms) would be part of our programme.

'Our community affairs policy concentrates its efforts in the area around Canary Wharf – the boroughs adjoining Tower Hamlets. The Community Affairs Department develops and maintains partnerships with reputable, effective local organisations that are working to regenerate the area.

'The current programme focuses on education, regeneration and employability issues, as this is where we can add value. The insights gained through volunteering are useful in our work to improve standards of personal finance education. The programme also helps regenerate the area through social inclusion initiatives.

'We are a founder member of the Heart of the City initiative, which aims to promote and encourage community involvement and charitable giving by City organisations, employees and individuals.'

Corporate giving

Although the authority has stated that it is unable to help charitable bodies financially because of the way it is funded (through an industry levy), it does appear to be able to make some small donations limited to organsiations within the vicinity of its London office.

In 2006/07, community contributions totalled nearly £333,000 of which £18,000 was in cash donations. Beneficiaries declared in its annual report and accounts included: Crisis (£10,200 – in lieu of producing a corporate Christmas card); Police Community Clubs of Great Britain (£660 – to purchase copies of a booklet against bullying and vandalism for use in Tower Hamlets); and West Ham and Plaistow Old People's Club (£80 – from the sale of old mobile phones).

In kind support

The FSA offer the use of conference rooms free to all community partners, local charities and local schools (local being Tower Hamlets and surrounding boroughs). PC donations are made in the local community through the Tools for Schools scheme (www.tfs.org.uk).

Employee-led support

The authority state: 'We have an established and varied community affairs programme offering employees a wide range of volunteering opportunities.

'This programme has grown from its early focus on education and business link activities to innovative initiatives aimed at social inclusion issues and regeneration. These include various schemes such as: mentoring, work placements, school

governors, board members and executive partnerships. We also offer staff the chance to participate in team challenges. Our schemes help the young, the unemployed through to employees assisting in non-executive type roles.'

Education: Over 300 of the authority's employees are actively involved in programmes delivered by Tower Hamlets Education Business Partnership. FSA staff provide help at nine primary and secondary schools in reading, numeracy, science, sports and computing.

Following the success in Tower Hamlets, similar employee volunteering schemes now exist at schools in Greenwich, Hackney, Newham and Lewisham.

Community: In partnership with East London Business Alliance (ELBA), the authority provide volunteers for ELBA's wide range of community programmes. These include executive partnership mentoring, trustees for local charities, team challenges and support for local community organisations.

Payroll giving: The authority runs the Give As You Earn scheme.

Findel plc

Company registration number 549034

Burley House, Bradford Road, Burley-in-Wharfedale, West Yorkshire LS29 7DZ

01943 864686; Fax: 01943 864986

Website: www.findel.co.uk

Correspondent: Dr I Bolton, Company Secretary

Chairman: Keith Chapman

Chief Executive: P E Jolly

Year end	Turnover	Pre-tax profit
31/03/2008	£645,058,000	£33,964,000

Nature of company business
Principal activities: the sale of greeting cards, paper products, gifts and educational supplies through mail order catalogues and the provision of e-commerce and mail order services to third parties.

Subsidiaries include: Health and Home Shopping Ltd, Philograph Publications Ltd, Express Gifts Ltd

Main locations: Ashby-de-la-Zouch, Accrington, Burley-in-Wharfdale, Swindon, Cheadle

UK employees: 3,636

> **Charitable donations**
>
> 2008: £72,716
> 2007: £332,853
> 2006: £78,826
> 2005: £79,550
> 2004: £76,000

Community involvement

The company supports local communities with a preference for local communities in the areas in which they operate (Yorkshire, Lancashire, Cheshire and the East Midlands).

Donations are made to organisations with particular emphasis on those working with children/youth, education, older people, medical research and sickness/disability, including many less well-known charities.

Exclusions

The company does not normally support appeals from individuals, animal welfare, the arts, enterprise/training, environment/heritage, science/technology, social welfare, sport, political or religious appeals or overseas projects.

Applications

In writing to the correspondent.

Corporate giving

In 2007/08, the company made cash donations of £72,716 (2006/07: £332,853) We have no details of the beneficiaries, but wish to point out that the exceptional figure for 2006/07 was due to a one-off donation to the Farepak Relief Fund.

In kind support

The group provides support by frequently donating products from home shopping and educational supplies catalogues to schools, hospices and other establishments in the areas in which they are based.

First plc

Company registration number SC157176

395 King Street, Aberdeen AB24 5RP

01224 650100; Fax: 01224 650140

Website: www.firstgroup.com

Correspondent: Arlene Craig

Chairman: Martin Gilbert

Chief Executive: Sir Moir Lockhead

Year end	Turnover	Pre-tax profit
31/03/2007	£4,707,600,000	£151,900,000

Nature of company business
The provision of passenger transport services primarily through provision of local bus and coach services and passenger railways.

Subsidiaries include: CentreWest London Buses Ltd, Great Eastern Railway Ltd, Northampton Transport Ltd, North Western Trains Co. Ltd, Leicester Cuty Bus Ltd, Hull Trains Company Ltd, Great Western Trains Co. Ltd

Main locations: London, Aberdeen

Total employees: 105,685

Charitable donations

2008: £120,000
2007: £100,000
2005: £40,000
2004: £34,000

Membership: BitC

Community involvement

According to the company's website, First plc's community strategy focuses on three key areas:

- community partnerships
- charitable giving
- employee volunteering.

Community partnerships: This will include looking at ways to extend initiatives across regions or to other companies with the potential to develop nationwide programmes where appropriate.

Charitable giving: A wide range of charitable giving takes place across First plc, through both the local operating companies and at group level. This includes monetary donations and extensive donations in kind such as the provision of buses free of charge for charitable events and initiatives. The group has also established a national charity partnership.

Employee Volunteering: First plc employees will be encouraged to participate in volunteering schemes, principally through the group's relationship with Business in the Community.

Charity of the year: Save the Children (2008).

Exclusions

Initiatives and causes that First plc do not fund include:

- political parties or bodies
- promotion of religious beliefs
- third-party giving organisations
- projects funded from local or central government
- the arts (unless the donation provides direct support to one of First plc's criteria)
- animal welfare
- research projects that are not directly associated with the needs of the business.

Applications
Charity and sponsorship

First plc have a charity and sponsorship committee which comprises 12 staff members who are geographically spread across the UK to encompass all operating areas. The committee considers and decides upon requests for funding and gifts in kind based on its charitable criteria, which includes:

- young people
- health
- the environment.

Applications which fall outside these charitable criteria will not be considered for funding.

However, if you meet the necessary funding criteria and would like to apply for charity or sponsorship support from First plc, please download and complete the application form available from the company's website.

When completed the form should be emailed to: cscapplications@firstgroup.com

Alternatively, you may post it to the correspondent.

Local partnerships

If you would like First plc to consider a proposal for your area, please contact:

Annalise Tyrie, Group Community Relations Manager, FirstGroup plc, 131–151 Great Titchfield Street, London

W1W 5BB. (Tel: 0203 008 7504; Email: annalise.tyrie@ firstgroup.com)

Information available: Corporate Social Responsibility Report 2008.

Corporate giving

In 2007/08, the company's charitable donations totalled £120,000 (2006/07: £100,000). The company does not keep a record of the cash value of its in kind support.

Besides supporting its charity of the year (Save the Children), through group partnerships help was also given to Outward Bound and UCAN. In addition, by emailing season's greetings to contacts and posting a seasonal message on its website, the savings made enabled about £12,000 to be set aside to support six staff nominated charities to the sum of £2,000 each. The charities were:

- Save the Children
- Girl Guiding Association – South Lanarkshire
- Excellent Development
- Royal National Lifeboat Institution (RNLI)
- Royal Society for the Prevention of Cruelty to Animals (RSPCA)
- Chavey Down Project (Part of Quarriers).

In kind support

First has provided the Archie branded bus which was key in promoting the Archie Foundation's message and brand.

Employee-led support

Employees' volunteering/charitable activities receive financial support from the company, which also matches their fundraising and giving.

Commercially-led support

Sponsorship: *Sport* – First plc have been a major supporter of the Paul Lawrie Junior Golf Development Programme for several years.

'The programme involves training teachers at participating primary schools to give lessons during PE periods for pupils from P4 upwards, using plastic clubs and sponge balls. It proceeds with support for coaching and the organisation of flag days and local tournaments throughout primary and secondary schools until the young golfer is ready to become a fully-fledged member of a golf club.'

First Plus Financial Group plc

Company registration number 3315543

Croescadarn Close, The Avenue Business Park, Pentwyn, Cardiff CF23 8FF

029 2030 3020; Fax: 029 2030 6265

Website: www.firstplus.co.uk

Year end	Turnover	Pre-tax profit
31/12/2007	£158,785,000	(£26,742,000)

Nature of company business
Personal finance company.

Main locations: Cardiff

UK employees: 350

Charitable donations

2007: £0
2005: £15,000
2004: £15,000

Community involvement

In order to be seen as a responsible member of the community and to involve staff in a worthwhile project, FIRSTPLUS formed Putting Cardiff Kids FIRST when it was less than one year old. This continues to be the sole focal point of the company's charitable support.

Exclusions

Appeals outside of the Cardiff postcode area and outside of the remit of Putting Cardiff Kids FIRST.

Applications

FIRSTPLUS invites applications for grants from organisations that have a Cardiff postcode and benefit children in the area. Application forms can be downloaded from the company's website (see under 'Our Community'). A panel of staff considers each application and makes awards.

Corporate giving

In 2005, over £15,000 was donated to charitable organisations and groups working on behalf of children in the Cardiff area. Recent beneficiaries have included: The Hollies Special School and Rubicon Dance.

Employee-led support

Money raised by staff through events such as summer balls, sporting or social occasions in aid of 'Putting Cardiff Kids FIRST' is matched £ for £ by the company. Over £200,000 has been donated since 1998.

First Trust Bank

Company registration number NI026401

First Trust Centre, 4 Queens Square, Belfast BT1 3DJ

028 9032 5599

Website: www.firsttrustbank.co.uk

Chairman: Dermot Gleeson

Chief Executive: Eugene Sheehy

Year end	Turnover
31/12/2005	£104,600,000

Nature of company business
Banking.

Main locations: Belfast

Total employees: 24,403

Charitable donations

2006: £1,052,724

Membership: A & B, BitC

Community involvement

First Trust Bank is a subsidiary of the Allied Irish Bank (AIB) and is a member of Business in the Community. However, despite a number of requests, we have been unable to obtain details of its current level of community support.

Previously, grants were available to organisations from Northern or Southern Ireland which had been established for at least 12 months. Support was also available under the AIB Better Ireland programme, but we were informed that this no longer extends to groups in Northern Ireland.

Exclusions

Previously have been advised that no grants are made towards: operating costs or salaries; international projects; third party fundraising activities; projects benefiting individuals rather than groups; private clubs; overseas travel; counter and public collections, or raffles; high-risk ventures, such as parachute or bungee jumping; or projects exclusively to a particular segment of society.

Corporate giving

According to the 2006 report of the now defunct PerCent Club, total community contributions amounted to £1,052,724. We have been unable to obtain a more recent figure.

Employee-led support

Business in the Community reported in 2008 that First Trust Bank 'Supports various groups through mentoring and educational programmes'.

Through the Allied Irish Bank's Partnership Fund, money raised by staff is either matched or a donation made to the organisation in recognition of the personal time given by the employee.

Commercially-led support

Sponsorship: *Sports* – Sport is sponsored at all levels, from grassroots golf, rugby and Gaelic sports, through to major events such as national rugby leagues and the Ryder Club.

FKI plc

Company registration number 164945

Precision House, Arden Road, Alcester B49 8HN

Website: www.fki.co.uk

Correspondent: Gary Barnes, Company Secretary

Chairman: Gordon F Page

Chief Executive: Paul Heiden

Year end	Turnover	Pre-tax profit
31/03/2007	£1,330,900,000	£65,300,000

Nature of company business
FKI plc is a major international engineering group quoted on the London stock exchange. Its specialised business areas are Lifting Products and Services, Logistex, Hardware and Energy Technology products, with operations principally from Europe and North America, it sells to customers in most countries of the world.

Subsidiaries include: Whipp & Bourne, Hawker Siddeley Switchgear Ltd, Bridon International Ltd, Brush Transformers Ltd, Brush Traction, CERTEX UK, Froude Consine, Brush Electrical Machines Ltd, Parsons Chain Company

Main locations: London

Total employees: 12,135

Charitable donations
2007: £100,000
2006: £100,000
2005: £100,000
2004: £100,000
2003: £100,000

Community involvement

The company allocates its charitable budget in March each year. This is distributed in April. The following extract is taken from the group's website:

'FKI businesses are encouraged to support the local communities in which they operate. FKI also supports charitable activities and donations to both local and international good causes through its corporate donations policy, updated in 2004 to include the potential for funds raised by employees towards charitable causes to be matched by donations from the group'.

Applications

In writing to the correspondent.

Corporate giving

In 2006/07, the company gave £100,000 in support of charities. This figure now appears to be the norm each year for donations.

Around 68% of FKI's businesses, representing 74% of employees, participated in local community activities, charitable events or made charitable donations to good causes, e.g. local charities, schools, hospitals and sports teams.

FKI also makes annual contributions to the Headstart scheme, part of The Engineering Development Trust which in turn is a component of The Royal Academy of Engineering's Best programme. The Headstart scheme promotes careers in science and engineering to 16–17 year olds through university-based, residential courses. The Group is also becoming more directly involved with Headstart through its graduate scheme, providing volunteer graduates to speak at a number of the residential courses. 'FKI embraces opportunities like this to re-invest in the engineering graduates of the future.'

A large percentage of FKI's US based businesses also support United Way, a charity which includes around 1,350 community-based organisations run by local volunteers. This support includes voluntary deductions from employee wages and locally organised fundraising events.

Employee-led support

Funds raised by employees towards charitable funds are matched by donations from the group.

Focus (DIY) Ltd

Company registration number 1779190

Gasworth House, Westmere Drive, Crewe CW1 6XB

01270 501555; Fax: 01270 250501

Website: www.focusdiy.co.uk

Correspondent: Public Relations Department

Chief Executive: Bill Grimsey

Year end	Turnover	Pre-tax profit
29/04/2007	£237,797,000	(£46,742,000)

Nature of company business
DIY and gardening retailer.

Main locations: Crewe

UK employees: 5,091

Charitable donations
2007: £14,570
2006: £33,380
2005: £29,960
2004: £35,255

Community involvement

Focus's website states: 'Focus has supported the Meningitis Trust since 2001 and makes an annual donation as well as raising much needed funds through:

- an 'Annual Fun Day' at all stores
- taking part in the London Marathon
- the sale of charity pin badges
- support centre 'Dress Down Days
- sample sales and raffles.'

Charity of the Year: The Meningitis Trust.

Exclusions
No support for individuals.

Applications
In writing to the correspondent.

Corporate giving

An annual cash donation is given to the Meningitis Trust. Although the company were not prepared to divulge the size of this, we assume it to be around £30,000 as in previous years.

In kind support
The company advised that it provides support through gifts in kind to UK charities and community groups.

Employee-led support
Staff are encouraged to become involved in local fundraising initiatives, as well as on behalf of the 'Charity of the Year'.

Payroll giving: A payroll giving scheme is in operation.

Commercially-led support
The company does not undertake arts or good-cause sponsorship.

Ford Motor Company Ltd

Company registration number 235446

Room 1/619, Eagle Way, Brentwood, Essex CM13 3BW

01277 252551; Fax: 01277 251439

Website: www.ford.co.uk/fbtrust

Correspondent: Andy Taylor, Director, Ford Britain Trust

Fax: 01277 251439

Chairman: Roelant de Waard

Year end	Turnover
31/12/2006	£7,845,000,000

Nature of company business
The Ford Motor Company Ltd is a wholly owned subsidiary of the Ford Motor Company of Dearborn, Michigan, USA.

Principal activity: the manufacture of motor cars and commercial vehicles, component manufacture and associated leasing and hire purchase activities.

The company and its subsidiaries operate principally in the UK and the Republic of Ireland. It is part of an integrated vehicle manufacturing group of Ford companies throughout Europe.

Main locations: Belfast, Bridgend, Halewood, Dunton, Essex, Southampton

UK employees: 12,000

Charitable donations
2006: £828,000
2004: £318,030
2002: £454,015

Total community contributions: £2,085,000

Membership: BitC

Community involvement

The company funds the Ford Britain Trust (Charity Commission no. 269410), a charitable organisation wholly supported by company contributions. Recipient organisations should preferably be registered charities. The majority of donations are one-off grants to local charities in the areas where the company has a presence. There is also a preference for charities in which a member of staff is involved.

Within these guidelines preference is given to projects concerned with education, environment, children and youth, the disabled, and projects that will provide a clear benefit to local communities.

National charities are rarely supported by the trust, and then only when the purpose of their application has specific benefits to communities in close proximity to Ford locations.

The objects of the trust are the 'advancement of education, and other charitable purposes beneficial to the community. The trust pays particular attention to organisations located near to Ford Motor Company Ltd locations in the UK. Currently these are: Essex; South Wales (Bridgend); Southampton; and Daventry.

The salary of the Director and his assistants is paid for by Ford Motor Company Ltd. The trust's income consists of donations from the company, and interest earned on those donations.

In addition, Ford Motor Company Ltd provides discount to specific charities for the purchase of vehicles and provides funding to BEN (Motor Industry Benevolent Society) and initiatives in the east of London (e.g. Invest in Thames Gateway).

Exclusions

Ford Britain Trust: National charities are rarely supported, except for specific local projects in Ford areas. Applications in respect of sponsorship, individuals, research, overseas projects, travel, religious or political projects are not eligible. Applications for core funding and/or salaries, revenue expenses, and major building projects are rarely considered.

Generally: no support for circulars, fundraising events, brochure advertising, individuals, purely denominational appeals, political appeals, local appeals not in areas of company presence or overseas projects.

Applications

Applications to the Ford Britain Trust are by application form available on their website – www.ford.co.uk/fbtrust

The trustees meet in July and November each year. Applications are considered in order of receipt and it may take several months for an application to be considered.

Although each application is carefully considered, the number of applications the trust receives far outstrips its resources and regretfully, therefore, the number of applicants it is able to help is limited.

Information available: Guidelines for applicants are given on the company's website at www.ford.co.uk/ie/fobtrust

Corporate giving

In 2006/07, the company made total community contributions in the UK of just over £2 million. Of this, cash donations totalled £828,000. Major beneficiaries were: BEN (£200,000); Ford Britain Trust (£150,000); Invest in Thames Gateway (£100,000); Lords Taverners (£60,000 – cash); and Gay Pride and Shakespeare Globe Theatre (£30,000 each).

Ford Britain Trust

The trust's income consists of donations from the company, and interest earned on these donations. In 2006/07 the trust made grants totalling £204,000 in the following categories: schools and education (£38,000); community service (£62,500); youth (£57,000); disability (£36,000); and special needs education (£10,500).

Applications in respect of new Ford vehicles are considered only when two-thirds of the purchase price is available from other sources. In such cases any resultant grant is unlikely to exceed £2,000.

Grants are not available for the purchase of second-hand vehicles.

In kind support

Examples include the loan of vehicles, free equipment, and education outreach support to a large range of charities such as Wooden Spoon, Lords Taverners, Gay Pride and so on, with a total worth of £325,000 in 2006.

Enterprise: The company supports local enterprise agencies. Support is given in the form of youth training, resources, equipment or management expertise.

Employee-led support

The company allows employees two days off per year for voluntary activities, gives financial support to employees' volunteering and gives contributions to employee fundraising.

Commercially-led support

Sponsorship: The company undertake good-cause sponsorship. Any proposals should be addressed to: Mark Jones (Tel: 01277 252086).

Fortis Insurance Ltd

Company registration number 3354568

Fortis House, Tollgate, Eastleigh, Hampshire SO53 3YA

023 8064 4455

Website: www.fortisinsurance.co.uk

Correspondent: HR Manager

Chief Executive: Barry Smith

Year end	Turnover	Pre-tax profit
31/12/2007	£692,300,000	£12,700,000

Nature of company business
Principally motor, travel and household insurance, and small commercial lines business.

Main locations: Eastleigh, Gloucester

UK employees: 1,174

Charitable donations
2007: £47,967
2006: £42,831
2005: £36,878
2004: £39,542
2003: £49,205

Community involvement

The company appears to support general charitable purposes. Although company foundations exist in the Netherlands and Belgium (the company's 'home' territories), support is limited to organisations within those countries.

Exclusions

No support for local appeals not in areas of company presence, general/circular appeals

Applications

In writing to the correspondent.

Corporate giving

In 2007, the company made charitable donations in the UK totalling nearly £48,000 (2006: £43,000). No details of the beneficiaries were available.

Employee-led support

Staff are encouraged to participate in volunteering and fundraising activities on behalf of charities and local community organisations.

Freshfields Bruuckhaus Deringer LLP

Company registration number GE000156

65 Fleet Street, London EC4Y 1HS

020 7936 4000; Fax: 020 7832 7001

Website: www.freshfields.com

Correspondent: Bea Malleson, Head of CSR and Community Investment

Joint Senior Partner: Dr Konstantin Mettenheimer

Joint Senior Partner: Guy Morton

Year end
27/03/2007

Nature of company business
International law firm.

Main locations: London

UK employees: 2,121

Total employees: 5,493

Charitable donations

2007: £490,447
2006: £481,994
2005: £245,949
2004: £246,500
2003: £296,653

Total community contributions: £2,537,587
Management costs: £220,838

Membership: BitC, L B Group

Community involvement

The firm state the following about their community support: 'Our community and pro bono programme is designed to make a positive difference to the communities where we have offices and, more broadly, to some of the wider legal and social issues that concern so many of us today, which is why we concentrate on investing in the community, including pro bono legal advice. In 2006/07, 92% of our firm-wide contribution was focused on community investment and 8% on charitable gifts'.

'The majority of our total firm-wide contribution is focused on our four themes. Each office, together with its community partners, is responsible for interpreting these themes in a way that is appropriate to their local community:

- promoting human rights
- improving access to justice for individuals and not-for-profit organisations in need by providing free legal advice
- reducing homelessness
- raising the levels of achievement and aspirations of young people from disadvantaged backgrounds, and improving their skills.'

Applications

In writing to the correspondent.

Information available: the firm provide an online corporate social responsibility report.

Corporate giving

In 2006/07, the firm provided cash support totalling £490,447 and made total UK community contributions of just over £2.5 million. This was broken down as follows:

- cash – £490,447
- gifts in kind – £96,668
- time – £1,950,472 (community: £347,000; pro bono: £1.6 million).

Freshfields state that in 2006/07, 736 (35%) of its people in London took part in one or more community and pro bono activities, contributing over 12,300 hours to pro bono legal advice and over 7,100 to community activities.

During this time, employee volunteers gave advice to around 1,000 people at legal advice centres; redecorated two centres for homeless people; created three gardens; encouraged, supported and informed around 450 children at Redlands Primary School and 1,000 pupils at Haggerston School for Girls; and provided support and advice to over 100 homeless people and work experience to over 20 people, including homeless people, teachers and pupils at local schools and colleges.

Comprehensive details of the firm's community involvement in London can be found on its website and covers:

- working with young disadvantaged people
- working with homeless people
- promoting access to justice
- promoting human rights
- community challenge.

In kind support

Through its Ready for Work programme, Freshfields has provides work experience placements to homeless people. Between 2000 and 2007, 126 individuals have completed successful placements at the firm, 14 of whom have taken up permanent jobs there. Others have gone on to work elsewhere.

In 2006/07, in association with Brent Council and The Learning Trust, which has responsibility for education in Hackney, Freshfields hosted the launch and graduation of the Black Leadership programme for 150 pupils from schools in these areas. The programme aims to equip young black students from disadvantaged areas with the skills and motivation to make better personal and career choices.

Employee-led support

Freshfields encourages every member of the firm to take part in an activity to help a charity or community-related project by providing time off to volunteer. In 2007, 35% of staff in London took part in one or more community affairs programmes surpassing the annual target of 30% staff participation in each office set by the entire firm.

The firm's website states that its philosophy is to promote active employee participation, rather than simply fundraising.

Payroll giving: The firm operate the Give As You Earn Scheme.

Commercially-led support

Sponsorship: *Homelessness* – In October 2007, Freshfields announced its £232,000, three-year sponsorship of Shelter's Keys to the Future initiative, which aims to end child homelessness in the UK. With this support, the charity is establishing the Children's Legal Service to fight for the rights of children and young people to have their housing needs met.

Friends Provident plc

Company registration number ZC000115

Pixham End, Dorking, Surrey RH4 1QA

0870 608 3678; Fax: 01306 654991

Website: www.friendsprovident.co.uk

Correspondent: Amanda Adey, Corporate Social Responsibility

Chairman: Sir Adrian Montague

Chief Executive: Trevor Matthews

Year end	Turnover	Pre-tax profit
31/12/2007	£2,506,000,000	(£113,000,000)

Nature of company business
Long-term insurance.

Subsidiaries include: Regional Properties Ltd, London Capital Holdings Ltd, Box Hill Investments Ltd, Preferred Assurance Co. Ltd, Larpent Newton & Co. Ltd

Main locations: Dorking, Exeter, Salisbury, Manchester

Total employees: 5,085

Charitable donations

2007: £83,202
2006: £169,724
2005: £204,248
2003: £324,337

Membership: BitC, L B Group

Community involvement

Friends Provident promotes two main themes of education and healthy lifestyles through its community investment programme. At a corporate level it has a significant giving programme supporting employee, as well as community, interests. 'Friends in the Community' is made up of three schemes: FRIENDS give, FRIENDS volunteer and FRIENDS raise.

Friends Provident also has corporate partnerships with a small number of national charities whose work relates to its business activities.

At a local level, in the communities around the main office sites of Dorking, Salisbury, Manchester and Exeter, the three objectives are to:

- partner local charities which focus on social and environmental needs relevant to that community
- support local sports and arts organisations that provide opportunities for our employees to maintain a healthy work/life balance
- build long-term relationships with schools close to our main office sites.

Support is also available from an 'independent', but closely-linked foundation (Friends Provident Foundation – Charity Commission no. 1087053) which received a substantial endowment of shares from the company in 2004. The foundation addresses issues relating to financial systems and poverty in the UK.

Exclusions

Please note the company does not support:

- individuals conducting their own fundraising for charity
- political or religious organisations, including local churches
- overseas trips and travel expenses
- applications for specialist school status or school building projects.

Applications

Enquiries regarding corporate support at a local level should be addressed to the appropriate person at the relevant site (Dorking, Salisbury, Manchester or Exeter).

The contact for the foundation is: The Secretary to the Friends Provident Foundation at the above address. Alternatively you can send an email to: foundation.enquiroes@friendsprovident.co.uk

Full details about how to apply to the foundation are available at: www.friendsprovident.com/foundation/

Corporate giving

Our request to the company for updated information did not receive a reply, which is unfortunate, given that some confusion exists regarding the value of its corporate community support.

In its 2005 annual report and accounts, the company stated that: 'The Friends Provident Foundation is an independent vehicle through which the company *may* make its charitable donations '. It then went on to give a total charitable donation figure which combined the giving of the group *and the foundation*. Due to the lack of any further information giving a breakdown of this total (£1,954,529), we decided to publish a figure showing what the group (which includes F&C Asset Management plc) paid to the foundation (£204,248). The same decision was applied to the 2006 figures.

The company's accounts for 2007, however, merely state that 'cash donations to charitable causes amounted to £1,548,699'. Whether this again includes donations made by the foundation we cannot tell. If it doesn't, then it would seem to include money raised by employees through the 'Friends in the Community' scheme for which a figure of £1.3 million is quoted in the company's corporate social responsibility report.

This lack of transparency does not help in ascertaining overall levels of corporate support in the UK. We have again, therefore, published a figure showing the total given by the group to the foundation (£83,202). This may well do a disservice to Friends Provident, but until the information they provide is clearer we feel we have no other choice.

Employee-led support

The company encourages employee volunteering and fundraising through the following schemes:

'FRIENDS volunteer:

- recognises employees that work for charitable organisations through 'recognition grants'
- supports community based team challenge days
- expands our well established schools programme

'FRIENDS raise, which supports individual fundraising as well as corporate fundraising days matching both activities £ for £.'

Payroll giving: FRIENDS give, which encourages payroll giving and through Give as you Earn Friends Provident matches employee donation up to £20 per month

Commercially-led support

Sponsorship: *The arts* – Friends Provident supports local (to company presence) events such as Salisbury Arts Festival.

Fujitsu Services Holdings plc

Company registration number 142200

Observatory House, Windsor Road, Slough, Berkshire SL1 2EY

0870 234 5555

Website: www. fujitsu.com/uk

Correspondent: Phillippa Holroyd, Head of Employee Policies and Procedures

Chairman: Richard Christou

Chief Executive: David Courtley

Year end	Turnover	Pre-tax profit
31/03/2007	£2,465,200,000	£172,000,000

Nature of company business
Holding company of an IT services group.

Subsidiaries include: FDK Electronics UK Ltd, Glovia International, Teamware Group

Main locations: Slough

UK employees: 11.919

Total employees: 18,390

Charitable donations

2007: £84,700
2006: £178,000
2005: £51,000
2004: £19,000
2003: £35,000

Membership: BitC

Community involvement

The following information was taken from the company's website:

'Fujitsu encourages the use of the technical and management skills of its employees to support local community and charitable activities. The company supports active participation in both company and locally initiated programmes, with particular focus on the areas of education, youth and health. Line managers are encouraged to support voluntary work and we provide funding and resources to support agreed initiatives.

'We fund a number of regional 'Impact on Society' groups in the UK, through which we seek to facilitate initiatives taken by, or sponsored by Fujitsu people in support of worthy causes in our local communities.

'We are patrons of the Prince's Trust directly supporting disadvantaged young people and are an active member of Business in the Community.'

Applications

In writing to the correspondent.

Corporate giving

In 2006/07, donations in the UK totalled £84,700 (2005/06: £178,000 including £100,000 donated to the Tsunami disaster relief fund). No further details were available.

In kind support

Fujitsu are involved in several programmes, which aim to increase both basic numeracy and literacy skills and IT skills in local primary schools in for example the Thames Valley, Northern Ireland, Glasgow and the Midlands. The company are also involved in mentoring in secondary schools and have hosted career and interview technique clinics for older children.

As part of the company's approach in working with the public sector, it is committed to working with local communities to act as a change agent for community regeneration programmes for example at its campus in Manchester, UK and its new centre in Derry, Northern Ireland.

Employee-led support

The company states: 'Our commitment to diversity extends into the communities in which we operate. Through our Charitable Support and Community Relations policy we encourage all our employees to become involved in helping to give something back to society'. We could not find a published copy of the policy on the website.

Payroll giving: A scheme is in operation to enable employees to make tax-efficient donations to charities. Also in the UK Fujitsu enable national insurance/tax-efficient donations through charitable giving with an additional contribution made by the company.

Future plc

Company registration number 3757874

30 Monmouth Street, Bath BA1 2BW

01225 442244; Fax: 01225 822836

Website: www.futureplc.com

Correspondent: Human Resources Department

Chairman: Roger Perry

Chief Executive: Stevie Spring

Year end	Turnover	Pre-tax profit
30/09/2007	£165,700,000	£9,200,000

Nature of company business
Publishing.

UK employees: 1,438

Charitable donations

2007: £49,000

Community involvement

Future's charitable donation policy provides for a matched contribution scheme. Employees raise money for their chosen charity and Future matches this amount, subject to a reasonable limit and to qualification under the rules of the scheme.

Exclusions

No support for individuals, political or religious appeals.

Applications

In writing to the correspondent.

Corporate giving

In 2007, Future made local charitable donations in the cities where it has offices. The total amount of charitable donations made by the group in the year was given as £27,000 (2006: £100,000), but this doesn't include the matched funding mentioned under 'Employee-led' support. We have included this in our figures, however.

In kind support

In Bath, Future run a 'Magazines for Charity' scheme where we make regular free deliveries of magazines to local medical surgeries, health centres, hospitals, schools and other community organisations.

Employee-led support

In 2007, £22,000 (2006: £41,000) was paid to support employees fundraising under the charitable match scheme mentioned earlier.

G4S plc

Company registration number 4992207

The Manor, Manor Royal, Crawley, West Sussex RH10 9UN

020 8770 7000; Fax: 020 8772 2000

Website: www.g4s.com

Correspondent: Nigel Lockwood, Group Communications Executive
Email: nigel.lockwood@g4s.com

Chairman: Alf Duch-Pedersen

Chief Executive: Nick Buckles

Year end	Turnover	Pre-tax profit
31/12/2007	£4,490,400,000	£216,800,000

Nature of company business
G4S plc provides security services, cash services and justice services internationally.

Main locations: Sutton

Total employees: 507,480

Charitable donations

2007: £311,000
2006: £94,000
2005: £300,000
2004: £328,000
2003: £121,000

Community involvement

G4S plc is implementing a five year programme of community projects which aims to support a range of health, welfare and community initiatives in countries around the world until 2012. No further information regarding the company's plans for the UK were available as at September 2008.

Exclusions

The group will not give political contributions. It is not known if there are any other exclusions.

Applications

Applications to the group communications executive.

Corporate giving

In 2007, the company declared charitable contributions by the group amounting to £311,000. It is not clear from the annual report whether the donations were made to UK charities/ organisations or to projects internationally. We have no details of the beneficiaries.

In kind support

Through HMP and YOI Parc, G4S Justice Services have participated in the 'Prison Me? No Way' programme for over five years helping to bring crime and safety awareness workshops to children aged between 13 and 15 years old at schools across the UK.

Employee-led support

G4S supports and encourages its employees to become involved its local communities through the 'G4S Sponsorship Matching' programme. The programme offers to double the money raised by them for local good causes and community projects.

Payroll giving: The company operates the Give As You Earn scheme.

Galiform plc

Company registration number 2128710

International House, 1st Floor, 66 Chiltern Street, London W1U 4JT

Website: www.galiform.com

Correspondent: Head of Marketing & Advertising

Chairman: Will Samuel

Chief Executive: Matthew Ingle

Year end	Turnover	Pre-tax profit
31/12/2007	£976,500,000	£44,400,000

Nature of company business
Manufacture, distribution and retail sale of kitchen cabinetry and related products

Subsidiaries include: Howden Joinery Ltd, Sofa Worshop, Hygena Ltd

Main locations: London

UK employees: 6,395

Charitable donations

2007: £410,000
2006: £376,000
2005: £515,000
2004: £400,000
2003: £300,000

Community involvement

The company provide cash and in kind support to a variety of generally, unspecified local causes. Leonard Cheshire is a key community partner with support being given towards its volunteer recruitment programme. Staff are also encouraged to fundraise on behalf of the charity during a fundraising awareness week.

Exclusions

No grants for overseas projects, political or religious appeals, science/technology or local appeals not in areas of company presence.

Applications

In writing to the correspondent.

Corporate giving

In 2007, the Director's Report section of the group's annual report and accounts contained the following: In addition to furniture products and services donated to various charities, the *group* made charitable donations during the period amounting to £410,000 (2006: £376,000)'.

However, on the group's website under 'Local communities – Getting involved' it states: 'This year, our *staff* made more than 1,400 donations to local good causes. This amounted to some £410,000 across the group and as well as cash donations and employee fund raising initiatives, included donations of joinery and kitchen equipment to local schools, village halls, care homes, local youth groups and sports clubs'.

These somewhat ambiguous statements (has the money come from the group, its staff or both?) do not suggest the company is being wholly transparent regarding its financial support of charitable organisations. That Galiform appear unable to present such information clearly is all the more unfortunate given that in 2007 it won a Third Sector Award for Excellence for the best UK Charity/Corporate Partnership (with Leonard Cheshire).

In kind support

This included the donation of joinery and kitchen equipment to local schools, village halls, care homes, local youth groups and sports clubs.

Employee-led support

The company financially assist employees' volunteering/ charitable activities.

Payroll giving: A scheme is in operation.

Gallaher Ltd

Company registration number 3299793

Members Hill, Brooklands Road, Weybridge, Surrey KT13 0QU

01932 372000; Fax: 01932 372532

Website: www.jti.com/english

Correspondent: Karen Orchin, Head of Community Relations – UK 01932 372531; Fax: 01932 372532
Email: ukenquiries@jti.com

Regional President (UK & Eire): Eddy Pirard

Year end	Turnover	Pre-tax profit
31/12/2006	£8,401,000,000	£565,000,000

Nature of company business
The manufacture and marketing of a range of cigarettes, cigars and pipes and handrolling tobacco products for the UK, Republic of Ireland. Gallaher is now part of the JTI Group (Japanese Tobacco Inc.).

Subsidiaries include: J R Freeman, Benson & Hedges Ltd

Main locations: Weybridge, Lisnafillan (N Ireland), Crewe, Cardiff

UK employees: 1,642

Charitable donations

2006: £405,392
2005: £451,747
2004: £624,358
2003: £393,250
2002: £423,861

Management costs: £10,000

Membership: A & B, BitC, L B Group

Community involvement

The company gives mainly to large national charities, and to smaller organisations working in areas of company presence (Weybridge, Cardiff, Crewe and Lisnafillan). Focus at a national level is on support for the elderly and adult education. Locations may support additional local causes with the exception of the specific exclusions listed herein.

Exclusions

Unable to support the following as a matter of policy: children's charities; medical/health-related charities. No support for circular appeals, telephone appeals, fundraising appeals, purely denominational (religious) appeals, local appeals not in areas of company presence or for advertising in charity brochures.

Applications

Applications are considered by the location community care committees which meet usually three or four times a year.

Regional contacts:

Steve Grundy – J R Freeman & Son, PO Box 54, Freeman House, 236 Penarth Road, Cardiff CF1 1RF.

Trevor Norwood – Virginia House, Weston Road, Crewe, Cheshire CW1 1GH.

Catriona McBride – 201 Galgorm Road, Lisnafillan, Gracehill, Ballymena, Co. Antrim, N Ireland BT24 1HS.

Debbie Price – Members Hill, Brooklands Road, Weybridge, Surrey KT13 0QU.

Corporate giving

In 2006, the company made charitable donations of £405,392 to projects and organisatiions in the UK. Donations in the UK are also made through the Charities Aid Foundation.

The company's focus is on developing partnerships with charitable organisations to make a meaningful and sustainable impact over time. The company identifies its own national projects, but local community care committees are able to respond to local requests.

Employee-led support

Payroll giving: The company operates the Give As You Earn scheme, with employees' donations being matched by the company to a maximum of £100 per month, or up to £1,200 in any one year.

Commercially-led support

Sponsorship: *The arts* – Gallaher is currently setting up a number of cultural and artistic sponsorships. Requests for individual sponsorships will not be considered.

GAP (UK) Ltd

Company registration number 3918195

Castle Mound Way, Rugby, Warwickshire CV23 0WA

01788 818300

Website: www.gapinc.com

Year end
31/01/2008

Nature of company business
Clothing supplier and manufacturer.

Main locations: London, Coventry, Rugby

Charitable donations
2007: £108,000
2005: £575,100

Community involvement

Whilst the company provides much information on its grant-making activities in the USA, little is available on its work in the UK except for a list of grant beneficiaries (see below). However, as all funding appears to come via the Gap Foundation, it can be assumed that the main areas of work supported here are as in the USA. These areas are: education, youth, health, welfare, arts and community work. The geographical focus of its UK support is Warwickshire and the surrounding areas. There also some support for charities based in London, where the company has an office.

Applications

Gap Foundation does not accept unsolicited proposals. Its strategy is to seek out and build strong partnerships with a limited number of national, regional and local community organisations.

Corporate giving

In 2007, cash donations in the UK via the Gap Foundation totalled around £108,000. The 11 organisations benefiting from this were: The Prince's Trust (£50,000); NCH Children's Charity (£13,000); Centrepoint (£10,000); Community Service Volunteers – London and Great Ormond Street Hospital for Children (£9,000 each); Coventry and Warwickshire YMCA (£6,500); Bradby Club – Rugby, Rugby Sea Cadets and Tall Ships Youth Trust – Hampshire (£2,500 each); Kingston College (£2,000); and Ravensbourne College of Design (£1,750).

Given that the foundation also matches funds raised by employees for qualifying charitable organisations, it is possible

that the total cash donations made by Gap in the UK are higher than that quoted. In addition, there appears to be a fair degree of in kind support (see below) for which, in relation to the UK, there is no value available.

In kind support

The company works with Gifts In Kind International and makes substantial product donations each year. In 2007, the company made product donations of around $59 million worldwide. (Note: We assume this figure to be at wholesale rather than cost price as is the norm in the US).

Employee-led support

The company states that through its foundation it supports employee volunteerism, both in the US and internationally. So, for example, it matches employees' donations dollar for dollar.

In addition to this, to find volunteer opportunities in their local communities, Gap Inc. employees worldwide use VolunteerMatch, a non-profit organisation that uses the internet to connect community groups with individuals interested in getting involved. Gap Foundation also organises volunteer events for employees in its corporate headquarters year-round.

GE Healthcare

Company registration number 1002610

Pollard's Wood, Nightingale Lane, Chalfont St Giles, Buckinghamshire HP8 4SP

01494 545200

Website: www.gemedicalsystemseurope.com/uk

Correspondent: David Boyd, Public Affairs Manager
01494 545200

Year end	Turnover	Pre-tax profit
31/12/2006	£193,464,000	(£6,350,000)

Nature of company business
Principal activities are the development, manufacture and sale of specialised products for research-based biotechnology supply and for the diagnosis and treatment of disease. Major UK locations are Slough, Amersham, Bedford and Hatfield.

Subsidiaries include: Amersham Pharmacia Biotech

Main locations: Amersham, Aberdeen, Cardiff, Chalfont St Giles, Little Chalfont, Gloucester

UK employees: 1.736

Charitable donations
2006: £22,810
2005: £34,628

Community involvement

GE states that in the UK, one of the key contributions it aims to make is through extensive community engagement. The company, primarily through its philanthropic arm the GE Foundation, develops and supports various programmes in its communities. This can be through either financial support or employee volunteering.

Exclusions

No support for advertising in charity brochures, animal welfare, appeals from individuals, the arts, fundraising events, overseas projects, political or religious appeals, sport or umbrella organisations raising monies for any such causes.

Applications

For local, small scale UK support, please apply in writing to the correspondent.

GE Foundation

The GE Foundation does not encourage unsolicited proposals. Through ongoing research in the field, the GE Foundation develops targeted initiatives and invites specific institutions and organisations to apply within those initiatives. Its capacity to review unsolicited proposals is extremely limited.

Corporate giving

Previously, we had thought that financial support to UK organisations was only available via the GE Foundation. However, it appears that small sums are donated by the UK company as their latest annual report and accounts reveal.

In 2006, GE Healthcare Ltd made charitable donations of £22,810 (2005: £34,628). By far the largest support, however, came from the GE Foundation which gave around £280,000 in the UK out of total worldwide contributions of £44 million.

Examples of organisation in the UK supported by the foundation include:

Sandfields School – GE is supporting a Neath Port Talbot Council project at Sandfields School, Port Talbot which aims to get at risk youngsters back into school. The initiative has been awarded a £50,000 grant.

Bristol Education Action Zone – GE is supporting an innovative project to develop the skills and confidence of children in four of Bristol's inner city schools. A grant of $75,000 (£38,000) was made to the Bristol Education Action Zone for its 'Learning Beyond the Classroom' project – aimed at raising attainment standards through making use of school time spent outside the classroom.

SETNET – GE is a major supporter of SETNET – the Science, Engineering, Technology and Mathematics Network, having awarded a grant of £125,000 to support SETNET's work.

In kind support

A current (2007/08) initiative is the knitting programme at GE Money in Greater London. Created to meet the needs of local hospitals and hospices. knitters of all ages come together every week to produce squares for blankets, pairs of bed socks, waistcoats, premature baby hats, burial gowns and cardigans.

Employee-led support

Across the UK, GE volunteers work in schools to improve reading and numeracy skills and to raise young people's aspirations. GE also supports a wide range of community organisations including hospitals, homeless shelters, and children's homes. Its employees help to enhance living and working environments in disadvantaged communities and better equip young people for the world of work through partnerships with Young Enterprise and SETNET, among others.

'In June 2007, during GE's global Volunteering Week, 1,100 GE volunteers in the UK gave over 7000 hours of service in their local communities. In September 2007, many sites took part in the World's Biggest Coffee morning fundraising for Macmillan Cancer Support.'

The GE Foundation provides a matching gift programme to support employee giving. However, we are unsure if this applies in the UK.

General Motors UK Ltd

Company registration number 135767

Griffin House, Osborne Road, Luton LU1 3YT

01582 721122

Website: www.vauxhall.co.uk

Correspondent: See 'Applications'

Year end	Turnover	Pre-tax profit
31/12/2007	£3,810,300,000	(£59,100,000)

Nature of company business
The company manufactures, markets and branded services passenger cars and light vans.

Main locations: Ellesmere Port, Luton

UK employees: 3,338

Charitable donations
2007: £231,418
2006: £218,446
2003: £264,432

Community involvement

Formerly Vauxhall Motors Ltd, the company changed its name to General Motors UK Ltd in April 2008. The following information was taken from the company's website regarding its community support (Note. This has not yet been updated to reflect the change in name, but is current policy):

'Vauxhall's charitable support starts at home. The company assists charities and community groups based where it operates, in Bedfordshire, and Cheshire and on the Wirral. Vauxhall allocates charitable funding via the Griffin Awards, awarded annually, and GM Community Grants, awarded quarterly in both locations. The company also designates an official Charity of the Quarter, for which employees are encouraged to get involved in fundraising and volunteering activities.

'Vauxhall's official charity policy is currently focused on organisations which support young people outside of school hours, as well as projects aimed at improving the local environment, whether from an ecological or from a social perspective. Initiatives from groups that demonstrate an active commitment to diversity and which focus on areas of community deprivation are particularly welcome.'

Exclusions

No grants for circular appeals, advertising in charity brochures, appeals from individuals, fundraising events, medical research, overseas projects, political appeals, religious appeals, science/technology, or local appeals not in areas of company presence. The company does not give raffle prizes or vehicle donations.

Applications

Griffin Awards

Application forms for the Griffin Award can be downloaded from the Vauxhall website. Once completed they should be sent to: Paul Patten, Vauxhall Griffin Awards CCAS, 80 Croydon Road, Beckenham, Kent BR3 4DF.

GM Community Grants

To apply for a GM Community Grant, please dowmload the application form from the company's website and tell them how well you would use the money.

Please Note: Applications from groups which can show commitment to diversity will be especially welcome. All winners must be prepared to be involved in publicity. The priority age group is those aged 11 to 20, but consideration will also be given to applications by groups which service those under 11. Judges are also looking to support specific projects, rather than contribute to general running costs.

Corporate giving

In 2007, General Motors (formerly Vauxhall Motors) donated a total of £231,418 (2006: £218,446) to charities in the UK.

Griffin Awards

In each region, Bedfordshire and the Wirral, a £10,000 first prize and three runner-up prizes of £1000 are donated to those organisations that are judged to meet the criteria that the judging panel believe will bring most benefit to the local community. Also, one organisation in each region will win the use of a Vauxhall vehicle, which they can use to support their charitable projects.

Recent (2005) winners were: Autism Bedfordshire and Groundwork in Wirral. A total of £26,000 was given in prize money during the year.

The two loan cars were won by the Luton Churches Education Trust in Bedfordshire and Age Concern Cheshire in Wirral.

GM Community Grants

GM Community Grants are run in conjunction with the Luton News and associated papers, the Ellesmere Port Pioneer and Wirral News Group. The £1,000 quarterly grants are awarded, alternating between charity and community groups in Bedfordshire and Cheshire. Judges look to help groups which support young people outside school hours. Applications are particularly welcome from local community groups and charities, although projects run by national charities working in Bedfordshire and Cheshire will also be considered.

In kind support

The company provide additional support through gifts in kind and joint promotions. For example, the Ellesmere Port plant has donated materials such as scrap wood and over 40 car engines to schools, colleges and universities for educational use.

Employee-led support

GM Volunteer Plus provides a donation of the sterling equivalent of $250 from the US-based GM Foundation, each time an employee or group of employees completes 50 hours of voluntary work for a registered charity.

Genting Stanley plc

Company registration number 1519749

Circus Casino Star City, Watson Road, Birmingham B7 55A

Website: www.stanleyleisure.com

Correspondent: Tan Sri Lim Kok Thay, Chairman

Chairman: Tan Sri Lim Kok Thay

Year end	Turnover	Pre-tax profit
31/12/2007	£206,400,000	(£15,400,000)

Nature of company business
The main activity of the company is that of casino operators.

Subsidiaries include: Pakm Beach Club Ltd, B J O'Connor Ltd

Main locations: Liverpool

UK employees: 4,188

Charitable donations

2007: £277,000
2006: £300,000
2005: £300,000
2004: £300,000
2003: £188,000

Community involvement

In 2007 Genting International plc paid £613 million to acquire Stanley Leisure and now trades as Stanley Casinos. The group owns three of the UK's most popular land-based casino chains – Circus, Mint and Maxims – and has a total of 46 casinos nationwide.

The company's social responsibilities focus mainly on promoting responsible gambling, and is an active contributor to the Responsibility in Gambling Trust. The trust funds research and education into problem gambling in the UK. In addition, the group supports the work of Gamecare, a registered charity, and publicises the services they offer to individuals with gambling problems.

Previously we were informed that the company prefers to support local charities in Northern Ireland and the North West of England, especially Merseyside, although this may have changed following the take over (the new head office is in Birmingham).

Exclusions

No support for appeals from individuals; the arts; environment/heritage; fundraising events; overseas projects; political appeals; religious appeals; or science/technology.

Applications

In writing to the correspondent.

Corporate giving

In 2007, the company made a donation of £215,000 to Responsibility in Gaming Trust (35 week period to 31 December 2006: £136,000). A further £22,000 was paid to various national charities (35 week period to 31 December 2006: £ nil) and £40,000 was paid to local charities (35 week period to 31 December 2006: £ nil). We have no details of the beneficiaries.

Employee-led support

Employees are encouraged to participate in charitable events, such as the BBC Children in Need Appeal.

Geopost UK Ltd

Company registration number 732993

Roebuck Lane, Smethwick, West Midlands B66 1BY

0121 500 2500

Website: www.geopostuk.com/

Correspondent: The Marketing Department

Email: marketing.dept@geopostuk.com

Year end	Turnover	Pre-tax profit
02/12/2006	£212,170,000	£23,936,000

Nature of company business
Part of La Poste (The French Post Office), the company is engaged in the provision of transport related services, which include the collection and delivery of parcels, distribution and logistics management.

Subsidiaries include: DPD UK Ltd, Homecall Ltd, Interlink Express Ltd, Mail PLus Ltd

UK employees: 4,081

Charitable donations
2006: £57,574
2005: £67,225

Membership: BitC

Community involvement

The company is a member of Business in the Community and is actively involved in supporting charitable and community organisations.

Applications

In writing to the correspondent.

Corporate giving

In 2006, the company made cash donations of £57,574 (2005: £67,225). We have no details of the beneficiaries.

In kind support

'DPD is also an active member of Business in the Community, a scheme through which employees give their time to support good causes, such as helping primary school children with their reading skills.'

Employee-led support

'Every year DPD UK (part of Geopost UK Ltd) employees take part in a wide range of fundraising events to support the Variety Club of Great Britain and every £raised is matched by the company. In 2007 DPD presented its 50th 'Sunshine Coach' to the charity and is proud to support an initiative that provides transport so that disadvantaged children can enjoy educational outings.'

GKN plc

Company registration number 66549

PO Box 55, Ipsley House, Ipsley Church Lane, Redditch, Worcestershire B98 0TL

01527 517715; Fax: 01527 517700

Website: www.gknplc.com

Correspondent: Grey Denham, Company Secretary

Chairman: Roy Brown

Chief Executive: Kevin Smith

Year end	Turnover	Pre-tax profit
31/12/2007	£3,869,000,000	£199,000,000

Nature of company business
An international company involved in the automotive and aerospace industries.

Main locations: Birmingham, London, Weston super Mare, West Bromwich, Sutton Coalfield, Walsall, Telford, Portsmouth, Redditch, Yeovil, Edgware, Eastleigh, Chesterfield, Lichfield, Leek, Isle of Wight

Total employees: 37,735

Charitable donations
2007: £166,800
2005: £236,900
2003: £840,000

Community involvement

The main emphasis of GKN's community involvement continues to be on education and community activities.

Preference is given to appeals from local and community organisations in areas where the company has a branch (particularly local to the Corporate Centre in Redditch, Worcestershire). Donations are made through the Charities Aid Foundation.

Exclusions

No response to circular appeals. No support for animal welfare, political appeals, religious appeals, sport or local appeals not in areas of company presence.

Applications

Appeals, in writing, should be addressed to the Company Secretary at the address shown above. Local appeals should be sent to local branches. Subsidiary companies make small grants independently of head office.

Advice to applicants: As a substantial proportion of the company's charitable budget is already committed to community projects/charities, only a small proportion remains for donations to individual appeals. Applicants should therefore ensure that they send only appropriate appeals.

Corporate giving

In 2007, worldwide community contributions totalled £581,500. Of this, £166,800 was given in cash donations in the UK – £144,500 for educational purposes and £22,300 for community activities. GKN now publish a list of beneficiaries on its website, although without reference to the size of the grant given.

In the UK, the following organisations were supported:

'Battle of Britain Memorial Trust; BEN; Birmingham Association of Youth Clubs; Birmingham Centre for Arts Therapies; Birmingham Women's Health Care Trust; Birmingham Women's Hospital; Brainwave; British Heart Foundation; British Occupational Health Research Foundation; Brownhills Community Colts; Cancer Research UK; Cerebral Palsy Midlands; CFKids; Children with Leukaemia; Children's Heart Federation; Christ Church Community Project; Christian Lewis Trust; Coundon Care Centre; Country Holidays for Inner City Kids; Darren Green Appeal Fund; Dorset Air Ambulance; Dream Holidays; Duke of Edinburgh's Award; Earl Mountbatten Hospice; Edward's Trust; Engineering Development Trust; First Steps Appeal; Great Ormond Street Hospital; Gurkha Welfare Trust; Handicapped Children's Action Group; Home Start Winson Green; Independent Age; Marie Curie Cancer Care; Midland Societies for the Blind; Missing People; NSPCC; Penydarren Country XI Cricket Club; Primrose Hospice Diary; REACH; Reactivate; Redditch Borough Council; Rosie's Helping Hands; Royal British Legion; Run For Home; Ryan Cockbill Trust; Salisbury Spinal Injuries Trust; Salvation Army; SENSE; Sequal Trust; Shropshire & West Mids Agricultural Society; Special Olympics – City of Birmingham; St Mungo's; Technology Tree; The Meningitis Trust; Trinity School; Victim Support; WaterAid Munro Challenge; Wimbledon Park Tigers; Women's Aid; Worcester Swimming Club; Worshipful Company of Glass Sellers Charity; Young Enterprise.'

In kind support

This may include the following, which is neither prescriptive, nor exhaustive:

- providing volunteer support for community projects
- making learning facilities available for local organisations and community bodies and promoting standards of literacy and numeracy within the local community as well as for all employees
- building regular links with local education establishments in order to promote engineering or manufacturing to students as a future career option
- providing professional mentors and coaches for young people about to enter the workplace
- providing structured work experience placements for young people from the local community.

Employee-led support

GKN state within its community policy that: 'It is for individual companies [within the group] to determine what is appropriate for their communities at any particular time'.

Generally, speaking, employees are involved in community projects, notably through fundraising. Staff fundraising at Corporate Centre is matched £ for £ by the company. Preference is given to supporting charities in which a member of staff is involved. Staff are allowed time off during working hours to volunteer.

Payroll giving: The company operates the Give As You Earn scheme.

Commercially-led support

Sponsorship: The company undertakes arts sponsorship.

Gladedale Holdings Ltd

Company registration number 3215228

Ashley House, Ashley Road, Epsom, Surrey KT18 5AZ

01372 846000

Website: www.gladedale.com

Correspondent: Gemma Alexander-Watson

Chairman: Remo Dipre

Chief Executive: David Gaffney

Year end	Turnover	Pre-tax profit
31/12/2006	£644,025,000	£85,227,000

Nature of company business
Gladedale is a privately owned, national residential housebuilding and property development company.

UK employees: 1,325

Charitable donations
2006: £100,000
2005: £24,000

Community involvement

We were unable to obtain any policy information regarding the company's community/charitable support, but believe there is some preference for causes local to its head office.

In 2007, Gladedale purchased Ben Bailey Homes, based in Yorkshire, a company which previously had a well established record of community support. However, we understand that this is unlikely to continue under the new ownership.

Applications

In writing to the correspondent. However, given the current state of the housing market/economy, we were advised that support is likely to be on a small scale in 2009.

Corporate giving

In 2006, the company's level of charitable donations quadrupled from £24,000 to £100,000. This entire amount was, however, donated to a single beneficiary – The Weedon Fire Museum.

GlaxoSmithKline plc

Company registration number 1047315

GSK House, 980 Great West Road, Brentford, Middlesex TW6 9GS

020 8047 5000

Website: www.gsk.com

Correspondent: Katie Pinnock, UK Corporate Contributions
020 8047 5000
Email: katie.apinnock@gsk.com

Chairman: Sir Christopher Gent

Chief Executive: Andrew Witty

Year end	Turnover	Pre-tax profit
31/12/2007	£22,716,000,000	£7,452,000,000

Nature of company business
The group's principal activities are the creation and discovery, development, manufacture and marketing of pharmaceutical products, including vaccines, over-the-counter medicines and health-related consumer products.

Subsidiaries include: Wellcome Ltd, Stafford-Miller Ltd, The Wellcome Foundation Ltd

Main locations: Stevenage, Hertfordshire, Stockley Park, Middlesex, Ulverston, Cumbria, Ware, Hertfordshire, Montrose, Tayside, Greenford, Middlesex, Dartford, Kent, Barnard Castle, County Durham, Beckenham, Kent

Total employees. 103,188

Charitable donations

2007: £6,000,000
2005: £4,000,000
2004: £4,000,000
2003: £4,000,000

Membership: A & B, BitC, L B Group

Community involvement

Within the UK GlaxoSmithKline (GSK) concentrates its corporate community support programme in the areas of health, medical research, science education, the arts and the environment.

The company state: 'We strive to be consistent in our selection of charities to support. We challenge them to be innovative, dynamic and cost effective with our donations. We expect to see something more – we try to see where we can add value in a creative way'.

All charitable donations made in the UK are agreed by the Corporate Donations Committee, which is a Board-level committee. Support is considered in four headings: healthcare; scientific education and medical research; the arts; and the environment. A six page document outlining the selection criteria used for each of these four categories is downloadable from the company's website at: www.gsk.com/community/criteria.htm

Exclusions

No support for appeals from individuals. For example, the company is unable to provide support for individual students or Raleigh International applicants, but does support organisations such as the British Medical Association Charity Trust, which in turn provides financial assistance to medical students. No support for fundraising events, advertising in charity brochures, purely denominational (religious) appeals, political appeals or sport.

Applications

Appeals for charitable support on a national scale should be addressed in writing to the correspondent.

Organisations seeking support for community projects within the locality or region of GSK sites should contact the relevant site to request the correct company contact.

Applicants are asked to supply a concise summary of their aims, objectives and funding requirements together with a copy of their most up-to-date audited accounts.

Corporate giving

In 2007 in the UK, GlaxoSmithKline made donations to charitable activities of £6 million, helping over 70 organisations in health, medical research, science education, the arts and the environment. No figure was available this year for in kind support in the UK.

Healthcare:

'The GSK Community Health IMPACT Awards: Working in partnership with the King's Fund, a leading independent health charity, GSK's annual IMPACT Awards programme recognises and promotes the work of small-to-medium-sized voluntary organisations in the UK, which have made a demonstrable impact on the health of their local communities. The awards give UK-registered charities the chance to win ten awards of £20,000, with one overall winner receiving an extra £10,000 on top. In addition, 10 highly commended organisations receive £5,000 each. The awards are open to charities that have been working in local community healthcare for at least three years with an annual budget of less than £1 million'.

Please note that the 2009 deadline for applications for this award has now passed.

Education

In the UK, GSK support a range of programmes, activities and resources designed to make science more relevant to young people and support professional development for science teachers.

Examples include the 'Puppet Project', which uses two puppets (Jasmin and Benny) who have dedicated themselves to getting primary school children interested in science (see: www.puppetproject.com), and the CREST Star Investigators education initiative.

The latter programme has been developed in partnership with the British Association for the Advancement of Science to provide science activities and awards for after school clubs in UK primary schools. 5,000 schools and 55,000 children are expected to be taking part by 2010.

The environment

'GSK has made a donation of £148,000 to fund a three-year programme aimed at increasing volunteering opportunities for participation in projects concerned with the conservation of the UK's natural resources. This donation will enable Earthwatch to increase the number of volunteer places for its 'Dyscovery Projects' from 150 to 500 and increase public understanding of science-based conservation.'

Employee-led support

The company also supports employees in the UK who are 'Making a Difference' in their own communities. Through the scheme staff are able to apply for funding for charity or community organisations that they are directly involved with.

Payroll giving: The company operates the Give As You Earn scheme

Commercially-led support

Sponsorship: *The arts* – The company may undertake sponsorship to enable or facilitate the performance, display or establishment of worthy arts projects.

Contact: Proposals should be sent for the attention of the Corporate Events Manager, at the above address.

Glencore UK Ltd

Company registration number 1170825

50 Berkley Street, London W1H 0LU

020 7629 3800; Fax: 020 7499 5555

Website: www.glencore.com

Correspondent: Colin Smith, Secretary to the Glencore Foundation

Chairman: W Strothotte

Year end	Turnover	Pre-tax profit
31/12/2006	£30,581,973,000	£36,242,585

Nature of company business
International commodity traders.

Subsidiaries include: Inomex Ltd

Main locations: London

UK employees: 241

Charitable donations

2006: £1,400,000
2004: £1,400,000

Community involvement

The company's donations are made through the Glencore Foundation (Charity Commission no. 1041859) which states its principal objectives are: 'To focus on the fields of education and welfare of children and youth, with particular reference to Israel.'

The company itself only supports local charities in areas of company presence (it has regional offices in Brechin, London and Thame). There is a preference for children and youth, medical, education and welfare. Preference is also given for supporting charities in which a member of staff is involved.

Exclusions

No support for circular appeals, fundraising events, advertising in charity brochures, appeals from individuals, culture and recreation, research, environment and heritage, local appeals not in areas of company presence or overseas projects.

Applications

In writing to the correspondent.

Corporate giving

In 2006, the company made charitable donations of £1.4 million of which £1.37 million was paid to the Glencore Foundation.

The Glencore Foundation

In 2006, the foundation made 86 grants totalling £1.14 million which were split between education (56) and welfare (30). We have no details of the beneficiaries but, in practice, grants are given throughout the world to Jewish organisations.

Employee-led support

The company has a matching scheme for fundraising by employees.

Payroll giving: The company operates a scheme on behalf of its employees.

The Go Ahead Group plc

Company registration number 2100855

3rd Floor, 41–55 Grey Street, Newcastle-upon-Tyne NE1 6EE

0191 232 3123; Fax: 0191 221 0315

Website: www.go-ahead.com

Correspondent: The Chief Executive

Chairman: Sir Patrick Brown

Chief Executive: Keith Ludeman

Year end	Turnover	Pre-tax profit
24/10/2008	£2,199,100,000	£131,100,000

Nature of company business
The principal activities of the group are the provision of integrated public transport – through its aviation, bus, parking and rail operations. Its subsidiaries provide transport solutions across London, the Home Counties, the North East and the South East of England.

Subsidiaries include: Tourist Coaches Ltd, Blue Triangle Buses Ltd, City of Oxford Motor Services Ltd, Aviance UK Ltd, Brighton & Hove Bus and Coach Company Ltd, Meteor parking Ltd, The Birmingham Omnibus Company Ltd, Reed Aviation Ltd, Hants & Dorset Motor Services Ltd, Abingdon Bus Company Ltd, Metrobus Ltd, Chauffeured Parking Services Ltd, London General Transport Services Ltd, Govia Ltd, New Southern Railway Ltd, Victory Railway Holdings Ltd, Wilts & Dorset Bus Company Ltd, London Central Bus Company Ltd, Thames Trains Ltd

Main locations: Brighton & Hove, Newcastle upon Tyne, London, North Eastern England, Oxford, Wiltshire, Dorset, Blackburn, Glasgow, Cardiff

UK employees: 27,627

Charitable donations

2008: £300,000
2007: £100,000
2006: £400,000
2005: £552,000
2004: £196,000

Total community contributions: £300,000

Community involvement

The company states on its website: 'Go-Ahead recognises that public transport is an integral part of the communities it serves. Our companies are closely involved in their local communities, through schemes to help make public transport a priority, and through charitable undertakings.'

'Go-Ahead Group plc makes various donations to charities throughout the year and is committed to making a positive impact on the local community, in the form of financial support. Our operating companies also provide 'support in kind', including providing resources such as bus services to a charity.'

The company has previously stated: 'In line with our devolved structure, each of our operating companies sets its own corporate responsibility objectives and targets. To monitor our progress in all these areas, we publish an annual online group-wide environmental and social report. Each of our companies also publishes individual annual environmental and social reports [to report directly to local stakeholders]'.

Exclusions

No support for advertising in charity brochures, animal welfare, appeals from individuals, environment/heritage, overseas projects, political appeals or religious appeals.

Applications

In writing to the correspondent.

Corporate giving

In 2007/08 the company provided charitable donations, sponsorship and community support in the UK totalling £300,000.

In kind support

In kind support includes providing bus services to charities, the donation of advertising space, and the development and delivery of programmes on safer bus travel for schoolchildren.

Education: Since 2002, the company has offered education resource packs to help teachers introduce 'transport' into the national curriculum.

Employee-led support

The company assists employees' volunteering/charitable activities through financial support.

Commercially-led support

Sponsorship: The company undertakes arts sponsorship.

Goldman Sachs International

Company registration number 2263951

Peterborough Court, 133 Fleet Street, London EC4A 2BB

020 7774 1000

Website: www.gs.com/uk/index.html

Correspondent: Charitable Services Group

Chairman: Peter Sutherland

Year end	Pre-tax profit
04/11/2007	£1,372,000,000

Nature of company business
Provision of investment banking, trading, asset management and securities to corporations, financial institutions, governments and wealthy individuals.

Main locations: London

UK employees: 5,489

Charitable donations

2007: £1,940,000

Community involvement

The company stated that it 'supports charities that are local to its office in London'. This appears to be restricted to education and youth projects concerned with business and entrepreneurship.

At an international level, we have previously been told to: 'Please note that there are not, and never will be, donations or grants made to organisations not currently supported by the company and no correspondence will be entered into.'

This appears slightly at odds, however, with advice given in The Goldman Sachs Foundation's grant guidelines. Whilst these clearly state that 'rarely will a grant be made in response to an unsolicited proposal', it does invite 'prospective applicants' to informally submit their ideas.

Although our request in 2008 for updated information went unanswered, neither were we advised that our reading of the Goldman Sachs Foundation's guidelines (as above) was incorrect.

Currently the foundation's priorities are as follows:

- to develop the abilities of promising high potential youth worldwide
- to support high quality education for young people in leadership, entrepreneurship and business education
- to enhance academic performance and prospects for life achievement of students at the secondary school level.

Exclusions

Grants will not be made to individuals; fraternal organisations; political causes, campaigns or candidates; or fundraising events.

Applications

UK applications should be made in writing to the correspondent, but please note the criteria stated at the beginning of this entry.

We were previously advised that a 'Programme Officer' had been added to the firm's London office to direct the foundation's international work. However, we have been unable to confirm if this is still the case.

The Goldman Sachs Foundation

This should take the form of a short letter (of around two pages) describing the project or organisation for which the grant is sought, its mission, accomplishments, budget size and current funding needs. 'Documentation of results achieved to date is highly desirable', as are copies of published project descriptions or brochures. On receipt, staff will decide whether additional materials are required and contact prospective grantees accordingly.

The address to write to is: The Goldman Sachs Foundation, 85 Broad Street, 22nd floor, New York, NY 10004, USA.

Corporate giving

In 2007, the company declared cash donations in the UK of £1,940,000. We have no details of the beneficiaries. The worldwide contributions made by the company and its foundation during the year are given below.

Goldman Sachs and its affiliates donated approximately $101 million (around £50 million) to various charitable institutions worldwide, including educational programmes, arts and cultural institutions, and social service agencies. Of the $101 million, $40.2 million was awarded directly to non-profit organisations, $50 million was granted to Goldman Sachs Gives and $10.8 million was donated to additional nonprofits through an employee matching gift programme.

In addition, The Goldman Sachs Foundation donated in 2007 approximately $19 million (about £10 million) to charitable and educational organisations worldwide. The foundation's mission is to promote excellence and innovation in education. Current areas of focus are: Developing High Potential Youth; Leadership, Entrepreneurship and Business; and Advancing Academic Achievement.

In kind support

As 'part of a long tradition of public service and socially responsible business practice', Goldman Sachs has established the Community Capital Group to promote public awareness and understanding of the role played by the modern market system in local communities around the world.

Through the sharing of its financial expertise and supporting innovative community projects it seeks to promote how use of efficient capital markets tools can increase local economic opportunity.

Employee-led support

Launched in 1997, Community TeamWorks (CTW) is an annual, global volunteering initiative that gives each employee one day off from work each spring to volunteer in a team-based project organised with local charities. It also offers a range of mentoring programmes for employees. The lists for both of these programmes are now full.

The company's website contains pictures of 'Community Team Works London – 2008', but no further information about who benefited was given.

Great Portland Estates plc

Company registration number 596137

33 Cavendish Square, London W1G 0PW

020 7647 3000; Fax: 020 7016 5500

Website: www.gpe.co.uk

Correspondent: Sally McLaren, Secretary to the Chairman

Chairman: Richard Peskin

Chief Executive: Toby Courtauld

Year end	Turnover	Pre-tax profit
31/03/2007	£42,900,000	£326,000,000

Nature of company business
The main activity of the company is property development and investment.

Subsidiaries include: Collin Estates Ltd, Petra Investments Ltd, B & H S Management Ltd, Knighton Estates Ltd, Courtana Investments Ltd, Pontsarn Investments Ltd, J L P Investment Co. Ltd, Ilex Ltd

Main locations: London

UK employees: 68

Charitable donations

2007: £45,350
2006: £98,650
2004: £78,700

Community involvement

The company supports both national and local charities, especially those concerning the homeless, children/youth, older people and sickness/disability.

Exclusions

No support for political appeals.

Applications

In writing to the correspondent.

Corporate giving

In 2006/07, the company made cash donations in the UK of £45,350. We have no details of the beneficiaries. We were previously advised that donations are paid in CAF vouchers.

Employee-led support

The company has an employee volunteering scheme which involves staff mentoring pupils at St Vincent's School, Marylebone. Employees are also given company time off in which to carry out charitable activities.

Commercially-led support

Sponsorship: The company undertakes good-cause sponsorship.

Greencore Group UK

Company registration number 372396

UK Centre, Midland Way, Barlborough Links Business Park, Barlborough, Chesterfield S43 4XA

01909 545900; Fax: 01909 545950

Website: www.greencore.com

Chairman: E F Sullivan

Chief Executive: P F Coveney

Year end
30/09/2007

Nature of company business
Manufacturer and supplier of convenience foods and ingredients to consumer, industrial and food service markets.

Subsidiaries include: The Roberts Group Ltd, W W Bellamy (Bakers) Ltd, Pauls Malt Ltd, Hazlewood Foods Ltd, Paramount Foods (UK) Ltd, Rathbones Bakeries Ltd, William McKinney (1975) Ltd, R & B (Bristol) Ltd

Main locations: Deeside, Hunslet, Kiveton, Lisburn, Runcorn, Worksop, Newmarket, Lydney

UK employees: 10,098

Community involvement

Eire-based Greencore Group primarily operates in the UK with the companies it acquired from Hazlewood Foods in 2001.

Greencore stated: 'Greencore Group plc supports the nominated charities of its customers and its trade charity, Caravan. Regrettably we are unable to make donations to additional charities unless they are within the immediate area (approx. 10 mile radius) of an operating site'.

Exclusions

No support for worthy local causes/projects unless within the immediate area (circa 10 mile radius) of an operating site.

Applications

Small local organisations seeking support will normally be aware of Greencore manufacturing facilities close to them. However, if you are unsure about this first check on the company's web site (www.greencore.com) to see if there is one close by. If so, there exists the means to log a request for support through the 'Contact Us' facility.

Greencore asked it be made clear that: 'Requests that ignore our clearly stated guidelines will not receive a response, but those with genuine enquiries will be assisted to discuss their projects with the appropriate contact'.

Corporate giving

We were advised that: 'Because of the decentralised nature of our [Greencore's] operations we do not account centrally for charitable donations or split out UK from elsewhere. UK charitable support is, however, likely to equal or exceed the £60,000 previously given by Hazlewood'.

In kind support

The company provides access to its expertise to a limited number of small non-competing businesses and in support of undergraduate business-focused training in a number of universities.

Employee-led support

Staff who set out individually to support a particular cause will be considered for 'sponsorship' by the company.

Greggs plc

Company registration number 502851

Fernwood House, Clayton Road, Jesmond, Newcastle upon Tyne NE2 1TL

0191 281 7721

Website: www.greggs.plc.uk

Correspondent: The Trust Manager, Greggs Trust
0191 212 7626; Fax: 0191 281 9536
Email: greggstrust@greggs.co.uk

Chairman: Derek Netherton

Chief Executive: Ken McMeikan

Year end	Turnover	Pre-tax profit
29/12/2007	£586,303,000	£51,143,000

Nature of company business
The principal activity of the group is the retailing of sandwiches, savouries and other bakery related products with a particular focus on takeaway food and catering. The majority of products sold are manufactured in house.

Main locations: Newcastle upon Tyne

UK employees: 18,827

Charitable donations
2007: £730,000
2006: £548,000
2005: £609,000
2004: £615,000
2003: £420,000
Membership: BitC

Community involvement

The following statement is taken from the company's website: 'Greggs plc is committed to being socially responsible in the way that we run our business and giving something back to those communities in which we operate. We believe that, as a growing and profitable business, we have a responsibility to help those less fortunate than ourselves. We also want to ensure that we progressively work to minimise the impact our business has on the environment.'

In support of this the company gives 1% of pre-tax profits in charitable donations, mainly through the Greggs Trust (Charity Commission no. 296590) and the Greggs Breakfast Club scheme. The main objective of the trust is the alleviation of the effects of poverty and social deprivation in the areas where the company trades. Projects in the fields of the arts, the environment, conservation, education and health will be considered, so long as they have a social welfare focus and/or are located in areas of deprivation.

In the North East the trust gives major grants to projects for core costs such as salaries and rent and rates. The 'Hardship Fund' makes grants to individuals in need who live in the region, and includes money donated by other local charitable trusts. These payments are for essential furniture, white goods and clothing.

Grants are assessed by fourteen divisional charity committees across the country. These committees are made up of staff volunteers from each division who allocate grants to worthy causes in their area.

Exclusions

Exclusions (major grants):

- animal welfare
- capital projects (including purchase, construction and refurbishment of buildings)
- events such as Conferences, Seminars and Exhibitions
- expeditions and Overseas Travel
- fee-charging residential homes, nurseries and care facilities
- festivals, performances and other arts and entertainment activities
- fundraising events
- holidays and outings
- hospitals, Health Service Trusts, medically related appeals and medical equipment
- individuals other than through the Hardship Fund
- large, well-staffed organisations with a greater fundraising capacity
- loans or repayment of loans
- national organisations and their regional branches
- mini-buses other than community transport schemes
- research – academic and medical
- religious promotion
- replacement of statutory funds
- retrospective grants

- schools other than for pre-school and after school clubs and activities promoting parental and community involvement
- sponsorship – organisations and individuals
- sports kit and equipment
- uniformed organisations e.g. scouts, guides and sea cadets.

Exclusions (Hardship Fund):

- payment of debts
- computer equipment
- sponsorship
- overseas expeditions.

Applications

The following outline regarding applications to the Greggs Trust is taken from its website (www.greggstrust.org.uk) where fuller information is available.

'Applications are welcomed from all sections of the community. Your organisation does not have to be a registered but it must have charitable objectives.

'We make donations under our 'Major Grants' programme to local, community-based projects.

'We also make grants through approved agencies to families and individuals under our 'Hardship Fund' programme.

'We don't consider applications for amounts below £1,000. However, divisional charity committees in Greggs plc's regional divisions make grants up to that level and applications received at this office may be passed on to them for their consideration.'

Corporate giving

In 2007, the company made charitable donations of £730,000 (2006: £548,000), including £280,000 to the Greggs Trust.

Greggs Trust

In 2007, the trust had a total income of £494,000 which was derived from donations from the company (as stated above), employees via Give as You Earn (£73,00), individuals (£129,500) and intangibles – donations from major shareholders and income from investments (£11,600).

Major grants – Under the major grants programme, funding is given for core costs (i.e. salaries and overheads) typically between £5,000–£15,000 per annum for one, two or three years.

During 2007, donations totalling £467,414 were made in the North East of England to benefit voluntary organisations.

Hardship fund – Grants up to a maximum of £150 are made for essential items including white goods, basic furniture and clothing to people in extreme social need who live in the North East of England. Priority is given to children and families, and applications must be made on behalf of a client by a recognised welfare agency.

Grants were made for hardship purposes amounting to a total of £87,527 with a further £91,000 paid in block grants for distribution by welfare agencies.

Divisional charity committees – These usually make smaller, one-off, grants, typically in the region of £500 each, to projects which are based in their own area. The Divisional Charity Committees awarded a total of £387,519

For more information on the Greggs Trust, see the *Guide to the Major Trusts Volume 1*, published by the Directory of Social Change.

In kind support

The company sponsors school 124 Breakfast Clubs in deprived areas across the UK.

Employee-led support

The company encourages its staff to work with local communities, and makes time available for them to do so.

Payroll giving: The company operates the Give As You Earn scheme, money from which is contributed to the Greggs Trust.

Commercially-led support

Sponsorship: *The arts/children* – the company has agreed a £150,000 three-year sponsorship with The Sage in Gateshead, establishing the Greggs Children's Room This is a centre where disadvantaged children are helped to gain confidence through participation in musical activities.

Grosvenor Group

Company registration number 3219943

The Grosvenor Office, 70 Grosvenor Street, London W1K 3JP

020 7408 0988; Fax: 020 7629 9115

Website: www.grosvenor.com

Correspondent: Virginia Parish

Email: virginia.parish@grosvenor.com

Chairman: The Earl of Home

Chief Executive: Mark Preston

Year end	Pre-tax profit
31/12/2007	£524,000,000

Nature of company business
The group's principal activities are property investment, development and fund management in Britain & Ireland, North America, Continental Europe, Australia and Asia Pacific.

Main locations: Liverpool, Edinburgh

UK employees: 365

Charitable donations
2007: £2,000,000
2006: £1,500,000

Membership: BitC

Community involvement

The group's community support is, in the main, routed through the Westminster Foundation (Charity Commission no. 267618) which supports a wide range of charitable causes. It has also recently established the Liverpool One Foundation (Charity Commission no. 1112697) in connection with the group's development of a 42-acre retail site ('Liverpool One') situated in the centre of Liverpool.

The Westminster Foundation makes grants to a wide range of causes. These are: Art; Church; Commemorative; Conservation (not building); Education; Medical (not research); Social welfare; and Youth.

The Liverpool One Foundation was formerly called the Liverpool Paradise Foundation, but changed its name in 2008 to reflect the name of the retail development mentioned above.

'The objectives of the foundation are to advance for the benefit of the people of Liverpool and its surrounding areas such exclusively charitable objects as the trustees shall from time to time determine, in particular (but not limited to):

- the prevention or relief of poverty
- the advancement of education
- the support of vocational training to establish children and young people in life
- the advancement of citizenship or community development
- the advancement of health or the saving of lives.'

Grants are directed towards geographical areas in which the Grosvenor Family and Grosvenor Group have a particular connection. Each operating company within the Grosvenor Group has its own charity committee and they put forward recommendations for grants for consideration at the quarterly foundation meetings.

Support for staff fundraising and volunteering on behalf of good causes is encouraged by the group.

Applications

Applications should be made in writing to the correspondent who will ensure that they are dealt with dealt with appropriately, i.e. passed on to the relevant foundation.

Corporate giving

In 2007, the group made charitable donations of £2 million of which £1.6 million went to the Westminster Foundation. We have been unable to ascertain how the remaining £400,000 was distributed.

Funding of The Liverpool One Foundation comes from a group of companies working on, or otherwise involved in the redevelopment of the centre of the City of Liverpool (the 'Liverpool One' project). This, of course, includes the Grosvenor Group which along with its fellow corporate founders have pledged, in total, to donate £250,000 a year to the foundation. However, as the project nears completion the involvement of many of the 'founders' will diminish. Nevertheless, the trustees believe that there is great scope to continue to benefit the people of Liverpool and its surrounding areas, and that the foundation should continue its work beyond the development phase of the project if sufficient support can be found.

The Westminster Foundation

In 2007, the foundation had an income of £3.8 million and made grants in the categories already outlined totalling £1.9 million. Fuller details are given in *A Guide to the Major Trusts Vol. 1*, also published by the Directory of Social Change.

The Liverpool One Foundation

In 2006/07 the foundation had an income of £316,000 and made grants totalling £86,000 under the following headings: community (£55,000); training and youth (£18,000); health (£7,500); and education (£5,000).

Employee-led support

The group supports staff fundraising efforts up to a specified limit. In 2007, for example, a cycle ride across the British Isles raised £27,800 on behalf of the Martha Trust, £10,000 of which was matched funding from Grosvenor

Guardian Media Group plc

Company registration number 94531

No. 1 Scott Place, Manchester M3 3GG

0161 832 7200; Fax: 0161 211 2042

Website: www.gmgplc.co.uk

Correspondent: P E Boardman, Company Secretary

Chairman: Paul Myners

Chief Executive: Carolyn McCall

Year end	Turnover	Pre-tax profit
01/04/2007	£716,100,000	£97,700,000

Nature of company business
Newspaper and magazine publishing. The group has national newspapers as well as regional evening and weekly papers in the North West, Berkshire and Surrey.

Subsidiaries include: Surrey and Berkshire Newspapers Ltd, Guardian Newspapers Ltd, Star Newspaper (Camberley) Ltd, GMG Radio Holdings Ltd, Workthing Ltd, Greater Manchester Newspapers Ltd

Main locations: Manchester, London

UK employees: 6,996

> ## Charitable donations
> 2007: £503,731
> 2006: £351,261
> 2005: £630,950
> 2004: £279,500
> 2003: £185,400
>
> Membership: BitC

Community involvement

The Guardian Media Group plc is wholly-owned by The Scott Trust. It has a board of 12 members who are chosen from areas of the media industry that reflect GMG's business interests. Its main aim is to ensure the commercial success of the group and to uphold the trust's values.

While each division of Guardian Media Group chooses to support its own charitable ventures, a more strategic focus has been placed at the centre of the group with the creation of the Scott Trust Foundation (Charity Commission no. 1027893), formerly the Guardian Foundation. Its remit reflects one of the trust's key objectives of 'promoting the causes of freedom of the press and liberal journalism both in Britain and elsewhere'. (The foundation's main purpose, however, is the training of journalists primarily in Eastern Europe and Africa.)

In 2005, the Scott Trust Charitable Fund was set up to support projects associated with independent journalism, journalist ethics, media literacy and journalist training in the UK and abroad. The fund includes representatives from all GMG divisions.

Exclusions

No support for animal welfare, environment/heritage, political or religious appeals.

Applications

In writing to the correspondent. Appeals sent directly to individual papers are dealt with separately.

Corporate giving

In 2006/07, the company made charitable donations totalling £503,731. Beneficiaries included: Scott Trust Foundation; The Newspaper Education Trust; The Samaritans; WaterAid; and Outward Bound.

The Scott Trust is currently spending £184,000 supporting the development of talented journalists in this country, providing bursaries for 16 aspiring writers to study journalism.

The Scott Trust Appeals Meeting takes place quarterly to review requests for charitable donations. Charities receive a maximum donation of around £250 each.

In kind support

The company gives additional support to charities through gifts in kind, training schemes, joint promotions and staff secondments.

Employee-led support

Employees fundraising efforts are matched £ for £ up a maximum of £100 per employee. Volunteering activities may also be carried out in work time.

Payroll giving: The Give As You Earn scheme is in operation.

Commercially-led support

Sponsorship: *The arts* – The company also sponsors the arts, especially theatre, music, modern arts, film and dance. For example, the National Youth Orchestra and the Royal Philharmonic Society have been supported recently. Good-cause sponsorship may also be undertaken.

Halfords Group plc

Company registration number 4457314

Icknield Street Drive, Washford West, Redditch, Worcestershire B98 0DE

01527 517601; Fax: 01527 513201

Website: www.halfordscompany.com

Correspondent: Barbara Cadd 01527 513571
Email: barbara.cadd@halfords.co.uk

Chairman: Richard Pym

Year end	Turnover	Pre-tax profit
30/03/2007	£744,000,000	£80,900,000

Nature of company business
The principal activity of the group is the retailing of auto, leisure and cycling products.

Main locations: Manchester, Brighton, London, Glasgow, Berwick on Tweed, Workington

UK employees: 10,325

Charitable donations

2007: £40,000
2006: £20,000
2005: £36,000
2004: £44,000

Membership: BitC

Community involvement

Halfords state that it is committed to supporting the Meningitis Trust throughout 2008. No indication was given about what other causes it may consider supporting.

Charity of the Year: The Meningitis Trust (2008).

Exclusions

The group will not fund appeals from individuals, applicants on behalf of individuals, private fund raising groups or organisations not registered with the Charity Commission.

Applications

In writing to the correspondent.

Corporate giving

During 2007, the group contributed £40,000 (2006: £20,000) to charities in the UK, comprising donations to Ben, a charity supporting individuals and families linked to the motor industry and associated trades, and a donation to help persons suffering from the failure of the Farepak Christmas hamper scheme.

In kind support

Small donations in the form of raffle prizes may be given to local organisations holding fund raising events. In this instance 'local' is defined as within a 20-mile radius of Head Office in Redditch.

The organisation must pick up any item. Halfords stores may also offer support to local charities/fund raising initiatives outside the beneficial area defined, as long as the remaining criteria are met. In these cases, Halfords will only provide a raffle prize or product donation; no cash will be given.

The company has taken various actions in order to meet their responsibilities regarding disability issues including training store colleagues in disability awareness, responding to some of the physical obstacles in stores and other access issues, and auditing their website for ease of navigation.

It is estimated that around eight out of ten child seats in the UK are wrongly fitted in cars, sometimes leading to injury or death of young babies and toddlers. As a retailer of child seats, Halfords has invested in training around 1,600 store staff in the demonstration and free fitting of child seats. They have also run roadshows at Halfords stores across the UK, working with road safety officers to give free advice and fitting services to parents and guardians.

The company also holds its own national child seat safety week at all superstores, to raise awareness of the issue.

Employee-led support

Support for the 2008 'Charity of the Year', will involve all of Halfords employees in the UK and the Republic of Ireland in fundraising initiatives for the Trust. The Halfords partnership will focus on raising awareness amongst staff and customers and raising money to support the charity's campaigns.

Hammerson plc

Company registration number 360632

10 Grosvenor Street, London W1K 4BJ

020 7887 1000; Fax: 020 7887 1010

Website: www.hammerson.com

Correspondent: Stuart Haydon, Company Secretary
Email: stuart.haydon@hammerson.com

Chairman: J F Jelson

Chief Executive: J G Richards

Year end	Turnover	Pre-tax profit
31/12/2007	£311,500,000	£110,400,000

Nature of company business
Property investment and development. 70% of the company's property assets are in the UK, with the remainder in France and Germany. Within the UK, the office property portfolio is mainly in London, with retail interests in Aberdeen, Birmingham, Brent Cross, Bristol, Leicester, Peterborough, Reading, and Southampton.

Main locations: Aberdeen, Birmingham, Brent Cross, Bristol, Leicester, Peterborough, Reading, Southampton, London

UK employees: 150

Charitable donations

2007: £94,100
2006: £117,944
2005: £112,670
2004: £103,385
2003: £109,000

Membership: BitC

Community involvement

A brief comment in the company's annual report states: 'donations are made to a variety of children's, medical, music and arts charities and to charities connected to localities where the group is represented. In addition to these charitable donations, the company provides financial assistance to other projects of benefit to the community.'

Exclusions

No support for political appeals.

Applications

In writing to the correspondent. Each application is considered on its merits, but about 95% of applications will be unsuccessful.

Information available: The company produces a Corporate Social Responsibility Report which can be accessed via their website www.hammerson.com

Corporate giving

In 2007, the company made charitable donations totalling £94,100. A concise breakdown of this amount was unavailable.

Hanson Ltd

Company registration number 4626078

Hanson House, Castle Hil, Maidenhead, Berkshire SL6 4JJ

01628 774100

Website: www.heidelbergcement.com

Chairman: Mike Welton

Chief Executive: Alan Murray

Year end	Turnover	Pre-tax profit
31/12/2006	£4,132,700,000	£160,800,000

Nature of company business
Hanson is a leading international building materials company. It operates in North America, the UK, Continental Europe, Australia and Asia Pacific.

Main locations: Bristol, Stewartby

UK employees: 6,500

Charitable donations

2006: £84,000
2005: £93,000
2004: £183,000
2003: £152,000
2002: £129,000

Community involvement

In August 2007, Hanson was acquired by HeidelbergCement Group Ltd for £8 billion. Although the Hanson website refers to its support for communities local to its areas of operation, fuller details were not available. We therefore repeat the information published previously, with figures updated where possible.

Hanson has a largely decentralised programme of charitable donations focused on the communities in and around its operational sites. Within this, it targets:

- community groups in the immediate vicinity, with the aim of building sustainable relationships with its neighbours
- support for employee volunteering and giving
- environmental organisations with an interest in habitat creation and management
- charities with links to the company's industry.

Hanson is often asked to support local projects by donating materials. There exists a general policy of supporting community projects in this way, particularly those close to its operations. Local management teams have overall responsibility for engagement with the communities in which they are located. Where the local community wants to meet formally with staff on a regular basis, community liaison groups are held. These provide an opportunity to meet and address concerns with input from a broad range of interested parties.

Exclusions

No support is given to circular appeals, fundraising events, appeals from individuals or for advertising in charity brochures.

Applications

Given the uncertainty that surrounds the company's current community support, we suggest that, in the first instance, you approach your nearest Hanson operating site.

Corporate giving

In 2006, the group made charitable donations worldwide of £348,000 (2005: £309,000), including £84,000 (2005: £93,000) in the UK. We have no details of the beneficiaries.

Previously, at corporate level, Hanson was a patron of CRASH the construction and property industry charity for the homeless, contributing to their core funding. We do not know if this remains the case.

In kind support

Goods and services are provided to local communities.

Employee-led support

In the UK Hanson has a programme which matches the first £500 of an employee's fundraising with a contribution from the company.

Hasbro UK Ltd

Company registration number 1981543

2 Roundwood Avenue, Stockley Park, Uxbridge, Middlesex UB11 1AZ

020 8569 1234

Website: www.hasbro.co.uk

Correspondent: Hasbro in the Community

Email: cathy.ranson@hasbro.co.uk / diana.potter@hasbro.co.uk

Year end	Turnover	Pre-tax profit
25/12/2006	£104,455,000	£4,810,000

Nature of company business
Toy and game manufacturer.

Main locations: Uxbridge, Newport

UK employees: 260

> **Charitable donations**
> 2006: £52,208
> 2005: £37,764
> 2004: £39,735

Community involvement

Hasbro provides comprehensive information on its website about the different types of support it provides to charitable and community organisations, along with details of how to apply.

Hasbro's criteria for donations are as follows:

- priority is given to charitable and community organisations that work with children and families
- for schools – Hasbro prioritise schools in the Hillingdon Borough (where its Stockley Park offices are based), or schools close to its Newport warehouse. The same applies to playgroups and pre-school nurseries

- the majority of donations take the form of toys and games donations
- cash donations/sponsorship are usually only given to its nominated charities of the year.

Exclusions

Hasbro will not:
- give donations to individual applicants, however needy
- support requests which do not come via, or are not on behalf of a registered charity or community organisation
- give donations to organisations concerned with animals
- undertake any form of advertising in souvenir brochures e.g. for a charity dinner.

Applications

General enquiries should be made in writing to the correspondent. or via email to one of the addresses given.

Product donations: No applications will be accepted in writing as all requests need to go via Hasbro's online system. If you have a question about how to complete the online form see the FAQ section on the company's website. If you need to speak to someone directly about your query please call 00800 22 42 72 76 and ask for Laura Bryant.

Corporate giving

In 2006, the company made donations to charity amounting to £52,208 (2005: £37,764). We have no information regarding the specific beneficiary organisations.

In kind support

The company operates an employee volunteering scheme under which staff are allowed work time off to become involved with the local community. Help has been given to primary schoolchildren with their reading, and community organisations which received computer, marketing or public relations advice.

Product donations: Qualifying organisations can apply for a 'Lucky Dip' box from Hasbro that contains a selection of its toys and games twice during the company's donating year which runs from January to November.

Employee-led support

Staff take part in 'Team Hasbro' volunteering activities through a programme of regular and one off events. If you would like to suggest a project close to the Hasbro UK offices for Team Hasbro to tackle, then please use the online 'Contact us' buttons to send full details about your project and how you think Team Hasbro could help.

Payroll giving: Staff take part in the Give as You Earn scheme that allows them to make tax free donations to the charity of their choice directly from their salaries.

Employees also have the opportunity to donate their last hour's salary of the year to charity.

Commercially-led support

Sponsorship: Hasbro have made a significant donation to the children's cancer charity CLIC Sargent to assist them in building their £5 million project the London Home from Home.

It has also sponsored the Sunshine magazine, a free local community magazine for families living in Hillingdon, since its inception.

Brands – Hasbro allow charities to use its brands in their fundraising activities free of charge. For example, the charity

Shelter have used the Monopoly logo and imagery in their recruitment advertising to encourage people to run the London Marathon whilst raising funds for them.

Please fill in the online request form to apply for permission to use Hasbro's intellectual property/products.

HBOS plc

Company registration number SC218813

PO Box 5, The Mound, Edinburgh EH1 1YZ

0870 600 5000; Fax: 0131 243 7082

Website: www.hbosfoundation.org

Correspondent: Angela Tinker, Head of HBOS Foundation

Chairman: Dennis Stevenson

Chief Executive: Andy Hornby

Year end	Turnover	Pre-tax profit
31/12/2007	£21,291,000,000	£5,474,000,000

Nature of company business
The group's principal activities are divided into five divisions, namely: retail banking, insurance and investment, corporate banking and treasury and asset management, and international.

Subsidiaries include: St James's Place Capital plc, Insight Investment Management Ltd, Clerical Medical Investment Group Ltd, CAPITAL BANK plc, BM Solutions, Colley's, esure.com, Godfey Davis, Hill Hire plc, Intelligent Finance, St Andrew's Group, Halifax plc

Main locations: Edinburgh

Total employees: 74,087

Charitable donations

2007: £12,740,000
2005: £10,470,000
2003: £5,800,000

Total community contributions: £18,610,660
Management costs: £93,000
CRM figure: £2,600,000

Membership: A & B, BitC, L B Group

Community involvement

HBOS plc was formed following the merger of the Bank of Scotland and Halifax plc, all charitable donations are channelled through the HBOS Foundation (Registered Charity no. SCO32942) which was launched in 2002. Additional support is provided through in kind giving, affinity cards, and the Bank of Scotland and Halifax's extensive corporate sponsorship programme.

HBOS Foundation

The foundation's activities are centered on three key areas:

- Large grants and the regional Community Action programme providing donations to charities and community groups across the UK
- Colleague fundraising via the £1 Million Challenge and colleague matched funding scheme
- HBOS volunteering providing encouragement, opportunities and support to colleagues who are donating their time to support the community in which they live and work.

Charity of the Year: CLIC Sargent (2008).

Exclusions

The HBOS Foundation will not provide support for: charitable advertising; sponsorship of fundraising events for registered charities; sponsorship of individuals or third party fundraising initiatives; any project or initiative which discriminate on the grounds of colour, race, sex or religious beliefs; political appeals; animal rights groups; overseas projects; or conferences.

Applications

If you are applying for a grant of over £50,000, for further information visit the HBOS Foundation website (www.hbosfoundation.org)for further information and instructions on how to apply.

If you are applying for a grant of under £50,000, further information is also available on the website, including a downloadable application form. Completed application forms should be posted to your nearest or most appropriate regional co-ordinator. HBOS Foundation Regional Co-ordinators are based across the UK and represent the majority of HBOS businesses, including subsidiaries. A map of the UK on the website shows where the regional co-ordinators are based.

Corporate giving

The HBOS foundation works on a national and local level to support a wide range of charities. During 2007, the foundation made charitable donations of £10,816,000.

Large grants – The foundation's large grants programme supports a mix of one year and multi-year projects and initiatives across Scotland, England, Wales and Northern Ireland. Managed centrally, by the HBOS Foundation, there's a proactive approach to sourcing potential nationwide projects and initiatives that enable the foundation to benefit different parts of the community. Projects tend to be aligned towards the money advice and financial literacy theme, but support a diverse range of organisations helping communities.

Examples of organisations supported during 2007 include: CAB and YouthNet (£300,000); Place 2Be (£290,000); Refugee Council (£250,000); and Pilotlight – Scotland (£150,000).

In addition to these large grants the foundation also made a grant of £840,000 towards a groundbreaking education programme that will be delivered by Leeds University and the Sutton Trust, to support young people from disadvantaged backgrounds into tertiary education.

Regional grants – As part of the foundation's commitment of supporting communities where HBOS plc does business, the foundation operate a structure of regional co-coordinators enabling it to work more closely with local communities and respond to local issues. Through the Community Action programme local grants of up to £10,000 to support a diverse range of projects can be provided – from funding equipment at a special needs school to supporting a debt advice service in an economically deprived area. The two key themes of the programme are money advice and financial literacy, and developing and improving local communities.

Charity of the Year – The HBOS Foundation matches pound for pound all money raised by colleagues, customers and shareholders for the HBOS Charity of the Year programme – the Million £Challenge. In 2007, including matched funding over £3.4 million was raised for the British Heart Foundation, WRVS and a partnership between the Family Holiday Association and RNLI.

In kind support

Each year the Foundation supports the three charities that are short listed as Charities of the Year by offering their pin badges each month for sale to customers and colleagues.

Charities may also be offered collection account facilities in the company's branches enabling them to raise funds for major appeals at low cost.

Employee-led support

Colleagues who regularly volunteer in their own time can apply to the foundation for an award of up to £250 on behalf of the organisation they volunteer with. Team challenge volunteering enables staff to apply for up to £250 per project.

The foundation also matches colleague fundraising up to £500 per colleague per year and colleague payroll giving to the Million £Challenge to a maximum of £600 per colleague per year.

HBOS colleagues are occasionally seconded to work in charities.

Payroll giving: The Give As You Earn scheme and Flexible Benefits Charitable Giving scheme are in operation.

Commercially-led support

Sponsorship: HBOS currently invests around £4 million a year in community sponsorship activity. Delivered under the Bank of Scotland and Halifax brands it is targeted at supporting the promotion and development of sport and the arts in Scotland and west Yorkshire Increasing access and participation for young people in sports and the arts is central to HBOS community sponsorship activity, with grassroots and educational activities underpinning flagship sponsorships. Community sponsorship activity is delivered through partnership with the recognised national organising or governing body.

Further information about community sponsorships can be found at www.hbosplc.com/community

Financial inclusion: HBOS financial inclusion strategy is driven by both commercial opportunity and a recognition that it is right to work towards bringing more consumers, especially those on lower incomes, into the financial system. HBOS strategy is aligned to the Government's aims to increase access to banking, asset ownership, money advice and credit. A full picture of financial inclusion activity is set out in its Financial Inclusion Report.

Examples of activity include:

Social banking: HBOS is a market leader in social banking, and is the only major bank to publish a target for new social banking accounts. HBOS is also the first major bank to produce a standalone, data driven Financial Inclusion Report, detailing performance and targets and plans for the year ahead and beyond.

Unlock: HBOS plc is working in partnership with Unlock, the National Association of Ex-Offenders, as part of its financial inclusion strategy. HBOS is delivering social banking provision to category C and B prisoners with a target of opening around 900 Easycash accounts for ex-offenders. HBOS has been running a pilot in two prisons, Cookham Wood and Coldingley, with the aim of opening bank accounts for up to 900 prisoners who were due for imminent release, so that they were active and ready to be used upon release. Social

banking accounts enable ex-offenders to rebuild their lives on release, making it easier for them to secure accommodation and employment. The success of the pilots means that the programme is being expanded from two prisons to four and is being integrated into business as usual.

ATMs and branches: In 2007, HBOS opened almost 100 new free-to-use ATMs in deprived areas of Scotland and the North of England. These ATMs have dispensed over £84 million. Customers using these machines have saved an estimated £1 million in fees compared with fee-charging machines.

HBOS also introduced a new 'mobile branch' to add to the six previous, to provide a full banking service to local communities, including villages, schools, retirement homes and community groups. These groups did not previously have convenient access to banking and face-to-face money advice, HBOS are the only major bank with branch and ATM expansion programmes in place to improve the amenities of deprived communities.

H J Heinz Company Ltd

Company registration number 147624

Hayes Park South Building, Hayes, Middlesex UB4 8AL

020 8573 7757; Fax: 020 8848 2325

Website: www.heinz.co.uk

Correspondent: Liz Keane, Trust Secretary 020 8848 2223
Email: charitable.trust@uk.hjheinz.com

Year end	Turnover	Pre-tax profit
31/12/2006	£570,700,000	£125,300,000

Nature of company business
Principal activities: the manufacture, processing, growing and distribution of food.

Main locations: Worcester, Hayes, Kitt Green, Leamington, Kendal, Grimsby, Westwick, Okehampton, Telford

UK employees: 2,179

Charitable donations
2006: £135,719
2005: £144,319
2004: £121,000

Community involvement

The HJ Heinz Company Ltd established the H J Heinz Charitable Trust (Charity Commission no. 326254) in 1983 as a vehicle for its charitable in the UK. It is committed to providing funding and support to promote the improvement of health and nutrition within its local communities. Priority support is given to charitable programmes and organisations that operate in areas where Heinz has significant operations and interests. In particular, it helps charitable organisations dedicated to maintaining and improving nutrition and nutritional education, youth services and education.

The charitable trust confines it's giving to purposes accepted in law as charitable in the following five key programme areas:

> nutrition – supporting improvements in, and a better understanding of, the medical aspects of nutrition and health in the community with a particular emphasis on paediatrics

youth and education – supporting the positive development of youngsters in our communities by strengthening systems that affect learning and by sustaining programmes that supplement the formal education process

local community – supporting and enhancing the local communities in which HJ Heinz has significant operations

quality of life – promoting programmes that support and add to the quality of life for residents in communities local to company operations, including support for the arts, as well as cultural and environmental programmes

volunteerism – supporting charitable work of Heinz employees through a programme that provides funding to nationally recognised charitable organisations in recognition of volunteer service.

Exclusions

The Heinz Charitable Trust does not:

support politically oriented causes in any way

consider religious appeals if the object is to promote denominational principles

take advertising space in charity programmes/brochures

support individuals undertaking educational/vocational studies

consider unsolicited research projects

directly support individuals or groups undertaking sponsored events

accept commercial sponsorship.

Applications

In writing to the correspondent or by using the online application form.

Please note that, generally, only organisations registered as national charity organisations will be considered.

The trustees meet once a year, usually in July or August to consider major appeals for donations. However, a sub-committee, which is authorised to make grants of up to £10,000, meets more frequently. This committee also selects applications to be considered by the trustees at their annual meeting.

Corporate giving

In, 2006, the company declared charitable donations in the UK of £135,719 (2005: £144,319). Of this, £90,000 was paid to the associated charitable trust and £28,970 to CARAVAN. A further £3,439 was donated by way of food.

H J Heinz Charitable Trust

In 2006, the trust had a total income of £65,000 and made 26 grants of between £200 and £2,000 totalling £19,000 (2005: £121,000). Beneficiaries receiving grants of £1,000 or more included: Well Child Trust and Hillingdon Hospital NHS Trust (£2,000 each); Move Europe, Brain and Spine Foundation, Breast Cancer Care, Core and the Paul Strickland Scanner Centre (£1,000 each).

In kind support

The company gives goods to raise money for local charities.

Education: The company is involved in local education/ business partnerships and provides educational materials for schools.

Commercially-led support

Sponsorship: Arts and good-cause sponsorship is undertaken.

Henderson Group plc

Company registration number 2072534

201 Bishopsgat, London EC2M 3AE

020 7818 1818; Fax: 020 7818 1820

Website: www.henderson.com

Correspondent: Director of Corporate Affairs

Chairman: Rupert Pennant-Rea

Chief Executive: Andrew Formica

Year end	Turnover	Pre-tax profit
31/12/2007	£455,900,000	£106,700,000

Nature of company business
The principal activities of the group are the provision of investment management services and the transaction of various classes of insurance business. The group has businesses in the UK, Europe and the US.

Subsidiaries include: Pearl Assurance plc, Henderson Fund Manangement plc, National Provident Life Ltd, Towry Law plc, London Life Ltd

Main locations: Bristol, Peterborough, Tunbridge Wells, Bracknell

Total employees: 881

Charitable donations

2007: £75,265
2006: £51,000
2005: £63,000
2004: £38,000
2003: £44,000

Community involvement

Formerly trading as HHG plc, the company changed its name in 2005 to Henderson Group plc. Its preferred charity since 1987 is Community Links, the inner city charity running community-based projects in East London.

Exclusions

No response to circular appeals or to sponsorship requests for individuals. No support for: fundraising events; advertising in charity brochures; religious appeals; or overseas projects.

Applications

In writing to the correspondent.

Corporate giving

Donations by the group during the year towards community and charitable causes amounted to £75,265 (2006: £51,000), which comprised social and welfare £6,700 (2006: £20,000); education and international £13,000 (2006: £8,000); and medical and other projects £55,565 (2006: £23,000).

Employee-led support

Employees are encouraged to get involved in charitable activities with the group matching £ for £ any money raised. Included in the total amount supporting charities, is donated £35,000 in employee matching grants during 2005.

Herbert Smith LLP

Company registration number 2202333

Exchange House, Primrose Street, London EC2A 2HS

020 7374 8000

Website: www.herbertsmith.com

Correspondent: Samantha Nicholson, Secretary to the Chairites Committee

Year end
31/12/2007

Nature of company business
International law firm.

Main locations: London

Charitable donations

Total community contributions: £2,670,000

Membership: A & B, BitC, L B Group

Community involvement

Herbert Smith was one of the first law firms to start an extensive community action programme and was a founding member of the UK-based charity, the Solicitors Pro Bono Group (Charity Commission no. 1064274).

For more than 16 years, Herbert Smith has supported community initiatives and encouraged all members of staff to take part. The firm's programme has developed with the following principles:

- we have a responsibility to invest our time, skills, energy and money in the wider community to help create a more inclusive and prosperous society

- by engaging in our pro bono and volunteering schemes, participants develop personal and professional skills and broaden their perspectives

- people at Herbert Smith enjoy the opportunity to 'make a difference'

- community activities can help to reinforce the sense of collegiality within Herbert Smith

- supporting the social, environmental, charitable interests and concerns of our people, clients and the wider community is a positive way of building relationships.

Herbert Smith's Community Investment Committee accepts requests for financial support from charities that meet its criteria. The criteria for making cash donations are:

- charities connected with our wider community investment programme

- charities connected with the provision of free legal services

- charities that provide educational services in areas of disadvantage local to our offices in London

- charities whose work has an impact in areas of disadvantage local to our London offices.

Charity of the Year (2007): Breast Cancer Care

Voted for by the firm's partners and staff and managed by sports and social committee, 'Charity of the Year' is the focus for many of the firm's fundraising efforts.

Charity of the year partnerships take place every two years. The nomination process to become the firm's charity of the year in 2009 is now closed. Please email CR@herbertsmith.com for more information on the selection process.

Exclusions

Donations are only made to UK registered charities.

Applications

In writing to the correspondent.

Corporate giving

In 2007, the value of community programmes in cash, time and in kind giving. was valued at £2.67 million

Below are some previous examples of the types of work the firm undertakes.

Legal advice: *Death Row Prisoners* – Herbert Smith is on the panel of London solicitors which deals with appeals for those facing the death penalty for murder in the Caribbean. Support is also given to Amicus, a UK charity working on behalf of death row prisoners in America.

Royal Courts of Justice – Herbert Smith is one of over 20 City firms which support the Citizen Advice Bureau located in the Royal Courts of Justice. The firm provides qualified solicitors on a rota basis who attend as honorary legal advisers to supplement the CABs full-time advisory staff.

Education: *The Thomas Buxton Junior School Project* – In conjunction with the Tower Hamlets Education Business Partnerships (THEBP) over 150 volunteers from the firm assist pupils at the school with their reading, writing and IT skills.

Also in partnership with the THEBP, the firm helps GCSE students studying foreign languages (French, German and Spanish) and, with the support of Herbert Smith's Charities Committee, sponsored a trip to Brussels for 21 language students.

In kind support

The firm have previously supplied and installed IT equipment for the pupils at Thomas Buxton Junior School in Whitechapel. On-going technical back-up will be provided as part of the package.

Employee-led support

Herbert Smith encourages staff to volunteer and in 2007, 39% of London based staff actively participated in the firm's pro bono and volunteering programme. Volunteering schemes cover pupils from nursery through to university and homeless people.

Commercially-led support

Sponsorship: *The arts* – 'Our programme of arts sponsorship is increasingly aligned to our corporate responsibility activities. In addition to the benefits we secure for client entertaining and employee engagement, we have also negotiated facilities and opportunities that can be utilised by schools and colleges who are part of our community action programme.

'We regularly work with the National Portrait Gallery to provide workshops and careers sessions to the schools we support in the communities near to our London office.'

HESCO Bastion Ltd

Company registration number 2600319

Knowsthorpe Way, Cross Green Industrial Estate, Leeds LS9 0SW

0113 248 6633; Fax: 0113 248 3501

Website: www.hesco.com

Correspondent: Patricia Laidler, Company Secretary
Email: info@hesco.com

Year end	Turnover	Pre-tax profit
31/01/2008	£196,453,361	£31,008,807

Nature of company business
The company develops and manufactures defence wall systems under the name of Concertainer*. Used for the purpose of force protection, flood protection and erosion control; the units are used within the military as a means of protecting personnel and facilities against secondary fragmentation.

UK employees: 308

Charitable donations

2007: £11,455,520
2005: £305,850

Community involvement

The company appears to have a preference for supporting organisations based in West Yorkshire, especially the Leeds area. working in health/ill health, respite care, medical research, children or conservation.

Exclusions

No support for local appeals from outside the West Yorkshire area. No support for individuals, political appeals or advertising in charity brochures.

Applications

In writing to the correspondent.

Further information about how to apply to the HASCO Bastion Fund is available from Leeds Community Foundation at: www.leedscommunityfoundation.org.uk

The foundation suggests that would be applicants initially complete the 'Expression of Interest' form on its website.

Corporate giving

In 2007/08, the company established the HESCO Bastion Fund with an exceptional donation of £10 million to the Leeds Community Foundation which will be responsible for running it.

A further £1.45 million was donated to various other charities, the main beneficiaries of which were: St James Hospital – Leeds (£1 million); Leeds Teaching Hospital and Sheffield Children's Hospital (£100,000 each); and Martin House, St Gemma's Hospice, Wakefield/Garforth Pilgrimages and Wheatfields Hospice (£50,000 each).

HESCO Bastion Fund

In 2008, some of the beneficiaries were:

Bridge Street Church – youth centre; Caring for Life – education block; FDM – community transport; Friends of Middleton Park – community activities; Leeds Mencap – activities for young children; People in Action – general activities; Sheffield Children's Hospital – general activities; Sick Children's Trust – home from home centre; Soccerworks – football coaching; St Cyprians – holiday scheme; St Philip's Osmondthorpe – roof appeal; Sue Ryder Care Wheatfields – general contribution; Unicef – general contribution; Martin House Children's Hospice – general contribution; St Gemma's hospice – general contribution.

Hess Ltd

Company registration number 807346

Level 9, The Adelphi Building, 1–11 John Adam Street, London EC2N 6AG

020 7331 3000

Website: www.hess.com

Correspondent: Andy Mitchell, Communications Manager – andy.mitchell@hess.com

John B Hess

Year end	Turnover	Pre-tax profit
31/12/2007	£737,382,000	£519,378,000

Nature of company business
The exploration and production of oil and gas. The ultimate holding company is the Hess Corporation based in the USA.

Subsidiaries include: Western Gas Ltd

Main locations: London, Aberdeen

UK employees: 222

Charitable donations

2007: £73,000
2006: £54,000
2004: £30,228

Community involvement

The Environment, Health, Safety and Social Responsibility Report for 2007 produced by the Hess Corporation states: 'We have a strong commitment to make a long lasting, positive impact on the communities. We have chosen to focus our efforts largely on health and education. We also support the community based volunteer activities of our employees'.

Previous information indicated that the UK company prefers to support appeals relevant to company business and local charities in areas of company presence.

Preferred areas of support are the environment, medical research, science/technology and sickness/disability charities. Support tends to be given to specific projects.

Exclusions

No support is given for advertising in charity brochures, animal welfare, appeals from individuals, purely denominational (religious) appeals, local appeals not in areas of company presence, overseas projects or political events.

Applications

Appeals from national charities should be addressed in writing to the correspondent. The Aberdeen office (1 Berry Street, Aberdeen AB25 1HS tel. 01224 841330) deals with appeals relevant to that region.

Corporate giving

In 2007, Hess invested more than $16 million worldwide; nearly triple the 2006 budget of $6 million. More than 57% went to improving education. In addition to programme support, Hess provided approximately $160,000 to disaster relief efforts principally in Indonesia, Ghana and Peru. The company also worked with a range of social development organisations including ones in the United Kingdom.

In the UK, the company donated around £73,000 in 2007 (2006: £54,000). Details of the beneficiaries were unavailable.

In kind support

In addition to charitable donations, the company also undertakes a range of activities in support of the communities in which it operates. For example in 2007, Aberdeen employees participated in the North Sea Chaplaincy Trust, which provides financial relief to those in the oil and gas industry or their dependants who find themselves with immediate financial problems.

Teacher fellowships in the UK – Partnering with Earthwatch, Hess created 30 fellowships to enable secondary school teachers to take part in environmental research projects and take their learning back into their class rooms and local communities.

Employee-led support

Employees in the UK have provided generous support matched by the company for Children 1st, a group that supports the Royal Scottish Society for the Prevention of Cruelty to Children.

Commercially-led support

Sponsorship: *Sport* – Through its partnership with the Lawn Tennis Association, support was given to the City Tennis Clubs programme.

Hewlett-Packard Ltd

Company registration number 690597

Cain Road, Bracknell RG12 1HN

Website: www.hp.com/uk

Correspondent: (See 'Applications')

Email: hp.philanthropy@porternovelli.co.uk

Managing Director: Stephen Gill

Year end	Turnover	Pre-tax profit
31/10/2007	£3,158,955,000	£151,894,000

Nature of company business
Hewlett-Packard Ltd is a subsidiary of the Hewlett-Packard Company incorporated in the USA. The principal activities of the group are the design, manufacture and marketing of measurement and computation products and systems.

Main locations: Bracknell, Bristol, Erskine (Glasgow)

UK employees: 5,654

Charitable donations
2007: £137,714
2006: £208,942
Membership: BitC

Community involvement

The following guidelines were provided by Hewlett-Packard:

'The majority of our EMEA (Europe, Middle East, Africa) grants are awarded through HP-developed grant initiatives that are aligned with our three focus areas Education, Economic Development and Environment. We launch these competitive grant initiatives at the beginning of each fiscal year (November).

'We will award grants only to eligible universities, schools and non-profit community organisations that meet the requirements of the specific initiatives. If you contact HP with an unsolicited grant request, you will receive a generic response that reiterates this policy.'

Exclusions

HP does not consider the following types of grant requests:
- requests from individuals
- requests for grants for religious activities, churches
- requests for sponsorships or grants for conferences, seminars, contests, fundraising activities, promotional items, sports events, marketing, TV and video production, research or feasibility studies
- requests from individual schools (unless through one of its grant initiatives)
- for-profit ventures
- requests from programmes that discriminate on the basis of race, creed, colour, religion, gender, national origin, sexual orientation, age, disability or veteran status
- requests for used or obsolete equipment
- discounted purchases.
- requests from organizations that provide support or resources to any individual or entity that advocates, plans, sponsors, engages in, or has engaged in terrorist activity; or to anyone who acts as an agent for such an individual or entity. Support or resources include currency or other financial instruments, financial services, lodging, training, safe houses, false documentation or identification, communication equipment, facilities, weapons, lethal substances, explosives, personnel, transportation, and any other services or physical assets. Any violation of this certification is grounds for return to the donor of all funds advanced to grantee.

Applications

HP EMEA (Europe, Middle East, Africa) does not accept unsolicited requests for grants.

Corporate giving

In 2006/07, cash donations in the UK totalled £137,714 (2005/06: £208,942). During the year Hewlett-Packard (HP) supported National Children's Home and The Prince's Trust.

HP also supports schools in their efforts to increase computer literacy and has a long-established, strong relationship with Kelvin School in Glasgow, a school for children who have multiple disabilities, including visual impairments.

HFC Bank Ltd

Company registration number 1117305

North Street, Winkfield, Windsor, Berkshire SL4 4TD

01344 890000; Fax: 01344 890014

Website: www.hfcbank.co.uk

Correspondent: Teresa Howlett, Community Affairs Executive 01344 890000 ext 2330

Chairman: David Keys

Managing Director: Gary Gilmer

Year end
31/12/2007

Nature of company business
The principal activity of the company comprises banking services.

Subsidiaries include: Hamilton Financial Planning Services Ltd, Hamilton Life Assurance Co. Ltd, Hamilton Insurance Co. Ltd, DLRS Ltd

Main locations: Winkfield, Birmingham, Bracknell

UK employees: 2,000

Charitable donations

2007: £30,000
2005: £176,730
2004: £164,067
2003: £150,000

Community involvement

Although now part of the HSBC Group, the company has a small charitable budget with which it supports local charities.

Exclusions

No support for advertising in publications and associated materials, appeals from individuals, the arts, heritage, medical research, overseas projects, political appeals, religious appeals, science/technology, social welfare or sport.

'Charity of the Year' proposals are not accepted.

Applications

In writing to the correspondent.

Information available: Potential applicants can obtain guidelines from the company.

Corporate giving

In 2007 the company made cash donations totalling £30,000. Beneficiaries included: Acorns Children's Hospice; Macmillan Cancer Support; BBC Children in Need; and Age Concern – Bracknell.

In kind support

Support is given through gifts in kind.

Employee-led support

Employees are actively involved in their own fundraising and are given company time off in which to volunteer. Employees fundraising efforts are matched up to a maximum of £500 per year.

Payroll giving: The Hands on Helping scheme is in operation.

William Hill plc

Company registration number 4212563

Greenside House, 50 Station Road, Wood Green, London N22 7TP

020 8918 3600

Website: www.williamhillplc.co.uk

Correspondent: Thomas Murphy, Group Company Secretary

Chairman: Charles Scott

Chief Executive Officer: Ralph Topping

Year end	Turnover	Pre-tax profit
01/01/2008	£940,400,000	£209,200,000

Nature of company business
The principal activities of the group during the period continue to be the operation of licensed betting offices and the provision of telephone and internet betting and online casino and poker services.

Main locations: Haringay

UK employees: 14,629

Charitable donations

2007: £581,000
2006: £423,000
2005: £351,000

Community involvement

The company's charitable donations are mainly focused on organisations involved in areas of greatest relevance to its business and include contributions to those involved in:

- promoting a responsible approach to gambling; undertaking research into problem gambling; and providing information, advice and help to those who are at risk or are experiencing difficulties with their gambling
- greyhound and racehorse welfare.
- support to disadvantaged individuals in horse and greyhound racing.

The group has established a Charitable Donations Committee, which reviews, on a quarterly basis, requests for charitable donations against the Board's agreed policy.

Exclusions

No support for circular or general appeals, or to political or religious organisations.

Applications

In writing to the correspondent.

Corporate giving

In 2007, the group made charitable donations of £581,000 (2006: £423,000) principally to industry-related charities serving the communities in which the group operates. e.g. Responsibility in Gambling Trust.

Employee-led support

The group is committed to providing support, wherever possible, to its employees through their own fundraising efforts. The group allocates a proportion of its annual charitable donations budget to match funds (up to a specified limit) raised by employees on local charitable projects.

During 2007 the nominated charities of staff members benefited by £25,000 from the matching scheme with staff endeavours including marathon running and parachute jumps.

Hiscox plc

Company registration number 2837811

1 Great St Helen's, London EC3A 6HX

020 7448 6000; Fax: 020 7448 6900

Website: www.hiscox.com

Correspondent: Alexander Neil Foster, Trustee, The Hiscox Foundation
Email: enquiry@hiscox.com

Chairman: Robert Hiscox

Chief Executive: Bronek Masojada

Year end	Turnover	Pre-tax profit
31/12/2007	£1,083,911,000	£237,199,000

Nature of company business
Insurance.

Charitable donations

2007: £616,572
2006: £567,000

Community involvement

The Hiscox Foundation (Charity Commission no. 327635), a charity funded by an annual donation from Hiscox, has been set up to give donations to deserving causes, i.e. to assist and improve education, the arts and independent living for disabled and disadvantaged members of society.

It gives priority to any charity in which a member of staff is involved with the aim of encouraging and developing such activity.

Through various sponsorships, individuals, the arts and equestrian and related fields are supported by the Hiscox brand.

Applications

In writing to the correspondent.

Corporate giving

In 2007, the company made charitable donations in the UK of £616,572 (2006: £567,000) of which £550,000 (2006: £500,000) was donated to the Hiscox Foundation. Normally, the amount given to the foundation by the company is around £50,000 a year, so these recent figures represent a significant increase.

The foundation's accounts note that this will greatly increase the level of investment income generated and therefore allow future donations to be significantly higher.

The Hiscox Foundation

In 2006/07, the foundation had an income of £532,000 and made grants totalling £30,150 to 61 charities.

Beneficiaries included: The British Heart Foundation; CLIC Sargent; Childline; Elizabeth Selby Infants School; Jo's Trust for Cervical Cancer; and Roche Court Educational Trust.

Employee-led support

Mentoring: 'Hiscox is a member of the Lloyd's Community programme, which supports local initiatives concerning education, training, enterprise and regeneration. In London for example, the Reading Partners scheme has continued, through which staff assist pupils at the Elizabeth Selby Infants School in Tower Hamlets. Employees also mentor students at Morpeth School in Tower Hamlets.'

Hiscox staff also continued their six year long support of the Richard House Hospice, raising over £30,000 through various initiatives during 2007.

Commercially-led support

Sponsorship: The arts – Hiscox supports the Public Catalogue Foundation which has been set up to photograph and record all oil, acrylic and tempera paintings in publicly-owned collections.

It is estimated that four out of five publicly owned paintings are hidden from public view. The aim of the foundation is to improve public access to these paintings.

The first catalogue for oil paintings in public ownership covers West Yorkshire and has been completed. For more information go to: www.thepcf.org.uk

Hiscox's regional offices undertake smaller, more locally relevant sponsorships separately.

Julian Hodge Bank Ltd

Company registration number 743437

30–31 Windsor Place, Cardiff CF10 3UR

029 2022 0800; Fax: 029 2023 0516

Website: www.jhb.co.uk

Chairman: John Mitchell

Deputy Chairman: Jonathan Hodger

Managing Director: D M Austin

Year end	Pre-tax profit
31/10/2007	£20,433,000

Nature of company business
Provision of a wide range of personal and business banking services and independent financial advice.

Main locations: Cardiff, Nantwich

UK employees: 112

Community involvement

The following information was taken from the bank's website: 'The group also recognises a social responsibility to the community and will continue to provide financial support for welfare, medical, academic (Julian Hodge Institute of Applied Macroeconomics and the Sir Julian Hodge Chair in Asset Finance) and educational concerns. Usually, this is through the medium of The Jane Hodge Foundation (Charity Commission no. 216053) or the Sir Julian Hodge Charitable Trust (Charity Commission no. 234848), charities which together own nearly 80% of the ordinary share capital of the bank's parent company, The Carlyle Trust Ltd'.

Applications

Please refer to the application criteria for the related trusts.

Corporate giving

Although we have been unable to obtain a figure regarding the banks level of support via the above trusts, full details of the trusts support criteria and application procedure can be found in the Directory of Social Change publications 'A Guide to the Major Trusts Volumes 1 and 2'.

In 2007, the Julian Hodge Bank through the Jane Hodge Foundation donated £10,000 towards the installation of a new infra red hearing system at The Sherman Theatre, Cardiff.

Honda of the UK Manufacturing Ltd

Company registration number 1887872

Highworth Road, South Marston, Swindon SN3 4TZ

01793 831183; Fax: 01793 831177

Website: world.honda.com/community

Correspondent: Corporate Communications Dept

Chairman: S Takagi

Year end	Turnover	Pre-tax profit
31/03/2007	£2,030,365,000	(£43,099,000)

Nature of company business
The principal activity of the company is the manufacture of motor vehicles, including the manufacture of motor engines and other vehicle parts.

Main locations: Slough, Swindon

UK employees: 4,458

Charitable donations

2007: £32,961
2006: £68,913
2004: £20,599
2003: £32,808

Community involvement

Honda in the UK summarises its philanthropic community initiatives under two categories:

- educational – leaders and sponsorships, especially in connection with young people
- community – local festival and event support. Help is also given through the donation of goods/prizes and by supporting its employees in their charitable works.

Support may also be given in connection with the environment and road safety.

There appears to be a strong preference for supporting organisations near to its manufacturing plants, e.g. Swindon.

Exclusions

No support for animal welfare, appeals from individuals, political appeals, religious appeals and large national charities.

Applications

In writing to the correspondent.

Corporate giving

In 2007, cash donations in the UK totalled £32,961 (2005: £68,913). Community contributions previously stood at around £200,000 a year, but we have been unable to confirm if it remains at this level.

We have no information about the organisations/events benefiting from the company's support.

In kind support

The main areas of non-cash support are gifts in kind.

Commercially-led support

Sponsorship: *Education* – The company undertake sponsorship of educational initiatives. For example, in 2007 the company organized the first Dream Factory at the Science Museum in Swindon.

Hoover Ltd

Company registration number 2521528

Pentrebach Factory, Pentrebach, Merthyr Tydfil CF48 4TU

01685 721222

Website: www.hoover.co.uk

Correspondent: Marion Heaffy, Hoover Foundation
01685 721222

Chairman: S Funagalli

Year end	Turnover	Pre-tax profit
30/12/2007	£156,390,000	(£420,000,000)

Nature of company business
Manufacture of domestic laundry, refrigeration, and vacuuming appliances.

Main locations: Glasgow, Merthyr Tydfil, Bolton

UK employees: 1,093

Charitable donations

2003: £86,687

Community involvement

The company appears to direct its grant giving through the Hoover Foundation (Charity commission no. 200274). Support is given to strategic UK charities working in education, health and welfare. Small grants are made to local organisations near its main sites in South Wales, Glasgow and Bolton.

Exclusions

No grants to individuals, including students.

Applications

In writing to the correspondent.

Corporate giving

The company's annual report and accounts for 2007 did not declare any charitable donations having been made. This, coupled with the overdue accounts for the foundation at the Charity Commission, do not assist in ascertaining what support, if any, the company give to charitable causes. For the time being, however, we will provide the information that is available.

Hoover Foundation

In 2007, the foundation had an income of £11,127 and a total expenditure of £145,089. Although fuller details were unavailable, the company's website states that the foundation supports Asthma UK. Assistance has also been given to Childline, along with support for the Welsh Young Consumer of the Year.

House of Fraser (Stores) Ltd

Company registration number SC021928

Granite House, 4th Floor, 31 Stockwell Street, Glasgow G1 4RZ

Website: www.houseoffraser.co.uk

Correspondent: Peter Hearsey, Company Secretary

Chairman: Don McCarthy

Chief Executive: John King

Year end	Turnover	Pre-tax profit
26/01/2008	£596,000,000	£12,900,000

Nature of company business
Department store operators.

Main locations: Glasgow, Swindon, London

UK employees: 4,951

Charitable donations
2008: £49,088
2007: £31,000
2006: £47,337
2005: £50,183

Community involvement

The House of Fraser makes charitable donations wherever possible and, along with its nominated charity of the year, the stores are encouraged to undertake their own fundraising events and activities for local charities.

Exclusions

Support is not generally given to circular appeals, appeals from individuals, purely denominational (religious or political) appeals, local appeals not in areas of company presence or overseas projects.

Applications

In writing to the correspondent. Local charities are supported at the discretion of the store managers in their region.

Corporate giving

In 2007/08, charitable donations totalled £49,088 (2006/07: £31,000). Although no breakdown of this amount was

available, we assume the majority went towards supporting its nominated charity of the year.

In kind support

The group actively supports Computers for Charity (CFC). CFC is a voluntary, non-profit-making organisation, the aim of which is to improve access to IT for community groups which it does by recycling computers. The group has sent some 200 PCs and a large number of laptops and printers to CFC over the last three years.

Employee-led support

In 2008, the company's annual Charity Golf Day was held on 9th July and raised approximately £72,000. This was split equally between the year's nominated charities: Walk the Walk, Southview School and Retail Trust.

Commercially-led support

Cause-related marketing; Each year the group produces a house-branded teddy bear for sale in its stores in conjunction with the RSPCA and Cancer Research UK. A portion of the selling price of each bear is donated to both charities.

HSBC Holdings plc

Company registration number 617987

Level 36, 8 Canada Square, London EC3R 6AE

020 7991 8888; Fax: 020 7992 4880

Website: www.hsbc.com

Correspondent: HSBC in the Community

Email: communityaffairs@hsbc.com

Chairman: Stephen K Green

Chief Executive: M F Geoghegan

Year end	Pre-tax profit
31/12/2007	£12,106,000,000

Nature of company business
The group provides banking and related financial services.

Subsidiaries include: The British Bank of the Middle East, First Direct, Midland Life Ltd, Midland Bank Ltd, East River Savings Bank, Eversholt Holdings Ltd, Samuel Montagu & Co. Ltd, HFC Bank, Forward Trust Ltd, James Capel & Co. Ltd

Main locations: Leeds, London

UK employees: 55,000

Charitable donations
2007: £18,400,000
2006: £16,400,000
2005: £15,800,000

Membership: A & B, BitC, L B Group

Community involvement

'HSBC supports the communities in which we operate both through the involvement of our employees and through donations. Our policy is to focus our efforts on education – particularly for young people – and on the environment. We aim to channel 75 per cent of our community giving into these two areas.'

'**Education:** HSBC believes that support for primary and secondary education, in particular for the underprivileged, is crucial to the future development and prosperity of every country.

'In addition to funding original education initiatives around the world, HSBC is keen to involve its experienced and supportive staff in building and developing mentoring programmes, and offering career guidance and job internships for talented young people.' Grants were made to schools and colleges in the UK through the HSBC Education Trust (Charity Commission no. 1084542).

'**Environment:** HSBC is deeply conscious of its responsibility to the environment

'We will always consider support for worthwhile environmental organisations and initiatives.'

Exclusions

No support for advertising in charity brochures, animal welfare, appeals from individuals, the arts, elderly people, fundraising events, political appeals, religious appeals, science/technology, sickness/disability, or sport.

Applications

In writing to the correspondent.

Corporate giving

In 2007, HSBC Holdings plc made donations within the UK totalling around £18.4 million (2006: £16.4 million). We have no specific information regarding the beneficiaries.

The HSBC Education Trust made grants totalling £4.7 million in 2007.

Employee-led support

Education: Around 1,000 HSBC employees in the UK work on a voluntary basis with the charity Young Enterprise, advising and encouraging young people to set up their own businesses.

Employees are given time off in which to volunteer, with their fundraising efforts being matched by the bank up to a maximum of £500.

Payroll giving: The bank operates the Give As You Earn scheme.

Alan Hudson Ltd

Company registration number 613979

Bevis Lane, Wisbech St Mary, Wisbech, Cambridge PE13 4RR

01945 583087

Correspondent: A D Salmon, Trustee

Year end	Turnover	Pre-tax profit
31/10/2007	£728,917	£113,982

Nature of company business
Fruit growers.

UK employees: 14

Charitable donations
2006: £117,527

Community involvement

The company is wholly owned by The Hudson Foundation (Charity Commission no. 280332) and donates its taxable profits for the year to the charity by way of Gift Aid.

The Hudson Foundation

The object of the foundation is the relief of infirm and/or older people, in particular the establishment and maintenance of residential accommodation for relief of infirm and/or older people and to make donations to other charitable purposes with a preference for the Wisbech area. The accounts state that 'whilst the trustees do make contributions to revenue expenditure of charitable organisations, they prefer to assist in the funding of capital projects for the advancement of the community of Wisbech and district.

Applications

In writing to the correspondent at: The Hudson Foundation, Whitegates, Barton Road, Wisbech, Cambridge PE13 1LE.

Corporate giving

In 2006, the company gift-aided £117,527 to the foundation which assets of £1.75 million and a total income of £784,000.

Grants were made totalling £148,000 the beneficiaries of which included: Wisbech Angles Theatre Council (£95,000); Methodist Homes for the Aged (£15,000); Wisbech Grammar School (£11,500); Wisbech St. Mary PCC (£9,600); Wisbech Swimming Club (£8,300); and Wisbech Sea Cadets (£1,500).

Hunting plc

Company registration number 974568

3 Cockspur Street, London SW1Y 5BQ

020 7321 0123; Fax: 020 7839 2072

Website: www.hunting.plc.uk

Correspondent: Ms Anna Blundell-Williams, Public Relations Coordinator
Email: anna.bw@hunting.plc.uk

Chairman: R H Hunting

Chief Executive: D L Proctor

Year end	Turnover	Pre-tax profit
31/12/2007	£1,949,500,000	£90,700,000

Nature of company business
The principal activity of the company is oil services.

Subsidiaries include: Irvin Group Ltd

Main locations: London

UK employees: 417

Total employees: 2,782

Charitable donations
2007: £57,000
2006: £49,000
2005: £49,000
2004: £26,000
2003: £24,000

Community involvement

Donations are generally made through the Hunting Charitable Trust (not a registered charity), which supports UK charities, both national and local, involved in welfare and medicine.

Local charities are usually only supported by subsidiaries if a member of staff has a particularly close connection with the charity.

Exclusions

The company does not make political donations.

Applications

In writing to the correspondent. The trustees of the Hunting Charitable Trust meet once a year, generally in November.

Corporate giving

In 2007, £57,000 was donated to UK charitable organisations. We have no details of the beneficiaries. A further £213,000 was donated to charitable causes overseas.

Commercially-led support

Sponsorship: *The arts* – the company sponsors the Hunting Art Prizes Competition. Subsidiaries also have their own sponsorship budgets.

Each year, as part of the Hunting Arts Prizes competition, a charity private view is hosted in order to raise money for good causes. The benefiting charity for 2005 was the Royal Hospital Chelsea and all funds raised at the private view and dinner were donated to its appeal to build a new Infirmary and updated Long Wards for the Pensioners.

Huntsman/Tioxide Europe Ltd

Company registration number 249759

Haverton Hill Road, Billingham TS23 1PS

01642 370300; Fax: 01642 370290

Website: www.huntsman.com

Correspondent: Jeanette Tomlinson, Community Action Team

Year end	Turnover	Pre-tax profit
31/12/2006	£206,626,000	(£850,000)

Nature of company business
The manufacture of titanium oxide and titanium compounds.

Main locations: Adlington, Billingham, Duxford, Grimsby, Hartlepool, Llanelli, Redcar, Shepton Mallet

UK employees: 613

Charitable donations
2006: £18,000
2005: £25,000
2004: £120,646
2003: £307,894

Community involvement

The company has factories in Adlington, Billingham (International Headquarters), Duxford, Grimsby, Hartlepool, Llanelli, Redcar and Shepton Mallet. Support is focused on charities local to these sites.

A wide range of causes in these communities are supported, with the preferred areas being children and youth, social welfare, medical and education.

Exclusions

No support for circulars, brochure advertising, local appeals not in areas of company presence, large national appeals, fundraising events or appeals from individuals.

Applications

Teesside (Billingham) charitable appeals should be made in writing to the correspondent.

For other local appeals in areas of company presence you will need to contact the appropriate office to obtain the contacts name.

Corporate giving

During the year 2006 the company made charitable donations totalling £18,000 (2005: £25,000). We have no details of the beneficiaries.

In kind support

Non-cash support is given in the form of gifts and occasional secondments.

IBM United Kingdom Ltd

Company registration number 741598

IBM (United Kingdom) Ltd, PO Box 41, North Harbour, Portsmouth, Hampshire PO6 3AU

0870 542 6426; Fax: 0870 542 6329

Website: www.ibm.com/uk

Correspondent: Mark Wakefield, Corporate Community Relations Manager
Email: wakefim@uk.ibm.com

Year end	Turnover	Pre-tax profit
31/12/2007	£3,674,100,000	£168,800,000

Nature of company business
IBM United Kingdom Ltd is the UK subsidiary of IBM Corporation. It is involved in the provision of information technology services and solutions, and the development, production and supply of advanced information technology products.

Main locations: London, Portsmouth, Glasgow

Total employees: 18,384

Charitable donations
2007: £800,000
2006: £800,000
2005: £800,000
2004: £900,000

Membership: BitC

Community involvement

IBM UK's support for charitable and community organisations is directed through its 'On Demand Community' grants programme which is supported by the

IBM United Kingdom Trust (Charity Commission no. 292462).

On Demand Community – The UK community grants programme is designed to support the 3,000+ IBM employees and the 150+ IBM retirees who have already registered as volunteers for the on demand community programme. The scheme provides money or IBM products to eligible community organisations and schools where IBM employees and retirees are actively volunteering, and in support of specific projects. In addition, the employee (and each member of the team) must have worked with an eligible organisation for at least five months and for a minimum average of eight hours monthly.

To be eligible an organisation must be a registered charity or other not-for-profit community organisation that offers assistance in areas such as education, the environment, arts/cultural activities, health and human services and so on. It must also be located in the community where the volunteer activity takes place.

Charities and schools may also be eligible for 'technology discounts'. IBM offers substantial discounts on many hardware and software products for schools and voluntary (not-for-profit) organisations supported by IBM volunteers.

Comprehensive information regarding the above support, eligibility and how to apply are provided on the company's website at: www-05.ibm.com/uk/news/ondemandcommunity/index.html or, should this link change, go to IBM UK's homepage > About Us > On Demand Community.

IBM UK Trust – The trust primarily achieves its aims by supporting the development and delivery of IBM's own community involvement programmes where these meet the charitable objectives of the trust. Effectively, support is provided for the majority of IBM's community involvement programmes in the UK, as well as for IBM's pan-European corporate social responsibility programmes within Europe, the Middle East and Africa.

Most of the trust's income comes from the IBM International Foundation or the IBM Corporation and its subsidiaries.

Exclusions

IBM will not support organisations which advocate, support, or practice activities inconsistent with IBM's non-discrimination policies, whether based on race, colour, religion, gender, gender identity or expression, sexual orientation, national origin, disability or age. Documentation (in the form of an Equality of Opportunity statement) demonstrating that organisations comply with the above statement will be required.

IBM reserves the right to determine which organisations are eligible for grants.

Applications

All requests for funding need to be requested by the employee rather than the recipient organisation, as organisations without an IBM employee volunteering cannot be supported. It might, however, be worth charitable and community groups based around company sites advertising voluntary positions on its intranet site to open up this avenue of funding.

For applications to the IBM UK Trust please contact Mark Wakefield, Corporate Community Relations Manager, IBM UK Trust, Mail Point 1PG1, 76 Upper Ground, London SE1 9PZ, telephone no. 020 7202 3608 or email – wakefim@uk.ibm.com

N.B. Unsolicited applications from organisations are not considered by the trust.

Corporate giving

In 2007, IBM UK made cash donations to charity of £800,000 (2006: £800,000). We understand that the majority of this is disbursed through the company's trust.

The latest accounts available for the IBM United Kingdom Trust are for 2006 when it had an income of just over £3 million. This mainly came from IBM subsidiaries (£1.6 million) and the IBM International Foundation (£1.3 million). Grants were made totalling £2,965,000 (this excludes support and administration cost) and went towards the advancement of education, educational research, improving the life of disabled and disadvantaged people, use and understanding of IT in the charitable sector and health, environment and poverty.

Some of the charitable activities supported by the trust were part of the company's community grants programme. These emphasise participation in and projects supporting IBM's key strategic efforts, including On Demand Community, Reinventing Education, MentorPlace, TryScience, KidSmart Early Learning and Web Adaptation Technology.

Employee-led support

Through its On Demand Community initiative, IBM encourages and supports employees and retirees to undertake voluntary work, organising its community involvement policies to motivate people to volunteer. The company's intranet site has a database of volunteer opportunities which allows staff to find a good cause which matches their interests. The UK Community Grants programme is designed to support the 3,000+ employees and 150+ retirees for the on demand community programme.

Payroll giving: The company operates the Give As You Earn scheme.

ICAP plc

Company registration number 3611426

2 Broadgate, London EC2M 7UR

020 7000 5000; Fax: 020 7000 5975

Website: www.icapcharityday.com

Correspondent: Nikki Studt, Charity Co-ordinator

Chairman: Charles Gregson

Chief Executive: Michael Spencer

Year end	Turnover	Pre-tax profit
31/03/2007	£1,106,300,000	£251,600,000

Nature of company business
The company is the world's largest interdealer broker and is active in the wholesale markets for OTC derivatives, fixed income securities, money market products, foreign exchange, energy, credit and equity derivatives.

Subsidiaries include: BrokerTec Europe Ltd, Exotix Investments Ltd, Garban-Intercapital Systems Ltd, Guy Butler Ltd, Harlow (London) Ltd, T&M Securities Ltd

Main locations: London

UK employees: 1,400

Charitable donations

2007: £9,200,000
2005: £2,100,000
2004: £2,100,000
2003: £2,000,000

Community involvement

The company donates to charitable causes the money raised each year during its 'Charity Day'. On this day the group donates its entire revenue, without any cost reductions, to various charities selected by local offices. This unique event includes the commission made by brokers as well as the company's revenue. It appears that employee fundraising efforts also add to the amount raised.

Support will be considered for the following: Advertising in charity brochures; Arts; Children/Youth; Education; Elderly People; Environment; Medical research; Overseas projects; Sickness/disability; Social welfare; and Sport.

Applications

In writing to the correspondent.

Corporate giving

In 2006/07, the company raised £9.2 million worldwide during its 'Charity Day'. We do not know what proportion of this was raised by the UK office.

Beneficiaries in the UK in 2007 included: National Centre for Young People with Epilepsy; Alzheimer's Society; Breast Cancer haven; Wellchild; and Asthma UK.

Employee-led support

The firm matches employees charitable fundraising and giving to a maximum of £250 per person, per year.

Payroll giving: The company operates the Give As You Earn scheme.

IMI plc

Company registration number 714275

Lakeside Solihull Parkway, Birmingham Business Park, Birmingham B37 7XZ

0121 717 3700

Website: www.imiplc.com

Correspondent: Elaine Morgan, Secretary – IMI Charitable Appeals Committee 0121 717 3700

Chairman: Norman Askew

Chief Executive: M J Lamb

Year end	Turnover	Pre-tax profit
31/12/2007	£1,599,000,000	£210,100,000

Nature of company business
IMI is a diversified engineering group operating in two main areas: Fluid controls and Retail dispense. It manufactures and sells internationally.

Main locations: Birmingham, Manchester, Liverpool, Yorkshire

UK employees: 2,721

Total employees: 14,700

Charitable donations

2007: £205,000
2006: £235,000
2005: £298,000
2004: £215,000
2003: £231,000

Total community contributions: £220,000

Membership: BitC

Community involvement

IMI believe that 'successful businesses cannot exist and operate in isolation from the culture in which they operate'. The group therefore supports a range of selected national charities and smaller charitable organisations operating in communities where it has a presence'.

'A sizeable proportion of total donations go into education, including establishments in engineering and technology.'

Exclusions

No support for circular appeals, advertising in charity brochures, appeals from individuals, fundraising events, local appeals not in an area of company presence, political appeals, large national appeals, or Christmas cards.

Applications

In writing to the correspondent. Grant decisions are made by an appeals committee which meets on an ad hoc basis. Local appeals should be sent to the relevant local plant or branch.

Advice to applicants: The company welcomes appeals from charities but its appeal mail is getting too large to handle. Applicants should therefore ensure that they can establish some link with the company in order to be considered for support.

Appeals should, where applicable, give details of the total amount to be raised and a description of how the money is to be spent. If possible, the latest statement of accounts should accompany the appeal.

Corporate giving

Community contributions totalled around £220,000 in 2007, of which charitable donations accounted for £205,000. Beneficiaries included: CIDA; Care for Children; and DebRA.

IMI has worked closely with Business in the Community on the following projects:

- garden refurbishment at a city primary school (2007) – prepared a plot of land for children to plant and cultivate a garden in a city environment
- Centre of the Earth office renewal (2006) – redesigned and rebuilt offices for the adult education centre near Watson Green Prison.

From 200 to 2006, IMI ran an Imagineering booth at the Town & Country Festival, promoting the field of engineering to 8–10 year olds.

In kind support

The main areas of non-cash support are secondments and gifts in kind.

In addition, non-cash support will be provided by many of IMI's subsidiary companies throughout the UK, but this support is not quantified.

Employee-led support

Support for employee charitable activity is provided at subsidiary level and is at the discretion of the management. It is not quantified in the overall company's community contribution.

Payroll giving: The company operates the Give As You Earn scheme.

Commercially-led support

Sponsorship: *The arts* – although the company is not a member of Arts & Business, IMI plc sponsors the Birmingham Royal Ballet and the Birmingham Hippodrome.

Contact: Corporate sponsorship proposals should be addressed to the Communications Manager.

Imperial Tobacco Group plc

Company registration number 3236483

PO Box 244, Upton Road, Southville, Bristol BS99 7UJ

0117 963 6636

Website: www.imperial-tobacco.com

Correspondent: Charlotte Maycock, Secretary, Charity Appeals Committee

Chairman: Iiain Napier

Chief Executive: Gareth Davis

Year end	Turnover	Pre-tax profit
30/09/2007	£12,344,000,000	£1,237,000,000

Nature of company business
Tobacco manufacturer.

Subsidiaries include: Sinclair Collis Ltd, Douwe Egberts Van Nelle Tabak

Main locations: Glasgow, Bristol, Liverpool, Nottingham, Farnham Royal

UK employees: 2,002

Total employees: 14,221

> **Charitable donations**
>
> 2007: £200,000
> 2006: £700,000
> 2005: £984,000
> 2004: £667,000
> 2003: £464,000
>
> Membership: BitC

Community involvement

The vast majority of the company's charitable funding is distributed through the Charities Aid Foundation in accordance with the company's charities policy.

It supports local causes in the communities in which it operates (mainly Bristol, Glasgow, Ipswich, Liverpool and Nottingham) and encourages employee participation in community affairs. There is a preference for supporting causes connected with the arts (sometimes local), education (sometimes local), elderly people, enterprise/training, environment/heritage, medical research, science/technology, sickness/disability charities and social welfare.

Exclusions

No support for government initiatives, advertising in charity brochures, animal welfare, appeals from individuals, children/youth, fundraising events, overseas projects, religious appeals, or sport.

Applications

The following information was provided by the company:

'We prefer to support charities and not-for-profit organisations which our employees already support by their own activities. Our own employees can apply for support through the company Intranet.

'If you wish to enter into a partnership with us at a regional or international level please complete the online form. If you have any supporting documentation, leaflets or other information about the organisation on whose behalf you are seeking our assistance, please make a note of this on your application form so you may be contacted with details of where to send the material.'

Corporate giving

In 2007, charitable donations worldwide totalled £2 million of which £200,000 was in respect of the UK (2006: £1 million/£700,000).

Employee-led support

Employees are encouraged to fundraise and make donations, which are matched by the company.

Payroll giving: The company participates in the CAF Give as you Earn scheme.

Inchcape plc

Company registration number 609782

22a St James's Square, London SW1Y 5LP

020 7546 0022; Fax: 020 7546 0010

Website: www.inchcape.com

Correspondent: CSR Committee

Chairman: Peter Johnson

Chief Executive: Andre Lacroix

Year end	Turnover	Pre-tax profit
31/12/2007	£6,056,800,000	£240,000,000

Nature of company business
Inchcape is a scale automotive retail group operating in Australia, Belgium, Greece, Hong Kong, Singapore and the UK. The group also has operations in a number of other global markets. It represents leading automotive brands and operates either a retail, or a vertically integrated retail model (i.e. exclusive distribution and retail), depending on the market.

Subsidiaries include: Maranello Concessionaires Ltd, Wadham Kenning Motors Group Ltd, Kenning Leaseline Ltd, Autobytel Ltd, Mann Egerton Vehicle Contracts Ltd

Main locations: London, Watford

UK employees: 6,592

Total employees: 14,121

Charitable donations

2007: £100,000
2006: £100,000
2005: £100,000
2003: £100,000

Community involvement

Inchcape established a corporate social Responsibility (CSR) committee in 2002. The group CSR programme is supplemented locally by a variety of sponsorships, donations and fundraising activities by individual businesses. Wherever possible, the company seeks to involve its employees and business partners in community activities.

Inchcape's head office donates to one nominated charity each year through a variety of fundraising events and employee collections.

Charity of the year: Moorfields Eye Hospital (2008).

Exclusions

Appeals which do not conform to Inchcape's policy.

Applications

In writing to the correspondent.

Corporate giving

Although the company's annual report and accounts makes reference to the page on which the amount of money given in support of charitable donations is quoted, we could not find it! However, based on the last eight years of accounts we assume the figure to be £100,000.

Inchcape Retail UK supports BEN, the motor industry benevolent fund. This support is shown through financial commitment, employee time commitment and various fundraising initiatives over the year.

Employee-led support

Employees contribute to a number of charities and trusts throughout the year that are of personal interest.

Informa plc

Company registration number 3099067

4th Floor, 27 Mortimer Street, London W1T 3JF

020 7017 5000

Website: www.informa.com

Correspondent: Community Steering Committee

Chairman: Derek Mapp

Chief Executive: Peter Rigby

Year end	Turnover	Pre-tax profit
31/12/2007	£1,129,098,000	£124,365,000

Nature of company business

Informa is an international provider of specialist information and services for the academic and scientific, professional and commercial business communities across 40 countries.

Subsidiaries include: IIR, Taylor & Francis Group

Main locations: Tunbridge Wells, Colchester, Ashford, Richmond, Byfleet, Victoria, London

Total employees: 8,740

Charitable donations

2007: £208,464
2005: £143,000
2004: £24,762
2003: £10,888

Community involvement

The company make the following statement regarding its community support: 'It is our aim to support ongoing charitable work as well as create new ways to support worthy causes. This could be through devising organisational initiatives which work in partnership with other groups or companies for mass benefit, or it could be by supporting employees with their own efforts. Our Community Steering Committee has the commendable task of developing and promoting more ways to help those around us'.

Exclusions

No support for political appeals.

Applications

In writing to the correspondent.

Information available: The company produce a corporate responsibility report.

Corporate giving

In 2007, the company made charitable donations of £208,464. We have no information regarding the beneficiaries, but believe the amount quoted may be a worldwide figure.

In kind support

The company supports the Mission to Seafarers (www.missiontoseafarers.org). Along with direct donations the company also carries the Mission's advertising free of charge.

Employee-led support

As part of the company's CR policy staff are encouraged to volunteer by, for example, participating in the Three Peaks Challenge.

Support has also been given to Book Aid, which provides books to libraries, hospitals and refugee camps and schools in over 40 countries, whilst staff worldwide contribute their time/donations to charities.

Innocent Drinks

Company registration number 5054312

Fruit Towers, 3 The Goldhawk Estate, Brakenbury Road, London W6 0BA

Website: www.innocentfoundation.org

Correspondent: Ms Ailana Kemelmacher, The Innocent Foundation

Year end	Turnover	Pre-tax profit
31/12/2006	£75,600,000	£9,200,000

Nature of company business
Production of natural fruit drinks.

Charitable donations

2006: £595,000
2005: £397,118
2004: £88,704

CRM figure: £111,000

Community involvement

The company channels its charitable donations through The Innocent Foundation (Charity Commission no. 1104289), a grant giving charity that works in partnership with community based projects and NGOs. To quote: 'Our vision is to work with local communities to create a sustainable future for people and their environment.'

The company donates 10% of profits to the foundation each year. The foundation's funding is focused on overseas projects. Please visit Innocent's website for details of current priority areas.

Exclusions

Only overseas projects are considered for support.

Applications

If you feel that you have a project that might be of interest, please contact the foundation before making a detailed proposal by filling in the short online form.

Corporate giving

In 2006, charitable donations made by the company to the foundation totalled £595,000 In turn, the foundation made donations to the following major beneficiaries: Care International – Ecuador (£42,400); Farm Africa – Tanzania (£13,500); Send a Cow (£10,000); and IDE – UK (£10,000).

Employee-led support

Payroll giving: The company operates a payroll giving scheme.

Commercially-led support

Cause-related marketing: In 2006/07, £111,000 was raised on behalf of Age Concern through the 'Big Knit'. This saw 50p donated for every Innocent drink that was sold topped with a special knitted hat.

Intercontinental Hotels Group plc

Company registration number 3203484

InterContinental Hotels Group plc, Broadwater Park, North Orbital Road, Denham, near Uxbridge, Buckinghamshire UB9 5HR

01895 512000

Website: www.ichotelsgroup.com

Correspondent: Jade Adnett, Charity Sponsorships

Chairman: David Webster

Chief Executive: Andrew Cosslett

Year end	Turnover	Pre-tax profit
31/12/2007	£863,000,000	£222,000,000

Nature of company business
Hospitality chain of hotels, soft drinks and public houses.

Subsidiaries include: Britvic Soft Drinks

Main locations: Windsor

Total employees: 10,366

Charitable donations

2007: £626,000
2005. £800,000
2003: £1,420,000

Total community contributions: £770,000

Community involvement

Intercontinental Hotels focus its charitable giving in the following five areas:

- children
- diversity
- education
- environment
- well-being.

Within this, all donations and sponsorships that the group grants must benefit communities where the company has a presence, and must enhance those communities by providing health and human services, education, arts and culture or community development initiatives.

At corporate level, the group directs all of its annual contributions to a group of carefully selected, major organisations that meet its criteria, and must decline most other requests for funding.

During 2007, the company has been looking to further align its charitable giving with its overall corporate responsibility strategy, focusing more on local community and environmental initiatives.

Exclusions

'Restrictions on giving:

- contributions are only made to organisations with verifiable charity status and those whose ethical principles are consistent with our Code of Ethics
- IHG does not support organisations that discriminate on the basis of race, religion, creed, gender, age, physical challenge or national origin. In addition, contributions generally are not provided to:
- individuals
- religious organisations
- general operating support for hospitals and health care institutions
- capital campaigns
- endowment funds
- conferences, workshops or seminars not directly related to IHG's business interests

'IHG generally does not commit to multi-year grants; only the first year of multi-year requests will be assured, but subsequent years will be dependent upon annual evaluation for future support

'IHG does not make political donations of any kind.'

Applications

In writing to the correspondent.

Please note that organisations to which the company is asked to contribute must have legal charitable status. Donations must be used for the sole benefit of the eligible institutions and are restricted to the use of the project for which the donation is being made.

Corporate giving

In 2007, the group made worldwide community contributions of £770,000 of which £626,000 was in cash donations. We do not know what proportion of this was given in the UK.

At corporate level, UNICEF is a major charitable partner of the group.

In kind support

The group makes in kind donations, such as hotel accommodation. As most of the hotels are franchised, such applications should be directed to the general managers of the individual hotels and not to the group.

Employee-led support

Employees are encouraged to give their time and skills to a variety of causes. Staff have held 'denim days' with the money raised matched by the company and donated to a charity selected at random from those nominated by the employees taking part.

Invensys plc

Company registration number 166023

Portland House, Bressenden Place, London SW1E 5BP

020 7834 3879

Website: www.invensys.com

Chairman: Martin Jay

Chief Executive: Ulf Henriksson

Year end	Turnover	Pre-tax profit
31/03/2008	£2,108,000,000	£199,000,000

Nature of company business
A leading provider of automation and controls for use in homes, offices and industry.

Subsidiaries include: Satchwell Control Systems Ltd, APV UK Ltd, Westinghouse Brake & Signal Holdongs Ltd, Eurotherm Ltd, Coutant-Lambda Ltd

Main locations: London

Total employees: 26,002

Charitable donations

2008: £200,000
2007: £300,000
2005: £100,000
2004: £300,000

Community involvement

Invensys made the following statement regarding its community investment: 'We continue to recognise the importance of our role in and relationship with communities in which we operate. Community outreach is encouraged by Invensys at the local level, where our businesses have ties with the communities where our employees work and live, and implemented by our site managers. Our businesses provide a variety of programmes such as matching gifts, sponsorships of activities and paid volunteer time that allow our employees to actively participate in community events.'

Exclusions

No support for appeals from individuals, or local appeals not in areas of company presence.

Applications

See 'Community contributions' section.

Corporate giving

In 2008, the company made worldwide cash donations to charities and community groups of £200,000 (2007: £300,000). However, as the company in the UK did not pay dividends during the year (2007: £100,000), it was decided that no donations should be made to charities here.

In kind support

'An initiative was introduced for our UK-based Rail Group employees which recognises employees consistently using 'green' options to travel to work (car sharing, walking, cycling and public transport). As a result of this initiative and in collaboration with the International Tree Foundation, 400 new trees will be planted on behalf of Westinghouse. They also continue to support local schools, providing sponsorship awards for outstanding science students.'

Employee-led support

The company's employees devote time to community fundraising projects in their local community, and receive support from the group wherever possible.

Invesco Asset Management Ltd

Company registration number 949417

30 Finsbury Square, London EC2A 1AG

020 7638 0731; Fax: 020 7065 3962

Website: www.invesco.co.uk

Correspondent: Ema Rearce, Company Secretary

Year end	Turnover	Pre-tax profit
31/12/2007	£66,169,942	£32,431,886

Nature of company business
Global investment management company.

Subsidiaries include: Perpetual Portfolio Management Ltd, INVESCO Asset Management Ltd, Perpetual Unit Trust Management Ltd, Perpetual Investment Management Services Ltd, INVESCO Private Portfolio Management Ltd, AIM, Atlantic Trust, Perpetual Investments Ltd, INVESCO UK Ltd, INVESCO Fund Managers Ltd

Main locations: London

Charitable donations

2006: £100,000
2005: £110,000
2003: £52,000

Community involvement

Invesco (previously AMVESCAP plc) seeks to support communities worldwide that are local to where its employees live and work. Help is given to various causes connected with the arts, education, the environment and sport, and may take the form of cash donations, in kind support or the provision of other resources.

Exclusions

No support for appeals from individuals or local appeals not in areas of company presence.

Applications

In writing to the correspondent.

Corporate giving

In 2006, the Invesco group of companies in the UK made charitable donations of £100,000 (2005: £110,000). We have no specific details of the beneficiaries, but understand that many charitable organisations were supported during the year, including some engaged in educational, sporting, civic and cultural activities.

In kind support

The company may provide unspecified resources to organisations.

Employee-led support

Employees are encouraged to become involved with communities local to sites of company presence.

IPC Media Ltd

Company registration number 53626

King's Reach Tower, Stamford Street, London SE1 9LS

0870 444 5000

Website: www.ipcmedia.com

Correspondent: Corporate Responsibility Manager

Chief Executive: Sylvia Auton

Year end	Turnover	Pre-tax profit
31/12/2006	£406,704,000	£98,665,000

Nature of company business
The publication of magazines.

UK employees: 2,135

Charitable donations

2006: £37,697
2005: £13,403

Membership: L B Group

Community involvement

The company states the following on its website: 'Corporate responsibility at IPC focuses mainly on the company's interaction with the wider community, in particular the local area of Southwark, and on engaging with the environmental issues that affect our industry. We highly value our employees' input and involvement, including volunteering, contributing environmental ideas, and participating in the fundraising activities of IPC's magazine and digital teams.

'We do provide ad hoc support to other charities, either by making a financial or an in kind donation. Such support is typically given to groups or organisations which are local to our offices or whose work is aligned with our key community priorities (young people, arts, education and literacy). A number of our magazines have also chosen one or more charities to support on an ongoing basis.'

Charity of the Year: British Institute for Brain Injured Children (2008).

Applications

In writing to the correspondent.

Corporate giving

In 2006, the company declared UK cash donations of £37,697 (2005: £13,403). We do not have a figure for its in kind support, but believe it may be fairly substantial.

In keeping with the company's business and its parent company's (Time Warner) focus on youth and arts education, IPC Media's major community initiative is the Schools Design Programme.

Working in association with Creative Partnerships in implementing and managing the programme, local schoolchildren in Southwark benefit from the input of IPC graphic design professionals with the objective of:

- encouraging secondary schoolchildren to view graphic design as a career option
- increasing skills development in the area of graphic design
- providing longer work placements and potential support through higher education
- influencing the skills development of teachers and the way creative arts training is provided in schools
- encouraging the participation of IPC designers in various aspects of the programme.

Towards the end of 2007, IPC developed the programme further by partnering with the London College of Communication (LCC), part of the University of the Arts. This partnership will offer students participating in the programme a range of additional benefits, including an additional week's work experience at the university and mentor support from LCC students.

In kind support

IPC Media is a key employer in the Roots & Wings Mentoring in the Community Project with which it has been involved since 1995.

IPC staff work with pupils at Northbrook School in Lewisham with the formal relationship between mentor and mentee spanning the full school year.

Employee-led support

Under the 'Volunteer Release Time' scheme, eligible employees can request up to a maximum of two days' paid time-off per year to participate in voluntary activities.

IPC staff also take part each year in the Time Warner 'Volunteer's Day', which provides the opportunity for staff to help out at a local community organisation.

ITV plc

Company registration number 4967001

200 Gray's Inn Road, London WC1X 8XZ

020 7156 6000

Website: www.itvplc.com

Correspondent: Birgitte Trafford, Communications Director
Email: responsibility@itv.com

Chairman: Michael Grade

Year end	Turnover	Pre-tax profit
31/12/2007	£2,080,000,000	£188,000,000

Nature of company business
Independent television company.

Main locations: Aberdeen, Bristol, Carlisle, Cardiff, Leeds, Southampton, Plymouth, Glasgow, Norwich, Newcastle, London, Manchester, Birmingham

UK employees: 5,700

Charitable donations

2007: £1,000,000
2006: £2,000,000
2005: £1,220,000

Total community contributions: £7,000,000
Management costs: £480,000

Membership: BitC

Community involvement

ITV's social investment programme has two strands – airtime donated to good causes, and cash donations made in support of charitable, social and environmental projects. As well as supporting the group's on-air national campaigns, ITV is active in each of its communities at regional level.

The ITV Trust (originally reliant upon Carlton Broadcasting Ltd for its income) appears to have been wound up in all but name. Income in 2006 was a mere £33 with expenditure being nil.

Applications

Applications for support from the company should be made in writing to the correspondent.

Information available: The company produces a corporate responsibility report.

Corporate giving

In 2007, the company made total community contributions of £7 million of which £1 million was in cash. Company information on its cash support is sketchy to say the least. As such, we have no details of the beneficiaries.

Employee-led support

Staff are encouraged and supported by the company in their volunteering activities.

Jaguar Cars Ltd

Company registration number 1672070

Whitley, Coventry CV3 4LF

Website: www.jaguar.co.uk

Correspondent: Les Ratcliffe, Public Affairs & Communications Manager
Email: lratclif@jaguar.com

Chief Executive: David Smith

Year end	Turnover	Pre-tax profit
31/12/2006	£1,428,000,000	(£258,000,000)

Nature of company business
The design, development, manufacture and marketing of high performance luxury saloons and specialist sports cars.

Main locations: Birmingham, Halewood, Coventry, Gaydon

UK employees: 7,583

Charitable donations

2006: £103,000
2005: £83,653
2004: £120,318
2003: £108,589

Membership: A & B, BitC

Community involvement

Following the take over of Jaguar by Tata Motors of India in June 2008, we have been unable to find out if any change in its community support policy is imminent. Furthermore, as the information contained on Jaguar's website appears to date from 2002/03, we have given a brief outline only of the company's support. We suggest you occasionally recheck the website for more up to date information.

The company gives support exclusively to local charities in areas of company presence (Birmingham, Coventry, Gaydon and Halewood – Merseyside) and charities in which a member of staff is involved. Within these geographical constraints, which are strictly adhered to, the company prefers to support organisations concerned with children and youth, education, environment/heritage, sickness/disability, social welfare and sport.

The company will support national charities if they have a local branch, or can in some way benefit the groups' employees and their families.

Charity of the Year: The company has supported the National Society for the Prevention of Cruelty to Children, the Juvenile Diabetes Research Foundation and BEN (Automotive Benevolent Fund).

Exclusions

No support is given to fundraising events, advertising in charity brochures, appeals from individuals, purely denominational (religious) appeals, large national appeals or overseas projects.

Applications

In writing to the correspondent at: Jaguar Cars Ltd, Banbury Road, Gaydon, Warwickshire CV35 0XJ (Tel: 01926 641111).

Corporate giving

In 2006, the company made donations totalling £103,000 (2005: £84,000).

In kind support

The company provides further support through gifts in kind, staff secondments, and joint promotions.

Education: The company is involved in local education-business partnerships and operates work experience schemes for pupils.

Employee-led support

The company allows employees company time off in which to volunteer and provides them with financial help in support of their charitable activities.

Payroll giving: The company operates the Jaguar Employee Charities Fund

Commercially-led support

Sponsorship: The group has a preference for prestige sports, arts and similar events. A major objective is to provide hospitality opportunities for dealers, and the group is not necessarily looking for TV exposure or press coverage. Typically, the group will spend up to £5,000 on an event sponsorship, or up to £10,000 on an exhibition. It prefers to be the sole or main sponsor.

Jardine Lloyd Thompson Group plc

Company registration number 1679424

6 Crutched Friars, London EC3N 2HP

020 7528 4444

Website: www.jltgroup.com

Correspondent: The Charity Committee

Chairman: Geoffrey Howe

Chief Executive: Dominic Burke

Year end	Pre-tax profit
31/12/2007	£95,212,000

Nature of company business
The company is a holding company of an international group of insurance broking companies and a Lloyd's members' agency.

Subsidiaries include: Agnew Higgins Pickering & Co. Ltd, JIB Group plc

Main locations: London

UK employees: 895

Total employees: 5,347

Charitable donations

2007: £267,210
2006: £388,950
2005: £462,000
2004: £430,000
2003: £246,000

Membership: BitC

Community involvement

The group charity committee consider many requests received for donations from a wide variety of local and national charities. All requests are considered carefully on their merits, but the group take particular interest in those charities that are connected to the communities local to its offices.

Jardine Lloyd Thompson Group has a special charity initiative called 'JLT Making a Difference'. This coordinates and supports staff charity activities and includes: a 'Charity Day'; staff volunteering; and matched funding.

Exclusions

No grants for fundraising events, advertising in charity brochures, appeals from individuals or large national appeals.

Applications

In writing to the correspondent. The charity committee meets four times a year.

Corporate giving

In 2007, the group made worldwide charitable donations of £267,210 (2006: £388,950). We have neither detail of the beneficiaries, nor of the amount given in the UK.

In kind support

UK staff are offered one day each year, a 'Charity Day', to help a charity or work in the local community.

In addition to the above, for example, members of staff from the London offices are encouraged to give up their lunch hours twice a week to visit the English Martyr's Roman Catholic School in Aldgate (a Lloyd's Community Programme partner) to help with IT training and support.

Employee-led support

The company will match £ for £ any amount raised by employees in fundraising activities they undertake for charity up to a maximum of £5,000). In 2007 this totalled more than £62,000.

Payroll giving: The company operates a Give as you Earn scheme. Donations under this scheme raised in excess of £25,000 for charity in 2007.

JJB Sports plc

Company registration number 1024895

Martland Park, Challenge Way, Wigan, Lancashire WN5 0LD

01942 221400; Fax: 01942 629809

Website: www.jjbcorporate.co.uk

Correspondent: Charity and Sponsorship Requests

Chairman: Roger Lane-Smith

Chief Executive: Chris Ronnie

Year end	Turnover	Pre-tax profit
27/01/2008	£811,754,000	£10,800,000

Nature of company business
The principal activity of the group is the retail of sportswear and sports equipment. The group also operates a separate leisure division which operates health clubs and indoor soccer centres.

Main locations: Aberdeen, Luton, Milton Keynes, Wrexham, Blackburn, Truro

UK employees: 12,017

Charitable donations

2008: £32,700
2007: £2,000
2005: £26,000
2004: £64,000

Community involvement

'JJB's main contribution to the community is delivered via its business activities. Our stores and health clubs play a vital role in satisfying the needs of our customers allowing the redistribution of wealth back into the community through the staff we employ and train.'

'JJB Sport's community programme provides support to nominated local and national charities and good causes. JJB also offers support to its employees who participate in chosen charity projects.'

Applications

In writing to the contact.

Corporate giving

The group made charitable donations of £32,700 during 2007/08. Beneficiaries included: Macmillan Cancer Relief, Breakthrough Breast Cancer, The British Heart Foundation and the Variety Club Sunshine Coaches.

In kind support

JJB's indoor soccer centres are available free of charge to local schools during school hours.

Employee-led support

The group lends its support to staff taking part in various charitable fundraising activities.

For example, management and staff from JJB's Golf department have for several years organised an annual charity golf tournament on behalf of the Variety Club of Great Britain. The monies raised from the 2007 event totalled to £60,000, being sufficient to purchase 4 Sunshine coaches to add to the 31 coaches already purchased from the proceeds of earlier year's tournaments.

Commercially-led support

Sponsorship: *health* – The group participates in the Macmillan Cancer Relief football badge campaign and has raised over £1.2 million through JJB since the campaign began in 1999.

During the 52 weeks to 27 January 2008, £20,000 has been raised through the sale of BHF locker tokens within JJB's fitness clubs.

S C Johnson Ltd

Company registration number 4166155

Frimley Green, Camberley, Surrey GU15 5AJ

01276 852000; Fax: 01276 852412

Website: www.scjohnson.co.uk

Correspondent: Natalie Bandtock, The Johnson Wax Ltd Charitable Trust
Email: givinguk@scj.com

Year end	Turnover	Pre-tax profit
30/06/2007	£130,989,000	(£3,404,000)

Nature of company business
The company manufactures and markets waxes, polishes and cleaning products for the consumer and industrial markets.

Main locations: Frimley Green, Egham

UK employees: 72

Charitable donations

2007: £317,000
2006: £319,779
2005: £178,000
2004: £180,000
2003: £210,000

Community involvement

'SC Johnson [is] helping to make our local community a better place to be by giving time and funding to support the local NHS Trust, build partnerships with local schools, help those who need support in their every day lives. The company's 'Giving Back' programme is about giving something back to the communities where we operate and in the UK we focus on health, education, environment, local community, arts, and sports for people with disabilities.'

Most contributions are directed towards the local communities around its two sites at Frimley Green and Egham, where the majority of its employees and their families live. Smaller amounts go to UK-wide programmes. Donations are generally made through the company's charitable trust – The Johnson Wax Ltd Charitable Trust (Charity Commission no. 200332).

Exclusions

A request falls outside of SC Johnson's corporate guidelines if it:
- benefits a single individual
- is an individual raising money for a charity
- is for another country
- is for attendance at a charity dinner, conference and so on
- is samples for gift bags or other marketing uses
- is payroll giving
- is in conflict with the interests of the company
- duplicates the services of another organisation or project already existing in the community
- duplicates a previous donation made within 12 months.

Applications

In writing to the correspondent.

Corporate giving

Although the company's annual report and accounts for 2007 makes no mention of its charitable donations, the report for the trust states that its primary source of income is derived from donations from the S C Johnson group of UK companies. In 2007, the trust received £317,000 (2006: £319,779) from the group.

The Johnson Wax Ltd Charitable Trust

Donations made by the trust in 2006/07 totalled £293,000 (2005/06: £327,045) and were broken down as follows: arts and sports £15,461 (2006: £92,846); employee matching scheme £18,137 (2006: £9,456): health related charities £29,709 (2006: £54,110); environment £39,095 (2006: £12,340); education £53,491 (2006: £47,097); June Community Day £55,396 (2006: £33,594); and local community £81,943 (2006: £70,848).

In kind support

Product donations are made, usually in the form of vouchers.

Employee-led support

As a company, SC Johnson encourages its employees to volunteer their time and talents to charities and not-for-profit organisations. Over the years we have contributed tens of thousands of volunteer hours in local effort around the world to help make people's lives better. Here in the UK we have three schemes that recognise these voluntary activities:

- 'employee matching – the Johnson Wax Charitable Trust will match employees fundraising activities £ for £ up to £500 when they volunteer their personal time and raise funds for a charity or not-for-profit organisation
- 'Pounds for Participating' – an award of £300 paid to a charity or not-for-profit organisation where an employee has given their personal time in sustained voluntary work of 25 hours or more. The organisation benefits twice, once from the contribution of time and secondly from this monetary award
- 'Samuel C Johnson Community Service Awards – named after the late chairman Sam Johnson, the top award of £3,000 is paid to a charity or not-for-profit organisation where an SC Johnson person has made a significant contribution through their voluntary work in community service. There are up to 3 additional 'specially recognised' awards of £500 for a charity or not-for-profit organisation where SC Johnson people have made noteworthy contributions.'

Additionally, once a year, for a day in June, the company closes down as much of the business as possible to give its employees the opportunity to volunteer for work on local community projects. For example, recently, approximately 180 volunteers worked at local schools to help create outdoor classrooms and improve outdoor and indoor areas for local children.

Commercially-led support

Sponsorship: *Arts/Sports* – SC Johnson has a long tradition in supporting arts and sports for people with disabilities in the UK. Alongside its support for national organisations, it also offers help to smaller organisations. Here are a few examples of past sponsorships:

- Stopgap Dance Company, Farnham – handicapped dance group
- First Bagshot Scout Group, Bagshot – money for new tables and benches

- CP Sport England and Wales – Helping people with cerebral palsy fulfil their sporting potential. Seeking funding to fund the SE Regional Boccia championships to be held at Farnborough leisure Centre on 2/3 February
- Surrey Heath Arts Council – organisation of 'Surrey Heath Young Musician of 2008'.

Johnson Matthey plc

Company registration number 33774

40–42 Hatton Garden, London EC1N 8EE

020 7269 8400; Fax: 020 7269 8466

Website: www.matthey.com

Correspondent: Madeka Panchoo, Corporate Communications Officer
Email: madeka.panchoo@matthey.com

Chairman: Sir John Banham

Chief Executive: N A P Carson

Year end	Turnover	Pre-tax profit
31/03/2007	£6,152,000,000	£242,600,000

Nature of company business
Johnson Matthey is a chemicals company focused on its core skills in catalysts, precious metals, fine chemicals and process technology.

Subsidiaries include: Cascade Biochem Ltd, Avocado Research Chemicals Ltd

Main locations: Enfield, Fenton, Hanley, Clitheroe, Cambridge, Newcastle upon Tyne, London, Heysham, Wallsend, Swindon, Royston, Sheffield, Reading

UK employees: 7,800

Total employees: 7,986

Charitable donations
2007: £282,000
2006: £330,000
2005: £340,000
2004: £279,000
2003: £323,000
Membership: BitC

Community involvement

Johnson Matthey has a long history of support for charitable causes aligned to issues to which the Johnson Matthey business makes a contribution and issues on which employees are passionate.

'The company's active and wide ranging donations programme encompasses medical research, education, care for the disabled and young people's charities as well as a number of worldwide community action programmes.

'Many employees contribute their own time, effort and money to support local community projects and annually, Johnson Matthey adopts a Charity of the Year which provides a focus for staff support and fundraising. Our Charity of the Year partnership commences in August each year.'

There is a trust associated with the company (Johnson Matthey plc Educational Trust – Charity Commission no.

313576), but this only gives support to the off-spring of and retired employees.

Charity of the Year: EveryChild (2007/08).

Exclusions

No support for advertising in charity brochures, appeals from individuals, political appeals or religious appeals.

Applications

In writing to the correspondent. A donations committee meets quarterly.

Note: Charitable donating is reviewed in March each year to set the programme for the following financial year, beginning in April. Please check for details of current areas of support.

Corporate giving

In 2006/07, the company donated £330,000 to charitable causes worldwide. Of this, £282,000 was donated in the UK to various beneficiaries including: Royal London Society of the Blind; Science Museum; English Heritage; and Generating Genius.

In kind support

Enterprise: The company has supported enterprise agencies in the past. It is also a primary supporter of the Prince of Wales Business Leaders Forum.

Employee-led support

The company has an employee volunteering scheme and allow employees time off in which to volunteer. Employee fundraising on behalf of the 'charity of the year' is matched in full by the company.

In 2006/07, staff raised £33,000 on behalf of the then 'Charity of the Year', Help the Aged.

Commercially-led support

Sponsorship: *The arts* – The company's arts programme has included sponsorship of Glyndebourne Festival Opera, Monteverdi Trust, National Gallery and Royal Opera House.

Johnson Service Group plc

Company registration number 523335

Johnson House, Abbots Park, Monks Way, Preston Brook, Cheshire WA7 3GH

01928 704 600; Fax: 01928 704 620

Website: www.johnsonplc.com

Correspondent: c/o The Donations Committee

Email: enquiries@johnsonplc.com

Chairman: Simon Sherrrard

Chief Executive: John Talbot

Year end	Turnover	Pre-tax profit
03/12/2007	£365,000,000	(£52,400,000)

Nature of company business
The company is principally engaged in textile rental, dry cleaning and facilities management.

Subsidiaries include: CCM Ltd, Hospitality Services, Workplace Management

Main locations: Bootle

UK employees: 7,330

Charitable donations

2007: £75,000
2006: £58,600
2005: £41,000
2003: £37,902
CRM figure: £19,000

Community involvement

Previously the company has informed us that charitable donations are largely arranged at local level through operating subsidiaries. Preference is given to charities in the fields of children and youth, social welfare, environment and heritage.

In September 2008 the company's website stated: 'The Johnson Service Group is acutely aware of its responsibilities to the communities in which it operates, and from which both its customers and employees are drawn. We are committed to progressively embedding Corporate Social Responsibility best practice into every aspect of our operations. The Group and its individual operating companies seek to be good neighbours, and work in partnership with our people to help their local communities.'

Exclusions

No support for circular appeals, appeals from individuals, religious appeals, local appeals not in areas of company presence, large national appeals or overseas projects.

Applications

In writing to the correspondent.

Corporate giving

In 2007, the group made charitable donations totalling £75,000. A further £19,000 was donated to its major charitable partner, Macmillan Cancer Relief, as a result of the return and re-use of clothes hangers. Other contributions are mainly made to local charities serving the communities in which the group operates.

There is a grant-making trust (The Johnson Group Cleaners' Charity) administered from the same address as the company. It receives most of its income from dividends on shares in the company, but does not appear to receive direct donations. It restricts its giving to the Merseyside area and to local registered charities dedicated to improving the well-being of the sick and the underprivileged. Further details can be found in *A Guide to Local Trusts in the North of England* published by DSC.

Commercially-led support

Cause-related marketing: £19,000 was donated to the company's major charitable partner, Macmillan Cancer Relief, as a result of the return and re-use of clothes hangers.

Johnston Press plc

Company registration number SC015382

53 Manor Place, Edinburgh EH3 7EG

0131 225 3361; Fax: 0131 225 4580

Website: www.johnstonpress.co.uk

Correspondent: PA to the Chief Executive

Chairman: R G Parry

Chief Executive: T J Bowlder

Year end	Turnover	Pre-tax profit
31/12/2007	£607,504,000	£124,704,000

Nature of company business
Newspaper publishers.

UK employees: 32

Charitable donations
2007: £136,000
2006: £133,000

Total community contributions: £1,936,000

Community involvement

Johnston Press made the following statement regarding its community support: 'Our aim is to serve local communities by meeting their needs for local news, information and advertising services through a range of media including print and digital channels which together achieve unparalleled levels of market reach.'

'Community

'Readers rely on local newspapers being at the heart of their communities – breaking major stories, campaigning on a wide variety of issues and spearheading fundraising initiatives. Johnston Press titles – together with their websites – are at the heart of local affairs, representing the interests of their local communities and acting as a catalyst for hundreds of charity campaigns.'

Applications

In writing to the correspondent.

Corporate giving

In 2007, the company made charitable donations of £136,000 (2006: £133,000). Although there are extensive examples in the annual report of various fundraising campaigns Johnston Press has been involved in promoting, there were no specific details of where the company's donations went.

However, this support facilitated the raising of £3.6 million on behalf of various charities. Furthermore, the company has given free advertising space to community and environmental campaigns to the value of £1.5 million and discounts to charity advertisers of £300,000.

In kind support

Through its various newspapers the company provides free space and discounted advertising to charitable organisations.

Jones Lang LaSalle Ltd

Company registration number 1188567

22 Hanover Square, London W1A 2BN

020 7493 6040; Fax: 020 7408 0220

Website: www.joneslanglasalle.co.uk

Correspondent: (see applications section)

Chairman (England): John Stephen

Chairman (Scotland): Andy Irvine

Managing Director (Scotland): Alan Robertson

Year end	Turnover	Pre-tax profit
31/12/2006	£134,912,000	(£2,911,000)

Nature of company business
Provision of real estate consultancy services.

Main locations: Edinburgh, Glasgow, Leeds, London, Manchester, Norwich, Birmingham

UK employees: 947

Charitable donations
2006: £30,258
2005: £5,757

Membership: BitC

Community involvement

The company has previously stated: 'Jones Lang LaSalle and its employees provide generous financial and other support to many worthwhile community programmes.' Areas of support included children's causes, education, older people's organisations, vocational training, environmental and heritage concerns, medical research, science, welfare, disability and sports. It has offices in Birmingham, Edinburgh, Glasgow, Leeds, Manchester, and Norwich and across London and it is likely that preference will be given to these areas.

Exclusions

No grants for: animal welfare; the arts; overseas projects; religious or political work; or for the benefit of one individual.

Applications

Contact your nearest office for further information.

Corporate giving

In 2006, the company declared charitable donations of £30,258 (2005: £5,757). We have no details of the beneficiaries.

Employee-led support

Payroll giving: The company participates in the Gift Aid Give As You Earn scheme.

Kaupthing Singer & Friedlander Ltd

Company registration number 970842

One Hanover Street, London W1S 1AX

020 3205 5000; Fax: 020 3205 5001

Website: www.kaupthingsingers.co.uk

Correspondent: David Griffiths, Personnel Director

Chairman: S Einarsson

Chief Executive: A Thorvaldsson

Year end	Pre-tax profit
31/12/2007	£56,676,000

Nature of company business
The group companies are involved in merchant banking, investment banking, stockbroking, investment management and property investment.

Subsidiaries include: Hillgrove Developments Ltd, Peninsular Park Developments Ltd, Gilbert Estates Ltd, Quinarius Investments Ltd, Collins Stewart Ltd, Straker Brothers Ltd, Ancomass Ltd, Sinjul Investments Ltd, Peaston Emerson's Green Ltd, Rowan & Co. Ltd, Sharepart Ltd, Millwalk Ltd

Main locations: London, Birmingham, Dorking, Isle of Man, Glasgow

UK employees: 649

Charitable donations

2007: £98,275
2006: £86,780
2005: £52,445
2004: £75,000
2003: £60,000

Membership: BitC

Community involvement

The following statement is taken from the company's website: 'On 8 October 2008 the High Court made an Administration Order in relation to Kaupthing Singer and Friedlander Ltd. Kaupthing Singer and Friedlander Ltd (KS&F) has not ceased to trade. The administration is necessary because of KS&F's financial position and to ensure that it can continue to operate, and to ensure the best interests of customers and creditors are served.'

In view of this, we cannot say with any certainty what the company's future support for charities, if any, will be. We therefore repeat (with updated figures) the previous information we received.

Previously the company had stated that: 'We actively contribute to the well being of the community by seeking to cater for the needs of all groups. We support social, medical, cultural and educational projects that place particular emphasis on supporting the under-privileged within society.'

Exclusions

No support for local appeals not in areas of company presence.

Applications

In writing to the correspondent.

Corporate giving

In 2007, charitable donations totalled £98,275 (2006: £86,780). We have no details of the beneficiaries.

Employee-led support

Employees are encourages to submit requests for support in which they are involved.

Kelda Group plc

Company registration number 2366682

Western House, Halifax Road, Bradford BD6 2LZ

01274 691111; Fax: 01274 372863

Website: csr.keldagroup.com

Correspondent: Anne Reed, Community Affairs Manager
01274 692515; Fax: 01274 372836
Email: anne.reed@yorkshirewater.co.uk

Chairman: John Napier

Chief Executive/Managing Director: Kevin Whiteman

Year end	Turnover	Pre-tax profit
31/03/2007	£878,900,000	£241,200,000

Nature of company business
The principal activities of the group are the supply of clean water and the treatment and disposal of waste water.

Subsidiaries include: Ridings Insurance Co. Ltd, 3C Waste, WasteNotts Ltd, Arbre Energy Ltd, Yorkshire Environmental Solutions Ltd, Derbyshire Waste Ltd, BDR Waste Disposal Ltd

Main locations: Bradford

UK employees: 3,259

Total employees: 3,259

Charitable donations

2007: £35,000
2006: £500,000
2005: £500,000
2004: £500,000
2003: £600,000

Total community contributions: £600,000

Membership: A & B, BitC

Community involvement

Kelda Group provided the following statement (abridged) regarding its community support:

'The Kelda Group has an extensive community support programme in place. Company policy has moved away from financial donations and towards volunteering, skills sharing and mentoring, because we believe [these] provide more benefits in terms of building good community relations and staff development opportunities.

'We have a large volunteering programme and, as a formal aspiration of our company vision, aim to be a national role model for volunteering by 2010. [Currently], 38% of our workforce is involved in in-house volunteering programmes.'

The group also funds an independent Yorkshire Water Community Trust (Charity Commission no. 1047923). This trust writes off the water bills of individuals who do not have the means to pay for the services and does not support organisations.

Applications

In writing to the correspondent.

Information available: The company produce a corporate social responsibility report which is downloadable from its website.

Corporate giving

Direct cash grants are no longer given by the group in response to external appeals. The only direct financial support provided by the group is through matched funding of employees fundraising efforts on behalf of WaterAid (to a maximum of £10,000 a year) and WaterWheelers (to a maximum of £5,000 a year). A donation of £20,000 was also made to SwimCare – an initiative to help key stage 2 pupils across Yorkshire to learn to swim.

In 2006/07, community contributions totalled £635,000 (including the above cash donations). Reference is made on the group's website to the value of employee time given over to voluntary work (£144,000), but this has not been included in the figures published by Kelda.

In addition to those beneficiaries already mentioned, support was also given to Cancer Research, Children in Need and Comic Relief.

In kind support

Through in-house volunteering programmes, opportunities exist for staff to take part in: Cares Challenges; GCSE mentoring; primary school mentoring; Halifax Rugby After School Club; Right to Read; Science & Engineering Ambassadors; WaterWheelers; Leeds United Learning Centre; Numbers partners; and Business Bridge mentoring.

One Million Green Fingers – 'Launched in September 2007 to coincide with the government's Year of Food and Farming in Education, the campaign will see the creation of sustainable gardens and allotments in primary schools across the Yorkshire region. The campaign is designed to educate children in an engaging way on a range of extremely topical issues that are relevant to our business and people's everyday lives, such as: sustainability, the environment, healthy eating, where food comes from, climate change, water conservation, and good citizenship. Over the next three years our volunteers are aiming to work with children at 350 schools to achieve One Million Green Fingers!'

Cares at Christmas – This initiative involves employees donating unwanted toys and gifts for distribution throughout the region to groups of deprived individuals.

Employee-led support

Employees are allowed time off in which to volunteer. The company matches employee fundraising to a maximum of £10,000 a year in respect of WaterAid, a charity which works to provide clean water and sanitation in the under-developed world.

Yorkshire Water employees have founded their own group, WaterWheelers, which organises fundraising events with the

income donated to local organisations. The fundraising effort is matched by the company, to a maximum of £5,000 a year.

Further information on the company's employee volunteering programme is available on request, or by visiting the community pages of Yorkshire Water's website at: www.yorkshirewater.co.uk

Payroll giving: The Give As You Earn scheme is in operation.

Kellogg Company of Great Britain

Company registration number 199171

The Kellogg Building, Talbot Road, Manchester M16 0PU

0161 869 2000

Website: www.kelloggs.co.uk

Correspondent: Community & Public Affairs Director, Community Affairs Team 0161 869 2226; Fax: 0161 869 2246 Email: communityaffairs@kellogg.com

Year end	Turnover	Pre-tax profit
31/12/2005	£833,074,000	£63,437,000

Nature of company business
The principal activity of the group is the manufacture, marketing and sale of cereal-based food products.

Main locations: Wrexham, Manchester

UK employees: 2,230

Charitable donations

2005: £548,000
2004: £449,000
2003: £432,132

Total community contributions: £804,000

Community involvement

The company focuses its resources, on local, regional and national organisations that are working in partnership with others to improve the quality of life for those at greatest disadvantage. Details of the company's partnerships and their joint achievements can be found on their website. The Kellogg's Community Affairs programme is primarily delivered by the Community Affairs Team, based at the UK and European Headquarters in Trafford, Manchester.

The company is committed to involvement in the communities in which it operates, recognising this as an important element of good corporate citizenship. The focus of its community involvement programme is mainly the areas around its manufacturing sites in Trafford Park and Wrexham, and its European headquarters in Old Trafford, Manchester. The communities of Old Trafford, Moss Side and Hulme, Wythenshawe and Wrexham are the principal beneficiaries of its local commitment.

Kellogg's Active Living Community Fund makes small donations to support activities, projects and organisations that actually promote sustained low cost participation in physical exercise for those people who need it most. A panel of Kellogg employees meets every month to assess applications for funding. The fund is not intended to support the running costs of existing sports clubs or to pay for resources where the panel consider it is the responsibility of statutory providers to pay for those resources. The fund will not support projects or activities that aim to promote sporting excellence.

Exclusions

Donations will not normally be given to circular appeals, advertising in charity brochures, animal welfare, appeals from individuals, the arts, fundraising events, medical research, overseas projects, political appeals, religious appeals, or science/technology.

Applications

All applications for support should be addressed to the Kellogg Community Affairs Team at the Talbot Road offices. Applications should be in writing either by email or post. Applications should include the following:

- a brief description of your organisation
- a brief description of how you would spend the donation
- who the donation will benefit, e.g. teenagers, disabled people, elderly people
- where the beneficiaries live, e.g. Manchester, Wrexham or, if applicable, a specific location such as Old Trafford
- who the cheque should be payable to.

The application process for the fund is designed to be quick, simple and applicant friendly. Kellogg's have reduced the need for supporting information to an absolute minimum, and endeavour to reply to all applicants within 6 weeks. However, due to the large number of applications received, Kellogg's are unable to explain their decisions or provide feedback to unsuccessful applicants. Please refer to the website for further details and advice.

Corporate giving

We did not receive a reply from Kellogg's to our request for updated information regarding its community investment. This information had previously been available on its website, but no longer is. Furthermore, despite looking at a number of accounts at Companies House, could not find any declaration concerning its charitable donations.

We therefore repeat the previously published details.

Total community contributions in 2005, were £804,000 (2004: £1,256,000) of which cash donations accounted for £548,000 (2004: £449,000).

Although most of the larger sums of money are 'locked up' in relationships with long-term partner organisations, the company will consider new applications for support. For smaller amounts of money the company's Active Living Community Fund is open to local charities and voluntary organisations all year round.

In kind support

Kellogg's has a dedicated Community Affairs team that offers significant time and expertise to partner organisations. Although this time is largely committed to existing partnerships, the company is always happy to consider new requests for support.

Other 'in kind' support includes the expertise and time of other Kellogg's employees, access to facilities and premises, and, occasionally, surplus office equipment and furniture.

Employee-led support

The group supports charitable activities by employees in their own time. In particular, it operates an employee matching scheme where the company matches £ for £, to a maximum of £500 (or £1,000 if a group of employees participate) funds raised by employees for charities of their choice.

Commercially-led support

Sponsorship: *Sports* – Kellogg's has announced a three year, £3 million partnership with the Amateur Swimming Association (asa) to help thousands of people get active by swimming as a regular part of their lives.

The sponsorship will provide support for the following: World Swimming Championships 2008; The Kellogg's/the asa Awards scheme; Kellogg's Swim Active; and Team Kellogg's. Details on each of these are available on the company's website.

In addition to the above Kellogg's is also providing swimming activities for employees and working with the asa on developing new swimming awards.

Health – Kellogg's has been working with a community learning charity called ContinYou since 1998 to promote the benefits of breakfast clubs in schools and other community settings.

A number of awards of up to to £3,000 each are available to Breakfast Clubs, although the application date for 2008 has now passed. Please visit www.continyou.org.uk for up to date information regarding the next round.

Kingfisher plc

Company registration number 1664812

3 Sheldon Square, Paddington, London W2 6PX

020 7372 8008; Fax: 0 20 7644 1001

Website: www.kingfisher.co.uk

Correspondent: Ray Baker, Director of Social Responsibilty
Email: social.responsibility@kingfisher.com

Chairman: Peter Jackson

Chief Executive: Ian Cheshire

Year end	Turnover	Pre-tax profit
02/02/2008	£9,364,000,000	£395,000,000

Nature of company business
Kingfisher is an international home improvement business operating in markets that fit strategic criteria of attractive scale, structure and economics. Operating principally through its main retail brands B&Q, Castorama, Brico Dépôt and Screwfix, Kingfisher operates in nine countries across Europe and Asia

Subsidiaries include: B & Q plc, Chartwell Land plc, MVC Entertainment Ltd, Time Retail Finance Ltd, Superdrug Stores plc, Comet Group plc, Halcyon Finance Ltd, Entertainment UK Ltd, VCI plc

Main locations: Middlesex, London, Croydon, Eastleigh, Harrow, Hull, Hayes, Leeds

UK employees: 64,320

Charitable donations

2007: £300,000
2006: £300,000
2005: £300,000
2004: £500,000
2003: £700,000

Total community contributions: £1,500,000

Membership: BitC

Community involvement

The company's website states: 'As a rule, Kingfisher will not consider unregistered UK charities as part of its annual sponsorship programme. This is because charities registered with the Charity Commission work to a set of legal and regulatory standards and requirements which are monitored by the Commission.

'From time to time, Kingfisher may enter in an agreement with an organisation linked to a government department or statutory authority. If this is the case, any funding which we give should not be used to replace that which is provided through public funds and evidence of additional benefits to people or communities must be given.

'Kingfisher will only select a small number of charities to support via our cash fund. These will be approved by the Director of Governance and Corporate Services and/or the Director of Social Responsibility and will be reviewed on an annual basis (Kingfisher financial year) to ensure a broad range of charities and issues are taken into account.

'Kingfisher also supports a selection of charities through its corporate centre fundraising activities. These charities are agreed by the Fundraising Committee (comprising representatives from Social Responsibility, HR & Communications) and are reviewed on an annual basis (Kingfisher financial year) to ensure a broad range of charities and issues are taken into account.

'The only exceptions to this annual review are Poppy Appeal, Children in Need and Comic Relief which are ongoing appeals. Kingfisher Communications also coordinates one-off fundraising activities e.g. for relief for victims of the Tsunami'.

In 2007/08, Kingfisher chose the following organisations as its 'charity partners': Save the Children; Motivation; Action for Blind People; and Community Payback.

B&Q

In addition to Kingfisher's giving, its operating companies have their own charity policies and nominated charities. For more information on B&Q UK's charity policies and nominated charities please visit the B&Q UK website www.diy.co.uk).

Exclusions

As policy, the company will not support the following:

- charity advertising space, unless specifically linked to a Kingfisher-funded project
- arts projects
- expeditions, overseas trips or adventure experiences for individuals
- support for political parties or political causes
- promotion of specific religious ideas or views
- support for religious bodies, except where the project is for the benefit of the general public and wider community

- year end deficits
- support for, or personal appeals by or on behalf of, individuals
- a charity's core costs, including buildings, salaries general running or management costs
- individual overseas projects not linked to Kingfisher's current partners
- anything that would replace funds provided by government or statutory authorities, and that does not bring additional benefits to people or communities.

Applications

In writing to the correspondent.

B&Q

The One Planet Living Grant is for local organisations to apply directly to their local B&Q store. For more information visit the relevant page on the company's website.

The One Planet Living Awards are launched every January. For more information visit www.diy.com/awards

Corporate giving

In 2007/08, community contributions totalled £1.4 million, including £300,000 given in cash donations.

B&Q

Donations policy: B&Q do not make cash donations, but instead operate a 'Better Neighbour Grant Scheme'. In 2008 the scheme was re-launched as the B&Q One Planet Living Grants.

The One Planet Living Grants

These offer between £50 and £500 of B&Q materials for projects supporting at least one of the following themes – environment/energy saving, natural habitats/wildlife and local culture/heritage.

Each store has a 'limited' budget and may not always be able to offer help should their budget be exhausted.

B&Q One Planet Living Awards

The OPL Awards allow community-based projects to secure up to £10,000 of B&Q products across the UK and Ireland. Projects need to demonstrate how their activities will support one of the following themes: environment/energy saving, natural habitats/wildlife and local culture/heritage.

In kind support

Kingfisher provides a voucher scheme which is designed to support small requests from local charities and community organisations e.g. requests for raffle prizes.

Employee-led support

Kingfisher offers various schemes to support personal fundraising. Employees may be involved in personal fundraising activities for charities that do not meet the company guidelines for the charities that it will support.

Volunteering – from February 2007, Kingfisher will allow corporate centre employees to spend one paid day per year volunteering for a charitable organisation.

Through the 'Double It' matched funding scheme, money that Kingfisher employees raise for a charity or good cause can potentially be matched pound for pound by Kingfisher, up to £500.

Payroll giving: Employees can choose to contribute to charities of their choice through a pay roll giving scheme.

Employees nominate an amount of money to be taken directly from their salary each month, tax free, and paid to their chosen charity.

Kodak Ltd

Company registration number 59535

Hemel One, Boundary Way, Hemel Hempstead, Hertfordshire HP2 7YU

01442 261122; Fax: 01442 240609

Website: www.kodak.co.uk

Correspondent: Kodak Sponsorship Department, Corporate Public Relations
Email: gb-sponsorship@kodak.com

Chairman and Managing Director: Julian Baust

Year end	Turnover	Pre-tax profit
31/12/2006	£173,900,000	£27,300,000

Nature of company business
Principal activities are the manufacture, supply and distribution of photographic film, paper, chemicals, digital imaging equipment, together with services associated with these activities. The company is a wholly owned subsidiary of the Eastman Kodak Company.

Subsidiaries include: Miller Bros Hall & Co. Ltd, Cinesite Ltd, Taylors Developing & Printing Works Ltd

Main locations: Hemel Hempstead, Harrow

UK employees: 1,681

Charitable donations

2006: £73,154
2005: £141,936
2004: £90,707
2003: £210,195

Community involvement

The Directors' Report contained in the 2006 annual report and accounts states: 'Kodak Ltd and our parent company Eastman Kodak Company, has always taken an active stance in its approach to charitable programmes and local community support and involvement.

'As well as a major corporate contributor to UNICEF (Save the Children), Breakthrough Cancer and The Prince's Trust, Kodak also supports a wide number of local community programmes and charities.. ... Kodak Ltd is a member of 'Business in the Community' ... Through this involvement we hope to develop and strengthen our community support programmes even further with greater direct involvement with local communities, not only through direct financial support, but through employee volunteer programmes and effective links with local education and school programmes.'

Exclusions

Kodak does not support advertising in charity brochures, purely denominational appeals, large national appeals, purely local appeals not in areas of company presence, appeals from individuals, overseas projects or circulars.

Applications

All appeals (charity, education or sponsorship) should be addressed to the correspondent.

Advice to applicants: The company welcomes appeals from charities, but it is receiving a large amount of mail. Applicants should therefore take note of the main areas of interest of the company as stated above.

Corporate giving

Charitable donations including those for scientific educational and research purposes in the UK in 2006 were £73,154 (2005: £141,936). Organisations supported by Kodak include: UNICEF; national Museum of Photography, Film and Television; Royal Photographic Society; Breakthrough Breast Cancer; Hope for Children; and The Prince's Trust.

In kind support

Kodak may donate products for raffle prizes, provide the use of premises for meetings, or help with graphic reproduction. It has helped UNICEF by donating a range of services including co-branding of picture CD packing and processing envelopes, on-line Christmas card collaboration and photo magic card initiatives.

Education: The office in Harrow coordinates a numberr of research fellowships each year, supporting individuals financially for three years during their PhD studies as well as collaborating between the university staff and group scientists and allowing the beneficiaries to present the results of their studies to the company's research and development centre.

Employee-led support

Employees are encouraged to fundraise on behalf of charities.

Commercially-led support

The company has sponsored Breakthrough Breast Cancer's Breakthrough £1,000 Challenge for a number of years. The event challenges individuals, groups and teams to raise £1,000 for the organisation's work a challenge which has been accepted by many of the company's employees.

KPMG LLP

Company registration number 3513178

Salisbury Square House, 8 Salisbury Square, London EC4Y 8BB

020 7311 1000; Fax: 020 7311 3311

Website: www.kpmg.co.uk

Correspondent: (see 'Applications')

Chairman: John Griffiths-Jones

Chief Executive: Colin Cook

Year end	Turnover	Pre-tax profit
30/09/2007	£1,607,000,000	£447,000,000

Nature of company business
The provision of professional services through the core functions of assurance, tax, consulting and financial advisory services (covering transaction services, corporate finance, corporate recovery and forensic). Legal services are provided by Klegal, an independent law firm associated with KPMG.

Main locations: Birmingham, Bristol, Cardiff, Cambridge, Edinburgh, Gatwick, Glasgow, Ipswich, Leeds, Leicester, Milton

Keynes, Newcastle upon Tyne, Liverpool, London, Manchester, Nottingham, Preston, Plymouth, Reading, St Albans, Southampton, Stoke on Trent, Watford, Aberdeen

Total employees: 10,890

Charitable donations

2007: £1,000,000
2006: £813,000

Total community contributions: £5,700,000

Membership: A & B, BitC, L B Group

Community involvement

There are two strands to KPMG's community involvement activity, namely, employee volunteering and a programme of charitable giving. KPMG's charitable giving policy states:

'KPMG's donation policy focuses on community and environment, particularly through education, to help enhance social inclusion for individuals and communities and to support charities that maintain and enhance biodiversity. Our donations budgets are to support the volunteering of our people.'

Support is also available from the KPMG Foundation (Charity Commission no. 1086518) which was established in October 2001 with a capital sum of £10 million from KPMG. The foundation states that it is a completely separate entity to KPMG LLP but, nevertheless, does have representatives from the firm on its board of trustees. The foundation's support costs are covered by the firm.

The focus of the KPMG Foundation is on education and social projects for the disadvantaged and under privileged, with particular emphasis on unlocking the potential of children and young people, up to 30 years of age, who for primarily social reasons have not fulfilled their educational potential.

In particular, the trustees have chosen to support four very distinct groups within this broad umbrella of 'disadvantage'. Those groups are:

- refugees
- young offenders
- children and young people who have been in care
- children and young people with dyslexia/literacy difficulties.

Charity of the Year: Help the Hospices.

Exclusions

Assistance to private educational establishments, political parties, or primarily evangelical causes and campaigns is not given.

Applications

Staff Charity of the Year: The application process for the 2008–10 KPMG Staff Charity has now closed. If you would like to register your interest in receiving information on the firm's 2010–12 Staff Charity please send a email to: csr@kpmg.co.uk

Applicants need to be UK registered charities and have the capability to support a charity of the year relationship across the firm's offices in the UK.

The KPMG Foundation: The foundation is pro active in seeking projects to fund and regrets that it is not in a position to respond to unsolicited grant applications.

Only registered charities are funded.

Corporate giving

In 2007, KPMG made total community contributions in the UK of £5.7 million (2006: £4.6 million), of which around £1 million was in cash donations.

Some of the projects supported by the firm during the year include:

Education – with finance and support from KPMG, the City of London KPMG Academy will open its doors in 2009. This will be a mixed and non-denominational school, with around 170 11-year-olds due to join in its first year. The company has committed over £1 million and many hours of its time to the school.

Disadvantaged groups in the workplace – KPMG's employability programmes aim to address some of the inequalities that exist between the least advantaged groups and communities and the rest of society by closing the opportunity gap and ensuring that support reaches those who need it most. The programmes include mentoring young entrepreneurs through The Prince's Trust Business Start-up programme as well as supporting ex-homeless people and refugees back into work through providing CV and interview skills coaching sessions.

KPMG Foundation

In 2007, the foundation had an income of £2.2 million (including £1.8 million from various partners in support of 'Every Child a Reader') and made grants totalling nearly £3.4 million. This was broken down as follows:

- refugees – £229,000
- young offenders – £543,000
- children and young people who have been in care – £127,000
- children and young people with dyslexia/literacy difficulties – £2.45 million (includes £2.3 million for 'Every Child a Reader' programme.

In kind support

The firm donates PCs and other IT equipment through the national Tools for Schools programme.

From time to time, furniture and other office equipment that is surplus to requirements are made available to community organisations.

Employee-led support
Employee volunteering/giving

'Community and environmental projects are an exciting way for our people to broaden their skills. KPMG the UK firm provides the following opportunities:

- everyone has 3.5 hours of firm time each month to volunteer
- we have donation budgets to support volunteering
- we run a Give As You Earn Scheme, with all donations made to our Staff Selected Charity, matched pound for pound up to the value of £100,000
- each of our offices has a CSR forum which decides its local priorities within a clearly defined national framework.'

In 2007, 3,600 KPMG employees volunteered their time, skill and energy during the working day. This amounted to 40,000 being contributed to the support of communities.

Payroll giving: Give as you Earn is available nationally and is supported by the firm.

Commercially-led support

Sponsorship: Minimal sponsorship opportunities exist in relation to the arts and good causes.

Kraft Foods UK Ltd

Company registration number 203663

St George's House, Bayshill Road, Cheltenham, Gloucester GL50 3AE

01242 236101; Fax: 01242 512084

Website: www.kraftfoods.co.uk

Correspondent: Corporate Affairs Department

Chairman: Nick Bunker (VP UK & Ireland)

Year end	Turnover	Pre-tax profit
15/12/2007	£552,958,000	£28,368,000

Nature of company business
The principal activity of the company is food manufacture.

Main locations: Cheltenham, Banbury

UK employees: 1,447

Charitable donations

2007: £94,000
2006: £191,000
2005: £97,500

Membership: BitC

Community involvement

Through its Kraft Cares global community involvement programme, the company focuses on three main areas; fighting hunger, advancing healthy lifestyles, and environment and sustainability. In identifying programmes to support that address important local needs and fit within these three areas, Kraft is reliant upon its offices, manufacturing facilities and sales locations worldwide.

Support is also given to communities in other ways through, for example, product donations and the provision of humanitarian aid to victims of natural disasters and other crises around the world.

The company also encourages its employees to support their local communities through various involvement programmes and a matched funding scheme.

Exclusions

Kraft Cares funding cannot be used to support the following:

- for-profit organisations
- political, religious or fraternal causes. However religious organisations may be considered if they are offered to the general populations and they have established a separate non-profit entity to run the programme
- organisations with a direct affiliation with a government or political institution or political party
- to influence, gain access to, or gain preferential treatment from a government official or entity
- hosting receptions
- for business causes, such as advertising or marketing seminars

- individuals
- membership fees.

Applications

If you wish to apply for support for a school or local community project that fits Kraft's categories, please contact the corporate affairs team on 01242 284511 or email ukcorporate@krafteurope.com

Corporate giving

In 2007, Kraft made cash donations in the UK of £94,000 (2006: £191,000). We have no details of the beneficiaries.

Since September 2004, the Kraft Cares programme in the UK – health 4 schools – has been run successfully in partnership with Business in the Community. The initiative promotes a healthy diet and active play to schoolchildren in Gloucestershire by encouraging them to eat breakfast, grow and cook their own food, and take part in physical play activities. Each school receives a package of support and resources worth nearly £5,000.

In June 2006, Kraft Cares announced its support for Shape Up, a new programme developed by leading European education specialists as a direct response to the European Union (EU) Platform on Diet, Physical Activity and Health call for action on rising obesity levels in children.

The three-year project will develop, test and evaluate practical in-school and community activities to influence the determinants of a healthy and balanced growing up in 26 cities across the region. This includes helping children investigate food, nutrition and physical activity. A Shape Up Competence Centre has been established at the University of Hull, which will be in charge of developing and implementing the project in the UK.

In kind support

The company makes product donations through designated country-specific relief or charitable organisations. The level of product donations can fluctuate significantly from year to year.

Employee-led support

Employees' fundraising is matched by the company in the US, but we were unable to confirm whether this was also the case here.

Kwik-Fit Group

Company registration number 5452193

3 Hardman Square, Spinningfields, Manchester M3 3EB

Website: www.kwik-fit.com

Chairman: David Reid

Group Chief Executive: Ian Fraser

Year end	Turnover	Pre-tax profit
31/12/2007	£857,600,000	£10,500,000

Nature of company business
The group's principal activities are: tyre, exhaust, MOT, servicing and car repair centres throughout Europe, and a financial services business in the UK.

Subsidiaries include: Apples Ltd, Ecology Tyre Collections Ltd, Tyreplus Autoservice Ltd, Superdrive Motoring Centres Ltd, Town and Country Tyre Services Ltd, Preston Paints Ltd

Main locations: Broxburn, Uddingston

Total employees: 10,192

Charitable donations

2007: £100,000
2006: £100,000
2005: £100,000
2004: £100,000
2003: £100,000

Community involvement

Kwik-Fit asked us to withdraw any information we intended publishing on its charitable support. However, we maintain our policy of including all companies relevant to our research.

The Kwik-Fit Group was acquired by PAI Partners, headquartered in France, in 2005 and is represented by four directors on the board of Speedy 1 Ltd. As the holding company of the Kwik-Fit Group, Speedy 1 Ltd's report and accounts are those we refer to here.

Previously, we have been advised that the group and its employees continue to support financially and in kind a wide range of charitable activities. In particular, there is an emphasis on initiatives that support children and young people, community development and road safety. We have neither received, nor found, any information to the contrary.

The company continues to be an active member of Scottish Business in the Community.

Exclusions

No response to circular appeals. No grants for advertising in charity brochures or appeals from individuals.

Applications

Kwik-Fit advised us that:' We are already inundated with requests for charity support and feel able to select the causes which we wish to support.'

In view of this, it would appear that any unsolicited applications the company receive are unlikely to be successful. However, if you are determined to write, we advise you NOT to send your letter to the registered office address given here. Instead, you should address it to the appropriate person at either the Broxburn office (car servicing), or the Uddingston office (insurance).

Corporate giving

In 2007, the company made charitable donations in the UK totalling £100,000 to national and local charities and community projects. During the year Kwik-Fit, along with a number of other Scottish-based companies, contributed to an ICT suite/resource library at the special needs Hollybrook Secondary School in Glasgow.

In kind support

Education: The company has been involved in many road safety initiatives, for example, 'Safer Roads for Children' programme. This includes study cards and fact sheets for schools, and a 'Kids' Code for the Road' for adults and children.

Enterprise: Activities include maintaining links with local schools, colleges and universities through Scottish Business in the Community, and acting as business advisors to students participating in the Young Enterprise Scheme.

Secondment: Employees participate in community assignments as part of their training and development, and can spend up to three months on secondment to a range of community based initiatives, through The Prince's Trust volunteers scheme. The company is also a Charter Founder Member of the Duke of Edinburgh's Award.

Employee-led support

Smaller charities also receive support from employees' commitment to the communities in which they operate.

Commercially-led support

Sponsorship: The company undertakes good cause sponsorship of local community events and competitions for local schoolchildren.

Previous examples of this are sponsorship of a local boys' football team in Beverley, a Teenage Pedestrian Road Safety Project and the Kwik Fit Charity Stadium Tour, when staff from Kwik Fit Financial Services set a target to raise £30,000 to purchase a minibus for Mavisbank School in Airdrie. The school caters for children and teenagers who have multiple disabilities and is well known for their expertise in dealing with children who are blind or have an identified visual impairment.

The company also regularly sponsor's Tyre Safety Weeks.

Ladbrokes plc

Company registration number 566221

Imperial House, Imperial Drive, Rayners Lane, Harrow, Middlesex HA2 7JW

020 8868 8899; Fax: 020 8868 8767

Website: www.ladbrokesplc.com

Correspondent: (see 'Applications')

Chairman: Sir Ian Robinson

Chief Executive: Christopher Bell

Year end	Turnover	Pre-tax profit
31/12/2007	£1,235,000,000	£344,200,000

Nature of company business
The group's principal activity is the provision of a range of betting and gaming services.

Subsidiaries include: Inter-National Hotel Services Ltd, Ladbrokes Ltd, LivingWell Health & Leisure Ltd

Main locations: Watford, Harlow

Total employees: 15,607

Charitable donations

2007: £720,000
2005: £54,000
2003: £152,000

Community involvement

It is unclear from Ladbrokes website and 2007 corporate responsibility (CR) report, just which organisations it supports and how (see 'Community contributions' section).

It was, however, a founding member of the Responsibility in Gambling Trust (RIGT) and has a significant partnership with Crimestoppers.

There is a trust associated with the company – Ladbrokes in the Community Charitable Trust (Charity Commission no. 1101804). However, according to the latest accounts at the Charity Commission, funding comes not from the company, but via the fundraising efforts of head office and shop staff, customers and 'Event Days'.

The trust seeks to support smaller local charities and groups through its countrywide network of betting shops. Its declared aims are to support causes concerned with education and training, medical/health/sickness issues, and sport and recreation.

Exclusions

No support is given to appeals for advertising in charity brochures, the arts, appeals from individuals, circular appeals, fundraising events, overseas projects, political appeals, religious appeals, or small, purely local appeals not in an area of company presence.

Applications

For Ladbrokes in the Community Charitable Trust, the procedure is to secure the support of your local shop in raising funds on behalf of your cause. Any monies raised are then banked with the trust, with consideration of additional funds being added by Ladbrokes taken by the trust's grants committee which meets every 5–6 weeks.

Corporate giving

According to its 2007 annual report and accounts Ladbrokes made charitable donations in the UK of £720,000. Its CR report, however, gives figures of £1,033,800 (total contributions by Ladbrokes – time resources given to Ladbrokes in the Community Charitable Trust) and £48,000 (total contributions in money, resources and in kind donated by Ladbrokes to all other charitable causes).

We have quoted the figure from the annual report and accounts on the grounds that this fulfils a legal requirement to disclose such information, but even so we are not confident that this is accurate.

Employee-led support

The group actively encourages its employees to undertake fundraising activities, particularly in support of Ladbrokes in the Community Charitable Trust.

Lafarge Aggregates & Concretes UK

Company registration number 297905

PO Box 7388, Granite House, Watermead Business Park, Syston, Leicester LE7 1WA

0116 264 8000; Fax: 0116 269 8348

Website: www.lafarge-aggregates.co.uk

Correspondent: Charity Advisor, Communications Department

Chairman: D M James

Year end	Turnover	Pre-tax profit
31/12/2006	£460,764,000	£16,823,000

Nature of company business
Supplier of asphalt, aggregate, concrete products and ready mixed.

Main locations: Leicester

UK employees: 1,949

Charitable donations
2007: £820,000

Membership: BitC

Community involvement

The following information was taken from the company's website in September 2008:

Lafarge in the Community

Although Lafarge is a global company, quarrying is very much a local activity and we recognise the importance of being a good neighbour, trusted business partner and employer of choice. We work hard to be actively involved in the communities close to where we operate.

Lafarge Aggregates & Concrete UK has a robust community relations programme which includes: community grants; community events; employee involvement; and education.

There are two ways local charities and community organisations can apply for grants: Lafarge charitable donations and the Landfill Communities Fund. Regarding the latter, Lafarge has produced a leaflet [downloadable from their website] to explain what the fund is and how local groups can apply for a wide range of community and environmental projects situated within 10 miles of a landfill site and close to a Lafarge Aggregates & Concrete UK operational site.

Exclusions

Local appeals not in areas of company presence.

Applications
Charitable donations programme

Charities and community organisations are encouraged to apply for a cash or materials donation. To be eligible for consideration, your organisation must be located within three miles of an operational Lafarge Aggregates & Concrete UK site or be otherwise affected by the company's operations – please contact Lafarge's charity advisor for further information. To find out which Lafarge Aggregates & Concrete UK site is nearest you, please refer to the 'Location finder' on their website.

All requests for cash or materials donations must be made in writing, with details of your organisation and/or project. If you are requesting a materials donation, please indicate the type and quantity of material, when it is needed and if you require delivery or will be collecting the material.

Lafarge endeavour to respond to all requests within 14 working days.

Corporate giving

Although Lafarge's accounts for 2006 (the latest available), did not declare any charitable donations having been made during the year, the community section of their website states that over £820,000 was donated in the UK in 2007. No figure was available regarding its in kind support which might well be substantial.

In kind support

Education: 'Lafarge Aggregates & Concrete UK is committed to developing relationships with schools close to our sites. The company also supports national education initiatives such as Enterprise Week.

'Schools and other education groups are welcome to visit Lafarge's operational sites including hard rock and sand & gravel quarries, landfill and recycling centres and Readymix plants. Tours of our head office in Leicestershire are also available. Your local Lafarge site manager is also available to speak to your class in school. Tours are dependent on weather and safety factors. To organise a visit or speaker, please contact the site manager directly. Or, contact our head office on 0116 264 8251.'

Environment: Lafarge works in partnership with a number of organisations such as wildlife trusts, national conservation organisations and local community groups on quarry restoration projects.

Employee-led support

'Lafarge encourages its employees to get involved in community activities, from speaking about geology, wildlife and biodiversity to local groups, to fundraising for local causes.

'If you'd like one of our experts to speak at your meeting or event, or would like to let us know about your fundraising activities, please contact us by writing to:

Community Involvement
Communications Department
Lafarge Aggregates & Concrete UK
PO BOX 7388
Granite House
Watermead Business Park
Syston, Leicester
LE7 1WA.'

The Laird Group plc

Company registration number 55513

100 Pall Mall, London SW1Y 5NQ

020 7468 4040; Fax: 020 7839 2921

Website: www.laird-plc.com

Correspondent: The Company Secretary

Chairman: Nigel Keen

Chief Executive: Peter Hill

Year end	Turnover	Pre-tax profit
31/12/2007	£140,300,000	£34,300,000

Nature of company business
The principal activities during the year were the design, manufacture and supply of products and services to the electronics, the residential building and the automotive industries. Prior to the year end, most of the automotive businesses were sold.

Main locations: London

UK employees: 12,297

Charitable donations
2007: £35,000
2006: £15,000
2005: £49,000
2004: £116,000
2003: £83,000

Community involvement

Laird states that the well-being of the communities in which the group operates is important to its long term development and success. In support of this, help is given to national and local charities, both financially and via in kind support. In addition to this, staff participate in fundraising events on behalf of various good causes.

Exclusions

No support for political appeals.

Applications

In writing to the correspondent.

Corporate giving

During 2007 the group gave £35,000 for charitable purposes (2006: £15,000). It supported a number of large UK charities including The Stroke Association, MacMillan Cancer Relief, CLIC Sargent and The Prince's Trust. Group businesses, many of which are long-established in their communities, supported a variety of local initiatives.

In 2007, the Laird Group plc Head Office sent electronic Seasonal Greeting cards and donated the money that would have been spent on traditional cards and their postage to SOS Children's Villages.

In kind support

Group companies support a variety of local sports teams through the provision of kit and equipment donations. They have also participated in an Annual Toys for Tots campaign through the purchasing of toys, the donation of unwanted Christmas gifts and active promotion of the regional programme which provides toys to needy families in the local community.

Enterprise support days at local schools and the provision of work experience placements are among other forms of in kind support provided by the company.

Employee-led support

In instances of major international disasters occurring, e.g. Hurricane Katrina and the Asian tsunami, money raised by employees in support of relief work has been matched by the company.

Commercially-led support

Sponsorship: *Sport* – Several group companies support a variety of local sports teams through the provision of team sponsorships.

Disability – In recent years staff at the Laird Group head office have sponsored trainee Guide Dog puppies.

Land Securities Group plc

Company registration number 4369054

5 Strand, London WC2N 5AF

020 7413 9000; Fax: 020 7925 0202

Website: www.landsecurities.com

Correspondent: Karen Saunders/Wendy Franks, CR Committee (Community)

Chairman: Alison Carnwath

Chief Executive: Francis Salway

Year end	Turnover	Pre-tax profit
31/03/2008	£1,561,200,000	£888,800,000

Nature of company business
Land Securities is the largest UK property group, involved in both property development and investment, and property outsourcing.

Subsidiaries include: Ravenside Investments Ltd, Ravenseft Properties Ltd, The City of London Real Property Co. Ltd

Main locations: Birmingham, London, Portsmouth, Sunderland, Cardiff, Gateshead, East Kilbride, Leeds, Glasgow

UK employees: 1,689

Charitable donations

2007: £487,600
2006: £559,000
2005: £580,000
2004: £804,000
2003: £774,000

Membership: A & B, BitC, L B Group

Community involvement

We were advised previously that: The group operates a sponsorship and charities committee which acts independently of the board of directors and comprises employees from each business unit. It administers a budget set by the executive directors each year. Support is generally only given for charitable work undertaken in the United Kingdom. Special consideration is also given to appeals from charities located in the areas of the UK where the group has an involvement.

However, the latest annual report and accounts (2007/08) refers to a Land Securities Foundation (not a registered charity) which arranges the company's community investment and employee volunteering. In addition to this, the company runs numerous regional grant programmes. The London Portfolio's Capital Commitment Fund, for example, is now in its third year and has supported 33 groups in Southwark and Westminster.

In general, support is directed towards the following: arts, children and young people, education, employability and enterprise.

Exclusions

No support for advertising in charity brochures, animal welfare, appeals from individuals, overseas projects, political appeals or religious appeals.

Applications

In writing to the correspondent. The charity committee meets every six weeks to choose the most suitable applications to support.

Information available: The company produces a corporate responsibility report.

Corporate giving

In 2007/08, the company made charitable donations in the UK of £487,600. SPEAR received its annual donation of £6,000. Details of other beneficiaries were unavailable.

In kind support

The group provides free floor space within its shopping centres to organisations wishing to promote their activities.

Employee-led support

The Land Securities Foundation is responsible for encouraging every employee to volunteer a minimum of one day a year in work time. It has supported 326 volunteers so far, clocking up more than 3,000 volunteering hours in total. This year (2007/08) around 20% of employees took part in projects. The company aim to have 50% of employees involved by 2010.

Some of the schemes supported by employee volunteers include:

- *enterprise* – Young Enterprise scheme launched to help young people interested in business to develop their skills and knowledge. Launched in 2008, the project is being run in London and the North West initially
- *education* – supporting literacy in schools in Tower Hamlets by buying books for their libraries and enabling more reading partners to come in and read to children
- *employability* – SPEAR mentoring programme. SPEAR is an eight-week programme for 16–24 year old unemployed people in West London. The course is run by experts in change management, education and youth work.

Employees who volunteer in their own time are encouraged to apply for matched leave. Volunteering 32 hours a year earns two additional days' leave, for example. To date 30 employees have taken a total of 45.5 days of additional leave.

Payroll giving: The Give as You Earn (GAYE) scheme is in operation. In 2007/08, Land Securities ran three GAYE promotions and increased the number of employees giving from 1% to 8.5%. This increase was boosted by the company's offer to match each employee donation with an additional 20%, up to a maximum of £5,000 per employee each year.

Lazard & Co. Ltd

Company registration number 162175

50 Stratton Street, London W1J 8LL

020 7187 2000; Fax: 020 7072 6000

Correspondent: Charities Committee

Year end	Turnover	Pre-tax profit
31/12/2005	£10,008,022,000	£76,065,000

Nature of company business
Financial advisor and asset management services.

Main locations: London

UK employees: 614

Charitable donations

2005: £140,753
2004: £224,120

Community involvement

Donations are no longer made through the Lazard Charitable Trust (Charity Commission no. 1048043) which ceased to exist as of October 2007.

We were advised that a Charitable Committee has been established to make donations to UK-registered charities which have a direct link with a member of staff. No further information is currently available.

Applications

Unsolicited applications are unlikely to succeed. Applicant charities must have a direct link with a member of staff at Lazard's in order to be considered for support.

Corporate giving

In 2005 the charity received total income of £108,908. A total of £140,753 was applied to charitable causes (92 grants).

Beneficiaries included the Amnesty International, Anna Trust, British Heart Foundation, Cystic Fibrosis Trust, English Pocket Opera Company, Habitat for Humanity, the Graham Layton Trust, Museum of London, NSPCC, National Society for Epilepsy, Royal Shakespeare Company and Universal Beneficent Society.

Sara Lee UK Holdings Ltd

Company registration number 1558575

225 Bath Road, Slough, Berkshire SL1 4AU

Website: www.saralee.com

Correspondent: The Charity Manager

Year end
31/12/2005

Nature of company business
Principal activities are: food and beverage; branded apparel; and household products. It operates in 55 countries and has nearly 150,000 employees worldwide.

Main locations: Nottingham, Worksop, Slough, Belper

Charitable donations

2005: £45,000

Community involvement

We have been unable to obtain any updated information on the company's charitable support. We repeat, therefore, the details previously published which we believe to be still valid.

The company has a structured policy for its grant making. Much information is available on the grant making activities of The Sara Lee Foundation, which provides grants around its headquarters in Chicago. The foundation's website states that grant policies outside of Chicago are at the discretion of the regional departments (presumably the UK headquarters).

Applications

In writing to the correspondent.

Corporate giving

The group donated £45,000 to charities during the year. No details were available on the size or number of grants in this year.

Leeds Building Society

Company registration number 320B

105 Albion Street, Leeds LS1 5AS

0113 216 7296; Fax: 0113 225 7549

Website: www.leedsbuildingsociety.co.uk

Correspondent: Sally Smith, Secretary of the Society's Charitable Foundation
Email: ssmith@leedsbuildingsociety.co.uk

Chairman: Robin Smith

Chief Executive: Ian Ward

Year end   Pre-tax profit
31/12/2007   £63,200,000

Nature of company business
The provision, to existing and prospective members, of residential mortgages and retail saving products.

Main locations: Leeds

Total employees: 987

Charitable donations

2007: £93,642
2006: £80,000
2005: £60,000
2003: £83,966

Community involvement

The majority of the society's charitable donations are made through the Leeds Building Society Charitable Foundation (Charity Commission no. 1074429). The following outlines the kind of projects the foundation will support.

'Generally, we will consider applications for community based projects which aim to provide relief of suffering, hardship or poverty, or their direct consequences. Some examples of the areas in which we have made donations include:
- support to homeless people;
- adults and children with physical and mental disabilities;
- older people
- underprivileged families
- deaf, blind and partially sighted people
- community projects benefiting local residents.'

'The project must operate in the area of one of our 57 branches. Church projects will be considered only where they involve community outreach and benefit, (e.g., supporting the homeless, disadvantaged families).'

Exclusions

The foundation is unlikely to make donations for:

- restoration or upgrading of buildings, including churches
- playgroups, Scout and Guide Associations
- environmental charities (unless there is a benefit to a disadvantaged community).

The foundation is unable to support:

- projects with religious, political or military purposes
- overseas charities or projects
- individuals, including sponsorship of individuals
- animal welfare projects
- medical research.

Applications

In writing to the secretary including:

- the name of your project and brief information about it
- a contact name, address and phone number
- your registered charity number
- details of what the donation would be used for
- who would benefit from it
- your nearest Leeds Building Society branch.

All applications will be acknowledged. The trustees usually meet quarterly in March, June, September and November. Following the meeting the foundation will write to you and let you know whether or not your application has been successful.

The foundation regrets that it is unable to support every application it receives and the trustees have sole discretion in the choice of projects which they wish to support. Usually the foundation is unable to consider applications if support has been provided in the last two years.

If you require further information or advice about applying, please rite to the secretary of the charitable foundation at the address above who will be happy to provide you with a copy of the foundation's current guidelines. Because the foundation operates independently of the building society, local branch staff are unable to answer questions about the foundation.

Corporate giving

In 2007, the group made charitable donations totalling nearly £94,000 of which £90,000 was paid to the foundation. Grants usually range from £250 to £1,000. Recent beneficiaries have included the 'talking newspaper' in Peterborough, the Citizens Advice Bureau in Kendal, the Motor Neurone Disease Association in Gloucestershire and a hospital radio project in Barnsley.

Commercially-led support

Cause-related marketing: The society offers a number of saver accounts to the public that are linked to a particular charity or community initiative.

The CaringSaver account offers payment by the society to three charities: Help the Aged, Save the Children and Marie Curie Cancer Care. An amount equal to 1% of the average balances in the account is divided equally between the three charities which, in 2007, totalled £44,000.

Legal & General plc

Company registration number 1417162

One Coleman Street, London EC2R 5AA

020 3124 2000

Website: www.legalandgeneralgroup.com

Correspondent: Graham Precey, Group CSR Manager
020 3124 2091

Chairman: Sir Rob Margetts

Chief Executive: Tim Breedon

Year end	Turnover	Pre-tax profit
31/12/2007	£18,202,000,000	£795,000,000

Nature of company business
The group's principal activities are: the provision of long-term insurance, investment management and general insurance.

Subsidiaries include: Arlington Business Parks Partnership, Gresham Insurance Company Ltd, Trident Componenets Group Ltd

Main locations: London, Brighton, Cardiff, Birmingham

UK employees: 9,269

Total employees: 10,067

Charitable donations

2007: £1,860,000
2006: £2,300,000
2005: £2,279,000
2004: £1,100,000
2003: £1,702,000

Total community contributions: £2,101,697
Management costs: £345,000

Membership: A & B, BitC, L B Group

Community involvement

Legal & General's policy is to provide support to three principal groups:

- a small number of national charities whose work is directly related to the group's core businesses. These are its 'Major Charitable Projects'
- charities and community groups local to its main offices
- UK employees who commit their own personal time and funds to help a local community or charity.

In addition, the company also operate a 'Young Excellence Scheme' which gives support to young people who have shown outstanding talent in a sporting or creative field.

Exclusions

Legal & General does not support animal charities, overseas based charities or international projects, religious organisations (except where it can be proven that the project is undertaken on behalf of the community as a whole) or political organisations.

Applications

Information about national charities which meet the group's guidelines should be sent to the correspondent. Appropriate local appeals should be sent to the relevant local contact.

National decisions are made by the charity committee and approved by the group board on an annual basis; local appeals are considered by individual offices. Overseas grants are handled by the subsidiary company in each country.

Corporate giving

In 2007, the company made total community contributions of £2.4 million of which £1.86 million was in cash donations. Legal & General calculated the cost of managing its community investment programme to be £345,000.

Major charitable projects supported by the company during the year, came under three headings:

- financial inclusion and education – for example, the *Money Trail Project with Age Concern* which is designed to mitigate pensioner poverty
- vulnerable community projects – for example, the *Safe Space Project* which offers a 'safe space' in a city centre church to provide support and practical assistance to intoxicated or vulnerable young people who find themselves in distress or difficulty over the Christmas period
- health and community projects – for example, *Hospice Care*.

In kind support

This can take the form of gifts in kind.

Employee-led support

Community awards scheme: Employees are encouraged to support charitable activities in their local communities. A 'Community Awards' scheme exists to recognise the good work of its employees in the community. Six winners are chosen from a list of nominees, each of whom receive £1,000 on behalf of the charity or group supported.

Community Volunteering Projects

Highlights in 2007 included the provision of staff skill, expertise and knowledge to: Beach Clean; National Museum & Galleries of Wales; The Prince's Trust Cymru Enterprise Challenge; Arts & Business Cymru Professional Development Programme; and Sussex Wildlife Trust.

In addition to the above, each year Legal & General donate to every school which has one of its employees as a governor.

Employees are entitled to Legal & General's Employee Sponsorship Matching Scheme as part of their employment package. The company match the first £750 raised per year per employee. 7.5% of its employees applied for matched funding in 2007.

Payroll giving: The company offer the Give As You Earn scheme. 12.4% of the company's employees participate in this scheme; 75% of these donations are to specific charities on a sustainable basis every month.

Employees are entitled to Legal & General's Employee Sponsorship Matching Scheme as part of their employment package. The company matches the first £750 raised per year per employee. 7.5% of Legal & General's employees applied for matched funding in 2007.

Commercially-led support

Sponsorship: *The Arts* – There is an established programme, which means it is difficult to make new commitments.

Youth/sports – The Young Excellence Sponsorship (YES) is designed to provide support for young people excelling in their chosen field whether that takes the form of sport or the arts.

Legal & General currently sponsors 21 young people as part of this scheme. It provides ongoing support designed to alleviate some of their financial worries as they pursue excellence in their chosen field.

In 2008, Legal & General were keen to support talented youngsters who are in need of financial assistance to achieve their goals in the run up to the 2012 Olympic Games.

John Lewis Partnership plc

Company registration number 238937

Partnership House, Carlisle Place, London SW1P 1BX

020 7828 1000; Fax: 020 7828 4145

Website: www.johnlewis.co.uk

Chairman: Charles Mayfield

Year end	Turnover	Pre-tax profit
26/01/2008	£6,052,200,000	£198,700,000

Nature of company business
The company trades under the name of John Lewis (department stores) and Waitrose (supermarkets).

The partnership is a retail business run on cooperative principles. All the ordinary share capital is held by a trustee – John Lewis Partnership Trust Ltd – on partners' (employees') behalf. Under irrevocable trusts the balance of profits is available to be shared among all partners after provision for prudent reserves and for interest on loans and fixed dividends on shares held outside. Management is accountable to the general body of partners, in particular through elected councils and through the partnership's journalism.

Subsidiaries include: Findlater Mackie Todd & Co. Ltd, Herbert Parkinson Ltd, Waitrose Ltd, Stead, McAlpin & Co. Ltd, J H Birtwistle & Co. Ltd

Main locations: Aberdeen, Bluewater, Watford, Welwyn Garden City, Trafford, Windsor, Norwich, Nottingham, London, Liverpool, Newcastle, Milton Keynes, Southsea, Southampton, Reading, Peterborough, Solihull, Sheffeld, Glasgow, Edinburgh, Kingston, High Wycombe, Cheadle, Bristol, Brent Cross

UK employees: 68,430

Charitable donations

2008: £2,846,361
2007: £2,599,163
2006: £2,040,000
2005: £2,080,000
2004: £1,650,000

Total community contributions: £5,112,701
Management costs: £1,078,397

Membership: BitC, L B Group

Community involvement

John Lewis's charitable giving is shaped to a significant degree by the following statement: 'As we are a partnership, it is important that we all have a say in how our collective contributions are spent, which is why partners are responsible for determining the recipients of more than 60 per cent of the total cash contributions we make.'

As such, 'The partnership favours charities in which partners are personally involved. We also like to give donations to smaller. local concerns, where we can make a real difference to our local communities. Areas we particularly support include: care for the sick and the disabled; youth and children; wildlife and conservation; care and housing for the elderly; medical research; and welfare and counselling services'.

In addition, the partnership actively encourages Waitrose and John Lewis shops to forge close links with local schools, charities and community groups.

In 2008, Waitrose introduced a new giving initiative – 'Community Matters' – which gives each branch a small, fixed sum of money to share out between three local good causes each month. Under the scheme customers nominate organisations for support, with the final nominations being decided upon by PartnerVoice Forums (Waitrose's local democratic bodies). Customers then vote for their preferred cause using the green token they are given each time they shop. The money each cause is given is directly proportional to the number of tokens (votes) they receive.

John Lewis established a 'Charity of the Year' scheme in 2007, raising money on behalf of YoungMinds.

Charity of the Year: Wallace & Gromit's Children's Foundation (2008).

Exclusions

The company does not support: individuals; religious, ethnic or political groups; third party fundraising activities; projects overseas; or the purchase of advertising space.

Applications

As the partnership's preference is now to support smaller, more local causes, qualifying applicants should contact the Community Liaison Coordinator at their nearest branch of John Lewis or Waitrose.

It is also possible to enquire about receiving support from the company by using the online 'Charity Donation Request Contact Form'. this can be found under the 'Contact us' link on their website.

Corporate giving

In 2007/08, the partnership made total community contributions of £6,191,098. This comprised: cash donations of £2,846,361; value of staff time of £1,525,332; in kind donations of £741,008; and management costs of £1,078,397.

In kind support

To mark the fiftieth anniversary of the establishment of the John Lewis business as a partnership in 2000, a £5 million trust fund was set up. Through The Golden Jubilee Trust partners are able to offer their time and expertise to good causes, while still being paid.

Secondments may last from one week to six months at projects with a clear local commitment and a specified objective. The scheme is run on a competitive basis with between 30 and 40 awards being made across the country each year.

The partnership provides additional support to charities through gifts in kind.

Employee-led support
Payroll giving: The company participates in the CAF Give as You Earn scheme.

Liberty International plc

Company registration number 1503621

40 Broadway, London SW1H 0BT

020 7960 1200; Fax: 020 7960 1333

Website: www.liberty-international.co.uk

Correspondent: Carolyn Kenyon, PA to the Chairman

Chairman: Patrick Burgess

Chief Executive: David Fischel

Year end	Turnover	Pre-tax profit
31/12/2007	£574,600,000	(£124,800,000)

Nature of company business
The principal activity is that of a property investment company. It is the leading company in the UK regional shopping centre industry.

Subsidiaries include: Portfolio Fund Management Ltd, Capital & Counties plc, Capital Shopping Centres plc

Main locations: London

UK employees: 507

Charitable donations
2007: £271,000
2006: £176,000
2005: £143,000
2003: £84,400

Total community contributions: £972,000

Community involvement

The following is taken from Liberty International's 2007 corporate responsibility report:

'We believe strongly in maintaining the bond with all generations, young and old, who regularly use our centres. Local management are encouraged to identify opportunities to work with their local community as appropriate in their area. Whilst the aims and objectives of organisations with whom we work are diverse and tackle a variety of problems across a broad spread of age groups, there is a central theme of providing support to the younger generation, especially those vulnerable members of society.

'Shopping centres are important hubs for their local communities, providing the facilities for social interaction, entertainment, trade and commerce. By forming central partnerships with national organisations, pre-eminent in their respective fields, in joint projects focused on youth, education and the prevention of anti-social behaviour. In concentrating on these three areas, we are addressing fundamental issues in modern society which are important to the long-term success of our business.

'Our contribution is provided by way of a combination of funding, provision of mall space, staff time and other support as appropriate. We assess the added value offered by each partnership before extending the initiative to other locations.'

Applications

In writing to the correspondent.

Information available: The company produces a corporate social responsibility report.

Corporate giving

In 2007, the company made total community contributions in the UK of £972,000 of which £271,000 was in cash donations. Organisations receiving support included: I CAN; the Sea Cadets; and the British Trust for Conservation Volunteers. Support was also given to a number of local community initiatives in the Covent Garden area of London.

In addition to the above, the work of many charities was supported in the group's shopping centres through the facilitation of 421 mall cash collections which raised an estimated £225,000. Some £50,000 of public donations made via fountains, Christmas grottos and so on, was also distributed by the group.

In kind support

Education: A significant part of the company's programme of supporting education involves working with the management team at The Sage Gateshead in organising 'The Big Sing'.

The programme enables children and their teachers to take part in a seven month group singing project to encourage the development of musical opportunities across the North of England. Resource materials, including a song book, are provided to the schools and musicians from The Sage Gateshead work alongside each school providing additional inspiration and guidance.

Employee-led support

In 2007, over 5,000 hours of the company's centre management time was devoted to the company's involvement with the local community. This involvement included a wide range of activities, including working with schools, both with the children and serving as school governors, assisting local community groups and contributing both time and resources to support town centre partnerships.

Eli Lilly and Company Ltd

Company registration number 284385

Lilly House, Priestley Road, Basingstoke RG24 9NL

01256 315000; Fax: 01256 315412

Website: www.lilly.co.uk

Correspondent: The Grants and Donor Administrator

General Manager: Andrew Hotchkiss

Year end	Turnover	Pre-tax profit
31/12/2007	£1,294,866,000	£182,007,000

Nature of company business
Eli Lilly & Company Ltd is a research-based corporation that develops, manufactures and markets human medicines, medical instruments, diagnostic products and agricultural products. Corporate headquarters are located in Indianapolis, USA.

Subsidiaries include: Elanco Products Ltd

Main locations: Basingstoke, Windlesham, Speke

UK employees: 2,400

Charitable donations

2007: £314,235

Community involvement

The following extract is taken from the company's website:

'Lilly UK has been reviewing its charity programme and has decided to discontinue the charity of the year scheme, replacing this with two new programmes.

'We believe these new programmes will actively encourage employee participation in fundraising and volunteering by providing employees with more choice as to how they support their charity.

'For 2008 we will be:

- Introducing a matching programme, whereby employees will be able to request a company donation to support their own chosen charities. This will include charities that are beneficiaries of both specific fundraising activities and payroll giving. We will be actively promoting our payroll giving scheme and are ambitious about the potential for expanding participation.

- Introducing a corporate volunteering initiative called Lilly's global 'Hands and Hearts'. This will involve different teams and departments within Lilly UK undertaking to carry out a specific volunteering project during 2008 that benefits a charity or their local community.'

'The decision to change our charity programme was based upon feedback from our staff and learning from what initiatives have been most successful elsewhere in the company. We are confident that the overall support that Lilly and our employees give to charitable causes will be increased following these changes.

'Lilly takes its responsibility as a major company very seriously and seeks to play an active role as a good citizen in the community in which it operates. As part of this approach, Lilly works in partnership with patient groups to provide funding to help with running costs or to work on specific programmes which benefit patients.

'In addition, at each of its three key locations (Basingstoke, Speke and Windlesham) the company operates a strong community relations programme, including working with local schools, enterprise and employee fundraising initiatives.

'The needs of the local communities around Lilly's UK sites vary enormously and the company seeks to be as responsive as possible. Each site runs a donations committee that assesses project and specific requests and in any 12 months up to 50 projects are initiated around the Lilly UK sites.'

Note: As at November 2008, details of the company's promised new 'Grants & Donations' procedure and forms for national applicants were unavailable. Please contact the correspondent for further information.

The Lilly Outstanding Achievement in Mental Health Awards

Now in their eighth year, the awards are designed to recognise and reward those people who help to 'breakdown misunderstanding and stigma and reintegrate individuals with severe mental illness into the community'. Any individual or team involved in developing and implementing activities and best practice designed to achieve community reintegration can apply.

▷ The Lilly Reintegration Award: entries are judged on their simplicity, innovation and how easily they could be replicated. The winner wins a Certificate of Excellence and a grant of £5,000 to invest in their winning project. Two runner-up entries win a Certificate of Achievement and grant of £2,000.

▷ Lilly Moving Life Forward Award: any individual who has suffered from severe mental illness can enter. The winner received a Certificate of Excellence and vouchers of their choice worth £500.

Patient group relationships

Lilly UK is committed to partnering with patient advocacy groups for the benefit of patients and in a way that is true to the ABPI Code of Practice and Lilly's policy.

Lilly UK has agreed with patient advocacy groups that it will make public the scope of its partnerships in the UK in order to increase transparency. This includes stating the amount of funding that Lilly provides (see 'Community contributions').

Full details of the policy pertaining to patient group relationships are available on the company's website.

Exclusions

No support for individuals, endowments, debt reduction, religious or political appeals, fraternal or veteran organisations, beauty or talent contests, fundraising activities related to individual sponsorship, conferences or media productions, non-accredited educational groups, memorials and local appeals not in areas of company presence.

Applications

Applications from national charities should be addressed to the correspondent. Applications from local charities should be addressed to 'The Secretary, Local Grants Committee', at the relevant operating unit (Basingstoke, Speke or Windlesham).

Patient group relationships: Ongoing relationships with patient groups are the responsibility of Lilly's Corporate Affairs department.

Unsolicited requests for support from patient groups are considered by the Lilly Grants Committee, details of which can be found on www.lilly.co.uk in the section called 'Making a difference'.

In addition, unsolicited requests for support from patient groups may be received at a regional level. Lilly's regional Corporate Affairs Managers are responsible for drawing up the 'Written agreement', details of which can be found on www.lilly.co.uk also in the section called 'Making a difference'.

Information available: The company produce a downloadable pdf document entitled: 'Lilly in the Community'.

Corporate giving

Although the company's 2007 annual report and accounts does not declare a charitable donations figure, from the grants quoted on its website financial support came to around £314,235. These grants were given through three separate avenues – Partner group relationships, Lilly grants committee and the United Way programme.

A complete list of the beneficiaries is include on the company's website under 'Making a difference' > 'Patient group relationships'.

In kind support

Education: Initiatives include involvement in local education/ business partnerships and the provision of work experience schemes for pupils and teachers, and educational materials for schools. In Speke, for example, it worked with other local businesses to create the country's first Partnership for Learning Centre.

Enterprise: Lilly supports the Young Enterprise 'Company Programme' in Basingstoke and each year has eight business advisers who provide help and support to youngsters in eight schools. Many of the business advisers carry on to complete more than one year.

Employee-led support

Preference is given to charities in which a member of staff is involved. Staff are also encouraged to become school governors.

Payroll giving: The company operates a scheme for employees.

Commercially-led support

Sponsorship: At national level this is very selective. At a local level some good cause sponsorship up to about £1,000 is undertaken, usually for health-related causes.

Lincoln Financial Group

Company registration number 1880345

Barnett Way, Barnwood, Gloucester GL4 3RZ

01452 374500; Fax: 01452 634300

Website: www.lincolnuk.co.uk

Correspondent: Isobel Mitchell

Email: isobel.mitchell@lincolnuk.co.uk

Chairman & Managing Director: Michael Tallett-Williams

Year end	Pre-tax profit
31/12/2007	£30,400,000

Nature of company business
Financial service company offering pensions, life assurance, health and disability cover, investment plans, unit trusts and ISAs.

Main locations: Gloucester

UK employees: 141

Charitable donations
2007: £100,953
2006: £104,632
2005: £117,647

Community involvement

The group runs a Community Partnership Programme (CPP) which is a scheme for making donations to charities and causes in the field of education, the arts and human services. The aim is to enhance quality of the life to empower and to support people in the communities where Lincoln has a presence.

The CPP has a dedicated committee who meet regularly to consider applications against their award criteria. They aim to make as much of an impact as possible with the donations that they make.

Priority is given to those projects that:

- enable support and service to help people realise their full potential or improve their quality of life
- enable education for disadvantaged people
- enhance quality of life through the arts and culture
- provide evidence that the partner is making a determined effort to help themselves
- provide opportunities for Lincoln to make a significant impact even with a comparatively small sum of money
- preferably give exclusivity for Lincoln
- preferably do not receive funding from elsewhere, e.g., from Lottery monies
- may be supported by employees who are contributing their own time or money.

Lincoln has a strong relationship with The National Star Centre, based near its headquarters, which is a secondary education college for young adults with physical disabilities.

Exclusions

The following types of projects are not usually supported: capital projects, such as the construction of a village hall or a scout hut; running costs, staffing costs, wages or general operating shortfalls; advertising support; general fundraising where the contribution would be merely a drop in the ocean rather than making a significant difference; schools, playgroups or colleges (except in exceptional circumstances); the services, such as ambulance, police and army; hospitals or health service projects that should normally be funded by the NHS; fraternal, political or religious organisations or activities; projects which are for the benefit of a single individual; travel or sports activities; or ventures partly or wholly outside of the UK.

Applications

On a form available from the correspondent, or downloadable from the website.

Corporate giving

During 2007, the group donated £121,111 to the CPP of which £95,593 was paid to charities in the UK. We have no details of the beneficiaries. The company paid an additional £5,000 to the Gloucester Flood Relief Fund.

The following information relates to 2005 (the most up to date available from the company's website):

Arts Cheltenham Festival of Music (£6,000); Gloucestershire Young Musician of the Year (£3,200); Gloucester Dance (£5,000); Everyman Theatre in association with National Star Centre (£6,839); and Gloucestershire Symphony Orchestra (£3,500).

Education Cheltenham Festival of Literature (£5,000); Gloucestershire Wildlife (£5,000); National Star Centre (£5,600); and Royal National Institute for the Deaf (£2,000).

Human Services Holiday Support (£1,350); Chamwell Holiday Playscheme (£5,000); Christian Lewis Trust (£2,200); The Spring Centre (£25,450); Children's Heart Federation (£6,300); and The Family Haven (£5,450).

In kind support

The CPP in the UK has taken an innovative approach to its award giving and decided to help address problems of adult illiteracy highlighted by a national survey carried out in the UK. This showed that one in five adults have problems with reading and/or writing.

With the help of an experienced and acclaimed adult literacy teacher, the CPP commissioned and published two books titled 'Help Yourself to Write a Letter' and 'Help Yourself to Fill in a Form'.

Employee-led support

Lincoln's Community Partnership Programme matches individual staff sponsorship efforts up to £100 per individual providing the end charity complies with all listed criteria. Where staff participate in a team, up to a cap of £1,000 may be added to the matching amount.

Commercially-led support

It has also operated a scheme which gave £10 to the National Star Centre for each new account opened during a month.

Linklaters

Company registration number 3604301

One Silk Street, London EC2Y 8HQ

020 7456 2000

Website: www.linklaters.com

Correspondent: The Community Investment Manager

Managing Partner: Simon Davies

Year end 31/12/2007	Turnover £543,000,000	Pre-tax profit £490,000,000

Nature of company business
International law firm.

Main locations: Colchester, London

Charitable donations

2007: £850,432

Total community contributions: £3,594,987
Management costs: £287,356

Membership: A & B, BitC, L B Group

Community involvement

Linklaters global charitable donations budget is based on 0.5% of its global profits. However, Linklaters recognise that there is more to community investment programme than just donating money. As such, it seeks to provide pro bono (i.e. free) legal advice and representation to those unable to afford it, and staff volunteers are actively involved in many projects local to the firm's 32 offices around the world. In the UK Linklaters focus its efforts in Hackney and Colchester.

The following areas have been identified: for support:

- achievement – empowering emerging talent to achieve its potential
- enterprise – encouraging enterprising and entrepreneurial people
- access to justice – asserting legal rights and responsibilities.

Exclusions

No support for appeals from individuals or local appeals not in areas of company presence.

Applications

In writing to the correspondent.

Corporate giving

In 2007, the firm made total community contributions in the UK of £3.6 million of which £850,000 was in cash donations. We have no details of the beneficiaries, but were advised that organisations working in the following areas are preferred: the arts; children/youth; education; and enterprise/training. Support is also given to a 'charity of the year'.

In kind support

Legal: *Pro bono clients* – this involves providing legal advice and legal services to a range of charities and voluntary organisations at no, or reduced, cost.

More than 15 community programmes are in operation, designed to support non-profit groups, charities, law centres, advice agencies and small businesses in the neighbouring boroughs of Tower Hamlets, Hackney, Newham and Southwark. These range from local school literacy and maths programmes to giving legal advice at law centres, ethnic minority undergraduate mentoring and supporting initiatives to tackle homelessness. Individual, group and firm-wide involvement is encouraged and much of this work is carried out during the working week.

Whenever possible, the firm also makes available meeting rooms for those charities and organisations which require the use of central London facilities.

Employee-led support

All staff are given a minimum of a day a year to volunteer. Besides the structured in kind support provided through pro bono work and established volunteering options, staff have raised money for a range of charities. This is matched £ for £ by the firm's matched giving scheme, up to a maximum of £500 for individuals and £1,000 for teams.

Linklaters LinkAid (Charity Commission no.: 1076058) is the firm's staff charity of the year. The fund is administered by a special committee comprising representatives from across the firm and staff are actively encouraged to promote charities of particular interest to them. In 2007, it raised £42,000. Beneficiaries have included Action for Kids, Barnardos, Central and Cecil Housing Trust, Childline, Colchester Emergency Night Shelter, London Symphony Orchestra and Lord Mayor's Appeal – Music for Everyone, NCH and NSPCC, Big Books, Princess Royal Trust for Carers, and Everyman.

In addition, a large number of staff make monthly fixed amount donations to specific charities of their choice through direct debit arrangements, whilst others create their own personal charity account into which they can place funds and from which they can donate to charities of their choice at a time they consider appropriate.

Payroll giving: The Give As You Earn scheme is offered by the firm to enable employees to give tax effectively to a charity/charities of their choice or to the firm's Link Aid Fund.

Commercially-led support

Sponsorship: *The arts* – Around 20% of the firm's annual donations budget goes towards supporting concerts in the City of London and Spitalfields Festivals.

LINPAC Group Ltd

Company registration number 4792926

3180 Park Square, Birmingham Business Park, Birmingham B37 7YN

0121 607 6700; Fax: 0121 607 6767

Website: www.linpac.com

Correspondent: Angela Thomas, PA to the Finance Director

Chairman: Bill Forrester

Chief Executive: Mike Arrowsmith

Year end	Turnover	Pre-tax profit
31/12/2006	£1,151,400,000	£18,000,000

Nature of company business
The principle activities of the group are the manufacture and marketing of plastic and paper products for packaging. The principal activity of the company is that of a holding company.

Subsidiaries include: Apex Storage System Ltd, Aquafilm Ltd, Billoway Engineering Ltd, Salter Paper Group Ltd

Main locations: Birmingham

UK employees: 9,285

Charitable donations
2006: £48,000
2005: £58,000
2004: £75,000
2003: £53,000

Community involvement

The company's website contained the following information regarding its charitable support:

'Across the LINPAC Group, we support numerous local charities and local initiatives to really help make a difference to their success and their aims. We also host visits to our manufacturing sites for local schools and community groups to help develop an understanding of what we do and why we do it.

'Examples of our support over the last year [include]:

- Our plastics factory in Featherstone, Yorkshire donates to Hemsworth Arts and Community College to help students learn about economic sustainable development and renewable energy resources. The college is using this financial support to build a wind turbine.
- LINPAC Recycling supported Royds School in Wakefield in their endeavour to supply materials to equip an educational facility in Belarus.'

Exclusions

No support for appeals from individuals. No support for local appeals not in areas of company presence.

Applications

In writing to the correspondent.

Corporate giving

The group made charitable donations amounting to £48,000 in 2006 (2005: £58,000).

Littlewoods Shop Direct Home Shopping Ltd

Company registration number 5059352

Skyways House, Speke Road, Speke, Liverpool L70 1AB

Website: www.shopdirect.com

Correspondent: The Head of Corporate Communications

Year end	Turnover	Pre-tax profit
30/04/2007	£1,308,531,000	£3,224,000

Nature of company business
Internet and catalogue home shopping.

Subsidiaries include: UKCL Ltd, Charities Trust Ltd, J & C Moores Ltd, Old Hall InsuranceServices Ltd, The International Import & Export Co. Ltd, CDMS Ltd, Stanley Insurance Services Ltd

Main locations: Preston, Liverpool, Oldham, Sunderland, Bolton

UK employees: 4,895

Charitable donations
2007: £600,000
2006: £600,000
2005: £500,000
2003: £300,000

Community involvement

The following was taken from the company's website in July 2008 under the heading 'Committed to long-term partnerships'.

'We are committed to supporting our local environment and are an active participant within the community.'

'We see the value in investing in charitable organisations, to ensure that they receive the full support and benefits that come from working in partnership with a commercial enterprise.'

'As part of our ongoing charitable and community support, we actively encourage all employees to join us in helping to make a difference to the charities we have committed to long-term partnerships with.'

'Our two charities of choice are Alder Hey Children's Hospital and its Imagine Appeal.'

Exclusions

No support for advertising in charity brochures, animal welfare, appeals from individuals, children/youth, elderly people, fundraising events, medical research, overseas projects, political appeals, religious appeals, science/technology, sickness/disability, social welfare or sport.

Applications

In writing to the correspondent.

Corporate giving

In 2006/07 the company made charitable donations of £600,000. Over a two-year period, Shop Direct Group has donated £2.25 million to the creation and funding of a specialist neurosciences wing at the hospital, the largest single contribution in the company's history of charitable giving.

In kind support

Previously, donations have been made in the form of recycled damaged, returned and surplus items to BDF Newlife and In Kind Direct.

Employee-led support

Littlewoods continues to be focused and committed in the area of employee involvement. Many of its colleagues actively volunteer in the Merseyside area and nationally.

Employees at the group's Crosby contact centre recently donated £5,000 to Alder Hey Children's Hospital enabling the purchase and installation of a new heart defibrillator.

Payroll giving: The company operates the Charities Trust scheme, and match employees' fundraising efforts and giving to limits set for specific campaigns/promotions.

Liverpool Victoria

Company registration number 61COLL

County Gates, Bournemouth, Dorset BH1 2NF

01202 292333; Fax: 01802 292253

Website: www.lv.com/

Correspondent: P B Cassidy, Company Secretary

Chairman: Dennis Holt

Chief Executive: Mike Rogers

Year end	Turnover	Pre-tax profit
31/12/2007	£625,700,000	£56,400,000

Nature of company business
The society is an incorporated Friendly Society which carries on insurance and financial services business in the UK.

Subsidiaries include: Frizzell Bank, Frizzell Financial Services Ltd, Frizzell Life & Financial Planning

Main locations: Bournemouth

UK employees: 1,973

Charitable donations
2007: £70,000
2005: £166,000
2004: £38,400
2003: £27,000

Community involvement

The following information is taken from the company's 2007 annual report and accounts: 'Throughout 2007 we have continued to strengthen and expand our community support programme. Our activities have been primarily focused upon our strategy of 'protecting our children and their future'. This approach concentrates on the areas our members and employees tell us matter most to them.

'Our community support is based on a long term view as befits an organisation providing long term products. Thus it is focused on the nation's children and their future. It is embedded in our operations through:

- our employee charity and community support initiatives
- our membership related fund raising activities
- our support for relevant projects that protect and enrich children's lives
- our sustainability programmes, ensuring our operations are as environmentally friendly as possible.'

Applications

In writing to the correspondent.

Corporate giving

The society makes charitable donations by periodic lump sum deposits to a Charities Aid Foundation account, from which payments are subsequently made. In 2007, this amounted to £70,000 and went to a range of causes including the Lord's Taverners minibus appeal, the Youth Cancer Trust charity, Help the Aged and Asthma UK.

Employee-led support

Employees are encouraged to devote their time and skills to a local Young Enterprise scheme, helping introduce school pupils to business skills and practices. In addition over 50 employees took advantage of the 'Employee Matching' scheme to add to the money they themselves have raised. As a result almost £17,000 has been added to funds raised by staff to support a range of causes including children's leukaemia support, breast cancer awareness and hospice care.

Commercially-led support

Sponsorship: *Education* – In 2007, the company launched a three year title sponsorship commitment to the LV= Streetwise Safety Centre in Bournemouth. This continues Liverpool Victoria's longstanding support for this award winning interactive education centre that uses real life street, transport and in-home situations to teach children basic safety skills.

Safety – Liverpool Victoria also relaunched and became title sponsor of LV= Kidzone, a beach safety scheme that helps to reunite lost children with their parents on crowded beaches. This simple but effective scheme pioneered the use of 'beach zones' combined with a free wristband given to children that helps them to find their parents.

Lloyd's

Company registration number 3189123

One Lime Street, London EC3M 7HA

020 7327 1000

Website: www.lloyds.com

Correspondent: Ms Victoria Mirfin, Lloyd's Charities Trust
020 7327 6075
Email: communityaffairs@lloyds.com

Chairman: Lord Levene

Chief Executive: Richard Ward

Year end	Pre-tax profit
31/12/2007	£3,846,000,000

Nature of company business
Insurance underwriting market.

Subsidiaries include: LPSO Ltd, LCO Marine Ltd, Lioncover Insurance Co. Ltd, Centrewrite Ltd, LCO Non-Marine and Aviation Ltd, Additional Securities Ltd

Main locations: London

Charitable donations
2007: £422,000
2006: £423,000
2005: £350,000

Membership: BitC

Community involvement

Lloyd's supports the community through The Lloyd's Charities Trust (Charity Commission no. 207232) and through its community programme.

The Lloyd's Charities Trust – Funded mainly by voluntary covenanted subscriptions from members of Lloyd's and by interest on its accumulated endowment, the majority of donations are made in support of three partner charities focusing on children and young people; social welfare development and medical health projects. The theme for 2007–2010 is 'At Risk' and the three partner charities have been selected on the basis of providing innovative projects. The partner charities for this period are Coram, FARM-Africa and Samaritans.

Occasionally, however, smaller one-off donations to charities are provided on an ad hoc basis. These donations are made to registered charities working in the following areas: medical/health; disability; social welfare; education and the environment.

The Lloyd's Community Programme – Set up in 1989, Lloyd's Community programme provides volunteering opportunities for individuals and companies from the Lloyd's insurance market to give their time and share skills in an effort to improve the opportunities and environment in neighbouring East London.

The programme is supported by individuals from over 65 underwriting agencies, insurance brokers and other associated companies who form part of Lloyd's insurance market. The agencies, brokers and associated companies pay an annual membership donation which is used to fund the Lloyd's Community Programme's projects.

In addition to the above, ad hoc income from covenants, bequests and donations is distributed through Lloyd's Patriotic Fund – established to further research into science, technology and business by way of fellowships and PhD business scholarships and Lloyd's Tercentenary Foundation – established to provide financial assistance to ex-servicemen and women and their widows and dependants.

Exclusions

No support for advertising in charity brochures, animal welfare, appeals from individuals, the arts, sponsorship, environment/heritage, fundraising events, medical research, political appeals, religious appeals, science/technology, sport or local appeals not in areas of company presence.

Applications

Lloyd's Charities Trust – For a one-off donation, apply in writing to the correspondent with a copy of your charities' annual accounts and a letter detailing the project for which funding sought. You should also give an example of what a donation of between £1,000 and £5,000 could do for your charity/project.

Lloyd's Community Programme – Lloyd's community programme funding is available to projects in Hackney and Tower Hamlets that fall within one of the six key themes. Priority is given to projects that provide opportunities for people from the market to get involved as volunteers. Although the website states that, 'All funds are currently committed to ongoing partnerships', it does imply that consideration may be given to new applicants. Please contact community affairs for further information.

Corporate giving

In 2007, the corporation donated to its charitable trust the sum of £422,000. This was used mainly to support the three charity partners in their work.

Also in 2007, with the support of Lloyd's Council, Lloyd's Charities Trust launched its new Special Award. This annual award is a one-off donation of £50,000 to a charity making a positive contribution to an issue or subject of interest to the Lloyd's market. The first recipient of this award was International Alert. International Alert is an independent peace building organisation that works to lay the foundations for lasting peace and security in communities affected by violent conflict.

In kind support

Lloyd's community programme supports schools and local businesses in Tower Hamlets and neighbouring East London boroughs.

Employee-led support

In 2007, 900 volunteers from the corporation and the market took part in opportunities in the East London community through Lloyd's community programme. Volunteering ranged from working with children in Tower Hamlets and Hackney to improve literacy and numeracy skills, to helping regenerate the local community through team challenges such as renovating local parks.

Commercially-led support

Sponsorship is not undertaken.

Lloyds Banking Group plc

Company registration number 2065

25 Gresham Street, London EC2V 7HN

020 7626 1500

Website: www.lloydstsb.com

Correspondent: Richard Cooper, Head of Corporate Social Responsibility 020 7356 2402
Email: richard.cooper@lloydstsb.co.uk

Chairman: Sir Victor Blank

Chief Executive: J Eric Daniels

Year end	Turnover	Pre-tax profit
31/12/2007	£18,228,000,000	£4,000,000,000

Nature of company business
The Lloyds TSB Group is one of the largest financial services companies in the UK, covering retail banking, commercial and corporate banking, mortgages, life assurance and pensions, general insurance, asset management, leasing, treasury and foreign exchange dealing.

Subsidiaries include: Abbey Life Assurance Co. Ltd, Scottish Widows Investment Partnership Group Ltd, Scottish Widows plc, Cheltenham and Gloucester plc, Black Horse Ltd, Scottish Widows Annuities Ltd, The Agricultural Mortgage Corpn plc

Main locations: London

UK employees: 67,616

Total employees: 69,553

Charitable donations
2007: £37,463,000
2006: £37,335,000
2005: £31,650,000
2004: £31,571,000
2003: £33,800,000

Membership: A & B, BitC, L B Group

Community involvement

Please note that Lloyds TSB Group plc was renamed Lloyds Banking Group on 19 January 2009, following the acquisition of HBOS plc. We do not know at this stage how, if at all, this will affect the related charitable foundations.

Lloyds TSB operates one of the largest community programmes in the UK. Cash donations are made through the four independent Lloyds TSB Foundations, which are grant-making trusts covering England and Wales, Scotland, Northern Ireland and the Channel Islands.

Foundation funding supports charities working to meet social and community needs. The main grants programmes are designed to address essential community needs and in particular, to support small under-funded charities.

Additional, and not insubstantial, in kind support is provided by the Lloyds TSB Group.

Corporate Charity of the Year: British Heart Foundation (2009).

Exclusions
For Lloyds TSB Foundations

'It is our aim to help charities working to improve the lives of disadvantaged people. However, we do not fund the following types of organisations and work:

'**Organisations:**
- organisations that are **not** registered charities
- second or third tier organisations (unless there is evidence of direct benefit to disadvantaged people)
- charities that mainly work overseas
- charities that mainly give funds to other charities, individuals or other organisations
- hospitals, hospices or medical centres
- rescue services
- schools, colleges and universities.

'Types of work:

* activities which a statutory body is responsible for
* capital projects, appeals, refurbishments
* environmental work, expeditions and overseas travel
* funding to promote religion
* holidays or trips
* loans or business finance
* medical research, funding for medical equipment or medical treatments
* sponsorship or funding towards a marketing appeal or fundraising activities
* work with animals or to promote animal welfare.'

Applications

For Lloyds TSB Foundations only:

Lloyds have recently launched a new online eligibility test. This consists of a three step process which, if you meet all the criteria, leads you to an eligibility questionnaire.

Further details of grant-giving policies and guidelines can be obtained by contacting the appropriate Lloyds TSB Foundation for your locality.

* Lloyds TSB Foundation for England and Wales
  Pentagon House 52–54 Southwark Street London SE1 1UN
  0870 411 1223; email: enquiries@lloydstsbfoundations.org.uk; website: www.lloydstsbfoundations.org.uk
* Lloyds TSB Foundation for Scotland
  Riverside House, 502 Gorgie Road, Edinburgh EH11 3AF
  0870 902 1201; email: enquiries@ltsbfoundationforscotland.org.uk; website: www.ltsbfoundationforscotland.org.uk
* Lloyds TSB Foundation for Northern Ireland
  2nd Floor, 14 Cromac Place, The Gasworks, Belfast
  BT7 2JB 028 9032 3000; email: info@lloydstsbfoundationni.org; website: www.lloydstsbfoundationni.org
* Lloyds TSB Foundation for the Channel Islands
  Lloyds TSB House, 25 New Street, St Helier, Jersey, Channel Islands JE4 8RG 01534 845889;
  email: john.hutchins@lloydstsb-offshore.com; website: www.ltsbfoundationci.org

Common reasons for unsuccessful applications

'The foundation cannot fund all eligible applications even if they are of a high quality because each year the total amount requested by eligible charities exceeds its budget.

'Other reasons for the foundation not being able to make a grant include:

* charities' core work not being sufficiently focused on our mission
* applications not falling within our guidelines
* charities not filling in the application form properly
* charities not having up to date annual returns or accounts filed with the Charities Commission or other relevant regulatory bodies.'

For Lloyds TSB Group plc only:

Contact: Richard Cooper, Head of Corporate Responsibility, Lloyds TSB Group plc, 25 Gresham Street, London EC2V 7HN.

Corporate giving

In 2007, cash donations to the four Lloyds TSB Foundations for distribution in cash grants to registered charities and community groups totalled £37,463,000. A similar figure was anticipated to be donated in 2008.

The Lloyds TSB Foundations

The four Lloyds TSB Foundations are, in aggregate, one of the UK's largest grant-giving organisations. Since 1996, and the merger of Lloyds Bank and TSB Group, the Lloyds TSB Foundations have received around £360 million to distribute to registered charities.

The foundations are shareholders in the Lloyds TSB Group and together they receive, under law, one per cent of the Group's pre-tax profits, averaged over three years, instead of the dividend of their shareholding.

The foundations focus their support on social and community needs and education and training. In particular, support is given to recognised charities helping disabled and disadvantaged people to play a fuller role in society. Within this general objective, each of the four foundations supports their own areas of special interest. Further details of the foundations proposed activities for 2009 can be had at: www.lloydstsbfoundations.org.uk

In kind support

The group has a large and dynamic property portfolio and surplus furniture is donated to local groups. Lloyds TSB also provides office space to the charity In kind Direct.

The group supports major charity appeals launched by the Disasters Emergency Committee, as well as certain sponsored appeals such as Children in Need, Comic Relief and the Royal British Legion. In addition, the group runs three nationwide pin badge appeals through its branch network.

Requests for local counter appeal support should be directed to the relevant branch. Please note, however, that no more than one counter appeal will be possible in any branch at any one time.

Employee-led support

Besides the foundations' support for local community causes, thousands of group employees volunteer to help in their communities, raise funds for the group's charity of the year or make direct donations to charity using the payroll giving system.

In 2007, the foundations provided matched funding for over 33,000 hours of time volunteered by Lloyds TSB employees in the community and also matched over £768,000 funds raised by employees for charities.

Through the 'Bank an Hour' volunteering scheme, Lloyds TSB will be supporting many different projects across the country. If you are part of an organisation which needs voluntary help, then please email Lloyds TSB at nationalccs@lloydstsb.co.uk with the following information:

* name
* address
* contact number
* organisation name (if applicable)
* what help you need.

Once your request has been received a community team member will contact you to see if they can help.

Payroll giving: The group operates the Give As You Earn scheme.

Commercially-led support

Sponsorship: The following is taken from the group's 'Community Investment Policy' leaflet:

'Sponsorship requests are those that provide a commercial return through exposure of Lloyds TSB's company name or brand.

'You should forward any local requests for sponsorship to your branch who will liaise with their Local Director office where local priorities are determined.

'As a general guide we do not support individuals or overseas activity and would prefer local initiatives to follow the national programme.

'The Group Sponsorship department deals with the national sponsorship programme. Any requests for sponsorship that refers to a specific product should be forwarded to the relevant business unit within Lloyds TSB.'

Lockheed Martin

Company registration number 2372738

Manning House, 22 Carlisle Place, London SW1P 1JA

020 7798 2850

Website: www.lockheedmartin.co.uk

Correspondent: Chris Trippick, Director of Communications

Chief Executive: Ian Stopps

Nature of company business
Systems integrator and supplier of high technology systems and service to defence and government customers.

Main locations: Farnham, Culdrose, Havant, Yeovil, Swindon, London, Malvern, Lincoln, Farnborough, Andover, Ampthill, Whiteley, Aldermaston

UK employees: 1,000

Total employees: 130,000

Community involvement

'For many years now Lockheed Martin UK has had a significant involvement in the local community, supporting various initiatives especially in the education field. In 2007 the company's commitment to the environment in which we live and work is as great as ever with Lockheed Martin not just wishing to be seen to be involved, but actively participating in many activities. We positively encourage our employees to become involved in activities outside work and a high percentage of our workforce is proud to contribute their time and energy.

'Lockheed Martin has a noticeable presence working with local communities and actively supports more than 20 charities in our main operating areas across the UK (Hampshire, Somerset and Cornwall).'

Applications

In writing to the correspondent.

Corporate giving

No UK community contributions figure was available. However, we do know that support has been given to: Charles Dickens Primary School in Portsmouth, for a behavioural unit as well as for trips to Marwell Zoo for high achievers; Culdrose Air Day; Emsworth Food Festival; and Hawke House Charity in Cornwall.

Lockheed Martin is a Charter Member of the Duke of Edinburgh's Award, providing financial and practical support to the self-development programme aimed at 14 to 25 year olds. The Prince's Trust is also regularly helped with the company supporting its funding stream for business start-up costs for young people in disadvantaged areas.

Employee-led support

The company has an annual Lend-a-Hand Day where staff are encouraged to volunteer with Portsmouth Housing Association to undertake tasks such as gardening, DIY and painting. About 10% of the workforce take part in the event.

Commercially-led support
Sponsorship: *The arts* – The company regularly support the Chichester Festival Theatre.

Lofthouse of Fleetwood Ltd

Company registration number 781277

Maritime Street, Fleetwood, Lancashire FY7 7LP

01253 872435; Fax: 01253 778725

Correspondent: Mrs D W Lofthouse, Trustee, Lofthouse Foundation

Chairman: Doreen Lofthouse

Managing Director: Tony Lofthouse

Duncan Lofthouse

Year end	Turnover	Pre-tax profit
31/12/2007	£31,949,807	£7,244,445

Nature of company business
Manufacturers of medicated confectionery.

Main locations: Fleetwood

Total employees: 312

Charitable donations
2007: £112,733
2006: £174
2005: £21,712
2004: £350,300

Community involvement

Manufacturers of the famous 'Fisherman's Friend', most of the company's charitable support is channelled through the Lofthouse Foundation (Charity Commission no. 1038728). The foundation was established in June 1994 with general charitable objects for the benefit of Fleetwood and its environs. There are three trustees, all of whom are members of the Lofthouse family.

Exclusions

The foundation does not support: advertising in charity brochures, animal welfare, the arts, overseas projects, religious appeals, science/technology or social welfare.

Applications

In writing to the correspondent.

Corporate giving

In 2007, the company made charitable donations of £112,733. Of this £112,000 was donated to the Lofthouse Foundation which granted the money to Fylde Coast YMCA. The company made two further donations during the year – £530 to UNICEF and £203 to Wear it Pink.

London Stock Exchange

Company registration number 2075721

10 Paternoster Square, London EC4M 7LS

020 7797 3322; Fax: 020 7588 3504

Website: www.londonstockexchange.com

Correspondent: Internal Communications Manager

Chairman: Chris Gibson-Smith

Chief Executive: Clara Furse

Year end	Turnover	Pre-tax profit
31/03/2008	£546,400,000	£234,700,000

Nature of company business
The London Stock Exchange is one of the world's leading equity exchanges and an international provider of services that facilitate the raising of capital and the trading of shares and debt securities.

Subsidiaries include: SE Mutual Reference Ltd, The Birmingham Stock Exchange Buildings Co. Ltd

Main locations: Birmingham, London

UK employees: 1,210

Charitable donations

2008: £196,000
2007: £99,000
2005: £124,000
2004: £101,000

Community involvement

The London Stock Exchange believes that it has a responsibility towards the wider society in which it conducts its business and to support its staff in their individual and collective efforts to make a contribution to the community. It does this by:

- making a positive contribution to the community by adopting a partner charity
- encouraging employee involvement in supported community projects and initiatives.

Charity of the Year: Princess Royal Trust for Carers (2007/08).

Exclusions

Political, overseas and purely religious charities are not supported.

Applications

Applications to be considered as a partner charity should be introduced by email to the named contact. Applications for ad-hoc financial support are not encouraged.

Corporate giving

There is a budget of £100,000 each year for the organisation's charitable support. The budget is split roughly 75% to 25% in favour of the partner charity, with the remaining funds going towards matching employees charitable contributions- around 30 to 40 charities receive small donations in this way.

In 2008, cash donations totalled £196,000 (2007: 399.000). The main focus of the exchange's charitable activity during the year has been its partnership with the Princess Royal Trust for Carers.

The partnership has being running since August 2007 and generated almost £100,000 for the Trust.

In kind support

Support was given to a number of charities by allowing them the use of the London Stock Exchange event facilities and in-house catering so they could hold business development events at zero cost.

Employee-led support

The London Stock Exchange has a staff matching programme which matches funds raised by staff for any UK registered charity, pound for pound, up to a maximum of £1,000 per employee. 2005 saw a significant increase (over 50 per cent) in staff matching applications on the preceding year. The company also makes 'community awards' to charities to recognise the time spent by members of staff performing voluntary work with them in their own time.

Payroll giving: The Give As You Earn scheme is in operation.

Low & Bonar plc

Company registration number SC008349

9th Floor, Marble Arch Tower, Bryanston Street, London W1H 7AA

2075353180; Fax: 2075353181

Website: www.lowandbonar.com

Chairman: R D Clegg

Chief Executive: P A Forman

Year end	Turnover	Pre-tax profit
30/11/2007	£311,800,000	£19,100,000

Nature of company business
Plastics, packaging and specialist material manufacture.

Subsidiaries include: Anglo-Danish Fibres Ltd, Fibrin Humberside Ltd

Main locations: Manchester, Bamber Bridge, Telford, Hull, Barnsley, Dundee, London

UK employees: 2,181

Charitable donations

2007: £15,000
2006: £15,000
2005: £20,000
2004: £15,000

Community involvement

Previously, donations were made through a company trust (the Low & Bonar Charitable Fund – SC010837). However, we have been advised that the assets of this fund have been used to create a new 'independent' charity called the Low & Bonar Charitable Trust (SC031663), which apparently has no connection with the company (name excepted!).

The charitable purposes of the new trust are listed on the Scottish Charity Register as:

- relief of poverty
- advancement of education
- advancement of health
- advancement of the arts, heritage, culture or science
- relief of those in need through age, ill health, or disability.

There is a preference for supporting smaller charities in the areas of Tayside and north east Fife.

Exclusions

No support for non-registered charities. No grants for local appeals not in areas of company presence; advertising in charity brochures; animal welfare; appeals from individuals; enterprise/training; fundraising events; political or religious appeals; science/technology; overseas projects, or sport.

Applications

It is unclear since the transferral of the assets of the company's charitable fund to the new 'independent' trust, whether it accepts unsolicited applications for support. Until clarification can be obtained on this, we suggest applications be addressed to: Nick Barclay, Administrative Secretary, Low & Bonar Charitable Trust, Thortons Law LLP, Whitehall House, 33 Yeaman Shore, Dundee DD1 4BJ. (email: nbarclay@thorntons-law.co.uk). Note: Only written applications are accepted by the trust.

The trustees meet quarterly. Support is only given to charities registered with the Charity Commission or, in Scotland, the Inland Revenue.

Corporate giving

Despite the changes detailed above that have taken place, the company still makes the majority of its donations via this new, unconnected, trust. In 2007, this amounted to £15,000 (substantially down on the average of £65,000 a year made through the company trust).

The trusts income in 2007/08 was £67,500. We have no details of the beneficiaries.

Man Group plc

Company registration number 2921462

Sugar Quay, Lower Thames Street, London EC3R 6DU

020 7144 1000; Fax: 020 7144 1923

Website: www.mangroupplc.com

Correspondent: Lisa Clarke, Secretary to the Charitable Trust

Chairman: John Aisbitt

Chief Executive: Peter Clarke

Year end	Pre-tax profit
31/03/2008	£1,039,500,000

Nature of company business
The company is a leading global provider of alternative investment products and solutions.

Main locations: London

UK employees: 743

Total employees: 1,731

Charitable donations

2008: £5,500,000
2007: £3,105,000
2006: £2,455,000
2005: £1,724,596
2004: £506,000

Management costs: £505,000

Membership: A & B, BitC

Community involvement

Through its website and various publications, the Man Group make available a wealth of information about its corporate community investment and the philosophy behind it. Whilst we can cover the salient points only here, others would do well to embrace the degree of openness and transparency the group display regarding its giving.

The following information is taken from Man Group's dedicated corporate responsibility website:

'Throughout our 225 years of operation, we have been committed to the communities in which our businesses operate and our people live and work.

'Our community engagement has three distinct strands:
- sponsorship – focused on literature, sport and climate change, which align with our core corporate values and our business proposition of innovation and excellence
- philanthropy – characterised by contributions of time, money and other resources to various good causes
- our people's engagement – which takes many forms, sometimes backed by Group financial assistance, sometimes simply involving our employees' time and effort.

'We take care to ensure that our community involvement reflects and is aligned with our core corporate values, as set out in our Ethical Policy [against each of the four core corporate values is listed the group's corresponding community involvement]:

'*Integrity* – disaster relief, humanitarian aid, meeting the needs of the elderly, the disabled and the vulnerable, youth programmes (help and development) and climate change.

'*Excellence* – the arts (scholarships and prizes), sport (fitness and health) and youth, particularly those in disadvantaged groups.

'*Innovation* – original and innovative approach to community, creative writing and literature.

'*Performance* – youth theatre projects, music and education.

'**Philanthropy:** Unlike sponsorship, we view our charitable activities as entirely separate from our marketing and public relations; any favourable publicity is a welcome spin-off, not a strategic objective. We give on a purely altruistic basis, in line with our core values.

'As well as money we encourage our people at all levels to invest their time and expertise in helping others. We match, up to an agreed limit, charitable contributions our people make, including via our Give As You Earn scheme, and contribute to the Man Group plc Charitable Trust based on the following formula:

- 2.5% of performance fee income, plus
- 0.25% of management fee income.

'The total above is subject at all times to a minimum set at 0.5% of the group's before tax profit.'

The main conduit for this philanthropic giving is the Man Group plc Charitable Trust (Charity Commission no. 275286), which is likely to support:

- charities that help young people develop self-esteem and reach their potential, for example through sport or the arts, or which help them address problems with, for example, addiction or homelessness
- charities that fund non-commercial medical research
- one-off disaster or emergency appeals
- The arts.

Charity of the year: The Anthony Nolan Trust (2008/09).

Exclusions

The Man Group plc Charitable Trust does not generally support: large national charities; charities which use external fund raising agencies; animal charities; charities primarily devoted to promoting religious beliefs; endowment funds; requests that directly replace statutory funding; individual beneficiaries; successful applicants from the previous twelve months.

Applications

In writing to the correspondent.

Information available: Besides producing an annual corporate responsibility report, the group also provide online access to its internal 'Corporate Responsibility Manual'. This provides an interesting insight into why the company does what it does for the community and how. Such levels of transparency are to be welcomed.

Corporate giving

In 2007/08, the group paid out £5.5 million to 150 charities selected by the trustees of the Man Group plc Charitable Trust and £500,000 through overseas offices. Percentage-wise donations were broken down as follows: young people (35%); vulnerable (16.5%); other (16%); international (12.4%); literacy (12%); and employee-related (8.1%).

Beneficiaries included: Teenage Cancer Trust (Charity of the Year 2006/07); Merlin; Co-ordinated Action Against Domestic Abuse; Every Child a Reader and Every Child Counts; The Prince's Rain Forest Project; Dyslexia Action; and Book Aid International.

In 2008/09 the group will contribute around £16 million to charities, the majority of which will be donated through the Man Group plc Charitable Trust. This will enable the group to broaden its geographic spread, and provide opportunities for its larger overseas offices to give more, and to provide a cushion for multi-year commitments.

Employee-led support

All staff are encouraged to become involved in charitable activities. Accordingly, 'In addition to the selected charities the trustees [of the group charitable trust] give preference to charities where a staff member has an involvement and they will generally match any sponsorship raised by staff members for charitable events'.

The trust will match up to £100 per person per month, individual employee fundraising efforts. There are no constraints as to which charity may benefit from these donations.

Payroll giving: The Give As You Earn scheme is in operation. Donations via the scheme rose to £214,000 in 2007/08 (2006/07: £112,000) with a further £86,000 being added through the group's matched funding. Membership in the scheme rose from 141 in 2006 to 200 in 2007.

Commercially-led support

Sponsorship: *The arts* – Selected arts sponsorship is undertaken. The most significant of these is the Man Booker Prize for Fiction.

Sport – Man sponsors London Youth Rowing, an Inner London sports initiative which encourages young people to experience the sport of rowing in three ways: Indoor rowing on Concept 2 rowing machines, on the water rowing at the London Regatta Centre in Newham, the Lea Rowing Club, Hackney and the Barn Elms Boat House in Wandsworth and an indoor and on the water Adaptive Rowing programme for people with disabilities.

The Manchester Airport Group plc

Company registration number 4330721

Wythenshawe, Manchester M90 1QX

0871 271 0711; Fax: 0161 489 3813

Website: www.manchesterairport.co.uk

Correspondent: Mrs Wendy Sinfield, Community Relations Manager

Fax: 0161 489 3467
Email: community.relations@manairport.co.uk

Chairman: Alan Jones

Chief Executive: Geoff Muirhead

Year end	Turnover	Pre-tax profit
31/03/2007	£385,500,000	£80,900,000

Nature of company business
International airport operation.

Subsidiaries include: Crow Aerodromes Ltd, East Midlands International Airport Ltd, Bournemouth International Airport Ltd, Humberside International Airport Ltd, Ringway Handling Ltd, Airport Advertising Ltd, Worknorth II Ltd, Worknorth Ltd

Main locations: Manchester

UK employees: 2,173

Charitable donations

2007: £189,000
2006: £150,000
2005: £150,000
2004: £100,000
2003: £100,000

Total community contributions: £639,000

Membership: A & B, BitC

Community involvement

Previously included under the name Manchester Airport plc, this has been amended to The Manchester Airport Group plc (MAG) to reflect its ownership of Bournemouth, East Midlands and Humberside airports.

In 2007, MAG completed a two-year project in conjunction with the Department of Trade and Industry and Manchester Metropolitan University which sought to deliver a leading edge, commercially beneficial corporate responsibility (CR) programme for the group. It identified that, although MAG has a long history of environmental and social commitments and a wide range of CR activities, these have never been brought together in one coordinated approach.

Whilst work is ongoing as to how best to implement the CR programme across the group and each airport site, we have, nevertheless, herein tried to reflect more fully the additional support given outside of Manchester Airport's well established trust fund (see below).

MAG focuses its community work on the areas closest to Manchester Airport and gives priority to those with the greatest social and economic need. MAG concentrates on supporting education and employment, recognising that these elements are of great importance not only to the communities that it serves, but also to the future growth of its businesses. Furthermore, support in kind is often more important than money. MAG therefore uses an internal network of employee community champions, through a community network of on site service partners and at Manchester through community links established with other businesses in the local community of Wythenshawe.

Comprehensive details of the group's various community programmes can be found on its website under 'Community Links'.

Manchester Airport Community Trust Fund

The airport company established the Manchester Airport Community Trust Fund (Charity Commission no. 1071703) as a community based initiative to promote, enhance, improve, protect and conserve the natural and built environment in areas which are affected by the activities of Manchester Airport.

Projects must be for the benefit of the whole local community or a substantial section of it, and not groups of an exclusive nature. Preference will be given to projects that have considered the needs of disabled or elderly people within the community.

Support is only given to organisations within a 20-mile radius of Manchester Airport (i.e. South Manchester, Altrincham, Bramhall, Stockport, Wilmslow, Borough of Congleton (excluding the town of Congleton), Borough of Macclesfield (excluding the town of Macclesfield), and up to, but not including, the town of Northwich. Exceptionally, local branches of national charities may also receive help.

An East Midlands Airport Community Fund (non-registered charity) also exists – see separate entry.

Exclusions

No support for appeals from individuals, commercial organisations, organisations which have statutory responsibilities such as hospitals or schools (unless the project is clearly not a statutory responsibility), those working for profit, or for organisations outside of the trust boundary.

Applications

Charities and schools in communities in close proximity to Manchester airport which do not qualify for funding from the trust fund may apply for prizes for fundraising by contacting the correspondent.

Grant applications to the Manchester Airport Community Trust Fund should not be made without first reading the policy guidelines. These, along with an application form, are available upon request from the Fund Administrator at the address given below. You can also get an application form and further information on-line from www.manchesterairport.co.uk

The Administrator
Manchester Airport Community Trust Fund
Community Relations
Manchester Airport
Manchester
M90 1QX

Tel: 0161 489 5281 (An answerphone is available for out-of-hours enquiries)

Fax: 0161 489 3467

Email: trust.fund@manairport.co.uk

Trustees meet quarterly. You should return your completed form to the administrator no later than the first Friday of March, June, September or December for consideration by the trustees the following month.

If you are successful you will usually receive a cheque a month after the trustees' meeting. You must send the trust fund original invoices/receipts for the works or goods you purchased within 3 months of receiving your grant cheque.

Corporate giving

In 2006/07, the group made total community contributions of £639,000. This comprised £450,000 of in kind support, a £150,000 cash donation to the community trust fund and £39,000 given in sound insulation grants. The latter, previously only available for domestic properties, has been extended in line with government recommendations to school and community buildings.

In addition to the above cash donation, Manchester Airport Community Trust Fund also received £61,350 as a result of environmental fines imposed on noisy operators. Successful applicants to the fund received grants of up to £5,000 each in 2007/08 including those to: Friends of Hesketh Park; Hope Direct; and National Library for the Blind – Stockport.

In kind support

Through a network of 'Community Champions' established right across its business, members of staff are encouraged to get involved in volunteering in local projects. Recent examples include: reading mentoring, mock interviews, 'World of Work' days, and the Airport Academy project – an employment and training programme helping unemployed people living in the Manchester South Regeneration areas and, particularly, in Wythenshawe.

Employee-led support

The company has an active employee volunteering scheme and allows employees company time off in which to volunteer.

Commercially-led support

Sponsorship: *The arts* – Last year the group's arts sponsorship was worth £1 million, covering several major events as well as ongoing sponsorship of world-class arts organisations. A huge variety of art forms were supported including theatre, music, poetry, fine arts, photography, fashion and new media.

New proposals should be relevant to at least one of the areas served by the group's airports, including the entire North West of England, Yorkshire, North Wales, Humberside, Bournemouth and the East Midlands.

Arts organisations based in the group's operational areas generally (though not always) have priority over other applicants. However, consideration will also be given to applications from arts organisations based elsewhere in the UK for projects touring the areas served by the group's airports.

Applications are particularly welcome from projects or organisations that encourage community-wide access to the arts or have outreach programmes.

All applications must be received by 31 December to be considered for sponsorship in the following year.

Contact: Sarah Brookes (Tel: 0161 489 2093).

Sport – Humberside and East Midland airports sponsored a number of youth football teams and youth sporting events located within their operational areas. We have no further information regarding this form of sponsorship.

Marks and Spencer Group plc

Company registration number 214436

Waterside House, 35 North Wharf Street, London W2 1NW

020 7935 4422; Fax: 020 7487 2679

Website: corporate.marksandspencer.com

Correspondent: Mike Barry, Corporate Social Responsibility

Chairman: Sir Stuart Rose

Year end	Turnover	Pre-tax profit
29/03/2008	£9,022,000,000	£821,000,000

Nature of company business
The principal activities are retailing women's wear, men's wear, lingerie, children's wear, beauty products, home products, food and the provision of financial services. Retailing activities are carried out under the Marks & Spencer and King Super Markets brand names.

Subsidiaries include: St Michael Finance plc

Main locations: London, Chester

UK employees: 71,613

Total employees: 75,359

Charitable donations

2008: £5,400,000
2007: £3,800,000
2006: £3,400,000
2005: £3,000,000

Total community contributions: £15,000,000
Management costs: £420,000

Membership: BitC, L B Group

Community involvement

Marks and Spencer (M&S) make donations to charitable organisations through its local stores. They each have a small, limited budget and focus their support towards issues that are important to their local community.

Through *Marks & Start,* its flagship community programme, the company helps people to prepare for the world of work. In particular it is aimed at: people who are homeless; people with disabilities; the young unemployed; schoolchildren, including those in deprived areas; students who are the first in their family to aim for higher education; and parents wanting to return to work.

In addition to the above, in kind support is given through the donation of food and clothing.

Exclusions

M&S stores are not able to support:

- personal appeals on behalf of individual people, including overseas trips
- advertising or goodwill messages
- political parties
- third party fundraising on behalf of a charity
- religious bodies, except where the project provides non-denominational, non-sectarian support for the benefit of the general project
- supplying clothing, other than in exceptional circumstances, as we already give clothes to BDF (Birth Defects Foundation) and Shelter.

Applications

Marks & Spencer receives over 50 requests a month for support. Of these about 12% are pursued and 6% accepted. To stand any chance of success, please check that your organisation can help to address key areas of the company's policy before applying.

Corporate giving

During 2007/08, the group made charitable donations to support the community of £15 million (2006/07: £13.9 million). These principally consisted of cash donations of £5.4 million (2006/07: £3.8 million) which includes the 'Marks & Start' community programme, Breakthrough Breast Cancer, Save The Children, World Wildlife Fund, and local community donations, £1.9 million (2006/07: £3 million) of employee time, principally on Marks & Start and school work experience programmes, and stock donations of £7.5 million (2006/07: £6.6 million) to a variety of charities including Shelter, FareShare and The Birth Defects Foundation.

In kind support

Donations of stock were made to a variety of charities, including Shelter, Fareshare, Birth Defects Foundation as well as to the local community.

Employee-led support

Employees are encouraged to give up their spare time to raise cash and volunteer for a wide range of charities and organisations.

Each year, in support of this, M&S set aside funds to match the charitable fundraising that its people do out of working hours. M&S encourage teamwork between colleagues through the programme's criteria which requires a minimum of five employees to be fundraising together for the same organisation.

Payroll giving: The Give as You Earn scheme is in operation. In 2007 over 2,800 M&S employees took advantage of the scheme, donating around £250,000 to over 300 charities.

Sharing the Caring, the payroll giving arm of the Charities Aid Foundation, is now visiting each of M&S's stores and head office locations annually in order to promote the scheme.

Commercially-led support

Cause-related marketing: *Breakthrough Breast Cancer* – 'M&S raises money through donations on sales of specially designed products during Breast Cancer Awareness month in October and as part of the Fashion Targets Breast Cancer campaign in April-May.

'Breakthrough Breast Cancer also benefits from a donation on the post surgery lingerie range which is sold all year round.'

Groundwork – 'M&S is donating all the profits (1.85p per bag) from our 5p food carrier bag charging scheme to environmental charity Groundwork; to invest in projects that will improve parks, play areas and public gardens in neighbourhoods around the UK.'

Marsh Ltd

Company registration number 1507274

Tower Place, Lower Thames Street, London EC3R 5BU

020 7357 1000; Fax: 020 7929 2705

Website: www.marsh.co.uk

Correspondent: Kathryn Pettifer, UK Community Relatiions Executive
Email: kathryn.s.pettifer@mmc.com

Chairman: Sir Peter Middleton

Chief Executive: M C South

Vice Chairman: Sir David W Brewer

Year end	Turnover	Pre-tax profit
31/12/2007	£210,044,000	£5,055,000

Nature of company business
Risk management and insurance services company. UK business conducted to identify, value, control, transfer and finance risk for clients that range from multinationals to small commercial and private businesses.

Subsidiaries include: Guy Carpenter & Co. Ltd, Global Broking Europe

Main locations: Liverpool, Birmingham, Edinburgh, Glasgow, Leeds, Bristol, Newcastle, London, Southampton

UK employees: 3,000

Charitable donations
2007: £318,984
2006: £31,918
Membership: BitC

Community involvement

The following information is taken from the company's website:

'Marsh Ltd is an operating unit of Marsh & McLennan Companies Inc. Marsh has had a long and well-established community relations programme in the UK. Through this programme we offer financial support and the time and skills of our employees to a wide variety of charities and community organisations in the cities and towns in which we operate.

'National charities – Marsh's donation programme is administered centrally. Under the theme of 'People and Communities at Risk', the company has established a multi-year partnership with eight national UK charities that provide support and services in response to a broad range of human needs.

'Every year, Marsh employees and other operating companies within MMC select a 'Charity of the Year' and then organise a series of fundraising events in support of it.'

Charity of the Year: Help the Hospices (2008/09).

Exclusions

Donations will not be made (other than in exceptional circumstances) to religious organisations or causes, political parties or causes, advertising in charity brochures, circular appeals, international crisis appeals, overseas causes, appeals for individuals' education, expeditions or recreation, animal welfare or sport.

Applications

For further information please contact the correspondent.

Corporate giving

In 2007. Marsh made cash donations in the UK of £318,984 (2006: £31,918 – community support programme under review). The majority of the company's donations during the year were made to its eight national charity partners in support of their work under the theme of 'People and Communities at Risk'. The eight partners were: The British Association for Adoption and Fostering; The Coram Family; Contact the Elderly; Crimestoppers; Crisis; Fairbridge; Home Start; and The Princess Royal Trust for Carers.

In kind support

In 2002, City of London Sinfonia (CLS) and the UK operating companies of MMC including Marsh, launched Music in the Community. Music in the Community brings CLS musicians and MMC volunteers into inner-city schools and community groups to encourage an appreciation of music and to promote self-confidence and teamwork through the medium of music. The nationwide programme, which focuses on cities in which MMC's operating companies have offices, has so far taken CLS musicians to Leeds, Southampton, Bristol, Chichester and London.

Employee-led support

Marsh's employee volunteering policy entitles every employee to a minimum of one day per year to take part in a programme that supports the community. Activities range from one-day 'Team Challenges' to one-to-one mentoring.

In addition, Marsh employees in the Bristol, Witham and London offices spend one lunchtime per week visiting local school children and helping them with their literacy and numeracy skills.

Through the 'Marsh MAGIC' scheme, the fundraising and volunteer efforts of employees, for the communities and charities of their choice, are matched by the company up to a ceiling of £300 per year.

Staff can also choose to donate the odd pennies from their pay slip to the 'Charity of the Year' under the Pennies from Heaven scheme.

Payroll giving; Marsh adds 10% to employees' payroll donations to charities of their choice via Give As You Earn.

Marshall of Cambridge (Holdings) Ltd

Company registration number 2051460

Airport House, Newmarket Road, Cambridge CB5 8RX

01223 373737; Fax: 01223 372472

Website: www.marshall-group.co.uk

Correspondent: Terry Holloway, The Group Support Executive
Email: th@marcamb.co.uk

Chairman: Michael Marshall

Year end	Turnover	Pre-tax profit
31/12/2007	£707,520,000	£24,047,000

Nature of company business
The principal activities of the group are car and commercial vehicle sales, distribution, service, hire and associated activities, together with general engineering connected with aircraft and military systems.

Subsidiaries include: Ted Salisbury & Sons Ltd, Tim Brinton Cars Lts, Fellhouse Ltd

Main locations: Ipswich, Huntingdon, Cambridge, Croydon

UK employees: 3,875

Charitable donations

2007: £1,065,000
2006: £195,000
2005: £29,000
2004: £35,000
2003: £36,000

Community involvement

A major engineering employee in Cambridge, the company takes an active role in the communities local to its operating sites. There is active participation by the group of companies in a wide range of community projects, including wildlife, the arts and environment and a diverse programme of visits to the company's Airport Works' premises. The company also supports a number of local charities and schools.

The company has strong links with Cambridge University (there is a Sir Arthur Marshall Institute within the Engineering Department), along with local schools and colleges and training and enterprise bodies.

Exclusions

No support for advertising in charity brochures, animal welfare, appeals from individuals, fundraising events, overseas projects, political appeals, religious appeals, or local appeals not in areas of company presence.

Applications

In writing to the correspondent.

Corporate giving

In 2007, the company made charitable donations in the UK of £1,065,000 (2006: £195,000). This substantial increase was due to a payment of £1 million being made to the D G Marshall of Cambridge Trust in memory of Sir Arthur Marshall. Although this was obviously an exceptional payment, the previous years figure also included a donation to the trust of £135,000. To our knowledge, it has not previously been the case that the group made donations to the trust. However, whether or not this will continue remains to be seen.

National projects which benefit from the encouragement and help of the group of companies include: The Air League Educational Trust, the Air Training Corps, the RAF Benevolent Fund, the Duke of Edinburgh's Award Scheme and BEN, the charity of the Motor Industry.

In kind support

Help is given through, for example, an adult retraining scheme and head teacher mentoring.

Employee-led support

Payroll giving: The group encourages staff charitable donations under the Give As You Earn scheme.

Commercially-led support

Sponsorship: *Education* – The company has formally taken on the sponsorship of Teversham Church of England Primary School, which is its nearest neighbouring school, in order to provide help and guidance with a wide range of technology projects.

Marshall of Cambridge also sponsors Bottisham Village College, a local secondary school. A Marshall Aerospace graduate engineer provides support for the school's technology projects and assists in a number of science related programmes.

Mascolo Ltd

Company registration number 770236

19 Doughty Street, London WC1N 2PL

020 7440 6660; Fax: 020 7440 6668

Website: www.toniandguy.com

Correspondent: Miss Ruth Ireland, Trust Administrator
Email: charitablefoundation@toniandguy.co.uk

Managing Director: Guiseppe Mascolo

Year end
31/08/2006

Nature of company business
Hairdressing and other beauty treatments.

UK employees: 546

Charitable donations

Total community contributions: £93,000 (2006)

Community involvement

Mascolo Ltd is the parent company of the 200-odd Toni & Guy hair salons in the UK, some of which are franchised or partially-owned by the company.

The company's charitable giving is directed through the Toni & Guy Charitable Foundation (Charity Commission no. 1095285).

Toni & Guy Charitable Foundation

Nominations for grants are generally elicited by informal means and include input from the Toni & Guy network of hairdressing salons. The current, main objective of the trust is the raising of funds for the new state-of-the-art children's ward at the Variety Club Children's Hospital at King's College Hospital in south east London.

Applications

In writing to the correspondent.

Corporate giving

In 2005/06 the foundation received nearly £93,000 from the company in the form of donated goods and services. Grants were made by the foundation totalling £111,000 to the following beneficiaries: The Variety Club – The Toni & Guy Ward (£80,000); King's College Hospital (£25,000); Italian Church Charity (£3,500); and The Variety Club – Children's Medical Pump Appeal (£2,400). A further £30,000 was donated to the Variety Club's Children's Hospital after the year end in December 2007.

In kind support

This constitutes the main form of charitable support provided by the company (see 'Community contributions/Corporate giving').

Employee-led support

Although salon staff at Toni & Guy are involved in fundraising activities, this does not appear to be matched by the company.

Bernard Matthews Ltd

Company registration number 625299

Great Witchingham Hall, Norwich NR9 5QD

01603 872611; Fax: 01603 871118

Website: www.bernardmatthews.com

Correspondent: David M Reger, Company Secretary

Chairman: B T Matthews

Year end	Turnover	Pre-tax profit
28/12/2006	£359,599,000	£19,891,000

Nature of company business
The principal activities of the group are the production and marketing of turkey and red meat products, oven-ready turkeys, day-old turkeys, fish products and other poultry products.

Main locations: Norwich

UK employees: 3,630

Total employees: 6,650

Charitable donations

2006: £197,349
2005: £303,611
2004: £463,563
2002: £397,156

Membership: BitC

Community involvement

Generally, the company has a preference for local charities in the areas where it operates (East Anglia). More specifically it states that: 'As a business we have five aims in the community which are central to us as a business and to our brand:

- food education
- preserving the local environment
- developing young people
- nurturing youth enterprise
- supporting local agriculture'.

Exclusions

No support for circular appeals, advertising in charity brochures, animal welfare, appeals from individuals, overseas projects, political appeals, sport, local appeals not in areas of company presence, or large national appeals.

Applications

In writing to the correspondent.

Corporate giving

In 2006, the company made donations to charitable causes totalling £197,349 (2005: £305,611). Full details of the beneficiaries were unavailable. Support was, however, given to the Duke of Edinburgh's Award Scheme, and The Prince's Trust. Local schools, youth activities and the arts (arts festivals, local museums and exhibitions) have also benefited.

In kind support

Environment: Support for the environment is a major consideration and a tree planting programme has been ongoing around the East Anglian sites, including a 30-acre future wood.

Employee-led support

The company supports employees' volunteering/charitable activities through financial support and allowing company time off to volunteer.

Mazars LLP

Company registration number 1485039

Tower Bridge House, St Katherine's Way, London E1W 1DD

020 7063 4000; Fax: 020 7063 4001

Website: www.mazars.co.uk

Correspondent: Katherine Moss, Chair of Mazars Charitable Trustee Committee
Email: katherine.moss@mazars.co.uk

Chairman: D Evans

Chief Executive: D Chapman

Managing Director: G Williams

Year end	Turnover	Pre-tax profit
31/08/2007	£83,000,000	£14,000,000

Nature of company business
Accountants and Business Advisers.

Main locations: London

UK employees: 1,200

Charitable donations

2007: £244,000
2005: £165,866
2003: £130,000

Membership: BitC

Community involvement

Support is given through the Mazars Charitable Trust (Charity Commission no. 287735) whose income is virtually all derived from donations received from Mazars LLP, which aims to donate 1.75% of its profits. The trust was established by a Trust Deed dated 23 August 1983 for the principal purpose of receiving contributions from the partners of the then firm of Neville Russell, Chartered Accountants and disbursing the same to charitable causes.

In the years since, the firm has twice changed its name and, on 1 September 2004, its status also from that of a partnership to Mazars LLP, a limited liability partnership. The name of the charity was also changed to its present form in 2003.

A wide range of charities receive support from the trust in the form of time and money. Resources are committed almost entirely to charities known to the partners and employees of the firm (charities' requests must be authenticated by a recognised agency). Unsolicited appeals are rarely considered.

The trust states it prefers to support specific projects (e.g. capital expenditure, research, an event) rather than normal revenue expenditure, although the latter will be considered provided that the applicant appears to be launching a strategic initiative and is financially sound.

It also: 'supports charities which reflect the corporate ethos of our donor, the UK firm of Mazars LLP. This ethos is being developed over time, but encapsulates the following sorts of charitable activity, associated with organisations which:

- will benefit significantly from receipt of a grant (i.e. the trust rarely supports large national charities)
- support professionals of whom our team are members (e.g. Chartered Accountants Benevolent Association)
- support disadvantaged people in the communities near which our offices are based
- seek to place people into employment and assist in housing (essential if a job is to be held down)
- seek to relieve hardship in deprived areas of the world in crisis situations
- as a firm, we wish to provide active support as a means of encouraging our team's participation in charitable activity (e.g. Business in the Community or The Prince's Trust in areas like mentoring, providing time and expertise in lieu of cash, or cash backing for voluntary work)
- our clients are encouraging us to support (subject always to careful adherence to independence criteria).

'It is hoped that by specifying these varying aims may over time lead to particular focuses in one form of activity in which initiatives are fostered by team members with the active support of the regional reps on the trust management committee and their regional managing partner or other manager reputed to manage the region's pot.'

In addition, applications for smaller amounts, usually between £50 and £500 may be made to one of the company's regions. These do not entail such detailed criteria and information can be obtained from the correspondent's secretary.

Exclusions

There is no support available for advertising in charity brochures, fundraising events, political appeals, science/technology or sport.

The company rarely supports large national charities as it prefers to welcome applications where a grant will make a significant impact.

The company will not permit a further application from a particular charity within a three year period of an earlier grant.

Commitment will not be made to on-going funding on the grounds that the future income of the trust is not assured.

The company does not generally support causes that are local to the partner/staff member proposing, as there is a regional allocation for smaller, less strategic applications to be made at the discretion of local managing partners.

Applications

In writing to any partner or employee of the firm. The trustees operate through a management committee which meets annually to consider applications for major grants which fit with the stated criteria. Some monies are allocated to five regional 'pot' holders who approve minor grant applications from within their own region.

Applicants for a national grant must be known to the team members of Mazars LLP. National and regional criteria are regularly reviewed but, in general, the trustees consider that the national grant making policy should avoid core funding and other activities that require funding over a number of years. Most national grants are therefore made towards one-off projects. Successful national applicants may not reapply within three years.

A copy of these criteria is available upon request to the trust administrator.

Corporate giving

In 2006/07, the LLP donated £244,000 (inclusive of Income Tax recovered) to the trust; the largest single donation received. The charity made donations to charitable causes totalling £224,267 during the year ended 31 December 2007.

In kind support

Additional support may be given in the form of gifts in kind and staff secondments.

Employee-led support

Employees are encouraged to get involved with community/ charitable projects/fundraising and grants from the trust are available on a meter funding basis. On occasion, match funding may be available for any charitable project/work in which a staff member becomes involved up to a maximum of £250.

Payroll giving: The company operates the Give As You Earn scheme.

Robert McAlpine Ltd

Company registration number 566823

Eaton Court, Maylands Avenue, Hemel Hempstead, Hertfordshire HP2 7TR

01442 233444; Fax: 01422 230024

Website: www.sir-robert-mcalpine.com

Correspondent: Brian Arter, Charity Co-ordinator

Year end	Turnover	Pre-tax profit
31/10/2007	£1,792,376,000	£45,904,000

Nature of company business
The principal business of the group is that of civil engineering and building contractors and renewable energy.

Main locations: Hemel Hempstead

UK employees: 2,834

Charitable donations

2007: £666,000

Community involvement

Robert McAlpine Ltd is the trading name of Newarthill Ltd; the ultimate parent company. End of year financial figures and charitable donations are those given in the annual report of Newarthill Ltd, but cover the whole McAlpine group of companies.

The company has a preference for local charities in areas where it operates and charities in which a member of the company is involved. Preferred areas for support are children and youth, and education.

There are two charitable trusts associated with the company – The Robert McAlpine Foundation and the McAlpine Educational Endowment. Details of each are given below.

Exclusions

No support for local appeals not in areas of company presence.

Applications

In writing to the correspondent.

Corporate giving

In 2007, the group made charitable donations in the UK of £666,000. We have no details of the beneficiaries.

The Robert McAlpine Foundation

The foundation generally supports causes concerned with children with disabilities, older people, medical research and social welfare. The trustees meet annually, normally in November. Successful applicants are informed at the end of the year. Applications should be addressed to the Secretary of the Trustees of the Robert McAlpine Foundation, at the address above.

The McAlpine Educational Endowment

This trust is for 13 to 18-year olds, who have sound academic ability, show leadership potential and are facing financial hardship. The trust favours 10 particular schools, with referrals coming from the headmasters. Applications should be addressed to the Secretary of the Trustees of the McAlpine Educational Endowment, at the address above.

McCain Foods (GB) Ltd

Company registration number 733218

Havers Hill, Scarborough, North Yorkshire YO11 3BS

01723 584141; Fax: 01723 581230

Website: www.mccain.co.uk

Correspondent: Claire Bentley, Secretary, Charities Committee

Managing Director: Nick Vermont

Year end	Turnover	Pre-tax profit
30/06/2005	£307,751,000	£23,080,000

Nature of company business
Manufacturer and supplier of frozen and ambient food products.

Subsidiaries include: SSHP Holdings Ltd, Everest Foods plc, Dansco Dairy Products Ltd, PAS Ltd, Britfish Ltd, Tolona Pizza Products Ltd, Everest Frozen Foods Ltd

Main locations: Scarborough, Peterborough, Montrose, Wolverhampton, Teddington

UK employees: 1,663

Charitable donations

2007: £87,657
2006: £69,023
2005: £80,806
2004: £75,406
2003: £20,000

Community involvement

The company prefers to give all cash donations locally (mainly in Yorkshire and particularly Scarborough). There is a preference for appeals relevant to company business. Preferred areas of support: children and youth; medical; education; recreation/sport; environment and heritage; the arts; enterprise/training.

Exclusions

Generally no support for: circular appeals; fundraising events; advertising in charity brochures; appeals from individuals; purely denominational (religious) appeals or local appeals not in areas of company presence.

Applications

In writing to the correspondent.

Corporate giving

During 2006/07, the company made charitable donations in the UK of £87,657. Although we have no information regarding the beneficiaries, we were advised that support is only given to charities and organisations 'in our own local area'.

In kind support

Additional support is provided through gifts in kind. Although not explicitly stated, we believe this to be in the form of product donations.

McDonald's Restaurants Ltd

Company registration number 1002769

11–59 High Road, East Finchley, London N2 8AW

0870 241 3300

Website: www.mcdonalds.co.uk

Correspondent: Joe Zammuto, Corporate Affairs
Email: joe.zammuto@uk.mcd.com

Year end	Turnover	Pre-tax profit
31/12/2007	£1,069,780,000	£39,973,000

Nature of company business
The activity of the company is quick service restaurants.

Main locations: London

Total employees: 37,644

Charitable donations
2007: £367,000
2006: £385,000
2005: £2,197,000
2004: £531,000

Membership: BitC

Community involvement

All of the company's charitable donations are given to the charitable trust, Ronald McDonald House Charities (Charity Commission no. 802047). The bulk of the charity's work is the creation of 'home away from home' accommodation for the families of children requiring in-patient care in hospitals or hospices.

Exclusions

No support for animal welfare charities, appeals from individuals, the arts, elderly people, medical research, overseas projects, political appeals, religious appeals, or science/technology.

Applications

In writing to the correspondent, preferably by email.

Corporate giving

McDonald's Restaurants Ltd, made charitable donations in 2007 of £367,000 (2006: £385,000). The sole recipient was Ronald McDonald House Charities.

Employee-led support

McDonald's has an employee volunteering scheme and allows staff company time off in which to carry out charitable activities. Please note, however, that staff are encouraged to participant in fundraising events for the company's own charity.

Commercially-led support

Sponsorship: *Sports* – the company supports a football coaching qualification provided by the national football associations of England, Northern Ireland, Scotland and Wales.

The scheme has helped to create over 13,000 new volunteer community football coaches across the UK since 2002, with an overall ambition to coach one million children by 2010.

Medtronic Ltd

Company registration number 1070807

Suite One, Building 5, Croxley Green Business Park, Watford WD18 8WW

01923 212213

Website: www.medtronic.co.uk

Correspondent: (see 'Applications')

Year end	Turnover	Pre-tax profit
28/04/2006	£57,034,000	£5,548,000

Nature of company business
The sale and marketing of medical technology to treat and manage conditions such as heart disease, neurological disorders, vascular illnesses and diabetes.

Main locations: Watford

UK employees: 240

Charitable donations
2006: £231,000
2005: £170,842

Community involvement

The Medtronic Foundation supports the following areas: community health; education and training opportunities; welfare; patient associations; and science education for children. Its two main programmes for UK applicants are as follows:

Patient Link – The programme is open to national/international patient associations that educate, support and advocate on behalf of patients and their families to improve the lives of people with chronic diseases.

Heart Rescue Grant Programme – The programme is open to local EMS agencies, hospitals and other non-profit organisations concerned with saving lives from sudden cardiac arrest through support of SCA awareness, prevention and treatment efforts.

Exclusions

The Medtronic Foundation does not support: continuing medical education grants; capital or capital projects; fundraising events/activities, social events or goodwill advertising; general operating support; general support of educational institutions; individuals, including scholarships for individuals; lobbying, political or fraternal activities; long-term counselling or personal development; programme endowments; purchases of automatic external defibrillators (AEDs); religious groups for religious purposes; private foundations; research.

Applications

Full information regarding the various grant programmes available, qualifying criteria and how to apply are available at: www.medtronic.com

Basically, organisations from outside of the United States wishing to apply firstly need to select the grant programme of interest. You will then be directed to complete a letter of inquiry and instructed on where to send it. Upon receiving the letter, a foundation representative may recommend that you submit a full application. At that time, an application form and a list of the required documents for organisations based outside the US will be provided.

Corporate giving

In 2005/06 (the latest year for which UK accounts were available), the company made cash donations of £231,000. Made predominantly to medical causes, the largest donation during the year was £25,000 to North Glasgow University Hospital NHS Trust.

We are unsure if the above support is given separately from any grants made in the UK by the Medtronic Foundation, or whether that is were the funding originates from.

In 2007/08, the foundation made grants worldwide of $26.2 million. Of this, around 16% was given outside of the United States ($4.2 million/£2.2 million).

In kind support

Products are available to international medical relief organisations.

Employee-led support

Employees are encouraged to carry out community work.

John Menzies plc

Company registration number SC4970

108 Princes Street, Edinburgh EH2 3AA

0131 225 8555; Fax: 0131 220 1491

Website: www.johnmenziesplc.com

Correspondent: Gordon McVinnie, Charity Funds Administrator

Chairman: William Thomson

Year end	Turnover	Pre-tax profit
29/12/2007	£1,541,000,000	£31,800,000

Nature of company business
Logistics support services group.

Main locations: Edinburgh, Hounslow

UK employees: 8,000

Total employees: 15,000

Charitable donations

2007: £86,000
2006: £112,000
2005: £125,000
2004: £94,000
2003: £100,000

Community involvement

The company prefers to support charities it categorises as working in the fields of: Health, education and medical research; Care, welfare, children and poverty; Sport (disabled) and arts; and Environment and heritage. Preference is given to charities in areas of company presence.

Each year the board approves a charitable budget of around one percent of gross dividends (as opposed to pre-tax profit) for the previous financial year. Support is given through the John Maxwell Menzies Community Fund, which solely assists employees in their voluntary work and the Charities Fund which is managed by a charities committee chaired by the chief executive.

We were advised by the company that from 2008 onwards, they intend increasing the size of individual charitable donations, but only make them to a few charities selected by them.

Exclusions

No support for animal welfare, appeals from individuals, enterprise/training, overseas projects, political appeals, religious appeals, or science/technology

Applications

Due to a change in the company's charitable giving policy, unsolicited applications are no longer considered.

Corporate giving

In 2007, the company donated £86,000 worldwide to various charitable, community and arts organisations. Donations vary between £250 and £1,000. Recent beneficiaries have included: Facing the World; NewstrAid; Yorkhill Children's Foundation; The Jolt Trust; and Educando Project – Peru.

Employee-led support

The John Maxwell Menzies Community Fund distributes funds to organisations in which company staff are directly involved.

Employees' fundraising and giving initiatives each may receive funding from the company to a maximum of £350 for individuals or £700 for teams.

Payroll giving: The company operates the Give As You Earn scheme, for which it meets the administration costs.

Merck Sharp & Dohme Ltd

Company registration number 820771

Hertford Road, Hoddesdon, Hertfordshire EN11 9BU

01992 467272; Fax: 01992 467270

Website: www.msd-uk.co.uk

Correspondent: External Affairs Manager

Managing Director: Vincent Lawton

Year end	Turnover	Pre-tax profit
31/12/2006	£383,061,000	£133,529,000

Nature of company business
Merck Sharp & Dohme Ltd is the UK subsidiary of Merck & Co. Inc., a research-driven pharmaceutical and services company. It discovers, manufactures and markets a broad range of innovative products to improve human and animal health.

Main locations: Hoddesdon, Cramlington

UK employees: 1,624

Charitable donations

2006: £32,111
2005: £51,089
2004: £69,580

Membership: BitC

Community involvement

We were advised by the External Affairs department at Merck, Sharp & Dohme – Hoddesdon, that: 'We have discussed this issue [our Corporate Community Support Survey 2008] with management and they have kindly advised that the report should be based on the already existing information that can be found on MSD's websites ... We regret that we can be of no further help'.

Unfortunately, the UK website appears somewhat out of date, with most examples of community support referring to 2005 or earlier (it is unclear whether the projects mentioned are still running). The US website meanwhile takes a more global perspective of the company's support and is not, therefore, helpful for our purposes here.

Merck, Sharp & Dohme states on its UK website that it: 'Aims to make a positive contribution to its local communities by supporting a wide range of charitable, educational and environmental initiatives. [and] strives to be a 'Neighbour of Choice' in the local communities where it is based.

The company has two sites in the UK: headquarters and pharmaceutical research and development laboratories in Hoddesdon, Hertfordshire; and manufacturing at Cramlington in Northumberland. The main thrust of the company's community support at these sites involves education and the environment.

Applications

In writing to the correspondent.

Corporate giving

In 2006, the company declared charitable donations in the UK of £32,111 (2005: £51,089). We have no details of the initiatives or groups supported in 2006.

Employee-led support

Employees are involved in educational and environmental projects within the local community.

The Mersey Docks and HarbourCompany

Company registration number ZC000189

Maritime Centre, Port of Liverpool, Liverpool L21 1LA

0151 949 6000; Fax: 0151 949 6300

Website: www.merseydocks.co.uk

Correspondent: W J Bowley, Secretary to the Dock Charitable Fund

Chairman: J Whittaker

Year end	Turnover	Pre-tax profit
31/03/2007	£85,523,000	£46,949,000

Nature of company business
The principal activities of the group are the operation and maintenance of port facilities on the Rivers Mersey and Medway, provision of cargo handling and associated services, and the conservancy and pilotage of the Ports of Liverpool and Medway and their approaches and the development of their respective dock estates.

Subsidiaries include: Woodside Business Park Ltd, Concorde Container Line Ltd, Marine Terminals Ltd, Link Transport Services Ltd, Spade Lane Cool Store Ltd, Roadferry Ltd, Portia Management Services Ltd, Portia World Travel Ltd, Medway Ports Ltd, Seawing International Ltd, Heysham Port Ltd, Coastal Container Line Ltd, Tankspeed Ltd, Sheerness Produce Terminal Ltd, Imar Ltd

Main locations: Sheerness, Liverpool, Heysham, Birkenhead

UK employees: 842

Charitable donations

2007: £168,458
2006: £150,773
2005: £110,000
2004: £126,425
2003: £133,913

Community involvement

The Mersey Docks and Harbour Company and acquired by Peel Ports Investments Ltd in July 2005, and now forms part of the Port of Liverpool and The Manchester Ship Canal. A large part of the company's donations are made through The Mersey Docks and Harbour Charitable Fund (Charity Commission no. 206913). There is a preference for local charities in the areas of company presence and appeals relevant to company business. Preferred areas of support are the arts, children/youth, education, elderly people, medical research, sickness/disability, social welfare and sport.

Exclusions

No support for circular appeals, advertising in charity brochures, appeals from individuals, fundraising events, religious appeals, local appeals not in areas of company presence, large national appeals or overseas projects.

Applications

In writing to the correspondent.

Corporate giving

In 2007, the company made charitable donations totalling £168,458 (2006: £150,773 – 15 month period). Besides the donation made to the associated trust (see below), we have no details of the beneficiaries.

The Mersey Docks and Harbour Charitable Fund

The fund gives grants annually to certain local charities. The trust was set up with three objectives:

- reward of people assisting in the preservation of the life of the crew of any ship wrecked in the port of Liverpool or in the preservation of the ship or cargo or in the preserving or endeavouring to preserve people from drowning
- relief of sick, disabled or superannuated men in the dock service or the families of such men who were killed in service
- benefit of charities in the town or port of Liverpool.

In the year to 31 December 2006, the fund had an income of £60,589, £60,000 of which was donated by the company (2005: £110,000).

Grants made during 2006 included: Community Foundation for Merseyside (£20,380); The Merseyside Mission to Seafarers (£10,000); Bootle High School (£5,000); Plaza Community Cinema (£3,000); Toxteth Citizen's Advice Bureau (£1,000); and Ainsdale Cricket Club (£500).

Michelin Tyre plc

Company registration number 84559

Campbell Road, Stoke-on-Trent ST4 4EY

01782 402000; Fax: 01782 402011

Website: www.michelin.co.uk

Correspondent: Christine Reynolds, Corporate Image Specialist
Email: christine.reynolds@uk.michelin.com

Managing Director: J Rickard

Year end	Turnover	Pre-tax profit
31/12/2007	£729,967,000	£41,318,000

Nature of company business
The manufacture and sale of tyres, tubes, wheels and accessories, maps and guides, and mobility support services.

Subsidiaries include: ATS (Investment) Ltd

Main locations: Ballymena, Stoke-on-Trent, Dundee

UK employees: 3,489

Charitable donations
2007: £125,315
2004: £57,713
2003: £99,020
Membership: BitC

Community involvement

The company has a usual preference for:

- national and local initiatives dedicated to improve mobility (road safety, environment and accessibility)
- local initiatives (Ballymena, Dundee and Stoke-on-Trent) concerned mainly with the progress of mobility, training and youth development schemes and other local development programmes.

Exclusions

No support for circular appeals, advertising in charity brochures, animal welfare, appeals from individuals, political appeals, religious appeals, or local appeals not in areas of company presence.

Applications

In writing to the correspondent.

Corporate giving

In 2007, the company made donations of £125,315. We have no details of the beneficiaries.

In kind support

Education: The company is involved in local education/business partnerships and links have been developed through the provision of educational assistance for schools, including work experience.

Enterprise: The company gives support to local enterprise agencies.

Environment: The company is involved in local schemes to improve wasteland and works with local business networks providing environmental expertise and training.

Other: The company also provides its sports and social facilities free of charge for local school sports events and training for local organisations such as the police and fire brigade.

Employee-led support

As well as preference being given to charities in which a member of staff is involved, employees are encouraged to become involved in the local community through acting as volunteers in both their own time and business hours when appropriate. The company provides matched funding to certain activities by its employees.

Payroll giving: The Give As You Earn scheme is operated by the company.

Commercially-led support

Sponsorship: The company is committed to improve the quality of mobility and may support various initiatives in road safety or environmentally friendly mobility issues.

Microsoft Ltd

Company registration number 1624297

Microsoft Campus, Thames Valley Park, Reading RG6 1WG

0870 601 0100; Fax: 0870 60 20 100

Website: www.microsoft.com/uk/community

Correspondent: Harsha Gadhvi, UK Community Affairs Manager

Year end	Turnover	Pre-tax profit
29/06/2007	£555,622,000	£53,763,000

Nature of company business
Computer software manufacturer and supplier.

Main locations: Edinburgh, London, Manchester, Reading

UK employees: 2,360

Charitable donations

2007: £258,213

2006: £187,962

2005: £223,142

2004: £373,888

Total community contributions: £258,213

Membership: BitC

Community involvement

Much of the following information regarding Microsoft's community support in the UK is taken from its website.

'At Microsoft in the UK, our aim is to build UK prosperity, both socially and economically, through our Citizenship programmes.

'One of the areas in which we work to make a difference socially within citizenship is through community affairs. Microsoft has successfully established an extensive network of non-profit partners who we work with to support community-based programmes and local projects which will enable more people to have access to technology. We give to a range of major charity projects both financially and through gifts in kind. In addition we support the investment of our employees in the community.

'Unlimited Potential is a global Microsoft community investment programme focused on improving the quality of life for people around the world through monetary grants, software, technology solutions, curriculum donations and employee volunteer hours.

'Microsoft Unlimited Potential (UP) is a global initiative, launched in 2003, which focuses on improving lifelong learning for disadvantaged young people and adults by providing technology skills through community technology and learning centres.

'In the UK, Microsoft has partnered with charities including: Leonard Cheshire, Age Concern, Fairbridge, NCH, Scarman Trust and Citizen's Online to bring IT and IT skills to over 10,000 disadvantaged people across Britain.

'In addition to Unlimited Potential programme, Microsoft also works with a number of other charities including the NSPCC and Ability Net and runs other programmes to aid communities in the UK.

'The NSPCC and Microsoft have been in partnership for 11 years and together aim to stop cruelty to children. Microsoft has been in partnership with Ability Net for the past 7 years and has provided funding for trainers in the Ability Net centres across the UK.

'Microsoft also operates a Software Donation scheme. The Microsoft Giving Programme provides support and software donations to hundreds of registered charities and non-profit organisations in the UK.

'The Microsoft Authorised Refurbisher (MAR) and Fresh Start programme are designed to make it easier for charities and schools to use donated computers and to acquire low cost, second use, refurbished PCs.'

Exclusions

Microsoft is only able to donate cash to selected major charity projects. They do not supply PC hardware, but do support a scheme to recycle PC's. No support is given, in any form, for political, religious or racially motivated projects.

Applications

In writing to the correspondent.

Corporate giving

During the period 2006/07, Microsoft Ltd donated £258,213 for charitable purposes. (2005/06:£187,962). No value was available for its in kind support.

Microsoft's community affairs website contains extensive information on, and examples of, its community support in the UK. The information below covers some of the main beneficiaries of Microsoft's support in the UK.

Black Country Consortium

'The Black Country Consortium (BCC) project is a long-term commitment supported by Microsoft to develop a stronger knowledge economy by improving the skills of the current labour force and providing basic skills to the unemployed. Through a network of 120 community technology centres, disadvantaged communities are receiving technology skills training in the Black Country region. The project ultimately aims to enable job growth and sustained economic opportunity in this economically depressed region. BCC works closely with Black Country Knowledge Society, to provide technology training at all levels, and with the Black Country Learning Net, to broaden digital inclusion in the community.'

Age Concern

'In Western Europe, there are limited work force opportunities for unemployed people over 50. As a part of the Black Country project, Age Concern's mission is to address unemployment in the Black Country region by supporting all people over 50 through a digital inclusion network as well as promoting micro-entrepreneurship through the PRIME initiative. The PRIME initiative is a charity linked to Age Concern, which strives to help people older than 50 consider options for self-employment and micro-entrepreneurship. In supporting this goal, Microsoft Unlimited Potential funding will be used to run community workshops on self-employment and to ensure appropriate IT skills training is delivered. It will help recruit mentors for potential micro-entrepreneurs and help track progress of people who are starting small businesses.'

Royal National Institute for the Blind (RNIB)

'Seventy-five percent of people who are blind or have low vision are unemployed in the United Kingdom. The Royal National Institute for the Blind (RNIB) is part of the Black Country project. Its mission is to empower people with visual disabilities to improve employment opportunities through IT skills training. The RNIB partnership will drive increased accessible IT skills training and access to employment for blind and partially sighted people of working age. Microsoft Unlimited Potential funding will support the cost of training trainers, making training centres accessible, and providing employer awareness training on disabilities in the workplace.'

In kind support

The Microsoft Giving programme provides in kind support to charities and community groups each year by donating software for use in fundraising or helping to run voluntary organisations.

'Microsoft Authorised Refurbisher (MAR) and Fresh Start programmes are specifically designed to make it easier for charities and schools to use donated computers and to acquire low cost, second use, refurbished PCs, using properly licensed software.

'Microsoft Community Affairs is working with Charity Technology Trust (CTT) a UK registered charity, to take over the management of the UK Microsoft product philanthropy programme. Effective from the 1st July 2006, CTT will be taking over the existing UK product donation programme and full details are available on the company's website.'

Employee-led support

Volunteering: 'At Microsoft we like to enhance our support by giving the community what we value most – the time and skills of our employees. With that in mind we introduced a formalised Employee Volunteering Programme in 2003. The UK programme enables employees to get involved in a way that suits them – whether they would like to spend a couple of hours helping out on a one-off key skills workshop or make a long term commitment to mentor a young person.

'Our volunteering is delivered through a number of external partners including The Prince's Trust, Central Berkshire Education Business Partnership, IT4Communities, The Prince's Scottish Youth Business Trust among others. In addition we aim to build volunteering opportunities into our Unlimited Potential Partnerships.'

Matching: 'Microsoft runs a matched giving scheme to encourage individual fundraising activities. The scheme matches staff fundraising up to £7,500 per annum, per employee. In 2005, Microsoft matched over £180,000 to help support over 55 organisations.'

Payroll giving: 'By signing up to GAYE, employees can choose to donate to a charity directly from their salary pre tax. Employees can choose any cause they wish to receive monthly donations and Microsoft will do the rest.'

Commercially-led support

Cause-related marketing: When choosing Microsoft Store to purchase Microsoft Office and Windows Vista this Christmas (2008), Microsoft will donate 15% from the purchase price to the NSPCC Child's Voice Appeal.

The Midcounties Co-operative

Company registration number IP19025R

Co-operative House, 234 Botley Road, Oxford OX2 0HP

01865 249241

Website: www.midcounties.coop

Correspondent: The Community Team

Email: communityteam@midcounties.coop

Chief Executive: Ben Reid

John Boot (Vice President); Patrick Gray (President); Viviian Woodell (Vice President)

Year end	Turnover	Pre-tax profit
26/01/2008	£550,369,000	£7,668,000

Nature of company business
The society has a number of diverse trading activities covering food, motor, property, travel childcare and funeral services.

Subsidiaries include: Oxford Garage Group Ltd, A W Bruce Ltd, North Oxfordshire Stores Ltd

Main locations: Gloucester, Oxford, Swindon

UK employees: 7,387

Charitable donations
2008: £203,790
2006: £150,000
2004: £212,000

Total community contributions: £520,051

Community involvement

In 2005, the Oxford, Swindon & Gloucester Co-operative Society Ltd merged with the West Midlands Co-operative Society to form the Midcounties Co-operative.

The Midcounties Co-operative is committed to supporting its community through a range of initiatives, including: Co-operative Community Funding; Co-operative Community Chequebook; and community volunteering.

Charity of the Year: Dogs for the Disabled (2008/09).

Exclusions

Applications from outside the operating area of the Midcounties Co-operative Society, i.e. Oxfordshire, Gloucestershire, Swindon, parts of Buckinghamshire and the West Midlands.

Midcounties Co-operative is also unable to help with funding for individuals and funding for overseas projects.

Applications

Applying for funding or for volunteer hours is simple. You can download a form from the Midcounties website, or you can request one by telephoning them on 01902 405700

As with all grant providers there are some conditions to be met – your project must:
- benefit a local community where at least one Midcounties Co-operative business trades
- have a charitable or community purpose.

Interestingly, given the negative responses we received when recently researching this exact topic, full details of the Midcounties Co-operative's terms and conditions are available on its application form.

If you think you may qualify for a Co-operative Community Chequebook donation, just pop into your local Co-operative store, Co-op Travel branch, Co-operative Funeral home, Motorworld franchise or Imagine Co-operative Childcare nursery and ask to speak to the manager.

Corporate giving

The Midcounties investment across the region in community initiatives during 2007/08 amounted to £520,051 which represents 6.8% of profit t before tax. The figure is derived from the total time, resources and money donated and invested. This compares with £619,051 in the previous year which represented 4.2% of profit before tax.

Cash donations during the year totalled £203,790 to deserving local community projects. Grants were used for a variety of purposes, for example, a new greenhouse for the residents of West View Sheltered Housing, story sacks to encourage reading at Eastrop Infant School in Highworth, and an automatic chemical dosing system for Highley outdoor pool. One of the largest events supported was the Oxford Children's

Food Festival held in July 2007 which attracted 18,000 visitors.

This support is given primarily in one of two ways:

- through Co-operative Community Funding which provides grants of up to £500 to support local community groups and projects
- through the Co-operative Community Chequebook which helps support local fundraising. Introduced into all its branches, these cheques can be used if a request is made for a raffle prize or small donation from the Co-op.

Employee-led support

A total of 14,847 hours were given to community work compared with 3,213 in 2006/07. Projects ranged from helping with riding for the disabled to reading with local school children and decorating health centres. This work would have cost £215,133 if it had been paid for.

Miller Group Ltd

Company registration number SC018135

Miller House, 2 Lochside View, Edinburgh Park, Edinburgh EH12 9DH

0870 336 5000; Fax: 0870 336 5002

Website: www.miller.co.uk

Correspondent: Stephen Dunn, Group HR Director

Chairman: Bob Speirs

Chief Executive: Keith Miller

Year end	Turnover	Pre-tax profit
31/12/2007	£1,232,800,000	£812,000,000

Nature of company business
Housing, property development and construction.

Main locations: Glasgow

UK employees: 2,090

Charitable donations
2007: £177,000

Community involvement

Miller states that it, 'endorses the need for a broader involvement in the community' and, accordingly, in 2007 established a new charity framework – "m'brace".

Besides introducing a payroll giving mechanism, it saw, for the first time, three employee-nominated 'lead charities' join three company-nominated ones. Each charity will receive direct financial and promotional support from the company as a result.

In addition to this, the group continues to provide charitable and sponsorship support for numerous communities across a wide range of causes from sport, to health and culture.

Employees are supported by the company in their personal fundraising efforts through a matched giving scheme. Staff and suppliers also contribute in kind to a wide range of community initiatives.

Applications
In writing to the correspondent.

Corporate giving

In 2007, the group made charitable donations of £177,000. Although not explicitly stated in the report and accounts, we believe the majority of this will have gone towards supporting the six lead charities.

Employee-nominated charities – Multiple Sclerosis Therapy Centres (UK), The Teenage Cancer Trust and Maggie's Centres.

Company-nominated charities – The Prince's Trust, the Duke of Edinburgh's Award scheme and The Place2be.

In kind support

Staff and suppliers contribute time, money and materials to a range of community initiatives, e.g. the building of playgrounds.

Employee-led support

Payroll giving: The Give As You Earn scheme is now available to employees.

Misys plc

Company registration number 1360027

One Kingdom Street, Paddington, London W2 6BL

020 3320 5000; Fax: 020 3320 1771

Website: www.misys.co.uk

Correspondent: Nigel Talbot-Rice, Director, Mysis Charitable Foundation

Chairman: Sir Dominic Cadbury

Chief Executive: Mike Lawrie

Year end	Turnover	Pre-tax profit
31/05/2008	£492,300,000	£48,900,000

Nature of company business
The development and licensing of application software products to customers in well-defined vertical markets within the financial services and healthcare sectors, together with transaction processing and professional services.

Main locations: London

UK employees: 4,975

Charitable donations
2008: £100,000
2007: £100,000
2006: £100,000
2005: £124,453
2004: £120,000

Community involvement

The following information is taken from the company's website.

'The Misys Charitable Foundation [Charity Commission no. 1065678] was created in 1997 with the goal of furthering education in information and communications technology worldwide. Its work focuses on three key areas: university scholarships, in the UK and overseas; funding for information technology (IT) equipment in UK state schools; and IT-related support for charities working in communities.

'The foundation is funded directly through donations from Misys plc, the global software company, whose board is firmly committed to the foundation's aims. One of these aims is to strengthen ties with the company's own 6,000 employees worldwide – many of whom are personally involved in local community and charitable activities.'

Exclusions

Appeals from local community organisations not in areas of company presence. Direct appeals from individuals outside of 'linked' schools or universities.

Applications

In writing to the correspondent.

Please note that scholarships are awarded on the recommendation of the foundation's partner institutions and not to individual applicants.

Corporate giving

In 2007/08, the company donated £100,000 (2006/07: £100,000) to the foundation in line with its stated commitment to provide minimum funding of £100,000 per annum for five years from 2003. What will happen to the foundation's funding after this year, we do not at present know.

Misys Charitable Foundation

For over 10 years the foundation has provided funding support for:

Students – support is given to able students studying IT - related subjects at university in the UK and abroad, with priority given to those in greatest financial need. Since it was established the foundation has supported 362 students at home and overseas.

Schools – support is given to schools, mainly primary, that are finding it difficult to raise the money required for their IT education programme. The foundation encourages employees to nominate schools in need of support, adding an important employee engagement aspect to its work.

Charities – help is given to organisations working to further IT education and the benefits of IT to the wider community, in particular charities giving IT training to the disabled.

During the calendar year the foundation donated:
- £121,000 in scholarships to students
- £20,000 to three schools
- £22, 000 to seven community projects.

In total 38 Misys Foundation scholarships were awarded to students studying at 12 British universities and colleges and at three universities and colleges overseas. Eight students had their awards extended.

In kind support

Misys donated redundant IT hardware to Digital Links International, a charity that arranges the refurbishment and dispatch of equipment to needy schools in Africa. The transport and training costs involved were covered by the foundation.

Employee-led support

Payroll giving: The company relaunched its 'Give as You Earn' scheme in the UK during 2006, and makes funds of up to £100,000 in total available for matched giving to specified charities designated by the company.

Mitchells & Butlers plc

Company registration number 4551498

27 Fleet Street, Birmingham B3 1JP

0870 609 3000; Fax: 0121 233 2246

Website: www.mbplc.com

Correspondent: Sally Ellson

Email: csr@mbplc.com

Chairman: Drummond Hall

Chief Executive: Tim Clarke

Managing Directors: Mike Bramley and Adam Fowle

Year end	Turnover	Pre-tax profit
29/09/2007	£1,894,000,000	(£48,000,000)

Nature of company business
Operator of managed pubs and pub restaurants.

Main locations: Birmingham

UK employees: 42,741

Charitable donations
2007: £215,000
2006: £200,000
2005: £143,000
2003: £71,000

Total community contributions: £500,000

CRM figure: £17,000

Community involvement

Mitchells & Butlers' charity policy is as follows:

'National charitable donations are supported at a corporate level through a centrally managed budget. In addition our Employee Community Award scheme encourages our employees to support a charity through their own fundraising activity or voluntary work.

'It is our policy that our retail managers are able to support those charities which are most important to their local community and we recognise these activities through our Heart of the Community Awards scheme. Our pub and pub restaurant raise thousands of pounds for charity and our Pub and Restaurant Community Awards Scheme enables our businesses who actively support a charity to apply for a company donation.

'Throughout the year we also make a number of in kind donations such as use of company facilities free of charge and donating complimentary meals in our businesses to local community groups, charities and schools.

'In relation to the donations we make the organisations we support must fall within the following criteria. The organisation must:

- show that they are a registered charity or an organisation with charitable objectives
- be based in the UK and meet the needs of local communities
- demonstrate that they have maintained up to date financial records and/or are financially sound
- show that their projects meet a local need and/or have a relationship with one of our businesses.'

Charity of the year: Barnardos.

Exclusions

The company will not fund charities or organisations to:

- provide expeditions or adventure travel for individuals
- fund advertising space
- restore historic buildings
- support political causes
- sponsor sporting events
- promote religious ideas or views
- fund year-end deficits.

Applications

In writing to the correspondent.

Corporate giving

In 2006/07, declared cash donations totalled £215,000 (2005/06: £200,000), although this figure does include unstated 'additional funds from Arts & Business'. Whilst noting that M&B's sponsorship of the Birmingham Royal Ballet (BRB) secured these additional funds and enabled BRB to host a series of educational dance workshops in primary schools across the West Midlands, we think including them as part of the company's declared donations brings a new and inappropriate meaning to the term 'leverage'.

In kind donations and employee volunteering time are estimated by the company to be around £500,000.

In kind support

This includes the use of company facilities, such as meeting rooms, free of charge, and donating complimentary meals to local community groups, charities and schools.

Employee-led support

The company operates an Employee Community Award Scheme which enables employees who actively support a charity through fundraising or voluntary work to apply for a company donation.

Commercially-led support

Sponsorship: *The arts* – Mitchells & Butlers has sponsored the City of Birmingham Orchestra for over 20 years. It also sponsors Birmingham Repertory Theatre. Birmingham Royal Ballet and ExCathedra.

Cause-related marketing: Ember Inns held its second annual 'Drink Pink' fundraising campaign for leading charity Against Breast Cancer. All Ember Inns pubs donated 5p per glass of rose wine sold, raising over £17,000 for the charity.

J P Morgan Chase

Company registration number 288553

10 Aldermanbury, London EC2V 7RF

Website: www.jpmorgan.com

Correspondent: Ketisha Kinnbrew, Secretary to the foundation 020 7325 1308; Fax: 020 7325 8195

Year end
31/12/2007

Nature of company business
Financial services organisation.

Main locations: London

Charitable donations
2007: £209,000
2006: £241,000
2004: £629,000
Membership: A & B

Community involvement

The company organises its giving through the JPMorgan Foundation (Charity Commission no. 291617). There is also a connecter trust, The JPMorgan Educational Trust (Charity Commission no. 325103), but this is being wound down over the next year and a half (from January 2009). All prior commitments of the trust will be met by the foundation.

The J P Morgan Fleming Foundation fund three major areas of social need.

- Community asset development – to encourage, sustain and develop economic self-reliance
- Youth education – to help young people succeed in life and in work
- Community life – to enrich communities with sponsorships and events focused on arts and culture

Funding is targeted to support the development of communities local to J P Morgan offices. In 2004 these location included London, Bournemouth, Edinburgh, Glasgow, Liverpool and a few UK-wide projects.

Exclusions

Projects that are not usually supported include: open appeals from national charities; direct appeals by individuals; charity gala nights and similar events; and medical charities.

Applications

In writing to the correspondent on two sides of A4. There are no application forms. Please set out your reasons for applying along with an indication of the amount of funding required. There are no specific closing dates for initial enquiries.

Applications are always acknowledged. Trustees meet in March, May, July, September and December. If your application is unsuccessful we suggest you wait at least a year before re-applying.'

Corporate giving

JPMorgan Foundation

In 2007, the foundation received a donation of £209,000 from JPMorgan Education Ltd. In turn, the foundation made 54 grants totalling £1,208,000 (2006: £546,000). The increase in giving is explained by the decision to award all grants, including those that would normally be made from the JPMorgan Educational Trust, from the foundation.

Examples of awards in 2007 within the three major areas of need include:

Community life (arts and culture) – £461,000 (38%) Beneficiaries included Whitechapel Art Gallery (£143,000), National Theatre (£105,000) and Royal Scottish Academy for Music and Drama (£30,000).

Community development – £409,000 (34%). Beneficiaries included Enterprise Education Trust (£132,500), Eastside Community Heritage (£21,550) and AFC Bournemouth Football in the Community Project (£7,500)

Youth education – £338,000 (28%). Beneficiaries included Into University (£75,000), Dorset Young Enterprise (£20,000) and First Step (£15,000).

Employee-led support

Payroll giving: employees are able to donate money to charities of their choice, through monthly donations.

Matched giving scheme: the company matches donations that employees give to charities of their choice.

The Morgan Crucible Company plc

Company registration number 286773

Quadrant, 55–57 High Street, Windsor, Berkshire SL4 1LP

01753 837000; Fax: 01753 850872

Website: www.morgancrucible.com

Correspondent: David Coker, Company Secretary
01753 837000; Fax: 01753 850872

Chairman: Tim, Stevenson

Chief Executive: Mark Robertshaw

Year end	Turnover	Pre-tax profit
04/01/2008	£693,200,000	£71,700,000

Nature of company business
The Morgan Crucible Company plc is the ultimate holding company of a group of subsidiary undertakings engaged in the manufacture and marketing of carbon and ceramic components for application in a wide range of industries and services.

Subsidiaries include: Morgan Matroc Ltd, Thermal Ceramics UK Ltd

Main locations: Windsor, Wirral, Worcester, Leeds

UK employees: 1,293

Total employees: 9,607

Charitable donations

2007: £86,970
2006: £92,507
2005: £168,882
2004: £89,257
2003: £51,563

Community involvement

The company states that its main support goes to relatively small 'niche' charities in the fields of medical care and research. Some limited support is given to the arts in areas of company presence. Grants are distributed by the Morgan Crucible Company Charitable Trust (Charity Commission no. 273507) which has categorised its donations as follows:

Medical development & research; care (including holidays) of people physically or mentally disabled; care (including holidays) of young people in deprived or undesirable circumstances; adventure or training holidays or courses for character development; local (Windsor area) good causes; character reform; arts; education; community services; and director recommended donations.

Exclusions

No support for: animal welfare; appeals from individuals; overseas projects; political appeals; religious appeals; science/technology; or sport.

Applications

In writing to the correspondent. Grant decisions are made by a donations committee which meets quarterly.

Corporate giving

In 2007, the company made worldwide charitable contributions totalling £193,598 (2006: £146,240) of which £86,970 (2006: £92,507) was donated in the UK. From the UK donations, £65,385 was covenanted to the associated company charity. We have no details of the beneficiaries.

Grants of between £100 and £500 are made nationally, but primarily in Wirral, Leeds, South Wales, South London, Worcester and Thames Valley. We believe that subsidiary companies have their own budgets for appeals, but no figures were available.

Morgan Stanley International Ltd

Company registration number 3584019

25 Cabot Square, Canary Wharf, London E14 4QA

020 7425 8000; Fax: 020 7425 8984

Website: www.morganstanley.co.uk

Correspondent: Ami Howse, Morgan Stanley International Foundation

Chairman: J C S Chenevix-Trench

Year end	Pre-tax profit
30/11/2005	£1,041,755,000

Nature of company business
Principal activities: the provision of financial services to corporations, governments, financial institutions and individual investors.

Main locations: London

UK employees: 4645

Charitable donations

2005: £2,610,256

Membership: BitC, L B Group

Community involvement

In June 2008, we were advised by the company that it is 'going through a strategy change at the moment', and that new guidelines regarding its community support would not be available until late September this year. We are still awaiting details.

The company makes a proportion of its charitable donations through the Morgan Stanley International Foundation (Charity Commission no. 1042671). The following guidelines for making charitable donations apply:

'The Morgan Stanley International Foundation (MSIF) is funded by Morgan Stanley International Ltd. It makes contributions to non-profit educational, health care and social service organisations which provide a benefit to our local communities. In London, this is primarily focused on the Boroughs of Tower Hamlets and Newham; in Scotland on Cumbernauld and Glasgow and in continental Europe on the cities in which our offices are based.

'The Foundation's grants are made to registered charities and state-funded schools which provide benefit to the communities local to our offices across Europe. The main thematic focuses are as follows:

▸ education and employability – particular emphasis is given to the provision of services to schools with which Morgan Stanley has an established relationship.

'In addition, but to a lesser extent, projects that provide support in the following areas will be considered:

▸ job training/remedial education/handicapped and homeless support – for adults and young people in order to prepare these people to become self-supporting.

▸ hospitals/health – support for hospitals and innovative healthcare projects in the East End of London. As a rule, the Foundation does not support organisations involved in the research of specific diseases.

'As a rule, the Foundation will give, consistent with the above guidelines, preferential treatment to those organisations which are actively supported through volunteer work or board representation by Morgan Stanley employees'.

The foundation also runs a 'Charity of the Year' programme in London and Glasgow. Employees are able to select a local charity to which all funds raised through company initiatives are donated.

Charity of the Year: Age Concern (2005/06).

Exclusions

'As a rule, grants will not be made to either national or international charitable organisations unless they have a project in one of these areas. In addition, grants will not be made to either political or evangelistic organisations, pressure groups, or individuals outside the Firm who are seeking sponsorship either for themselves (e.g. to help pay for education) or for onward transmission to a charitable organisation.'

Applications

All initial funding enquiries should be directed to Louise Ellison at the Morgan Stanley International Foundation (MSIF): louise.ellison@morganstanley.com

There is no pro forma for grant applications. Please send details of the project for which you are seeking funding, along with a copy of your latest report and accounts, to the correspondent.

Grant applications are considered quarterly in March, June, September and December by the MSIF trustees. The trustees are senior representatives from across the Firm's divisions.

Please note that the MSIF takes a proactive approach to grant making and rarely responds to unsolicited requests.

Corporate giving

During 2005, subsidiaries of the company made donations to various charities of over £3.9 million (2004: £2.3 million). Of this, around £2.6 million was paid to the Morgan Stanley International Foundation for the foundation's financial years 2005 and 2006.

Morgan Stanley International Foundation

In 2005, the foundation had assets of £2.76 million and an income of just over £2.69 million most of which came from a donation from Morgan Stanley and Co. International Ltd. Just over £1.78 million was distributed or committed in grants.

The largest grant of £155,521 was made to the foundation's 'charity of the year', Age Concern There were a further 135 grants made of over £1,000 each including: Save the Children (£100,000); Community Links (£75,769); London Bomb Appeal (£50,000); East Side Educational Trust and Tower Hamlets Summer University (£25,000 each); Trees for Cities (£16,500); and Crime Concern (£12,500).

In kind support

Education – As part of the Tower Hamlets Education Business Partnership's 'Take Our Students to Work Day' programme, 30 local students, aged 13–14 spent a day in the Cabot Square offices.

Morgan Stanley also provided paid summer internships to two local 'A' Level students as part of the Corporation of London's Business Traineeship Programme.

Employee-led support

The company encourages its employees to get involved with the local community and the chosen 'charity of the year'. Fundraising efforts by staff on behalf of Age Concern raised over £150,000 in 2005/06.

Staff contributions to charities of their own choice are matched by the foundation up to a maximum of £2,000 per employee, per event. Additionally, employees can apply to the foundation for matching of their time in volunteering. The size of the grant is dependent upon the employee's length of service with both Morgan Stanley and the benefiting organisation.

Commercially-led support

Sponsorship: The company are sponsors of the 'Great Britons' Awards in partnership with The Daily Telegraph. Members of the public have been invited each year since 2004, to nominate individuals who have achieved success in a particularly 'British' way.

Nominations are made across seven categories: arts; business; campaigning; creative industries; public life; science and innovation; and sport.

To complement Morgan Stanley's recent sponsorship of The Old Vic Theatre, the company funded 'Soapbox', an innovative pilot project created by The Old Vic Education Department. The programme harnesses the skills of actors, writers, producers, directors, education facilitators and Morgan Stanley employees in order to help children communicate more effectively.

Involving 250 pupils over two summer months, the workshop was converted into a curriculum insert aimed at primary schools across London. Following the success of the pilot project, Morgan Stanley funded an expanded 'Soapbox' programme in 2006.

T J Morris Ltd

Axis Business Park, East Lancs Road, Gillmoss, Liverpool, L11 0JA

0151 530 2920

Website: www.homebargains.co.uk

Correspondent: Sue Ion

Email: sue.iom@tjmorris.co.uk

Year end	Turnover	Pre-tax profit
30/06/2007	£322,543,242	£30,205,673

Nature of company business
The principal activity of the company during the year was wholesale distribution and retailing of toiletries, cosmetics and other household products.

UK employees: 3,081

Charitable donations
2007: £184,280
2006: £44,614

Community involvement

T J Morris Ltd (trading as Home Bargains) is a Liverpool-based retailer that has grown over the years and now operates over 140 stores nationwide. Some preference may be given to supporting Merseyside organisations.

Exclusions

No support for individuals, political appeals or local appeals not in areas of company presence.

Applications

In writing to the correspondent.

Corporate giving

In 2006/07, the company made charitable donations of £184,280. We have no details of the beneficiaries.

Commercially-led support

Sponsorship: As part of Liverpool's Capital of Culture celebrations, Home Bargains is sponsoring a number of projects to actively involve the people of Merseyside in creating art. Further details can be found at: www.gocreate08.co.uk/

Wm Morrison Supermarkets plc

Company registration number 358949

Hillmore House, Gain Lane, Bradford BD3 7DL

0845 611 5000

Website: www.morrisons.co.uk

Correspondent: Philippa Hadfield, Charities Administrator

Chairman: Sir Ian Gibson

Chief Executive: Marc Bolland

Year end	Turnover	Pre-tax profit
03/02/2008	£12,969,000,000	£612,000,000

Nature of company business
Retail distribution of goods through the medium of supermarkets.

Subsidiaries include: Erith Pier Co. Ltd, Farmers Boy Ltd, Returnvital Ltd, Lifestyle Wholesale Distribution Ltd, Nathanspire Ltd, Farock Insurance Co. Ltd, M1 Discount Stores Ltd

Main locations: Bradford

UK employees: 117,454

Charitable donations
2008: £100,000
2007: £300,000
2006: £200,000
2005: £153,000
2004: £130,000

Community involvement

Each year a single (usually national) charity is nominated as the company's 'Charity of the Year' and supported throughout the stores through fundraising and collection points. One of the main criteria for selection is that the money raised in a particular area, is used by the charity in that area. The company also contributes to this cause.

Other appeals are supported on a small scale through the Wm Morrison Supermarkets plc Charitable Trust (Charity Commission no. 1007857). Support is given to a wide range of charities within the definition of 'general charitable purposes'.

Charity of the Year: Help the Aged and Childline (2008/09).

Exclusions

No response to circular appeals or support for the arts, overseas projects, or political appeals.

Applications

In writing to the correspondent.

Corporate giving

In 2007/08, the company made charitable donations of £100,000 (2006/07: £300,000). However, unlike in some previous years, the money was not donated to the company's charitable trust. We assume most of the money was given in support of the chosen 'Charity of the Year', although support has also been given to CSV Action Earth.

Wm Morrison Supermarkets plc Charitable Trust

No accounts have been placed on file at the Charity Commission since year ending 30 January 2005. The trust then exceptionally had an income of just over £3 million as a result of a general appeal on behalf of the Tsunami victims. Income since has varied between £5,000 and £11,000 with expenditure varying between £17,000 and £38,000. We have no details of the beneficiaries.

In kind support

Main areas of non-cash support are gifts in kind, joint promotions and training schemes.

Mothercare plc

Company registration number 1950509

Cherry Tree Road, Watford, Hertfordshire WD24 6SH

01923 241000

Website: www.mothercare.com

Correspondent: Charity Administrator, The Mothercare Charitable Foundation 01923 206077; Fax: 01923 206376 Email: debra.barnes@mothercare.co.uk

Chairman: Ian R Peacock

Chief Executive: Ben Gordon

Year end	Turnover	Pre-tax profit
29/03/2008	£676,800,000	£4,500,000

Nature of company business
Principal activities: selling, by retail and mail order, clothing, household goods, furniture and furnishing. The company operates mainly in the UK, US and Europe.

Subsidiaries include: Storehouse Finance plc, Mothercare UK Ltd

Main locations: Watford

UK employees: 7,626

Charitable donations

2008: £100,000
2007: £100,000
2006: £100,000
2005: £250,000
2004: £150,000

Community involvement

In order that Mothercare could have a more focused approach to charitable activities, the Mothercare Group Foundation (Charity Commission no. 1104386) was created and registered with the Charity Commission on 16th June 2004.

The Mothercare Group Foundation

The foundation aims to help parents in the UK and worldwide meet their needs and aspirations for their children and to give their children the very best chance of good health, education, well-being and a secure start in life. Specifically, the foundation welcomes applications from registered charities and research organisations associated with the following criteria:

- ensuring the good health and well-being of mums-to-be, new mums and their children
- special baby-care needs and premature births
- other parenting initiatives relating to family well-being.

The foundation also makes available two discrete funds for Mothercare group employees:

- the Chairman's Fund – an annual allocation donated following a competition among Mothercare staff to propose the most deserving or inspiring cause
- an Area Managers' Fund which is available and responds to requests from local charities made to the group's area managers.

Exclusions

Previous information stated that unsolicited appeals are unlikely to be successful. No response to circular appeals. Support is not given to: animal welfare, appeals from individuals, the arts, elderly people, environment/heritage, religious appeals, political appeals, or sport.

Applications

Requests for donations will only be considered when made in writing on the application form that can be printed from the company's website. Applications are welcomed from registered charities whose objectives match those of The Mothercare Group Foundation. Applications should be accompanied by details of your charity's financial status.

If your cause does not match those of The Mothercare Group Foundation please do not make an application. All applications received that do not meet the criteria will automatically be rejected.

Please note that meetings of the foundation that consider applications for support normally take place on a quarterly basis.

Whilst successful applicants will be notified, the process may take several weeks. If you have not heard from us within 6 months of submitting your application you should assume that your application has been rejected and should not reapply within six months.

Information available: The company produces a social responsibility report. Policy guidelines are available for those considering applying to the foundation.

Corporate giving

In 2007/08, the group made a donation of £100,000 to the Mothercare Group Foundation which during the same year donated £95,000 to charitable causes. The main projects supported were: Wellbeing of Women (£40,000); The New Children's Hospital Appeal (£20,000; Tirupur Maternity Hospital (£15,000); and Richard House Hospice (£15,000).

Other beneficiaries included: KidsOut; The Jennifer Trust; The Peace Hospice; The Child Care Action Trust; and Handicapped Children's Action Group.

In kind support

The group has started a relationship with In-Kind Direct – a national charity linking in kind donors with suitable recipients. Its donations last year included over 100 pallets of goods, donated to more than 200 recipient charities.

Employee-led support

Past information suggested that employees are encouraged to fundraise on behalf of selected charities.

Mott MacDonald Ltd

Company registration number 1243967

St Anne House, 20–26 Wellesley Road, Croydon, Surrey CR9 2UL

020 8774 2000; Fax: 020 8681 5706

Website: www.mottmac.com

Correspondent: Steve Wise

Email: stephen.wise@mottmac.com

Chairman: Peter Wickens

Managing Director: Keith Howells

Year end	Turnover	Pre-tax profit
31/12/2007	£508,491,000	£9,422,000

Nature of company business
The company is one of the world's leading engineering, management and development consultancies.

Main locations: Aberdeen, Belfast, Colwyn Bay, Glasgow, Liverpool, Preston

Total employees: 5,986

Charitable donations

2007: £303,000
2004: £156,185
2003: £89,463

Membership: BitC

Community involvement

A significant proportion of the company's financial support for charitable activities is channelled through the Mott McDonald Charitable Trust (Charity Commission no. 275040). Support is mainly given for education and training purposes in the fields of civil, structural, mechanical, electrical and allied engineering.

Employees are encouraged to get involved with their local communities and to raise funds on behalf of their chosen charity.

Through its not-for-profit arm, the Cambridge Education Foundation, the company supports lectures, research and publications in education focusing on learning and development.

As a member of Business in the Community, the company has agreed to set aside 1% of pre-tax profit towards charitable and community initiatives.

Applications

In writing to the correspondent.

Corporate giving

In 2007, the company declared support 'to recognised charities' totalling £303,000 including a donation of £167,000 to its associated charitable trust. Although we don't have details of those benefiting directly from the company's support, we do have a breakdown of the trusts donations.

Mott MacDonald Charitable Trust

Grants in 2006 totalled £199,389 and were broken down into the following categories:
- scholarships £80,000
- bursaries £103,500

- ICE Quest £5,700
- Milne award £2,850
- best paper award £3,000
- project manager of the year £2,500
- chairman's award £2,000.

In kind support

In helping develop the Global School Partnership, Cambridge Education Foundation has been able to support teachers in the UK and in developing countries to share their knowledge.

Employee-led support

Employees involved in a particular charity are able to apply through the Mott MacDonald Community Award for a grant of up to £1,000 on its behalf.

Muir Group

Company registration number 18632R

Old Government House, Dee Hills Park, Chester, Cheshire CH3 5AR

01928 728000; Fax: 01244 404030

Website: www.muirgroup.org.uk

Correspondent: The Community Engagement Officer
01925 790624; Fax: 01244 404026
Email: fomg@muir.org.uk

Chairman: Anthony Diggle

Chief Executive: John Bellis

Year end	Turnover	Pre-tax profit
31/03/2008	£17,441,000	£1,583,000

Nature of company business
The principal acytivity of the association is the provision of affordable housing to people in housing need, either by way of rent or by sale on a shared ownership basis

UK employees: 133

Charitable donations

2008: £98,535

Community involvement

The Muir Group Housing Association established the Friends of Muir Group (Charity Commission no. 1100471) in 2002 for the following purposes:
- to assist and further the charitable purposes of the group
- to provide support and advice to people in financial hardship or who are elderly or disabled
- to promote education
- to provide recreational facilities to people in need
- the advancement of training and retraining
- the relief of unemployment in areas of social deprivation.

Applications

Applications are open to:
- any individual Muir resident
- any resident group or community group operating in an area where Muir Group residents live

any organisation or partnership that benefits an area where Muir Group operates.

A grant application form and application guidance notes are downloadable from the group's website.

Applications can be made by writing to the correspondent at: Friends of Muir Group, Mere's Edge, Helsby, Cheshire WA6 0DJ. Alternatively, you can apply by telephone (01925 790624); by fax (01244 404026); or, by email (fomg@muir.org.uk).

Applications are considered every three months from March onwards. Notification of a decision normally occurs within four weeks of a meeting taking place.

Corporate giving

In 2006/07, the charity had an income of £101,000 of which over £98,000 was donated by the group. Total grants payable amounted to £58,000 and werte broken down as follows:

- youth (£31,000)
- community (£19,000)
- special needs (£5,000)
- elderly (£3,100).

The majority of funds were spent on arts and sports, with the remainder being spent on health, education and the environment.

National Express Group plc

Company registration number 2590560

7 Triton Square, London NW1 3HG

Website: www.nationalexpressgroup.com

Correspondent: The Group Communications Secretary

Chairman: David Ross

Chief Executive UK Division: Ray O'Toole

Chief Executive: Richard Bowker

Year end	Turnover	Pre-tax profit
31/12/2007	£2,615,400,000	£149,900,000

Nature of company business
The principal activities of the group are the provision of passenger transport services in coaches, buses, airports and trains in the UK, USA and Australia.

Subsidiaries include: Eurolines, Stansted Express, Airlinks The Airport Coach Company Ltd, Stansted Express, c2c Rail Ltd, Travel Midlands Metro, Dot2Dot, King's Ferry

Main locations: London

Total employees: 41554

Charitable donations

2007: £374,000
2006: £296,000
2005: £286,000
2004: £210,000

Community involvement

The National Express Group's Charity Policy has previously stated that it seeks to form partnerships with a range of charities who meet the following criteria.

Charities should ideally be:

- registered (local groups such as football clubs should be encouraged to contact the company's local operators who have more flexible policies)
- national with local branches that connect with the group's local and regional operations
- promoting public transport
- minimal on their administration costs
- involved in one or more of the following areas: education, environment, the arts.

The group has also indicated that within the above criteria, support would be considered for organisations concerned with advertising in charity brochures, children/youth, the older people, enterprise/training and environment/heritage.

Exclusions

The group does not support political or religious organisations and is unlikely to provide corporate assistance to high profile charities with significant existing corporate support.

Applications

Further information is available in writing to the correspondent. All charitable applications are reviewed on a quarterly basis with the Charity Committee providing a regular input.

Information Available: The company produces a Social Responsibility Report.

Corporate giving

The company made cash donations of £374,000 in 2007.

In kind support

The company also gives support in the form of gifts in kind and joint promotions.

Employee-led support

The company supports its staff in their charitable activities where practical. It also matches employee fundraising to an amount which varies.

Payroll giving: A payroll giving scheme is in operation.

Commercially-led support

The company provides arts and good-cause sponsorship.

National Grid plc

Company registration number 2367004

National Grid House, Warwick Technology Park, Gallows Hill, Warwick CV34 6DA

Website: www.nationalgrid.com/uk

Correspondent: Julian Buttery, Head of UK Community Relations 01926 655278; Fax: 01926 655633 Email: julian.buttery@uk.ngrid.com

Chairman: Sir John Parker

Chief Executive: Steve Holiday

Year end	Turnover	Pre-tax profit
31/03/2008	£11,423,000,000	£2,192,000,000

Nature of company business
The principal operations of the company are the ownership and operation of regulated electricity and gas infrastructure networks in the UK and the US, serving around 19 million consumers directly and many more indirectly. Interests in related markets, include electricity interconnectors, metering services, liquefied natural gas (LNG) facilities and property in the UK, LNG storage and transportation, unregulated gas transmission pipelines and home energy services in the US.

Subsidiaries include: Utility Metering Services Ltd, SecondSite Property, Advantica, Fulcrum Connections, Network Mapping Ltd

Main locations: London, Warwick

UK employees: 10,223

Total employees: 27,557

Charitable donations

2008: £600,000
2007: £2,900,000
2005: £1,352,000

Total community contributions: £9,200,000

Membership: A & B, BitC, L B Group

Community involvement

National Grid has provided the following information concerning its work with the community:

'We believe that the best way of conducting our business is in a manner which encourages and supports social growth and development. Our community involvement programme, 'supporting employees, supporting communities' reflects our commercial needs and is designed to develop our business and enhance our reputation by engaging our employees and supporting the local community.

'The main themes of the programme are:

- **education and skills**, forming sustainable partnerships with schools and community groups with a particular focus on skills which support our business such as engineering
- **environment and energy,** demonstrating our commitment to ensuring that energy is used wisely and is available to all at a minimal impact to the environment
- **community development**, supporting the development of diverse, vibrant and prosperous communities.'

'We deliver this by managing a range of social and community programmes which include our environmental education centre network; national partnerships and sponsorships such as Special Olympics Great Britain and The Tree Council; local community project support; employee volunteering.'

Exclusions

Support is not given to circular appeals, advertising in charity brochures, appeals from individuals, overseas projects, political appeals, religious appeals, and local appeals not in areas of company presence.

Applications

In writing to the correspondent. For innovative grants, applications must be submitted on a form by a senior manager of one of the group's businesses rather than the applicant charity.

Information available: A leaflet on National Grid's sponsorship and donations policy is available on request.

Corporate giving

In 2007/08, total worldwide community contributions amounted to £9.2 million (2006/07: £8.9 million) of which cash donations comprised £600,000 (2006/07: £2.9 million). We do not know the reason for the significant fall in cash donations to charity, or to whom specific donations were made.

However, National Grid is engaged in a number of strategic national partnerships which they described to us as follows:

'We have supported The Tree Council's Tree Warden Scheme since 1997. The scheme is a national force of local volunteers, dedicated to their communities' trees. With the help of the Tree Wardens, and expert advice from The Tree Council, we work hard to manage trees near our assets in a safe and sustainable way.

'Our network of environmental education centres are run in partnership with local authorities and environmental charities. They help meet our commitment to operating as a socially and environmentally responsible business, through mitigating the impact of substations on rural environments. They also help by improving the environmental status and biodiversity of the land on which we operate and provide work for staff and hundreds of volunteers.

'We recently became the first ever official partner of Special Olympics Great Britain which is a community driven organisation, with over 200 clubs across Great Britain. It provides people with learning disabilities with everyday opportunities to participate in sport. Supporting the Special Olympics at local events and clubs is an extension of our existing community involvement, demonstrating how we take our responsibilities and the impact we have on communities through our infrastructure works very seriously.'

In addition to the above, to ensure that the company is addressing areas of need in its community they will work with quality assured organisations such as:

- Business in the Community 'Cares' employee volunteering initiatives for decorating/gardening/painting challenges in schools and charities
- Wildlife Trusts for environmental and conservation projects
- National Grid Environmental Education Centres for environmental challenges
- National Parks Authority for conservation challenges.

In kind support

Education: National Grid Company is involved in a number of liaison activities with schools and universities. It also supports educational materials for schools through the Electricity Association's 'Understanding Energy' service.

Environment: National Grid supports beneficial environmental initiatives, both on its own land and elsewhere. The company has established a major network of environmental education centres, with the active involvement of local education authorities.

Employee-led support

The company supports its employees in their community fundraising and giving through:

- matched giving – £400 per annum to match employee fundraising efforts
- employee community grants – cash for significant volunteer work
- Give As You Earn – donations to charity direct from your salary.

'Individual employees also encouraged to volunteer to become involved in educational and community support programmes such as:

- literacy, numeracy and enterprise supporters
- imagineering club tutors
- local charity trustees
- Prince's Trust business advisers.'

Commercially-led support

Sponsorship: The company has two national sponsorships, in partnership with the Improvement & Development Agency (National Grid Community 21 Awards Scheme), and the Tree Council (National Grid Tree Warden Scheme).

Contact: Julian Buttery, Head of UK Community Relations.

National Magazine Co. Ltd

Company registration number 112955

National Magazine House, 72 Broadwick Street, London W1F 9EP

020 7439 5000

Website: www.natmags.co.uk

Correspondent: Team Secretary – MD's office

Chairman: F A Bennack

Year end	Turnover	Pre-tax profit
06/01/2006	£347,609,000	£13,975,000

Nature of company business
The main activities are the publishing and distribution of magazines and periodicals.

Main locations: London

UK employees: 1001

Charitable donations

2006: £12,480
2005: £44,770
2004: £30,768

Community involvement

The National Magazine Company states that 'each year The National Magazine Company offers The Soho Family Centre financial support and also assists and works together on a number of projects to further the aims of the Centre'.

The company also states that it does not make ad hoc donations to charities, but that it is able to offer a number of annual subscriptions on request. Outside of this, support appears only to be given to the community local to its offices in Soho.

Exclusions

Local appeals not in areas of company presence.

Applications

In writing to the correspondent.

Corporate giving

In 2006 the company made charitable donations of £12,480 (2005: £44,770). Althought this is considerbly lower than the previous year, it may be a blip.

In kind support

Staff have assisted the Soho Family Centre through writing and designing its annual report, redesigning and equipping a new kitchen and playroom, donating equipment and resources, and raising extra funds.

Employee-led support

The company supports employees' volunteering/charitable activities with financial help.

Nationwide Building Society

Company registration number 355B

Nationwide House, Pipers Way, Swindon SN38 2SN

Website: www.nationwide.co.uk

Correspondent: The Community Affairs Manager

Chairman: G M T Howe

Chief Executive Officer: G J Beale

Year end	Turnover	Pre-tax profit
04/04/2008	£2,276,900,000	£686,100,000

Nature of company business
The group provides a comprehensive range of personal financial services.

Main locations: Swindon

UK employees: 17,296

Charitable donations

2008: £2,448,191
2007: £2,380,565
2006: £2,324,287
2005: £1,343,009
2004: £1,296,965

Membership: BitC, L B Group

Community involvement

The society has made the following statement: 'Nationwide has a strong history of involvement in community projects and is firmly committed to supporting the communities from which it has grown. Through sponsorship, fundraising and other activities, Nationwide supports hundreds of events and initiatives across the country each year.

'The Community Affairs team are responsible for co-ordinating charitable activity and making decisions on requests for sponsorship and funding made to Nationwide'.

The majority of the group donations are made through the Nationwide Foundation (Charity Commission no. 1065552). As a separate legal entity the foundation is not part of the Nationwide Group and is controlled by an independent board of trustees which determines the policies. However, as requests for charitable donations made to the society are referred to the foundation, we include it here.

The Nationwide Foundation

The Nationwide Foundation was set up in 1998 by the society from which, as its main benefactor, it receives an annual donation.

Over the past 10 years, the foundation's funding criteria have encompassed a number of diverse themes. The current grant-making strategy, Supporting Families, comprises the themes of domestic violence, prisoners' families and young offenders. The strategy incorporates two grants programmes, the Small Grants Programme and the Investor Programme. The Investor Programme is designed to offer long term flexible support and core funding to a selected number of charities, over three years, whilst encouraging and funding partnership working among them. The Small Grants Programme offers one-off grants of up to £5,000 to registered charities with an income of under £500,000.

For more information and to keep up to date with the foundation's criteria, please see its website (www.nationwidefoundation.org.uk).

Exclusions

No response to circular appeals. No support for advertising in charity brochures, animal welfare, appeals from individuals, medical research, overseas projects, political appeals, religious appeals, or for commercial (as opposed to community related) sponsorship.

Applications

Applications to the company for donations or sponsorship should be sent to the Community Affairs Manager.

For applications to the Nationwide Foundation, further information can be obtained from the foundation's website (www.nationwidefoundation.org.uk).

On a local basis, giving depends on the local area managers, who have small budgets for local community projects.

Corporate giving

In 2007/08 the society made charitable donations of £2.4 million of which £2 million went to the Nationwide Foundation.

The Nationwide makes an annual donation of to Macmillan, its flagship charity since 1993.

In kind support

Non-cash support in the form of equipment, consultancy, furniture, prizes/merchandise, and print/design is provided.

Employee-led support

Payroll giving: Nationwide operates the Give As You Earn payroll giving scheme and supports employee fundraising in various ways.

Nestlé UK Ltd

Company registration number 51491

PO Box 207, York YO91 1XY

01904 604 604; Fax: 01904 603 461

Website: www.nestle.co.uk

Correspondent: Mrs Vicky Whitelock, Consumer Services

Chairman: A Sykes

Managing Director: Paul Grimwood

Year end	Turnover	Pre tax profit
31/12/2007	£1,269,000,000	(£62,400,000)

Nature of company business
Manufacture and sale of food products and associated activities.

Main locations: Hayes, Castleford, Croydon, Dalston, Fawdon, Girvan, Halifax, York, Tutbury

UK employees: 4,848

Charitable donations
2007: £1,005,954
2006: £1,200,000
2005: £1,700,000
2004: £1,900,000

Membership: BitC, L B Group

Community involvement

Nestle provided the following information regarding its community support in the UK:

'The company supports young people (aged 11 to 18) in the following areas:
- nutrition, health and wellness
- out of school childcare and education.'

'Nestlé UK supports community projects that focus on our company strategies of nutrition, health and wellness and sustainability.

'The company's key charity partners are 4Children (formerly Kids' Club Network), Fareshare, Allergy UK and Purely Nutrition (PhunkyFoods). The single largest charity partner is 4Children with whom the company have worked since 1996 and have partnered with them in the Make Space campaign, which calls for new style youth clubs for young people. On 1 July 2008 Nestlé launched the Make Space for Health programme which focuses on nutrition, health and wellness awareness among youth workers and promotes healthy lifestyles to young people outside the classroom.

'We support schools, charities and community groups local to our offices and factories mainly by way of product donations.'

Exclusions

No support is given towards student expeditions, individuals, political causes, third-party fundraising events or the purchase of advertising space in charity programmes.

Applications

Applications should be made to nearest local site. Few national financial donations are given.

Corporate giving

The company made charitable donations totalling just over £1 million during 2007 (2006: £1.2 million). Details of the specific amounts given to the company's key partners and/or other organisations were not available.

In kind support

Nestlé's main area of non-cash support is gifts in kind – the company providing product, furniture and equipment donations to local good causes.

Employee-led support

The York site has their own employee charitable trust, which raises funds from employees and is donated in small grants to local organisations in which employees hold an interest. The trust is The Nestlé Rowntree York Employees Community Fund Trust (Charity Commission no. 516702). Please contact Jackie Johnson for further information.

Payroll giving: A scheme is operated through an internal company community fund.

Network Rail Infrastructure Ltd

Company registration number 4402220

Kings Place, 90 York Way, London N1 9AG

020 3356 9595; Fax: 020 3356 9245

Website: www.networkrail.co.uk

Chief Executive: Iain Coucher

Ian McAllister

Year end	Turnover	Pre-tax profit
31/03/2008	£5,960,000,000	£1,597,000,000

Nature of company business
Network Rail owns operates and maintains Britain's rail network.

UK employees: 34,770

Charitable donations

2008: £793,000
2007: £973,000
2006: £886,000
2005: £1,087,000

Membership: BitC

Community involvement

Network Rail completed a two-year charity partnership with Cancer Research UK in March 2008. Since April 2008, the company are working with the NSPCC for two years.

The company supports staff in their volunteering and fundraising activities.

Applications

In writing to the correspondent.

Corporate giving

In 2007/08, the company made charitable donations in the UK of £793,000 which included £285,000 in good-cause

sponsorship (2006/07: £496,000/£477,000). We have no specific details of the beneficiaries, but assume Cancer Research UK to have been one.

Employee-led support

Network Rail encourages employees to support charities. Its charitable giving scheme offers employees up to five days' paid volunteer leave with a supported charity and matches employees' fundraising up to £1,200 a year.

Payroll giving: The Give as You Earn is in operation with contributions matched (up to £1,200 per annum). Employees raised £423,980.71 for charity as well as giving 281 days in volunteer leave.

Newcastle Building Society

Company registration number 233B

Portland House, New Bridge Street, Newcastle upon Tyne NE1 8AL

0191 244 2000

Website: www.newcastle.co.uk

Correspondent: Corporate Communications Manager

Chairman: Chris Hilton

Chief Executive: Colin Seccombe

Year end	Pre-tax profit
31/12/2007	£17,600,000

Nature of company business
Building society.

Subsidiaries include: NBS Financial Services Ltd, Newton Facilities Computer Leasing Ltd, Newton Facilities Management Ltd, Newton Facilities Computer Purchasing Ltd

Main locations: Newcastle upon Tyne

UK employees: 1,015

Charitable donations

2007: £100,000
2006: £100,000
2005: £100,000
2004: £90,000
2003: £98,625

Membership: A & B, BitC

Community involvement

The society supports community groups and organisations through their sponsorship programmes and its community fund. The Community Foundation serving Tyne and Wear and Northumberland (Charity Commission no.: 700510) manages the the Newcastle Building Society Community Fund. There is a strong focus on projects that help improve the community, nurture talent and support education. Grants are mainly of £1,000 or less. Since the community fund began, the society has helped hundreds of voluntary projects and charities in the areas in which it has branches.

Charity of the Year Scheme: In 2008 Newcastle Building Society introduced a Charity of the Year Scheme which challenges its staff to raise money for a local cause. The target for the year was £25,000 for a new Maggie's Cancer Caring Centre at the Freeman hospital.

Exclusions

No grants for: sponsorship and fundraising events; small contributions to major appeals; large capital projects; endowments; political or religious groups; or work which should be funded by health and local authorities, or government grant aid.

Applications

Applications to the Newcastle Building Society Community Fund should be made using an application form available from The Community Foundation serving Tyne and Wear and Northumberland, Cale Cross, 156 Pilgrim Street, Newcastle upon Tyne NE1 6SU (0191 222 0945; email: grants@communityfoundation.org.uk, website: www.communityfoundation.org.uk).

Applications should include background information and a full explanation of how any grant will be used. Applications can be received at any time and are acknowledged.

Full grant guidelines can be obtained from the society's website.

Corporate giving

Each year the Newcastle donates around £100,000 to worthwhile charities and individual causes. The society has also established the Newcastle Building Society Community Fund. Considerable' in kind support is also given.

Charitable projects that have recently received a grant include the Cricket Foundation's Chance to Shine at Gateshead Fell Cricket Club, which will receive £25,000 over five years to pay for extra coaching sessions in schools. We have also donated £13,000 so far to The Children Foundation's Whoops! Project, which aims to stamp out bullying in local schools.

In kind support

In addition to charitable donations, support is given through gifts in kind, joint promotions, and advice and mentoring.

Commercially-led support

Sponsorship: The Newcastle has been involved in several key sponsorship projects that have benefited the communities in which it operates.

Working with the Sponsors Club for Arts and Business, the society adopted a three-year, former Universal Building Society project, with Seven Stories, the Centre for Children's Books, which aims to bring the joy of story telling to children.

For the opening of its new office at Cobalt Business Park in 2008, the society commissioned both established and budding local artists to produce pieces for display throughout the building. The society also ran an art competition with local universities and colleges with a £1,000 top prize.

The Members' Community Fund

In 2003 the society launched The Members' Community Fund which allows members to make an annual donation from one of their Newcastle Building Society savings accounts.

The society selects three charitable themes aimed at covering a wide cross section of people and activities, including children's education, adult literacy and numeracy and IT schemes for the over 55s.

The money raised is then divided among these themes so that if 30% of respondents choose to support children's education, 30% of the funds will go to causes related to this.

As with the community fund, the funds are also held and distributed by The Community Foundation serving Tyne & Wear and Northumberland.

News International plc

Company registration number 81701

1 Virginia Street, London E98 1XY

020 7782 6000

Website: www.newscorp.com

Correspondent: The Community Affairs Manager

Chairman: K R Murdoch

Year end: 30/06/2007
Pre-tax profit: £383,600,000

Nature of company business
Main activity: the printing and publishing of national newspapers. Other activities include newsprint storage and distribution.

Subsidiaries include: News Group Newspapers, Times Newspapers Holdings, The Times Supplements, Broadsystem, Convoys

Main locations: Glasgow, Knowsley, London, Peterborough

Charitable donations
2007: £900,000
2006: £1,200,000
2005: £1,200,000
2004: £900,000

Community involvement

We have been unable to obtain any up-to-date policy information for the company, but confirm the contact to be correct.

Subsidiary companies: Local appeals are dealt with by the company's plants in Glasgow, Knowsley, and Peterborough which are encouraged to pursue their own community affairs programmes. Unfortunately, no details were available regarding what this might cover.

Exclusions

No support for advertising in charity brochures, appeals from individuals, fundraising events, medical research, overseas projects, religious/political appeals, science/technology, sport or local appeals not in areas of company presence. As a general rule the company does not make contributions to capital building projects.

Applications

In writing to the correspondent. A charities committee meets regularly. Unsuccessful applicants are given reasons and the corporate policy is explained.

Appeals to subsidiary companies should be made to managing directors, managing editors or editors.

Corporate giving

According to the company accounts for 2006/07 filed at Companies House, charitable contributions for the year amounted to £900,000 (£1.2 million 2005/06). No details of the beneficiaries were available.

Employee-led support

Previously, we were advised that there is a preference for supporting charities in which a member of staff is involved. Staff are encouraged to become volunteers in their own time and to become school governors.

Payroll giving: A scheme is operated by the company.

Next plc

Company registration number 4521150

Desford Road, Enderby, Leicester LE19 4AT

0845 456 7777

Website: www.next.co.uk

Correspondent: Jeanette Cooper-Hudson, Charities Co-ordinator

Chairman: David Barton

Chief Executive: Simon Wolfson

Year end	Turnover	Pre-tax profit
28/01/2008	£3,329,000,000	£498,000,000

Nature of company business
The principal activities of the group are high-street retailing, home shopping, customer services management and financial services.

Subsidiaries include: First Retail Finance Ltd, Vetura

Main locations: Bradford, Leeds, Leicester

UK employees: 61,751

Charitable donations
2008: £499,000
2007: £383,000
2006: £350,000
2005: £708,000

Total community contributions: £1,021,000

Membership: BitC

Community involvement

The company's 2006/07 Corporate Responsibility Report states that: 'At Next we look for opportunities to develop and maintain positive and healthy relationships with the communities in which we operate in by contributing to the wellbeing of those communities through donations of funding, product or the time and expertise of our employees. In 2006 we have focused our resources on projects that support communities throughout the United Kingdom as well as providing sponsorship to a wide variety of organisations and charities. In addition to our direct community contributions, we support charities by organising fundraising events on their behalf which allows the charity to attract additional funding at the event as a direct result of the support they have received from Next.'

Exclusions

It does not second staff to voluntary organisations. No support is given to political causes and the company prefers not to give for adverts in publications and/or sponsorship of an event or individual – the company's involvement in these areas is limited.

Although a member of Business in the Community, the company does not support enterprise agencies, nor is it involved in any local economic development initiatives.

Applications

All donation requests should be sent to the Personnel Department where they will be carefully considered, with priority being given to local charities, i.e. local to Leicester and Leeds (this is where the majority of employees are based). A budget has been specifically allocated for this purpose. As such, all letters and telephone requests should be directed to the Charity Co-ordinator and she will reply.

Full details of the company's involvement are carefully recorded and further information can be obtained from the correspondent. Details of charitable donations will be presented to the Board and be available for all members of the Charity Committee.

Corporate giving

Next made donations in 2007/08 totalling £499,000. We have no details of the beneficiaries, however we believe some of this was distributed via The Next Charitable Trust (Charity Commission no. 1107877).

In kind support

Product donations – Next make use of damaged stock by donating it to charities for them to either sell in their shops, help individuals, or recycle and make into new product to sell on.

Charity Christmas Cards – Next raised £522,000 by donating 25p from each pack sold.

Employee-led support

The staff at Next have a charity committee which raises money.

One of the company's main fundraising events is its Annual Next Charity Golf Day.

Commercially-led support

Sponsorship: Next have sponsored a number of fashion and sports organisations. It also gives support to local sporting teams, especially where there is direct employee involvement with the team.

Nike (UK) Ltd

Company registration number 1887016

One Victory Way, Doxford International Business Park, Sunderland, Tyne & Wear SR3 3XF

0191 401 6453; Fax: 0191 401 2012

Website: www.nike.com

Correspondent: Carole Ewart

Year end	Turnover	Pre-tax profit
31/05/2006	£62,790,159	£11,106,390

Nature of company business
Multi-national manufacturer of sports clothing and equipment.

Main locations: Sunderland

UK employees: 218

Community involvement

The company supports projects which help children get active and become involved in teamwork through sport. Currently, there is a strong push towards supporting adolescent girls in sport

Exclusions

Only registered charities can be supported. No grants are made to individuals, sports teams, non-registered charities, for-profit groups, religious groups, capital campaigns, endowment funds, memorials or political activities.

Applications

The following application guidelines are taken from Nike's corporate website (www.nikebiz.com) to which you should refer for fuller information.

Cash grants

'For those seeking cash support, we invite proposals from non-profit organisations or collaborations among organisations. Before preparing your proposal, please ensure that your non-profit or NGO organisation meets the eligibility criteria outlined in these guidelines. Proposals should include the following information in this order:

- description of the organisation, including its mission, major accomplishments, governance, area, and population served
- detailed description of the project or activity for which support is being requested, including the amount of the grant request
- operating budget for the current fiscal year
- identification of funding sources for the current fiscal year and amounts received (include foundation, corporate, individual, and public support)
- list of any previous funding received from Nike, Inc. or the Nike Foundation and short project description
- project budget
- list of current board members and key staff
- most recent financial statement
- copy of the organisation's tax-exempt notification letter from the IRS or equivalent documentation.'

Product donations

'Each year, Nike proactively donates product to non-profit organisations and NGOs dedicated to youth physical activity, and disaster relief efforts around the world. In 2005, Nike donated more than $23 million in footwear, apparel and equipment to non-profit organisations.

'Nike will not provide product donations to individual sports teams in order to clearly separate our philanthropy from our marketing efforts.

'Product donations are made based upon availability. If you are requesting product in support of an event, Nike must receive your request at least 12 weeks before the event date.

'Requests for product should include the following information:

- description of the organisation, including its mission, major accomplishments, governance, area, and population served
- detailed description of the project or activity and those benefiting for which product is being requested
- specific purpose for product, type of product, quantity and size run
- method of distribution, and accountability for delivery and utilization of product
- project budget
- list of any previous product support received from Nike, Inc. and short project description
- copy of the organisation's tax-exempt notification letter from the IRS or equivalent documentation.

'Nike may request additional information. Proposal materials, including photographs, videos, CDs, and special binders cannot be returned.

'Email or fax proposals will not be accepted.'

All applications are processed centrally from its US office. The address is: Global Community Affairs, Nike Inc, PO Box 4027, Beaverton, OR 97076, USA.

Applicants are generally notified of a decision within eight weeks (although as this probably means a reply is sent within eight weeks of it receiving a request, transatlantic applications may extend slightly beyond this barrier).

Corporate giving

In 2005/06, Nike contributed $100 million in cash and products to non-profit partners around the world.

Nike's UK annual report and accounts for 2006 does not declare any charitable donations, Furthermore, we have been unable to locate any examples of support given in the UK, although we assume from past examples (see below) it continues to be given.

Previously, Nike's major programme in the UK was *Zoneparcs*. Working with the Youth Sport Trust, the UK Department for Education and Skills, Nike set out to radically transform recess and lunchtime at schools. The intent was to promote physical and mental activities that were creative, positive and sporting. What started as a pilot programme in one school in east London has spread out to 300 schools across the UK. Nike has committed more than £500,000 since the scheme started in 2000.

NikeGO – Sport for Social Change, is an initiative that seeks to effect positive change through sport in excluded young people's lives. In its EMEA (Europe, the Middle East and Africa) Community Book, the following organisations are listed as having received support under the scheme either through grants, volunteer time or product donations: Community Service Volunteers, London; Youth Sport Trust (Girls in Sport); Northumbria Police & Gateshead MBC (Offbeat); Sunderland Youth Development Group (Young Achievers); Hoop Dreams; Hylton Redhouse Primary School; St Aloysius R.C. School, London; Richard Cobden Primary School, London; and Ecclesbourne Primary School.

Support is also provided through the Nike Foundation, although this mainly seems to be proactively initiated by Nike through what is termed the 'Requests for Proposals' process. Basically, this means that if you haven't been invited by Nike to apply to them, then don't waste your time doing so.

In kind support

Much of Nike's community work involves the donation of its products.

Employee-led support

Employee activism is encouraged through Nike's Sport4ACause Fund. Employees engaged in charitable sporting events have the funds they raise matched by the company.

Nike's 'EXTRA TIME' programme gives employees six days per year for volunteer activities.

Norbert Dentressangle

Company registration number Sc7173

Norbert Dentressangle House, Lodge Way, New Duston, Northampton NN5 7SL

01604 662600; Fax: 01604 622605

Website: www.norbert-dentressangle.co.uk

Correspondent: Marketing and Communications Manager

Chairman: David Fish

Chief Executive: Stewart Oades

Year end	Turnover	Pre-tax profit
31/03/2007	£899,000,000	£44,100,000

Nature of company business
Principal activities: logistics and food services.

Subsidiaries include: Inverleith Insurance Co. Ltd, Inveralmond Insurancce Ltd

Main locations: Northampton, Edinburgh

UK employees: 8,970

Total employees: 14,090

Charitable donations
2007: £26,796
2006: £30,551
2005: £23,649
2004: £22,000
2003: £45,000

Community involvement

Previously included here under the name of Christian Salvesen plc, the company was acquired by Norbert Dentressangle in December 2007.

At this point it is unclear how, if at all, the change of ownership will affect the company's community support. We have therefore repeated the last information we were provided with.

Exclusions

The company does not make political donations.

Applications

Apply in writing to the contact. The Group Charities Committee meets quarterly.

Corporate giving

In 2007, the company made cash donations totalling £26,796 (2006: 30,551) to a variety of registered UK charities.

In kind support

The company works closely with Remploy in promoting economic independence for disabled people through helping them back into work and has won awards for the work done in this area at its Motherwell depot. As a result of this partnership, the company has succeeded in employing over fifty registered disabled people in a variety of roles.

Company staff are occasionally seconded to the community.

Employee-led support

The company supports projects that involve the community through both financial aid and by in kind support such as employee involvement. A wide range of events and activities is organised and takes place at individual sites to support local and national charities and community based projects. In some instances the company will match the funds raised locally.

Commercially-led support

Sponsorship: *Education* – The company sponsors an MSc student each year on the Logistics and Supply Chain Management course at the Heriot-Watt University School of Management. The student is given the opportunity to complete their MSc projects within the company and will also be considered for the Group's Graduate Management Development Programme.

Medical Research – The company also supports SPARKS (Sport Aiding medical Research for Kids) during each year by sponsoring a celebrity golf challenge.

The company is a founder member of TransAid, the leading charity specialising in effective transport solutions in the developing world and continues to have an active involvement with the charity.

Northern & Shell Network Ltd

Company registration number 4086475

Number 10 Lower Thames Street, London EC3R 6EN

0871 434 1010

Website: www.northernandshell.co.uk

Correspondent: (see 'Applications')

Chairman: R C Desmond

Year end	Turnover	Pre-tax profit
31/12/2007	£484,974,000	£54,945,000

Nature of company business
Holding company in the Northern & Shell group of companies principally engaged in newspaper publishing and printing, magazine publishing and television broadcasting.

UK employees: 1,257

Charitable donations
2007: £547,000
2006: £868,000

Community involvement

Northern & Shell make donations to charitable causes both in its own right and through the RD Crusaders Foundation (Charity Commission no. 1014352). The foundation's aim is to use donations in a focused and informed way and allocates funds to a large number of smaller charities.

Exclusions

No support for individuals, political or religious appeals.

Applications

Applications to the foundation should be made in writing and sent to: Mrs Allison Racher, The RD Crusaders Foundation, Northern and Shell Building, Number 10 Lower Thames Street, London EC3R 6EN. (Tel: 0871 520 7760; Email: allison.racher@express.co.uk).

Corporate giving

In 2007, the company made charitable donations of £547,000 (2006: £868,000) of which £419,000 (2006: £588,000) was paid to the RD Crusaders Foundation.

RD Crusaders Charitable Trust

Richard Desmond (Chairman of Northern & Shell) and his wife are trustees of the above charity.

In 2007, 96 grants of £413,544 were made, including large donations to Jewish Care, Fight for Sight, Elton John Aids Foundation and Civitas. Whilst in 2006, 97 grants of £605,684 were made, including large donations to AJJDC (UK) Trust, The Disability Foundation, Breast Cancer Campaign.

The foundation's aim is to distribute all income received, leaving a zero balance.

Northern Foods plc

Company registration number 471864

2180 Century Way, Thorpe Park, Leeds LS15 8ZB

0113 390 0110

Website: www.northern-foods.co.uk

Correspondent: The Corporate Social Responsibility Officer

Chairman: Anthony Hobson

Chief Executive: Stefan Barden

Year end	Turnover	Pre-tax profit
01/04/2008	£931,900,000	£50,100,000

Nature of company business
A leading supplier of high-quality chilled foods under the own labels of the major multiple retailers, with strong brands of its own in premium quality biscuits, fresh chilled dairy products, frozen food and savoury pastry products. The company has a strong operating presence in Nottingham, Sheffield, Greater Manchester, Batley and Lancashire.

Subsidiaries include: Cavaghan & Gray Group Ltd, Cavaghan & Gray Ltd, Fletchers Bakeries Ltd, F W Farnsworth Ltd, Convenience Foods Ltd, NFT Distribution Ltd

Main locations: Accrington, Bolton, Batley, Sheffield, Nottingham, Oldham, Market Drayton, Manchester, Worksop, Wakefield, Corby, Carlisle, Hull

Total employees: 10,767

Charitable donations
2008: £60,000
2007: £59,600
2006: £89,000
2005: £273,000
2004: £291,000
Membership: BitC

Community involvement

Following the completion of a comprehensive review of its corporate social responsibility commitments in 2006, the company is to concentrate on supporting the promotion of healthy balanced lifestyles. In 2007/08 it continued its support of Phunky Foods, the unique primary school programme which delivers healthy lifestyle education for 5 to 11 year olds.

Exclusions

The company does not generally support the larger national charities, religious or political bodies. Support given to health charities and the arts is extremely limited. No grants for circular appeals, advertising in charity brochures, animal welfare, appeals from individuals, elderly people, environment/heritage, fundraising events, medical appeals, science/technology, sickness charities or sport.

Applications

In writing to the committee, including supporting information. Applications are considered by a committee comprising Directors and Executives which meets on a quarterly basis.

Corporate giving

During the year the group donated £60,000 (£59,600 2006/07) for charitable purposes.

Previous beneficiaries have included Samaritans, Wybourn Youth Trust – Sheffield, Fairbridge – Greater Manchester, Youth at Risk – Nottingham, Opera North Community Education, Sobriety Projects – Yorkshire, Parents at Work, the Warren – Hull, Fair Play – Batley, First Data – Nottingham and Hope for the Homeless – Worksop.

In kind support

Education: In addition to financial support, support for education includes: gifts in kind to schools and universities, particularly those close to its companies or from which it recruits staff.

Enterprise: The company supports enterprise agencies. In kind support is also given in the form of stock or equipment and the provision of professional services free of charge.

Employee-led support

The Northern Foods Association covers all employees. Though primarily a sports and social club its activities include fundraising for charities, which is encouraged by the company. Employees at many of the companies are involved in charitable and community activities and a number have participated in short assignments or longer-term secondments to community projects. A number of directors and senior managers serve as trustees, advisers or non-executive directors of these groups.

Payroll giving: The Give As You Earn scheme is operated.

Northern Rock plc

Company registration number 3273685

Northern Rock House, Gosforth, Newcastle upon Tyne NE3 4PL

0191 285 7191; Fax: 0191 284 8470

Website: www.northernrock.co.uk

Correspondent: Colin Taylor, Group Secretary

Chairman: R A Sandler

Year end	Pre-tax profit
31/12/2007	(£167,600,000)

Nature of company business
The main purpose of the group is the provision of housing finance, savings and a range of related personal financial and banking services.

Subsidiaries include: Indemnity Company Ltd

Main locations: Newcastle upon Tyne

UK employees: 6,334

Charitable donations
2007: £14,300,000
2005: £24,700,000
2003: £19,300,000

Membership: A & B

Community involvement

The conversion of Northern Rock Building Society into a public company was completed on 1 October 1997. An integral part of this was the formation of a charitable body, the Northern Rock Foundation (Charity Commission no. 1063906). This was launched in January 1998 and is entitled to receive a covenant of about five per cent of annual pre-tax profits of Northern Rock plc.

In February 2008, Northern Rock was taken into temporary public ownership. As part of this arrangement the Chancellor announced that the foundation would receive a minimum of £15 million a year in 2008, 2009 and 2010 from Northern Rock. The foundation's trustees intend to spend up to £11 million through their grant programmes [in 2008].

Maintaining this arrangement is a condition of any sale of the bank in that period. The government has asked the bank's board to identify a viable long-term future for the foundation.

Organisations that already have grants and those that receive them in the future can be absolutely assured that funds have been set aside to meet all outstanding commitments. Grants awarded over several years will be paid as planned.

Currently, the foundation is accepting applications under its four grant programmes.

- **Independence and choice** – services for people with mental health problems, people with learning disabilities, older people and carers
- **Building positive lives** – one-to-one help for young people at risk, homeless people, substance misusers and groups that face prejudice and discrimination
- **Safety and justice** – reducing the incidence and impact of domestic and sexual violence, abuse and hate crimes
- **Culture and heritage** – inspiring, enjoyable and diverse culture programmes and events that raise our region's

profile and make it a better place for everyone to live and enjoy life.

The foundation goes on to say that: 'As part of our support for older people's projects in Independence and Choice, we are accepting applications from organisations providing welfare benefits advice and targeted benefit take-up campaigns.

'Overall, we are continuing our policy of funding fewer, better grants, and engaging with applicants and grant-holders to help them maximise their effectiveness. We are also making grants for work across the North East and Cumbria. If your work fits within one of these four programmes, you can apply now in the normal way. All the information you need is on this website.'

Please note: At the time of writing (December 2008), the trustees announced that they plan to continue their current funding priorities into 2009, when they expect to award up to £11.3 million through their grants and other initiatives.

Exclusions

'There are certain organisations, projects and proposals that we will not consider for grants. You should be aware that it costs the equivalent of several small grants to administer ineligible applications each year. If your organisation or your project falls into one of the categories below please do not apply to us for a grant.'

Activities which are not recognised as charitable in law; applications for under £1,000; charities which appear to us to have excessive unrestricted or free reserves (up to 12 months' expenditure is normally acceptable), or are in serious deficit; national charities which do not have a regional office or other representation in North East England or Cumbria; grant-making bodies seeking to distribute grants on Northern Rock's behalf; open-ended funding agreements; general appeals, sponsorship and marketing appeals; corporate applications for founder membership of a charity; retrospective grants; replacement of statutory funding; activities primarily the responsibility of central or local government or health authorities; individuals and organisations that distribute funds to individuals; animal welfare; mainstream educational activity, schools and educational establishments; medical research, hospitals, hospices and medical centres; medical treatments and therapies including art therapy; fabric appeals for places of worship; promotion of religion; expeditions or overseas travel; minibuses, other vehicles and transport schemes except where they are a small and integral part of a larger scheme; holidays and outings; playgrounds and play equipment; private clubs or those with such restricted membership as to make them not charitable; capital bids purely towards compliance with the Disability Discrimination Act; amateur arts organisations; musical instruments; sports kit and equipment.

Applications

The foundation has different grant application processes: one for requests from £1,000 to £20,000; the other for requests over £20,000. Please make sure you complete the correct application form.

Applications can be made online, or by downloading the appropriate form from the foundation's website at: www.nr-foundation.org.uk which also contains all the information you will need to assess your eligibility.

Alternatively, application forms can be obtained by writing to the Grants Manager, The Northern Rock Foundation, The Old Chapel, Woodbine Road, Gosforth, Newcastle upon Tyne NE3 1DD.

(Tel: 0191 284 8412; Fax: 0191 284 8413; Email: generaloffice@nr-foundation.org.uk).

The pack contains comprehensive information on how to apply and on the foundation's current policy. It is important to be aware of the latter as the criteria can change from year to year.

The foundation will acknowledge all applications and let you know straight away whether or not it is eligible. If it is eligible, you will be told which staff manager will assess it. They will be your main contact should there be any queries. They will usually visit your organisation, but sometimes assessment interviews are carried out by telephone. Others may be asked about your organisation or proposal, so let the foundation know if there is anything confidential about your plans or situation which should not be divulged.

Trustees make their decisions based on the staff manager's assessment. They meet five times a year to make decisions on grants over £20,000. For grants over £20,000, the aim is to give a decision within six months of receiving the application, though sometimes it necessarily takes longer. For grants under £20,000 there are more regular meetings, and a response within two to four months can be expected, though, once again, some applications take longer.

Please avoid telephoning to enquire about progress.

Corporate giving

The company's covenant to the foundation for 2007 amounts to £14.8 million (2006 full year – £31.4 million) representing the charge for the first half of 2007.

The Northern Rock Foundation

During 2007, the foundation awarded 226 grants totalling £17 million under its main grant programme.

The most recent grants awarded were announced by the foundation in December 2008. These included: Contact a Family (£233,252 over three years); Norcare (£160,000); Fairbridge (£142,313); Bell View (£103,960); Northumbria Coalition Against Crime (£99,786); and Homeless Action Group (£44,559).

Employee-led support

The foundation runs a scheme where it matches money donated to UK charities by Northern Rock employees. In 2007, the foundation double-matched donations, giving £2 for every £1 raised or given by staff.

The total raised and matched in 2007 was £1.9 million.

Payroll giving: The Give As You Earn scheme is in operation.

Northern Trust Group Ltd

Company registration number 2776907

Lynton House, Ackhurst Business Park, Foxhole Road, Chorley PR7 1NY

01257 269400; Fax: 01257 269997

Correspondent: J C Kay, Director

Chairman: T J Hemmings

Year end	Turnover	Pre-tax profit
31/03/2007	£59,394,000	£17,190,000

Nature of company business
Property, leisure and investment.

Main locations: Chorley

UK employees: 402

Charitable donations
2007: £25,000
2006: £63,000
2004: £650,000
2003: £1,150,500

Community involvement

Previously, we noted that Northern Trust Group Ltd appeared to channel its charitable support through the TJH Foundation (Charity Commission no. 1077311) by virtue of the charity's accounts declaring receipt of substantial donations from the company in 2003 and 2004.

Although a director of the company, Mr J C Kay, continues to be a trustee of the foundation, the company has not made any significant donation to the charity of late, but has made small charitable donations of its own. Unfortunately, we have no information concerning the beneficiaries, nor about the types of cause likely to be considered for support.

Applications
In writing to the correspondent.

Corporate giving

In 2007 the company donated £25,000 to charity. No further information was available.

Northumbrian Water Group

Company registration number 2560626

Abbey Road, Pity Me, Durham DH1 5FJ

0870 608 4820

Website: www.nwl.co.uk

Correspondent: The Community Relations Manager

Chairman: Sir Derek Wanless

Managing Director: John Cuthbert

Year end	Turnover	Pre-tax profit
30/03/2008	£670,400,000	£170,300,000

Nature of company business
Northumbrian Water Group plc is one of the UK's ten water and sewerage businesses. The company and its subsidiaries work in three related areas: the supply of water and waste water services within the UK; international water management; and a range of supporting technical and consultancy services.

Subsidiaries include: ULG Northumbrian Ltd, Fastflow Pipeline Services Ltd, Entec UK Ltd

Main locations: Durham

UK employees: 3,070

Charitable donations

2008: £134,702
2007: £128,555
2006: £122,411
2005: £89,369
2004: £33,084

Membership: A & B, BitC

Community involvement

'NWG gives not only money but also time and facilities to help its communities. These activities are mainly targeted to support projects which make the areas served better places in which to live, work or invest. The key elements of the programme include:

- an extensive community involvement programme supporting the work of community foundations and encouraging voluntary time through the 'Just an hour' scheme and funding through 'Cheque it out'
- health and environmental campaigning, including our innovative 'Water for health' initiative
- educational programmes which range from curriculum support to 'Back to Business' where NWL is a lead partner in a pilot scheme to link schools and businesses
- environmental partnerships and campaigns where, as well as being a member of many environmental organisations, NWL has developed some key partnerships to help the conservation and biodiversity of our sites, for example, with the Essex Wildlife Trust at Hanningfield
- regional support for local community organisations and support for our adopted charity, WaterAid.'

Exclusions

No support for circular appeals, local appeals not in areas of company presence, large national appeals or overseas projects (other than support for WaterAid).

Applications

In writing to the correspondent.

Corporate giving

During 2007/08 the company made charitable donations of £134,702.

In kind support

The company gives additional support through gifts in kind, joint promotions and encouraging employee volunteering.

Up to 2008, over £225,000 has been provided for water coolers in schools. Over 500 have been supplied to date in over 300 schools.

Employee-led support

An employee volunteering scheme launched in 2002, Just an Hour, encourages employees to spend an hour of work time a month providing support to community or environmental initiatives. In 2008, 23% of employees participate in the scheme, giving over 5,431 hours to the community.

The 'Care for Safety' scheme, which encourages employees to reduce accidents and associated lost time, has triggered payments totalling £49,890 for NWG's nominated charities: Great North Air Ambulance Service, Mencap's Dilston College, RNLI, St Teresa's Hospice and East Anglia's Children's Hospices.

Commercially-led support

Sponsorship: *The arts* – in recent years the company has sponsored the RSC.

Norwich & Peterborough Building Society

Company registration number 437B

Peterborough Business Park, Lynch Wood, Peterborough PE2 6ZA

01733 372372

Website: www.npbs.co.uk

Correspondent: Pat Turner, General Manager – HR

Chairman: Keith Bedell-Pearce

Chief Executive: Matthew Bullock

Year end	Pre-tax profit
31/12/2007	£24,300,000

Nature of company business
Independent building society offering a range of financial products and services.

Subsidiaries include: Hockleys Professional Surveyors and Valuers

Main locations: Lowestoft, Norwich, Great Yarmouth, Peterborough, Stamford, Southwold, King's Lynn, Ipswich, Lincoln, Bury St Edmunds, Cambridge

UK employees: 1,000

Charitable donations

2007: £218,000
2005: £89,000
2003: £147,000

Total community contributions: £292,000

Membership: BitC

Community involvement

The society only supports organisations based in East Anglia and Lincolnshire and prefers to support those that focus on environmental causes, sickness/disability and social welfare. Through its 'community' budgets, branch managers are able to lend support to deserving organisations and groups within their area.

As a mutual building society it was decided to draw up an agreement requiring customers opening new savings accounts to assign any windfall benefits to charity. Although certain exemptions apply to this, any eligible windfalls will go to the Charities Aid Foundation.

Applications

In writing to the correspondent.

Corporate giving

In 2007, the society made total community contributions of £219,000 of which £218,000 was in cash donations. A major beneficiary during the year was the Peterborough Environment City Trust.

In kind support

This takes the form of gifts in kind.

Employee-led support

Subject to budget, employee fundraising is matched to maximum of £500. Employee giving is topped-up by the society by 10%.

Payroll giving: The society operates the Give As You Earn scheme.

Commercially-led support

Neither arts nor good-cause sponsorship is undertaken.

Nottingham Building Society

Company registration number 411B

5–13 Upper Parliament Street, Nottingham NG1 2BX

0115 948 1444

Website: www.thenottingham.com

Correspondent: Anna Croasdale, Public Relations Manager
Email: anna.croasdale@thenottingham.com

Chairman: David Thompson

Chief Executive: Ian Rowling

Year end	Pre-tax profit
31/12/2007	£8,236,000

Nature of company business
Independent building society offering a range of financial products and services.

Main locations: Nottingham

UK employees: 521

Charitable donations

2007: £22,720
2005: £45,630
2003: £55,538

Community involvement

The following statement is taken from the Society's annual report:

'The society's community schemes aim to support causes which help to protect people's homes and communities. In the autumn, we joined forces with regional press to launch the 'Safe As Houses' awards, which seek to reward groups and organisations with funding for projects which help to make their communities safer. We also gave community awards to numerous groups and organisations as we helped to make a difference to the quality of life in our communities.'

A wide variety of groups are supported, including large and small registered and non-registered charities. Only groups in areas of society presence are supported, i.e. Nottinghamshire, Lincolnshire, Derbyshire and South Yorkshire.

Exclusions

No support for advertising in charity brochures, appeals from individuals, children/youth, education, elderly people enterprise/training, overseas projects, political appeals, part funding of a larger project, travel expenses, rent or property maintenance, staffing costs or projects which are the responsibility of statutory organisations.

Applications

Application forms are available from the society or from local branches.

Corporate giving

In 2007, the society made cash donations of over £22,720 primarily through its Community Spirit Awards scheme. Donations of up to £1,000 are available under three categories.

(i) *Crime Reduction and Security* – Helping to keep people safe in their homes and whilst they are out and about

(ii) *Health and Quality of Life* – Helping to promote health and improving the quality of life of those living with illness or disability

(iii) *Education and New Talent* – Helping to provide opportunities to learn and to encourage new talent

In addition to the above, charitable donations are made on an ad hoc basis in response to written appeals received from groups or organisations based in an area in which the society has a presence.

In 2007 support was given to many charities and good causes, including Long Eaton St John's Ambulance for medical equipment and to Cleethorpes Friendship at Home for wheelchairs.

Employee-led support

The society encourages employee volunteering.

Commercially-led support

Cause-related marketing: Support was given to Nottingham Forest Football Club's Youth Academy through its Nottingham Forest Saver Account.

Novae Group plc

Company registration number 5673306

71 Fenchurch Street, London EC3M 4HH

020 7903 7300; Fax: 020 7903 7333

Website: www.novae.com

Correspondent: Reception ('Charities')

Email: enquiries@novae.com

Chairman: Paul Selway-Swift

Chief Executive: Matthew Fosh

Year end	Turnover	Pre-tax profit
31/12/2007	£221,000,000	£41,000,000

Nature of company business
Novae Group plc is the holding company of a group that carries on insurance business and associated financial activities.

UK employees: 213

Charitable donations

2007: £70,000

Community involvement

Novae continues to support community programmes that are appropriate to the business and that contribute to society.'

Besides the major help it provides as a corporate patron, Novae have also established a charities committee which has a set annual budget to support charities nominated by employees.

The company also supports its staff in their fundraising and volunteering activities.

Applications

In writing to the correspondent.

Corporate giving

In 2007, the company made cash donations in the UK of around £70,000. The following extract is taken from the annual report and accounts for the year and provides, in part, a breakdown of this figure (see also 'Employee-led support').

'We are patrons of The Prince's Trust, to which we contributed £52,000 in 2007: £25,000 through our corporate membership; and £27,000 through fundraising events, participation in and sponsorship of The Princes' Trust Challenge 2007 and other activities.

'We have committed £10,000 in corporate support for the 2008 Polar Challenge, as part of a charitable fundraising initiative to support pharmaceutical research into child oncology led by the Institute of Cancer Research. This has enabled over £40,000 to be raised for the Institute.

'Our charities committee has a separate annual budget of £10,000, which is used to support charities nominated by employees and for which a donation would make a real difference.'

In kind support

To encourage shareholders to receive their copy of the annual report and accounts electronically, the Novae Group plc and Computershare Investor Services support 'eTree'. This is an environmental incentive programme designed to promote electronic shareholder communications by rewarding every shareholder who registers, with a sapling donated to the Woodland Trust's 'Tree for All' campaign by Novae Group plc.

Tree for All is aiming to plant 12 million trees – one for every child in the UK. It addresses not only the fact that children are losing touch with nature, but also that the UK has one of the lowest woodland populations in Europe.

Employee-led support

The company also support staff that choose to give their time and effort to the Lloyd's Community Programme. Total donations to charities from these activities amounted to £24,963 in 2007.

Payroll giving: The Give As You Earn scheme is in operation.

Old Mutual plc

Company registration number 3591559

5th Floor, Old Mutual Place, 2 Lambeth Hill, London EC4V 4GG

020 7002 7000

Website: www.oldmutual.com

Correspondent: The Head of Corporate Social Responsibility

Chief Executive: Jim Sutcliffe

Year end	Turnover	Pre-tax profit
31/12/2007	£16,864,000,000	£1,668,000,000

Nature of company business
Provision of financial services.

Main locations: London

Total employees: 54,630

Charitable donations

2007: £352,000
2006: £359,000
2005: £382,000
2004: £234,000
2003: £222,000

Community involvement

Old Mutual plc makes donations to charities through its Bermuda Foundation (not a registered charity). The funds are split into different pots: staff choice, staff matching, ad hoc donations and a CEO selection. In 2007 Old Mutual plc staff selected three charities to receive support through the staff choice programme. The Lavender Trust, Habitat for Humanity and Thames 21 were chosen and each charity received £10,000.' Donations from the ad hoc fund supported music workshops in schools by the City of London Sinfonia for a second year.

Ad hoc donations from the Bermuda Foundation were made throughout the year. The main project that received support was the Lord Mayor's Appeal. Further support was given to Crisis, the homelessness charity, both through the Crisis Square Mile Run and the Christmas Card Challenge. Staff also attended a number of charity dinners during the year, including the Railway Ball, a charity gala night raising money to stop abuse of children living on the streets.

Exclusions

No grants towards: sports; religious organisations; capital projects; non-registered charities; organisations without published, audited accounts for the last three years; or organisations whose total administrative and marketing expenses exceed 12% of the income.

Applications

In writing to the correspondent.

Corporate giving

In 2007, the company, its subsidiaries in the UK, and the Old Mutual Bermuda Foundation collectively made charitable donations of £352,000 during the year.

In kind support

Applications for gifts in kind are considered on a case-by-case basis.

Employee-led support

'Staff participated in a number of fundraising events in 2007, many of which received matching. One member of staff raised over £2,000 for the neonatal unit at Barts Hospital. Many members of staff took part in running events, in support of nominated charities from the Race for Life to the Great South Run.'

Commercially-led support

Cause-related marketing: Additional money was raised for the Lavender Trust through Breast Cancer Awareness Month. The office sold pin badges and had a Wear it Pink day to raise funds.

Oracle Corporation UK Ltd

Company registration number 1782505

Oracle Parkway, Thames Valley Park, Reading, Berkshire RG6 1RA

0118 924 0000; Fax: 0118 924 3000

Website: www.oracle.com/uk

Correspondent: Caroline Hockey, Corporate/Community Senior Director 0118 924 6468
Email: stacey.torman@oracle.com

Managing Director: Ian Smith

Vice President: Chris Baker

Year end	Turnover	Pre-tax profit
27/05/2006	£33,256,000	(£22,203,000)

Nature of company business
Producer of IT solutions and database software.

Main locations: Manchester, London, Reading, Edinburgh, Bristol, Birmingham, Belfast

UK employees: 2,814

> ### Charitable donations
> 2006: £6,825
> Membership: BitC

Community involvement

Oracle focuses its efforts in three primary areas across the UK – advancing education, protecting the environment and enriching the community. In order to achieve meaningful change in each of these areas it has four key programmes, namely:

- education initiatives
- hands-on support/enriching the community
- green programmes
- charitable giving.

Applications

In writing to the correspondent.

Corporate giving

In 2006, Oracle in the UK donated £6,825 to charitable causes. Although the information currently available on its website is less than in previous years (non-existent as far as we can tell), as a member of Business in the Community we believe it still provides sufficient in kind support to warrant inclusion. Below are examples of some of the past community support given by the company.

Advancing education: Oracle UK has previously made a million pound pledge to the government to support 'Specialist' schools.

Hands-on activities/enriching the local community: In conjunction with Central Berkshire Education Business Partnership, the company sponsored the first 'Leadership Challenge' for sixth-form students from five reading area schools. The programme gave 17–18 year old students the opportunity to deal with real-world business challenges.

Green programme: Oracle UK donated four high-spec bicycles to the police force.

In kind support

The Oracle Internet Initiative provides software and resources to educational establishments for use in degree programmes. In June 2003 it began a four-year, £1 million programme to support 40 specialist schools in creating and delivering maths, science and IT lessons.

The company has helped Berkshire schools create materials to enhance financial coursework in business studies programmes and has established a number of resources, such as Think.com and Oracle Internet Academy, which provide free educational information for teachers and students alike.

Employee-led support

All employees are encouraged to participate in renovation projects in disadvantaged areas.

In addition to this work, its global parent company organizes global volunteering days each year when all employees are encouraged to participate in community work during a fortnight.

Orange PCS Ltd

Company registration number 2178917

St James Court, Great Park Road, Almondsbury Park, Bradley Stoke, Bristol BS12 4QJ

0870 376 8888

Website: www.orange.co.uk

Correspondent: Head of Charities

Year end	Turnover	Pre-tax profit
28/12/2007	£4,395,000,000	£311,000,000

Nature of company business
The company was acquired by France Telecom in August 2000. Main activity is the provision of wirefree personal communications services.

Subsidiaries include: Hutchinson Ltd

Main locations: Bristol

UK employees: 10,024

Community involvement

Orange state on its website (November 2008) that: 'Charity is a key part of out corporate responsibility programme and we are currently reviewing all activity in this area.'

Perhaps because of the above review, little information is available about the company's charitable support. Previously, the company had a two-and-one-half year partnership with Sense which the company encouraged its employees to support through fundraising and volunteering.

Although mention is made of an Orange Foundation (formerly the France Telecom Foundation) this is not registered with the Charity Commission. We assume, because of its previous name, that the foundation is based in France and therefore has a preference for supporting organisations in that country.

The Orange Foundation's focus is concentrated in three areas:

- healthcare – helping autistic people and giving people with visual or hearing impairment greater independence and quality of life
- education – joining the battle against illiteracy and promoting education for girls in developing countries
- culture – encouraging group singing.

Exclusions

Orange do not support applications for projects:

- for work that does not primarily benefit those with sensory disabilities
- for the benefit of individuals rather than a group
- for beneficiaries outside the UK
- for work that has already taken place
- for core funding (operational running costs such as staff salaries or administration costs)
- for fundraising events, receptions or trips
- for the promotion of religion or politics.

Applications

In writing to the correspondent.

Corporate giving

In 2007, the company made charitable donations of £67,120 (2006: £563,865). We do not know the reason for the large fall in donations and assume the majority of support given in the year went to Sense.

Employee-led support

Orange's most recent partnership with the national deaf-blind charity Sense, came to an end in March 2008. Over the 2 ½ years of the relationship, its staff raised £470,000 for the charity through a variety of events. From cycling from London to Paris, to skydiving to running the London Marathon.

The money raised has supported outreach workers across the UK who meet with deafblind children and adults and breakdown the isolation ensuring their lives are enriched with opportunities and choices.

Payroll Giving: Orange operates a payroll giving scheme, which allows employees to make contributions directly from their salary before tax is deducted. Employees can choose to contribute to up to 12 different registered charitable organisations.

Commercially-led support

Sponsorship: Orange sponsors a variety of events nationwide in music, culture, and sport. These range from regional free festivals to grassroots music projects and writing initiatives.

Osborne & Little Ltd

Company registration number 923748

Riverside House, 26 Osiers Road, London SW18 1NH

020 8812 3000; Fax: 020 8877 7500

Website: www.osborneandlittle.com

Correspondent: Vanessa Zoil, Human Resources
Email: oand@osborneandlittle.com

Chairman: Sir Peter Osborne

Year end	Turnover	Pre-tax profit
31/03/2007	£28,040,000	£1,704,000

Nature of company business
The main activities are the design and distribution of fine furnishing fabrics and wallpapers.

Subsidiaries include: Tamesa Fabrics Ltd

Main locations: London

UK employees: 178

Community involvement

We were advised by the company that they did not wish to be included in our guide, even though they continue to support good causes. In line with our policy of including all relevant companies we repeat the information previously published with a few additions.

The company prefers to support local charities where it operates, appeals relevant to its business and those where an employee is involved. Preferred areas of support are children and youth, education (design) and arts (design).

Exclusions

The company does not advertise in charity brochures.

Applications

In writing to the correspondent.

Corporate giving

In 2007, the company made charitable donations in the UK totalling nearly £16,000 (2006: £20,746). We have no details of the beneficiaries.

Palmer & Harvey McLane Ltd

Company registration number 2274812

P&H House, 106–112 Davigdor Road, Hove,
East Sussex BN3 1RE

01273 222100; Fax: 01273 222101

Website: www.palmerharvey.co.uk

Correspondent: James Hussey, Charities Administrator

Chairman: Christopher Adams

Chief Executive: Chris Etherington

Year end	Turnover
04/04/2004	£6,445,100,000

Nature of company business
The main activity of the company is tobacco and confectionery distribution.

Subsidiaries include: Snowking Ltd

Main locations: Tonbridge, Coventry, Hove, Haydock

UK employees: 4,000

Charitable donations
2004: £40,000

Community involvement

The company holds an annual Charity Greyhound Evening in order to raise money for the Confectioner's Benevolent Fund, a charity dedicated to caring for people who have worked in the confectionary industry.

Previous information suggested that other than support for certain trade charities, the company has no set policy, although it prefers to support 'people charities' local to its branches.

Exclusions
Past information suggested the company provides no support for local appeals outside areas of company presence.

Applications
In writing to the correspondent.

Corporate giving

Despite not being able to obtain an updated donations figure, the appointment of a 'Charities Administrator' indicates the company's continued commitment towards its communities. However, we cannot be sure whether donations remain at around £40,000 a year as previously advised.

Panasonic UK Ltd

Company registration number 1069148

Panasonic House, Willoughby Road, Bracknell RG12 8FP

01344 862444

Website: www.panasonic.co.uk

Correspondent: Kelly Hales, Manager – MD's Office
01344 853103; Fax: 01344 853722
Email: kelly.hales@eu.panasonic.com

Year end	Turnover	Pre-tax profit
31/03/2007	£625,979,000	£1,738,000

Nature of company business
The ultimate holding company is Matsushita Electric Industrial whose main businesses are video equipment, audio equipment, home appliances, communication and individual equipment, electronic components, kitchen-related products, and others.

Main locations: Bracknell, Northampton

UK employees: 351

Charitable donations
2007: £75,000
2005: £134,050
2004: £56,057
2003: £47,000

Total community contributions: £125,000

Community involvement

We understand that each office/site has its own budget to support local charities in its area. Panasonic predominately supports causes local to its main office in Bracknell and its other regional site in Northampton.

The company's charitable giving has been directed towards the following categories:

(i) *General* – charities and groups which assist those in need, particularly people who are disadvantaged, disabled, sick or elderly people, plus local schools and playgroups

(ii) *Cause related* – charities with a theme chosen by staff

(iii) *Key project* – support for one or two major projects per year within the immediate local area.

The company is patron of the Berkshire Community Foundation, an independent community foundation serving the wider community where it is based. The Berkshire Community Foundation seeks to address the changing needs within the county of Berkshire.

The Panasonic Trust

The Panasonic Trust (Charity Commission no. 290652), administered by the Royal Academy of Engineering, funds the updating and retraining of qualified engineers, particularly in new engineering developments and new technologies. Since its inception in 1984 the Panasonic Trust has awarded grants to more than 800 engineers. The majority of these grants have been awarded to enable the engineers to undertake part time modular MSc courses, the structures of which appeal to both the individual and the employer. Globally Panasonic's Corporate Outreach Programme concentrates its resources in three strategic areas: – education, civic and social welfare and arts and cultural. Within each of these strategic areas Panasonic has particular interest in projects that are targeted to address the needs of women and diverse populations.

Exclusions

The company does not normally respond favourably to unsolicited requests. No support for advertising in charity brochures, animal charities, appeals from individuals, enterprise/training, heritage, medical research, overseas projects, political appeals, religious appeals science/ technology, or sport.

Appeals for 'charity of the year' status are not considered.

Applications

In writing to the correspondent.

Applications to the Panasonic Trust should be made via the Royal Academy of Engineering. Full details are available at: www.raeng.org.uk/education/professional/panasonic/awards.htm

Corporate giving

In 2006/07, the company's charitable contributions in the UK totalled £125,000 of which £75,000 was in cash donations. Major beneficiaries were the Panasonic Trust, Berkshire Community Foundation and various charities, schools and voluntary groups in the Berkshire and Northamptonshire areas.

In kind support

The company prefers to donate equipment for either office use or fundraising purposes wherever possible and responds to requests received accordingly.

Employee-led support

Employees' giving is matched by the company to a maximum of £100. Employees' fundraising may also be matched, but this is considered on a case by case basis.

Commercially-led support

Sponsorship: Arts and good-cause sponsorship are undertaken. Proposals should be addressed to the named correspondent.

Pearson plc

Company registration number 53723

80 Strand, London WC2R 0RL

020 7010 2000

Website: www.pearson.com

Correspondent: The Communications Manager

Chairman: Glen Moreno

Chief Executive: Marjorie Scardino

Year end	Turnover	Pre-tax profit
31/12/2007	£4,162,000,000	£468,000,000

Nature of company business
The company is an international media group.

Subsidiaries include: Pearson Education, The Penguin Group, Financial Times Group Ltd

Main locations: London

Total employees: 32,692

Charitable donations

2007: £7,200,000
2006: £3,600,000
2003: £605,000

Management costs: £260,000

Membership: BitC, L B Group

Community involvement

'Through the Pearson Foundation [www.pearsonfoundation.org], we focus our charitable giving on education and literacy projects around the world. We encourage our employees to support their personal charities by matching donations and payroll giving and by providing volunteering opportunities.'

The majority of Pearson's giving is in the US. Overseas projects are also supported in France, Spain and South Africa.

Exclusions

No support for advertising in charity brochures, animal welfare, appeals from individuals, enterprise/training, environment/heritage, fundraising events, medical research, political/religious appeals, science/technology, sickness/disability charities, social welfare or sport.

Applications

Appeals should be addressed to the correspondent. Local and trade appeals should be sent directly to the relevant subsidiary company.

Corporate giving

In 2007 the company's worldwide community contributions totalled £7.2 million. In addition to cash donations, Pearson also provides in kind support such as books, publishing expertise, advertising space and staff time.

In kind support

The operating companies also respond to trade and local causes through in kind donations. The main area of non-cash support is via gifts in kind.

Employee-led support

Wherever possible, employees are encouraged to become involved in charitable work in their local communities.

Payroll giving: The company runs and matches the Give As You Earn scheme.

Commercially-led support

Sponsorship: Support of the arts is undertaken. The Pearson Gallery of Living Words was opened at the British Library in 1998. It is one of three galleries open free to the public and reflects the diversity of the Library's collection through a series of special exhibitions. The Pearson Playwrights' Scheme offers bursaries to writers working in the theatre and awards to the authors of plays that are staged.

Pennon Group plc

Company registration number 2366640

Peninsula House, Rydon Lane, Exeter EX2 7HR

01392 446688; Fax: 01392 434966

Website: www.pennon-group.co.uk

Correspondent: Ms Lorna Shearman, Communications Manager
01392 443022; Fax: 01392 443018
Email: lshearman@southwestwater.co.uk

Chairman: Kenneth George Harvey

Chief Executive: Chris Loughlin/Colin Drummond

Year end	Turnover	Pre-tax profit
31/03/2007	£748,300,000	£131,100,000

Nature of company business
The provision of water, sewerage services and waste management.

Subsidiaries include: South West Water Ltd, Orbisphere UK Ltd, Viridor Ltd, Viridor Waste Ltd, Viridor Instrumentation Ltd, Exe Continental Ltd, ELE International Ltd, T J Brent Ltd, GLI International Ltd, Viridor Contracting Ltd, VWM (Scotland) Ltd

Main locations: Exeter

UK employees: 3,200

Total employees: 3,200

Charitable donations

2007: £183,000
2006: £131,000
2005: £100,000
2004: £60,000
2003: £60,000

Total community contributions: £500,000

Community involvement

Formerly South West Water plc, the company is now known as Pennon Group plc. Its main subsidiaries are South West Water Ltd and Viridor Waste Ltd.

The group's financial involvement in the community is channelled through a number of initiatives:
- charitable donations (Pennon)
- community sponsorship programme (South West Water & Viridor Waste)
- Landfill Tax Credit Scheme (Viridor Waste)
- environmental fund committee (Pennon)
- special assistance fund (South West Water customers).

The company website states that the group recognises its responsibilities by providing financial and other support to assist those communities and organisations in which it operates, i.e. Devon and Cornwall, to enhance their local environment.

Areas considered for support are advertising in charity brochures, animal welfare, appeals from individuals, the arts, children/youth, education, elderly people, enterprise/training, environment/heritage, fundraising events, science/technology, sickness/disability, social welfare and sport.

Charity of the Year (2007): WaterAid (South West Water); Scope and Primary Immunodeficiency Association (Viridor Waste).

Exclusions

No support for circular appeals, medical research, political appeals, religious appeals, local appeals not in areas of company presence or overseas projects.

Applications

In writing to the correspondent.

Information available: The company produces an annual social responsibility report which is available online.

Corporate giving

In 2006/07, the group made total UK community contributions of £500,000. Cash donations to charities operating in Devon and Cornwall totalled £183,000. Examples of beneficiaries included: Duke of Edinburgh's Award; Dartington International Summer School; Cornwall Wildlife Trust; Broadclyst Victory Hall – Devon; St David's Church – Exeter; Headwat – Devon; and NSPCC.

Initiatives the company are involved with (as mentioned above) are detailed here:
- charitable donations by Pennon Group plc are primarily to charities operating in Devon and Cornwall, the average donation being around £500. Total donations in 2006/07 were £50,000
- South West Water Community Sponsorship Programmes are delivered across a wide range of activities and totalled £77,000 during the year ending 31 March 2007
- Landfill Tax Credit Scheme (LTCS) enables Viridor Waste to deliver lasting environmental and social benefits for communities in the vicinity of its landfill operations. £7.2 million was awarded during 2006/07
- Pennon – Environmental Fund Committee was formed with the specific aim of bringing environmental and social benefits to the communities within South West Water's operating area by utilising some of the Viridor Waste's landfill tax credits. £56,000 was awarded in 2006/07
- South West Water Special Assistance Fund was established to provide help to customers trying pay their water and sewerage bills but, for reasons of severe financial or personal difficulties, were having problems paying the full amount

In kind support

Education: Group companies provide advice and support ranging from organising site visits relating to waste treatment, waste and recycling process for school pupils and students, to providing a training service to plumbers and ground workers under the Water Industry Approved Plumbers Scheme. Also, demonstrate the 'Science of Water' to secondary school children at Torbay Science Fair.

Students at Plymouth University have also been provided with work placements through the 'Year in Industry' scheme.

Employee-led support

Viridor Waste supports employees in their volunteering and fundraising efforts. For example, employees carrying out charitable/community work are given time off during working hours in which to do so. Whilst the company matches £ for £ individual employees fundraising (up to £1,000) and charitable giving (also up to £1,000).

Commercially-led support

Sponsorship: The company undertakes both arts and good-cause sponsorships. In 2006/07, the South West Water Community Sponsorship programme made awards totalling £77,000. Examples of beneficiaries include: The Pony Club (Tiverton branch); Padstow School (reading programme); Devon Youth Games 2006; and Surf Life Saving Association.

Contact: Chris Mills on 01392 443035.

Pentland Group plc

Company registration number 793577

The Pentland Centre, Lakeside, Squires Lane, London N3 2QL

020 8346 2600

Website: www.pentland.com

Correspondent: Community Involvement Officer

Chairman: R S Rubin

Chief Executive: A K Rubin

Year end	Turnover	Pre-tax profit
31/12/2007	£972,600,000	£66,000,000

Nature of company business
The main activities of the subsidiary companies are footwear, clothing and sports, consumer products and international trading.

Subsidiaries include: Ellesse Ltd, Boxfresh International Ltd, Onetruesaxon Ltd, Mitre Sports International Ltd, Airborne Footwear Ltd, Sportsflair Ltd, Kangaroos International Ltd, Speedo International Ltd, Red or Dead Ltd, Berghaus Ltd, Airborne Leisure Ltd

Main locations: Sunderland, London, Nottingham

UK employees: 10,446

Charitable donations

2006: £271,000
2005: £1,859,000
2004: £253,000

Community involvement

The company states on its website that: 'We work with many different organisations around the globe to support programmes that care for those in need. We are always amazed at how much our employees are prepared to dedicate their time, skills and energy to support a number of meaningful causes'.

Under the heading of 'Making a Difference', Pentland list six areas within which they give support. These are: People; Health; Environment; Education; Arts and Sport.

There is a preference for charitable and community projects associated with the group's products and business activities and local to its offices and factories. The group is also particularly keen to provide seed corn funding for projects that have a multiplier effect in generating money for a charity from other sources.

Exclusions

No support for local appeals not in areas of company presence.

Applications

In writing to the correspondent.

Corporate giving

In 2007 the group declared worldwide charitable donations of £1,209,000 'of which £1,168,000 was made directly by the company'. It also states in its annual report and accounts for the year that 'donations were primarily made to the Rubin Foundation'.

The Rubin Foundation (Charity Commission no. 327062) is closely linked to the company, which it primarily relies on for its income. In 2006/07 the foundation had an income of £101,000, in the previous year the sum of £1 million was received from the company.

In 2006/07 grants made by the foundation totalled £461,000, most of which went to the same set of recipients as in the previous year. Beneficiaries of the largest grants were: World Swim for Malaria (£75,000); Resources for Autism (£19,500); and British Friends of the Leo Baeck Education (£10,000).

The Pentland Group's website lists a number of UK charities it has supported including:

- People – The Prince's Trust; and Crimestoppers.
- Health – British Lung Foundation; Dementia Relief Trust; Leuka; North London Hospice; and Teenage Cancer Trust.
- Environment – Earth Charter.
- Education – Barnet Educational Bursaries Parnership; Holocaust Education Trust; and Trialogue Education Trust.
- Arts – Arts and Business; Donmar Warehouse; Royal Festival Hall; Royal Opera House Foundation; and Royal National Theatre.
- Sport – British Wheelchair Sports Foundation; Penathlon Foundation; Greenhouse Schools Project; and Peace and Sport.

Employee-led support

Employees are encouraged to support local good causes.

PepsiCo UK

Company registration number 123910

1600 Arlington Business Park, Theale, Reading, Berkshire RG7 4SA

Website: www.pepsico.co.uk

Correspondent: The Corporate Affairs Department

Year end	Turnover	Pre-tax profit
25/12/2004	£349,647,000	£8,222,000

Nature of company business
The group's activities include the manufacture, warehousing, marketing, distribution and sale of snack foods, the bottling and distribution of soft drinks and the supply of services on behalf of group companies.

Main locations: Reading, East Durham, Warrington, Leicester

UK employees: 5,480

Charitable donations

Membership: BitC

Community involvement

Although we have been unable to update the financial information for the company, it is clear from the information taken from its website (see below) that its support for charities and communities is quite extensive. On these grounds (and as a trans-national consumer-orientated business) we feel it should remain part of our research findings.

Charities: 'In our charity work, we have a number of long lasting commitments with local, national and international campaigns. For example, we have undertaken significant national activity to support Comic Relief.

'To further support and encourage our employees to participate in our charitable activity, we have provided staff with an easy, tax-efficient way of contributing to a chosen organisation. PepsiCo employees have the opportunity to make donations direct from their pay packet to a registered charity of their choice.'

Communities: 'With thirteen sites across the UK and Ireland, we have an opportunity to make a difference for staff and local families across the UK. For example, as part of the government's Skills for Life programme, PepsiCo has funded learning centres in Peterlee and Warrington. Open to employees, their families and members of the community they provide a wide range of courses to help people develop their basic skills and build self-belief and esteem.'

PepsiCo also provides support for local environmental improvements, particularly where there are health benefits for children to be had.

Applications

It is unclear whether this company accepts unsolicited applications from charities. However, with over thirteen sites around the UK, more success may be had at a local level.

Corporate giving

Despite the lack of an overall charitable donations/community contributions figure, an example of the level of support given by PepsiCo for a particulat project is mentioned on its website.

Environment: 'In both Leicester and Reading, we have worked with local councils to plan new children's playgrounds in public parks, as well as donating £100,000 towards their construction.'

Helping our communities

'All our sites have a range of longstanding commitments to local charities and good causes. These include:

- The Children's Adventure Farm – Northern Regional Distribution Centre, Warrington (NRDC)
- The Children's Hospital Manchester – NRDC
- Air Ambulance – Theale, Lincoln and NRDC
- St Barnabis Hospice – Lincoln
- Hartlepool Hospice – Peterlee.

In kind support
'Education

'*School and community partnerships* – Each of our sites partners with local schools and the community to provide children with a safe, comfortable place to learn and play. Activities we take part in range from fundraising to more hands-on projects, like painting a classroom, creating a garden area or clearing a common.'

Employee-led support

Education: '*Reading buddies* – Volunteers from PepsiCo support 20 schools across the country by listening to children read so they can enjoy the benefits of literacy in later life. In addition, we provide a range of support materials and funding for books.

'*School Governors* – There is a real shortage of school governors in the UK. PepsiCo encourages employees to volunteer as governors and works in partnership with School Governors' One-Stop Shop – a charity that puts volunteers in touch with schools that would benefit from their support.'

Payroll giving: PepsiCo offer this option to employees wishing to donate to the charity of their choice directly from their pay packets. The company then add 10% to this amount.

Commercially-led support

As official Red Nose Day sponsors, the PepsiCo business raised over £1 million for the charity in 2007.

Persimmon plc

Company registration number 1818486

Persimmon House, Fulford, York YO19 4FE

01904 642199; Fax: 01904 610014

Website: www.persimmonhomes.com

Correspondent: G N Francis, Company Secretary 01904 642199

Chairman: John White

Chief Executive: Mike Farley

Year end	Turnover	Pre-tax profit
31/12/2007	£3,010,000,000	£582,700,000

Nature of company business
Principal activities: residential building and development. Persimmon Homes is based in Anglia, Midlands, North East, North West, Scotland, South Coast, South East, South West, Thames Valley, Wales, Wessex, and Yorkshire.

Main locations: Leicester, Peterborough, Exeter, Fareham (Hampshire), Hamilton, York, Weybridge, Northampton, Llantrisant (Mid-Glamorgan), Lowestoft, Malmesbury (Wiltshire), Newcastle, Doncaster, Bristol, Lancaster, Leeds, Maidenhead, Warrington, Wolverhampton

UK employees: 5,501

Charitable donations

2007: £210,000
2006: £251,000
2005: £203,000
2004: £81,500
2003: £89,000

Total community contributions: £540,000

Community involvement

Persimmon supports national and local charitable and community initiatives at a group and regional operating business level.

Applications

In writing only to the correspondent. Each application is considered on its merits.

Information available: The company produce an annual corporate social responsibility report.

Corporate giving

In 2007, community contributions totalled £540,000 (generated by the group, its employees and suppliers) of which cash donations amounted to £210,000. Beneficiaries included: Marie Curie Cancer Care; York Minster; Dreams Come True; Samaritans; and St Leonard's Hospice.

Over the next ten years, from 2005, the group will donate over £700,000 to help train apprentices in the ancient craft skills which will be used to repair and conserve the east front of York Minster.

It is also involved in two educational initiatives entitled 'Homing in on Opportunity' which aims to promote the education of young people and advise them of the career opportunities within the house building sector and the 'Surveyors Committee' which amongst other things has looked at ways to encourage young people to join the business and train to become qualified quantity surveyors.

In kind support

The company provides gifts in kind by providing labour, material and, where appropriate, staff time. However, donations of gifts in kind and time made by individual businesses are not collated centrally.

Employee-led support

The company matches £ for £, and in full, employee fundraising and giving to charitable causes.

Personal Group Holdings plc

Company registration number 3194991

John Ormond House, 899 Silbury Boulevard, Central Milton Keynes MK9 3XL

01908 605000; Fax: 01908 201711

Website: www.personal-group.com

Correspondent: Dr J Barber, Trustee
Email: jbarber@personal-group.com

Chairman: C W T Johnston

Managing Director: K W Rooney

Year end	Turnover	Pre-tax profit
31/12/2007	£26,401,000	£8,571,000

Nature of company business
The provision of accident and health insurance, employee benefits, financial advice, and personal insurance and reinsurance broking services.

UK employees: 185

Charitable donations

2007: £80,000
2006: £80,000

Community involvement

Personal's corporate social responsibilitypolicy states: 'The group is committed to ensuring that the way in which its business is conducted has a positive impact on its employees and on the communities in which it operates'. Its activity in this respect includes a charitable fund to which Personal Assurance plc presently contributes approximately half of one percent of premium income. The group supports a range of voluntary sector and community activities, primarily where its own employees or employees of host companies from whom the group derives its business are actively involved'.

Personal Insurance Charitable Trust (PACT)

The trust was set up in 1993 to provide a source of funds for good causes from the revenues generated by the company.

Only Personal Assurance policyholders can nominate a charity or charitable purpose for the trustees to consider a donation.

Exclusions

Individuals or groups who are not policyholders with, or employees of, Personal Insurance plc.

Applications

If you are a Personal Assurance policyholder and would like to nominate a charity to receive assistance from PACT, please send an email to: pact@personal.com

Alternatively, you may complete the online PACT nomination form and post it to the relevant party.

Corporate giving

In 2007, the company donated £80,000 to charity, all of which went to PACT.

The largest donation made by the trust was to support the St John Ambulance schools first aid competition.

Other past beneficiaries have included MK Community Foundation (£5,000), TGWU Northern (£3,000) and Milton Keynes Sea Cadets (£1,000).

Pfizer Ltd

Company registration number 526209

Walton Oaks, Dorking Road, Tadworth, Surrey KT20 7NS

01737 330713; Fax: 01737 332526

Website: www.pfizer.co.uk

Correspondent: External Affairs

Managing Director: John Young

Year end	Turnover	Pre-tax profit
30/11/2006	£1,298,193,000	£151,252,000

Nature of company business
Pfizer Inc is the world's largest research-based pharmaceutical company and discovers, develops, manufactures and markets prescription medicines in 11 therapeutic areas including oncology, cardiovascular, pain, neuroscience, and infectious diseases, including HIV/AIDS. Pfizer is also the world's largest animal health company.

Subsidiaries include: Howmedica International Ltd, Unicliffe Ltd, Shiley Ltd

Main locations: Sandwich, Tadworth

UK employees: 5,500

Charitable donations

2007: £1,845,528
2006: £338,000

Total community contributions: £2,195,846
Management costs: £300,000

Membership: BitC

Community involvement

Pfizer's sites in the UK are at Sandwich, Kent and Walton Oaks, Surrey. Both seek to work closely with many diverse charitable, local organisations and statutory agencies using two main mechanisms for their corporate giving:

- Pfizer UK Foundation – a national initiative which supports organisations across the UK working at community level to deliver projects which address local health inequalities
- community funds – relevant to Pfizer sites, these are available to organisations local to the Sandwich (East Kent) and Walton Oaks (East Surrey) facilities.

The Pfizer UK Foundation

Applications are welcomed from organisations that:
- are based in Scotland, Northern Ireland, Wales or England
- are charities, community-led organisations, PCTs, local health boards, local authorities and academic bodies
- clearly address a defined health inequality
- are based in a deprived or marginalized community, targeting a specific local area
- can demonstrate a tangible impact on a defined group of people
- require funding of between £3,000 and £50,000
- intend to use the grant within a calendar year of payment.

Community funds

Sandwich – Pfizer's key aim is to contribute to initiatives that improve the health and well-being of communities in East Kent. Almost 60% of grants are committed to projects related to improving health through the Pfizer 'Healthy Communities' programme.

In addition to health spending, Pfizer actively supports personal and social education and welfare through local sports and community groups.

Walton Oaks – newly established in 2008, the fund supports projects that:

- align with Local Community Action Plans (LCAP)
- supports local health needs (outside statutory funding), specifically, healthy living initiatives
- directly respond to the local community's priority.

Exclusions

Unfortunately, these programmes cannot support applications from organisations that:
- are sectarian or political
- are ex service, fraternal, trade unions or professional societies
- represent personal appeals by, or on behalf of, an individual
- are seeking core funding i.e. building, equipment or on-going staff costs
- represent research projects.

Applications
Pfizer UK Foundation

If you feel your project/organisation meets the criteria, please send an email to pfizerukfoundation@pfizer.com to request an application form. Once you have received this, complete the form in full and send it back to the same email address. In this email, attach any supporting documents you feel would help the Pfizer UK Foundation board in assessing your application. If you do not have these in electronic format, send them by post to:

Pfizer UK Foundation
External Affairs
Pfizer Ltd
Walton Oaks
Dorking Road
Tadworth
Surrey
KT20 7NS

The foundation's board meets three times a year (February, June and October) to consider submissions, assess applications against the key criteria and make funding decisions.

The application process takes a maximum of four months from the receipt of the application to payment of the approved grants. Applications are kept informed of the process at regular intervals.

Community funds

Walton Oaks – for further information on applying to this local fund for assistance, please write to External Affairs at the above address, telephone them on 01737 330713, or send a fax to 01737 332526.

Sandwich – for further information on applying to this local fund for assistance, please write to Community Liaison, Ramsgate Road, Sandwich, Kent CT13 9NJ. Alternatively, you may telephone them on 01304 616161.

Note: local appeals outside of these two areas will not be considered.

Corporate giving

Although we are currently only able to supply financial data for year end November 2006, community investment figures for the following year were provided by the company.

In 2007, Pfizer made total community contributions in the UK of nearly £2.2 million of which £1.8 million was in cash. The following examples of support were given.

Pfizer UK Foundation – £1 million donated each year to organisations in England, Scotland, Wales and Northern Ireland. In 2007, donations were made to 39 community organisations, including:

- Fraserburgh Community School (£50,000)
- Ash Wales (£49,968)
- The Belfast Carers' Centre (£49,482)
- BD3 Ltd (£44,417)
- Children in Crisis (£40,500).

Sandwich Community Investment Panel – local initiative for organisations in East Kent. Donations above £5,000, totalling £135,514 made in 2007, including:

- Elements CIC – HIV counselling (£17,780)
- Age Concern Sandwich (£10,000)
- Options Pregnancy Crisis Centre (£10,000)
- Pilgrims Hospices (£11,868)
- Cancerbackup (£9,275).

Note: The Walton Oaks Community Fund was only established in 2008, so figures are not currently available.

In kind support

The company cites three examples of 'gifts in kind': the use of premises, including the use of equipment, e.g. use of projector and/or screens and photocopying; staff secondments; and training schemes.

Employee-led support

'Engaging colleagues in community activities is a core tenant of Pfizer's policy. In addition, Pfizer encourages its employees to share their skills and expertise with local voluntary organisations. Pfizer's ' Health Relief' (Walton Oaks) and 'Reaching Out' (Sandwich) volunteering programmes allow employees to take up to five days paid leave a year to work with a range of community projects.'

'In addition, for 'Health Relief', £250 is available to projects where additional materials (paint, plants and so on) are required to complete the task.

'Financial support is also given by the company to employees involved in charitable activities. The company matches employee fundraising (to a maximum of £150 per individual and £350 per team).'

Payroll giving: The company operates a payroll giving scheme, where it matches employee individual donations to a maximum of £100 per calendar month.

Commercially-led support

Sponsorship: Neither arts nor good-cause sponsorship are undertaken.

Philips Electronics UK Ltd

Company registration number 446897

Philips Centre, Guildford Business Park, Guildford, Surrey GU2 8HX

01293 815000

Website: www.philips.co.uk

Correspondent: The Quality Manager, (Social Sponsorship)

Chairman & Managing Director: Peter Maskill

Year end	Turnover	Pre-tax profit
31/12/2003	£682,200,000	£65,900,000

Nature of company business
The manufacture and supply of electrical and electronic equipment, supported by a research and development activity.

Main locations: Guildford, Reigate, Redhill, Manchester, Colchester, Hamilton (Lanarkshire)

UK employees: 1,802

Charitable donations
2006: £125,515
2005: £35,476

Community involvement

Philips has made the following statement regarding sustainability and responsibility:

'In the UK, Philips operates a social sponsorship programme that focuses on supporting activity that improves individuals' health and their quality of life.

'Our current policy is to concentrate our activities in three main areas:

- working with a national charity that places emphasis on improving the health and well-being of individuals
- sponsoring a range of projects in the Guildford area that support improving the health and quality of lives for the underprivileged
- working with the Surrey Community Foundation as a founder sponsor to support their work in providing grants that make a genuine difference to the lives of people in Surrey.'

'Philips receives a high number of requests for support and in order to have a proposal reviewed it must meet the objectives of the Philips social sponsorship programme. If it has been successful then Philips will contact the applicant directly to discuss this in more detail. Unfortunately we are unable to respond to every request.'

Charity of the Year: Tommy's – the baby charity (2007/08).

Applications

If you are a registered charity, or seeking sponsorship that meets the listed criteria, please write to Philips with details about your charity, what participation you are seeking, and the objectives you are planning to achieve by working with Philips.

Letters should be addressed to the correspondent.

Corporate giving

In 2006, the company declared charitable donations in the UK of £125,515 (2005: £35,476). We have no details of the beneficiaries, but assume a large proportion of this will have gone to national charity Philips chose to support in that year.

Pilkington Group Ltd

Company registration number 41495

Prescot Road, St Helens, Merseyside WA10 3TT

01744 28882; Fax: 01744 692660

Website: www.pilkington.com

Correspondent: Julie Woodward, Public Relations

Chief Executive: Stuart Chambers

Year end	Pre-tax profit
31/03/2007	(£309,000,000)

Nature of company business
Producer of glass and related products worldwide.

Subsidiaries include: Triplex Safety Glass Ltd

Main locations: Doncaster, St Helens, St Asaph, Kings Norton

UK employees: 4,000

Charitable donations

2007: £181,000
2006: £181,000
2005: £199,000
2004: £204,000
2003: £235,000

Membership: BitC

Community involvement

In June 2006, Pilkington was acquired by NSG UK Enterprises Ltd and became a member of the NSG Group, a wholly-owned subsidiary of Nippon Sheet Glass Co. Ltd of Japan.

Previously, we were advised that: 'The group and its employees also work closely with non-profit organisations through a wide range of voluntary work programmes and charitable contributions covering education, arts, medicine, welfare and young people and programmes that help create jobs and promote urban renewal. [This complements] the significant inputs of the time and skills of employees.'

We have been unable to find out how, if at all, the above acquisition has affected this policy.

Exclusions

No support for appeals from individuals, enterprise/training, overseas projects, political appeals or religious appeals.

Applications

In writing to the correspondent.

Corporate giving

In 2006/07, donations to charitable organisations in the UK totalled £181,000 (2005/06: £181,000). We have no detail concerning the beneficiaries, but can confirm the contact to be correct as at August 2008.

In kind support

The company provides non-cash support through gifts in kind.

Pilkington management time is given in support of young people in St Helens running their own business under the Young Enterprise scheme.

Employee-led support

UK employees and retirees regularly give their time to a variety of educational projects, including helping children with their reading, the twinning of managers with head teachers and employment and career advice.

Payroll giving: The Give As You Earn scheme is in operation.

Commercially-led support

Sponsorship: *Education* – In November 2006, the company announced its sponsorship of two Arkwright Scholarships.

Founded in 1991, the Arkwright scheme identifies young innovators and encourages the top engineers of the future

Each scholarship consists of an award of £950 over two years, which is divided between the successful scholar – to support their sixth form studies – and the Technology Department at his or her school.

PKF (UK) LLP

Company registration number 991270

Farringdon Place, 20 Farringdon Road, London EC1M 3AP

Website: www.pkf.co.uk

Correspondent: The Press Office

Managing Partner: M R Goodchild

Senior Partner: I E Mills

Year end
31/03/2008

Nature of company business
Principal activities: chartered accountants and management consultants.

Main locations: Bristol, Cardiff, Coatbridge, Derby, Lancaster, Ipswich, Leeds, Leicester, Edinburgh, Glasgow, Great Yarmouth, Sheffield, St Asaph, Liverpool, London, Northampton, Manchester, Lowestoft, Nottingham, Norwich, Stoke, Birmingham

UK employees: 120,181

Total employees: 122,880

Community involvement

'At PKF we have long recognised that local businesses and local communities are inextricably linked. The firm plays an active role in contributing to society through both financial support and through enabling our people to take part in activities organised by the firm as well as supporting them in their own initiatives. We encourage all of our people to take part in charitable and voluntary activities as we recognise that this strengthens our bond with the communities in which we work. Activities arranged by individuals include events such as Easter and Christmas collections and themed dress-down days.'

Previously we were advised that the company supports national charities and local charities near regional offices; also, that many PKF offices throughout the country contribute to their local communities by way of cash donations and the provision of employees' time and skills to local community initiatives.

The company is actively involved in Business in the Community initiatives.

Exclusions

No support for circular appeals, fundraising events, advertising in charity brochures, individuals, purely denominational (religious) appeals, local appeals not in areas of company presence, large national appeals or overseas projects.

Applications

In writing to the correspondent.

Corporate giving

As with all professional firms, there is no legal obligation on PKF to make publicly known any charitable donations they may have made. For this reason we are unable to provide a figure for 2007/08.

In kind support

From time to time the firm provide professional advice to charitable and community groups on a pro bono basis.

Employee-led support

PKF allows all partners and staff up to one week per year to take part in community activities.

Payroll giving: The Give As You Earn system is in operation.

Commercially-led support

Sponsorship: *The arts* – Support has been given to Royal National Theatre and Millstream Touring.

Premier Foods plc

Company registration number 5160050

Premier House, Centrium Business Park, Griffiths Way, St Albans AL1 2RE

01727 815850

Website: www.premierfoods.co.uk

Chairman: David Kappler

Chief Executive: Robert Schofield

Year end	Turnover	Pre-tax profit
31/12/2007	£2,247,600,000	(£73,500,000)

Nature of company business
Premier's principal products are bread, "ambient" or shelf stable groceries and chilled foods.

UK employees: 17,937

Charitable donations
2007: £158,000
2006: £52,000

Community involvement

Premier Foods annual donations budget is administered locally to a policy directed predominantly towards assisting those communities in which the group's businesses are located. In addition to this the group also makes donations to national charitable organisations.

Exclusions

No support for local appeals not in areas of company presence; or, political appeals.

Applications

Requests for a donation should simply be addressed to the company as they will be passed to the appropriate person for consideration. You may, if you so wish, put '(Fundraising)' after the company name in the address.

Corporate giving

In 2007, the group made charitable donations in the UK totalling £158,000 (2006: £52,000). We have no details of the beneficiaries.

PricewaterhouseCoopers LLP

Company registration number OC303525

1 Embankment Place, London WC2N 6RH

020 7583 5000; Fax: 020 7822 4652

Website: www.pwc.com/uk

Correspondent: Matthew Sugden, Corporate Responsibility Manager 020 7212 3164
Email: community.affairs@uk.pwc.com

Chairman: Ian Powell

Year end	Turnover	Pre-tax profit
30/06/2008	£2,244,000,000	£686,000,000

Nature of company business
Professional services firm.

Main locations: Leeds, Bristol, Southampton, Manchester, London, Birmingham

Total employees: 15,189

Charitable donations
2006: £1,500,000
2004: £1,107,914

Total community contributions: £6,800,000

Membership: A & B, BitC, L B Group

Community involvement

Generally Price Waterhouse Cooper (PwC) is proactive in selecting initiatives in the following fields:

- raising educational achievement in primary and secondary schools and encouraging citizenship
- developing employability schemes, encouraging enterprise and overcoming social exclusion in its local communities.

Support is given nationwide, but particularly where the firm have offices, i.e. Southwark and Westminster in London, Birmingham, Bristol, Leeds, Manchester and Southampton.

Exclusions

No support for circular appeals, advertising in charity brochures, animal welfare, appeals from individuals, the arts, elderly people, environment/heritage, fundraising events, medical research, overseas projects, political or religious appeals, science/technology, sickness/disability, social welfare, sport, or local appeals not in areas of company presence.

Applications

In writing to the correspondent. Donations are approved after consideration by a charities committee.

Information available: A Corporate Social responsibility Report can be downloaded from the firm's website (www.pwc.com/uk) along with further information for applicants.

Corporate giving

Total community contributions in 2008, including cash, time and in kind support totalled £6.8 million. Unfortunately, we were unable to find out the cash element of this.

Previous beneficiaries have included the Prince's Trust, Shakespeare's Globe, several local Community Foundations and Wings of Hope, which offers support to orphaned and poor children by providing free education.

In kind support

The firm runs a secondment programme for a small number of staff each year.

Employee-led support

In 2008, 4,650 staff were supported in their volunteering activities by the firm. Through its matched giving programme, employees can have up to £250 per year donated to the charities for which they fundraise. Tye form also donate through its 'Volunteering Awards Scheme', which is open to those who have a sustained involvement with a charity or community organisation.

Payroll giving: The Give As You Earn scheme is operated.

Commercially-led support

Partnerships: Projects include Our Theatre, a partnership with Shakespeare's Globe and Southwark Council that has involved over 4,000 students from 48 Southwark schools since 1997.

Principality Building Society

Company registration number 455B

PO Box 89, Principality Buildings, Queen Street, Cardiff CF10 1UA

029 2038 2000

Website: www.principality.co.uk

Correspondent: The Coporate Communications Manager

Chairman: David Williams

Chief Executive: Peter Griffiths

Year end	Pre-tax profit
31/12/2007	£30,600,000

Nature of company business
The provision of housing finance and a range of insurance and financial services.

Main locations: Cardiff

Charitable donations
2007: £25,000
2005: £10,674
2004: £8,528
Membership: BitC

Community involvement

The Principality supports a number of initiatives such as cultural events, sport at various levels and the volunteering and fundraising efforts of its staff.

Applications

In writing to the correspondent.

Local branch managers should be contacted to find out more about the branch sponsorship programme.

Corporate giving

In 2007 a total of £25,000 was given via the Principality Give me Five award. Five projects from each of the operating regions across Wales received support.

Employee-led support

Staff members have been involved in various community projects.

Commercially-led support

Sponsorship: *The arts* – For over 25 years the society has sponsored the National Eisteddfod of Wales.

The society has also sponsored various events, such as National Science Week at the Techniquest Centre in Cardiff Bay.

As well as sponsoring a number of national projects, Principality's branch network is involved in local level sponsorships through its 51 branches based throughout Wales and the borders, to support schools, local groups and community projects.

Private Equity Foundation

Company registration number 5882818

CAN Mezzanine, Downsstream, 1 London Bridge, London SE19BG

020 7785 3810

Website: www.privateequityfoundation.org

Correspondent: Shacks Ghosh, Chief Executive Officer
Email: info@privateequityfoundation.org

Year end
31/07/2007

Charitable donations
2007: £4,028,606

Total community contributions: £4,188,606

Community involvement

'Established in 2006, the Private Equity Foundation (PEF) is both a company limited by guarantee and a registered charity (Charity Commission no. 1116139). It is included here because it is funded by over 70 private equity firms and their advisors, including banks, law firms, accountancy firms, consultants and search firms. It describes its aims as follows:

'Our mission is to empower young people to reach their full potential. We seek to do this by investing both money and expertise from the private equity community, to help excellent charities achieve a step-change in their impact.

'The foundation aims to broker strong relationships between the business and charity worlds. Our hope is that charities will benefit as much from our skills as they do from our donations. Engaging with charities to build truly great organisations has the additional benefit of protecting and enhancing our donors' investments. Each charity we back is rigorously assessed before it is chosen to appear in our portfolio. Once a charity is selected, the foundation provides a package of support to ensure that the chosen charity's work is scaled up and made available to more young people.'

In 2008, the eight directors (who perform the role of trustees of the charity) of PEF were: David Blitzer (The Blackstone Group International Ltd); Scott Collins (Summit Partners Ltd); Todd Fisher (Kohlberg Kravis Roberts & Co.); Charlie Green (Candover Partners Ltd); Carl Parker (Perira Advisors LLP); Stephen Peel (Texas Pacific Group Capital); Dwight Poler (Bain Capital Ltd); and Ramez Sousa (Tower Brook Capital Partners UK LLP).

In addition to financial support, the foundation's backers may also provide pro bono and volunteer help.

Applications

Private Equity Foundation has its own charity selection process. It makes information available on its website when it is seeking new charities to join its portfolio.

Information available: The foundation's Annual review 2006/07 is available online.

Corporate giving

In 2006/07 the foundation had an income of £4.6 million, of which £4 million came from donations. A further £160,000 was provided to the foundation in services in kind. Grants totalled £2.4 million.

During the year the following UK-based charities were supported: Community Links (£270,000); IntoUniversity (£300,000 over four years); Leap Confronting Conflict (£200,000 over two years); NSPCC Treatment and Therapeutic Services (£1.1 million); The Place2Be (£576,000); and Volunteer Reading Help (£500,000 over three years).

In 2008, investments were approved for the following charities: Every Child a Chance Trust; Fairbridge; School-Home Support; Skill Force; and Tomorrow People.

In kind support

Examples of in kind support provided by the foundation's backers include:

▹ provision of a board member to Volunteer Reading Help by Bridgepoint

▹ provision of resources around strategic planning and financial training by Intermediate Capital Group and PwC

▹ 'adoption' of Community Links by TPG's staff.

Procter & Gamble UK

Company registration number 83758

The Heights, Brooklands, Weybridge, Surrey KT13 0XP

01932 896073; Fax: 01932 896233

Website: www.uk.pg.com

Correspondent: Mrs J S Butler, Community Matters Co-ordinator, UK & Ireland
Email: butler.js@pg.com

Chairman: A G Lafley

Chief Executive: A G Lafley

Year end
30/06/2008

Nature of company business
Procter & Gamble UK is a wholly owned subsidiary of The Procter & Gamble Company, USA. The principal activities of the company and its subsidiaries are the manufacture and marketing of innovative consumer products, with associated research and development services.

Main locations: Seaton Delaval, Skelmersdale, Weybridge, Manchester, Newcastle upon Tyne, West Thurrock, Egham, Harrogate, Bournemouth

UK employees: 5,000

Charitable donations
2004: £150,118
2001: £598,841
2000: £545,200

Total community contributions: £3,686,297

Membership: A & B, BitC, L B Group

Community involvement

Procter & Gamble (P&G) only supports local charities in areas of company presence across a wide range of causes covering education, economic well-being and leisure/social welfare.

Through its UK and Ireland Community Matters Programme, P&G's chosen area of support is primarily assisting with the development of children in need, from birth to 13 years – in line with its corporate cause Live, Learn and Thrive. The company also aim to support Educational; Health & Hygiene and Strategically Aligned Projects to those local communities in which we live and work.

P&G helps its local communities by providing:

▹ people involvement
▹ funding, where appropriate
▹ product donations
▹ time and expertise
▹ business skills and resources.

P&G also encourages its employees to pursue their own voluntary activities and to share their time and expertise to help establish sustainable benefits to their local communities.

Further information about P&G's UK and Ireland Community Matters programme, including objectives, strategy, principles and guidelines, can be downloaded from their website.

Exclusions

No support is given to circular appeals, advertising in charity brochures, appeals from individuals, fundraising events, medical research, overseas projects, political or religious appeals, or local appeals not in areas of company presence.

Applications

Applications should be by letter only and addressed to the correspondent.

For financial grants in Tyne & Wear, and Northumberland only, call the 'P&G Fund' at The Community Foundation (0191 222 0945). Applications should be made on the standard foundation form.

Information available: The company produces a social responsibility report and provides policy guidelines for applicants. The company also produces a newsletter entitled "Community Matters".

Corporate giving

Procter & Gamble have been, and remain, an elusive company to pin down with regard to its financial and community investment figures for the UK. As we did not receive a reply to our request for information we have repeated the last figures we were able to obtain. The remainder of the information has been checked as far as possible for accuracy.

In 2005, the company made donations totalling almost £3,700,000 in the UK, according to Business in the Community's PerCent Club (now defunct) figures. No figures for 2006 were available in the company's literature for 2006.

P&G Fund

The Community Foundation for Tyne & Wear and Northumberland manages the above fund on behalf of Procter & Gamble to support the company's charitable giving. Procter & Gamble have pledged to build a £1 million fund over ten years to support charitable groups in the North East.

Applications are welcomed:

- from charitable groups in Tyne & Wear and Northumberland
- from projects requiring £500–£5,000 with the majority of grants around £1,000
- for capital purposes for equipment, or revenue support for running costs.

Procter & Gamble aims to improve the quality of life for local people and grants are made in a broad field of activity to spread support across the community. Support is offered to:

- organisations which deliver sustained benefit to the community in areas of education, cultural and leisure amenities, and social well-being.

Procter & Gamble will target support at those groups which can demonstrate a sustained and long-term benefit to the communities they work with.

Future Friendly Awards

The Future Friendly Awards, developed in partnership between brands [e.g., P&G's 'Ariel' and 'Fairy'] and leading sustainability experts in saving energy, water and waste, is designed to celebrate the local heroes that take small scale, positive action to help make a difference. The awards focus on recognising and developing the work of those who actively demonstrate and lead the way in encouraging others to adopt sustainable principles.

The overall prize is a £20,000 bursary – 50% in funds to progress the commendable work that that individual, group or community has already put in place, and 50% consultancy time with one of the partners to guide the winner on next steps and ideas.

Further information about making an application can be found at: www.futurefriendly.co.uk

In kind support

The company also contributes through gifts in kind, training schemes and provision of employee time/expertise, for example, marketing, finance and so on. to community projects. Company employee skills and expertise are also used by many community projects in the areas of education, economic well-being, leisure and social welfare projects.

The In Kind Direct/Procter & Gamble partnership continues the work of distributing donations of toiletries to a vast number of charities and voluntary organisations in the UK. In 2007 alone, just under £1 million worth of goods have come from P&G.

Employee-led support

Employees undertake voluntary work in both company time their own time can request funds to support the project, when appropriate.

Payroll giving: The company operates an Employee Charitable Fund scheme, matching employee giving on a pound for pound basis.

Commercially-led support

Sponsorship: The company undertakes local arts and good-cause support.

Cause-related marketing: Procter & Gamble runs joint promotions on behalf of a variety of causes, many to do with young children and animals.

Provident Financial plc

Company registration number 668987

Colonnade, Sunbridge Road, Bradford, West Yorkshire BD1 2LQ

01274 731111; Fax: 01274 727300

Website: www.providentfinancial.com

Correspondent: Brent Shackleton, Community Affairs Manager
Email: brent.shacleton@providentfinancial.com

Chairman: John van Kuffeler

Chief Executive: Peter Crook

Year end	Turnover	Pre-tax profit
31/12/2007	£669,200,000	£115,200,000

Nature of company business
Personal credit and insurance.

Subsidiaries include: Colonnade Insurance Brokers Ltd, Greenwood Personal Credit Ltd

Main locations: Bradford

UK employees: 3,100

Charitable donations

2007: £776,751
2005: £677,751
2004: £450,083
2003: £270,820

Total community contributions: £837,982
Management costs: £142,272

Membership: A & B, BitC, L B Group

Community involvement

The company states on its website that: 'Our community programme aims to help people who live and work in the areas in which we operate – our customers, agents, employees and the local community. We work with local partners to offer new opportunities and to play our part in the development of neighbourhoods and communities.

'The aim of our programme is to create new opportunities for young people. The projects and associations we support are wide-ranging and varied.'

Additionally, through the 'Provident in the Community' programme, support and encouragement is given to employees and agents to initiate and take part in fundraising activities within the communities in which they live and work.

Exclusions

No support for appeals from individuals, heritage, medical research, overseas projects, political appeals, or religious appeals.

Requests for 'Charity of the Year' status are not considered.

Applications

In writing to the correspondent.

Corporate giving

Total community contributions by the company in 2007 were £837.982 of which £776,751 was in cash donations. A further £142,272 was attributed to management costs. Major beneficiaries included: Yorkshire Playhouse; Scottish Youth Hostel Association; L'Ouverture; and Axis Theatre. Further details of some of these are given below.

Community partnerships

'Spark – Spark is our flagship art education project in the UK and Ireland. This exciting, innovative three-year project links theatres with local schools and encourages children to take part in stimulating arts activities.

'Working together with the West Yorkshire Playhouse arts development team, which co-ordinates the project, we aim to raise the aspirations of children from inner-city communities and give them new opportunities to enjoy the arts and broaden their horizons.

'Spark embraces a wide range of visual and performing art forms from street dance to storytelling and junk percussion to puppet-making.

'The project targets key stage two (KS2) school children and involves over 50 schools and 6,000 children a year. Working through eight regional theatres, the project works with local schools where there is traditionally little access to the arts. Local freelance artists work with four classes in each school to undertake five weeks of bespoke art sessions.

'L'Ouverture – L'Ouverture provides unique opportunities for young people to learn about the arts and the media. Attention is focused on those young people unlikely to find such opportunities elsewhere, including those from deprived inner-city areas and those who have fallen between the cracks of the formal education system.

'L'Ouverture teaches young people about the traditional arts, including drama, dance, singing, drawing and creative writing, as well as the media industry – both about how it works, and about relevant media skills such as design, web building and video making.

'Our funding helps the organisation work with young people from Lewisham, Tower Hamlets, Southwark and Lambeth in the provision of in-school sessions, holiday and Saturday clubs.

'Give us a Break – Give Us a Break aims to provide new opportunities for young people to take part in outdoor activities and so increase their confidence and self-esteem. We have joined forces with the Scottish Youth Hostel Association (SYHA) and its sister organisation in Ireland, the Irish Youth Hostel Association, to deliver these enjoyable learning opportunities.

'Give us a Break provides schoolchildren with a free, two-day break in a youth hostel. Each group undertakes activities linked to the national curriculum, as well as gaining access to new cultural experiences. We provide additional support through our employees and agents who attend the breaks and supply practical materials such as t-shirts, caps and water bottles.

'Since the project began, over 7,000 young people have taken part in these valuable breaks.'

Employee-led support

Provident in the Community – This programme supports and encourages employees and agents to initiate and take part in fundraising activities within the communities in which they live and work. Provident see it as a direct way of building on the relationships built between its customers and their agents, their families, friends and associates.

Support is provided in the form of financial donations, practical help, materials and advice. Provident believe that its involvement in such projects builds a greater understanding of the communities in which their customers, staff and agents live and work. It also encourages the development of new skills and creates a sense of pride in what can be achieved.

In the last twelve months employees and agents across the UK home credit businesses gave time and raised funds for more than 200 local good causes through the scheme. Activities undertaken ranged from raffles to fun runs, mentoring to DIY skills. Through their efforts community groups and charities benefited from more than £150,000.

Prudential plc

Company registration number 1397169

Laurence Pountney Hill, London EC4R 0HH

020 7220 7588; Fax: 020 7548 3528

Website: www.prudential.co.uk

Correspondent: Tina Christou, Head of Corporate Responsibilty
Email: tina.christou@prudential.co.uk

Chairman: Sir David Clementi

Chief Executive: Mark Tucker

Year end   Pre-tax profit
31/12/2006 £893,000,000

Nature of company business
Prudential plc, through its businesses in Europe, the US and Asia, provides retail financial products and services.

Subsidiaries include: Scottish Amicable Life plc, M&G Investment Management Ltd, Jackson National Life

Main locations: Belfast, Chelmsford, Reading, Nottingham, London, Stirling

UK employees: 6,000

Charitable donations

2006: £3,150,000
2005: £3,500,000
2003: £2,800,000

Total community contributions: £4,724,000 (global)
Management costs: £904,456

Membership: A & B, BitC, L B Group

Community involvement

Prudential's corporate community involvement is part of its wider commitment to corporate social responsibility. Each business within the group has its own community investment plan in place. However, identified as a key issue across all locations, is the need to improve financial literacy within communities. This is therefore dealt with at group level.

National (UK) and local charities are supported in areas where the company has offices.

Exclusions

No support for appeals for sponsorship of individuals or groups, fundraising events, advertising in charity brochures, circular appeals, political organisations, purely denominational (religious) appeals, local arts or drama groups, animal welfare, heritage and building projects, medical research, or science/technology.

Applications

Further information can be sought from the Corporate Responsibility team at the above number.

Corporate giving

In 2006, the group made total community contributions worldwide of £4.7 million. Within this, direct donations to charitable organisations amounted to £3.15 million, of which £2.3 million came from European Union (EU) operations. This was broken down as follows: Education (£1.1 million); Social and Welfare (£809,000); Environment and Regeneration (£82,000); Cultural (£149,000); and Staff Volunteering (£242,000).

Beneficiaries included: Citizens Advice; Specialist Schools and Academies Trust; National Institute of Adult Continuing Education; and Personal Finance Education Group.

In kind support

A range of in kind support is offered to organisations on a local basis. This includes employees' time and skills, office space, meeting rooms, computers and office furniture.

Employee-led support

A new international employee volunteering programme, The Chairman's Award, was launched across the group in December 2005. The initiative encourages employees to volunteer with charities within their local communities.

Payroll giving: The company operate the Give As You Earn scheme.

Psion plc

Company registration number 1520131

Alexander House, 85 Frampton Street, London NW8 8NQ

020 7535 4253; Fax: 020 7535 4226

Website: www.psionteklogix.com

Correspondent: Group Communications

Chairman: Dr David Potter

Chief Executive: John Conoly

Year end   Turnover   Pre-tax profit
31/12/2007 £199,740,000 £10,792,000

Nature of company business
Development, manufacture and supply of mobile, digital communication and computing technology.

Subsidiaries include: Trivanti Ltd, Symbian Ltd

Main locations: Milton Keynes, London

UK employees: 1,229

Charitable donations

2007: £17,606
2006: £12,694
2005: £20,293
2003: £41,000

Community involvement

Psion focuses its support principally on organisations local to its production sites and those in which an employee is involved through volunteering.

Exclusions

No support for appeals from individuals or local appeals not in areas of company presence. The company does not provide support for political parties.

Applications

In writing to the correspondent.

Corporate giving

In 2007, Psion made charitable donations totalling £17,606 (2006: £12,694). We have no details of the beneficiaries.

QinetiQ Group plc

Company registration number 4586941

Cody Technology Park, Ively Road, Farnborough, Hampshire GU14 0LX

08700 100 942

Website: www.qinetiq.com

Correspondent: Brenda Jones

Chairman: Sir John Chisholm

Chief Executive: Graham Love

Year end	Turnover	Pre-tax profit
31/03/2008	£1,366,000,000	£51,400,000

Nature of company business
The group's principal activity is the supply of scientific and technical solutions and services.

Main locations: Farnborough

UK employees: 11,024

Charitable donations

2008: £184,000
2007: £19,000
2006: £54,000
2005: £57,000

Membership: BitC

Community involvement

The company states: 'Investing in community programmes enable our people to commit their time and expertise to support local and wider society issues. In addition to fundraising activities for a range of good causes, we are proud of our education outreach programmes through which we aim to inspire the next generation of scientists and engineers.

'Throughout the group, we support a number of charities that are important to our employees. Charitable giving initiatives included matched giving, payroll giving and volunteering. QinetiQ sites continue to support a range of local issues in their communities.'

Applications

In writing to the correspondent.

Corporate giving

In 2007/08, cash donations to UK charitable organisations amounted to £184,000. Past beneficiaries included: The National Trust for Scotland, whom it helped secure St Kilda's dual world heritage status; St Richard's Hospice in Malvern; and support for two schools in attaining specialist science status – St Augustine's, Malvern and Cove, Farnborough.

Through the Community Foundation for Wiltshire and Swindon, the company established the QinetiQ Boscombe Down Fund which is designed to improve the life of disadvantaged people through education and science.

In kind support

To increase awareness of science and technology in local schools, the company is piloting the use of 'Lab in a Lorry' in Boscombe Down. In addition, a particular emphasis has been placed on investigating ways to make a contribution through technology support for the Royal National Lifeboat Institute (RNLI) and Cancer Research UK.

Employee-led support

In support of 'charities that matter to our staff', QinetiQ has implemented a match-funding arrangement through which certain identified charities are given funding priority. These charities include: Cancer Research UK, St Richard's Hospice, NSPCC, RNLI, Royal British Legion and SSAFA. As a result of this over £15,000 was provided by the group.

Payroll giving: The company funds a payroll giving scheme.

Commercially-led support

Sponsorship: *Education* – QinetiQ sponsor the following events: the Schools Aerospace Challenge, the Stockholm Prize at the BA Crest Science Fair, the Cheltenham Science Festival, Generation Science as part of the Edinburgh Science Festival, and the Engineering Education Scheme.

RAB Capital plc

Company registration number 3694213

1 Adam Street, London WC2N 6LE

020 7389 7000

Website: www.rabcap.com

Correspondent: Ben Pope, Facilities Manager
Email: info@rabcap.com

Chairman: Michael Alen-Buckley

Chief Executive: Stephen Couttie

Year end	Turnover	Pre-tax profit
31/12/2007	£124,346,000	£51,047,000

Nature of company business
The company is a listed alternative asset manager which specialises in managing absolute return funds (often referred to as 'hedge' funds).

UK employees: 137

Charitable donations
2007: £5,260,000
2006: £2,400,000

Community involvement

According to a report in The Financial Times, dated 16 April 2007, one of the co-founders of RAB Capital, Philip Richards, advocates paying a tithe to charity. In line with this, the company's annual report shows that the two highest paid directors (one of whom is Philip Richards) chose to sacrifice anticipated personal emoluments (bonuses) which were then paid to charity.

Applications

In writing to the correspondent

Corporate giving

In 2007, the company's annual report declared charitable donations of £5.26 million (2006: £2.4 million). We have no details of the beneficiaries, but believe there may be some preference for Christian causes.

Rank Group plc

Company registration number 3140769

Statesman House, Stafferton Way, maidenhead SL6 1AY

01628 604000; Fax: 01628 504042

Website: www.rank.com

Correspondent: Karen Doogan, Company Secretary

Chairman: Peter Johnson

Chief Executive: Ian Burke

Year end	Turnover	Pre-tax profit
31/12/2007	£257,000,000	£76,600,000

Nature of company business
The Rank Group is one of the UK's leading leisure and entertainment companies and an international provider of services to the film industry. Leisure and entertainment activities include casinos, bingo clubs, pub restaurants and holiday resorts. Rank also owns film processing and video and DVD duplication and distribution facilities. Rank operates primarily in the UK and North America, although it has activities in Continental Europe and other parts of the world.

Subsidiaries include: Deluxe Laboratories Ltd, Deluxe Video Services Ltd, Grosvenor Casinos Ltd, Mecca Bingo Ltd

Main locations: London

UK employees: 8,169

Charitable donations	
2007: £236,000	
2006: £244,000	
2005: £269,000	
2004: £233,000	
2003: £275,000	

Community involvement
The company supports local and national charities with major support going to industry related trusts.

Exclusions
No response is given to circular appeals. No support for individuals is granted – students, expeditions and so on. No grants for advertising in charity brochures, animal welfare, the arts, fundraising events, overseas projects, political appeals, religious appeals, science/technology, sport, or local appeals not in areas of company presence.

Applications
In writing to the correspondent.

Corporate giving
In 2007, charitable donations made in the UK amounted to £236,000 (2006: £244,000). The largest donation of £220,000 was to BCA Gaming Industry Trust.

Subsidiary companies support a variety of local and national charities. For example, in 2008 Mecca Bingo is supporting Whizz-Kidz as its official charity. Whilst during 2007,

Grosvenor Casinos raised money for a variety of charities including the British Heart Foundation and Breakthrough Breast Cancer.

Ravensale Ltd

Company registration number 1476675

115 Wembley Commercial Centre, East Lane, North Wembley, Middlesex HA9 7UR

020 8908 4655

Correspondent: Bruce D G Jarvis, Charity Correspondent

Year end	Turnover	Pre-tax profit
30/06/2007	£6,711,738	£2,190,819

Nature of company business
The principal activity of Ravensale Ltd is property development and investment, and the design and manufacture of ballpoint pen components.

UK employees: 43

Charitable donations	
2007: £1,795,000	
2006: £1,893,000	
2005: £1,903,000	
2004: £959,471	

Community involvement
Ravensale Ltd directs all its charitable giving, which is substantial, through the registered charity, The Joron Charitable Trust (Charity Commission no. 1062547) of which two of the directors are trustees. The trust is established for general charitable purposes and makes grants to registered charities in various fields where it can be demonstrated that the grants will be used effectively.

There is no formal grant application procedure and the trustees retain the services of a charitable grants advisor and take advice when deciding on grants.

Exclusions
No support for political organisations.

Applications
There is no formal grant application procedure. Apply to the contact in writing.

Corporate giving
During the year ending 30 June 2007 the company donated £1,795,000 (2006: £1,893,000) to The Joron Charitable Trust. The trust in turn made 30 grants totalling £1,048,608 (2006: £974,678).

The beneficiaries included: UNICEF UK (£133,110); The Princess Royal Trust for Carers (£106,893); Keech Cottage, Jewish Care and RNIB (£100,000 each); CSV People for People (£50,000); Theodora Children's Trust (£30,000); Tree House (£20,000); AT Society (£10,000); and Community Trading Ltd (£2,000).

Reckitt Benckiser plc

Company registration number 527217

103–105 Bath Road, Slough, Berkshire SL1 3UH

01753 217800

Website: www.reckittbenckiser.com

Correspondent: The Corporate Communications Department

Chairman: Adrian Bellamy

Chief Executive: Bart Becht

Year end	Turnover	Pre-tax profit
31/12/2007	£5,269,000,000	£1,209,000,000

Nature of company business
Principal activities: The manufacture and sale of household and healthcare products.

Main locations: Derby, Hull, Slough, Windsor, Swindon

Total employees: 23,400

Charitable donations

2007: £606,000
2006: £599,000
2005: £568,000
2004: £496,000
2003: £367,000

Community involvement

'Reckitt Benckiser continues to invest over £1 million per year towards projects that really make a difference to people in the communities in which we operate around the world. As well as the company providing much needed financial support, our people also give unselfishly of their time on a range of projects that assist those who can benefit from some help and support.'

Exclusions

No grants for animal welfare charities, the arts, elderly people, political appeals, religious appeals, science/technology, sickness/disability or sport.

Applications

In writing to the correspondent. Applications are considered by the Community Involvement Committee which meets four times a year. In addition to authorising donations, the committee is concerned with the implementation of policy relating to the company's community programme.

Corporate giving

Donations to charitable organisations in the UK in 2005 were £606,000, of which £300,000 was donated to Save the Children the company's nominated charity.

'In 2007, we gave more than £1.5 million worth of support to community programmes worldwide. Our employees also gave their time and money to many fundraising projects. Our main focus is still Save the Children, our global charity partner, because most of our products are bought by families. And, in line with our business expertise, we also choose to focus our support on health and hygiene programmes. Reckitt Benckiser operates a community involvement policy executed through

its Community Involvement Committee (CIC) which consists of senior executives from the company.'

In kind support

Additional support may be given through gifts in kind.

Employee-led support

The company matches employee fundraising. In 2007 its four UK offices each supported local family, children's and health charities like Home-Start and Prospect Hospice.

Redrow Group plc

Company registration number 2877315

Redrow House, St David's Park, Flintshire CH5 3RX

01244 520044; Fax: 01244 520720

Website: www.redrowcsr.co.uk

Correspondent: Simon Bennett, Marketing Director
01244 520044; Fax: 01244 520580

Chairman: Alan Bowkett

Chief Executive: Neil Fitzsimmons

Year end	Turnover	Pre-tax profit
30/06/2008	£650,100,000	(£139,900,000)

Nature of company business
The principal activities are housebuilding and commercial development.

Subsidiaries include: Bates Business Centre, Poche Interior Design, Harwood Homes

Main locations: Barnsley, Bexhill on Sea, Liverpool, Flintshire, Leek, Falkirk, Aberdare, Preston Brook, High Wycombe, Leigh, Cardiff, Launceston

Total employees: 1,271

Charitable donations

2008: £281,000
2007: £334,000
2006: £304,000
2004: £96,000

Membership: BitC

Community involvement

In March 2006, Redrow established the Redrow Foundation. This independent charitable trust which is a registered charity seeks to relieve poverty and sickness in the UK, and in particular to provide accommodation and related assistance, including respite care, especially for children, the elderly and those who are sick or infirm.

The company and its employees also support educational initiatives, arts, craft, sport and small charities at a local level.

Exclusions

No support for circular appeals, advertising in charity brochures, purely denominational (religious) appeals, large national appeals, overseas projects or local appeals not in areas of company presence.

Applications

In writing to the correspondent, or, via email to: foundation@redrow.co.uk. You will then be informed of the foundation's full criteria, together with the next date when the trustees are to meet to discuss the merits of each submission.

In considering each request, the trustees will be looking for evidence of leverage on the funds. Please state, therefore, how you intend to match or increase any donation you may receive in your application.

Corporate giving

In 2007/08 the company gave £281,000 in charitable donations during the year. A total of £217,000 was given in respect of national charities and £64,000 in support of local charities.

The Redrow Foundation

Redrow has made an initial donation to the foundation of £100,000 and, thereafter, will contribute £50 for every Redrow home purchased. In the year ended June 2008, Redrow paid £50 per home legally completed to the Redrow Foundation. The amount paid to the foundation is included within the charitable donations in respect of national charities disclosed above and amounted to £196,000 in 2008. The economic climate of 2008 which has seen a downturn in the property market may have an undue effect on future giving.

In kind support

In kind help may be given through the donation of furniture to needy causes such as care homes, or the development of curriculum resource packs for primary school children. Suitable IT equipment may also be donated to local schools as the company updates its hardware.

Employee-led support

All employees are encouraged to take part in fundraising on behalf of their local community. Each of Redrow's regional companies is encouraged to adopt a local charity and fundraise on its behalf.

Reed Executive plc

Company registration number 2061422

Academy Court, 94 Chancery Lane, London WC2A 1DT

Website: www.reed.co.uk

Correspondent: (see 'Applications')

Chairman: Alec Reed

Year end	Turnover	Pre-tax profit
28/12/2007	£9,251,000	£3,440,000

Nature of company business
Specialist recruitment and HR services provider

UK employees: 69

Charitable donations
2007: £34,874
2006: £44,824

Community involvement

Reed comprises a family of companies of which Reed Executive is but one. Others include Reed in Partnership plc, Reed Employment plc and Reed Learning plc. It may well, therefore, be worth checking these out as possible benefactors. However, it is not clear from the information available whether they would be open to unsolicited applications.

Historically, to quote from its website: 'Reed has a long-standing commitment to social initiatives and charitable concerns. Since opening the first Reed branch in 1960, our founder Alec Reed has ensured that an ethos of involvement in charitable and social initiatives has been integral to the company's mission and aims.'

Charities

Alec Reed has founded the following charities: The Reed Foundation; Ethiopiaid; and Women at Risk.

Applications

The contact for the foundation is: The Secretary, The Reed Foundation, 6 Sloane Street, London SW1X 9LE (Tel: 020 7201 9980). However, the trust states that it does not respond to unsolicited applications.

Corporate giving

In 2007, the company made charitable donations totalling £34,874 (2006: £44,824). We have no details of the beneficiaries, but believe some of the money may have been given in support of The Reed Foundation (Charity Commission no. 264728).

The Reed Foundation

The trust has general charitable purposes, but historically has had an interest in womens causes in the develolping world.

In 2005, the trust had assets of £15 million and an income £183,000. Grants totalled £529,000. Beneficiaries included Women at Risk (£335,000), Academy of Enterprise (£82,000), Ethiopiaid Sweden (£40,000), Speed International (£7,500), Marie Curie (£5,000) and Donmar Warehouse (£1,000).

In kind support

Reed works inpartnership with TimeBank to raise awareness of the value of giving time and skills back to the local community. Although promoting this to its employees, no examples of Reed employee volunteering are given.

Employee-led support

Payroll giving: The Give As You Earn scheme is in operation.

Renishaw plc

Company registration number 1106260

New Mills, Wotton-under-Edge, Gloucestershire GL12 8JR

01453 524524

Website: www.renishaw.com

Correspondent: David Champion, Chairman, Charities Committee
Email: genenq@renishaw.com

Chairman: Sir David McMurtry

Chief Executive: Sir David McMurtry

Year end	Turnover	Pre-tax profit
30/06/2008	£201,157,000	£43,059,000

Nature of company business
The main activities are the design, manufacture and sale of advanced precision metrology and inspection equipment, and computer aided design and manufacturing systems.

Subsidiaries include: Wotton Travel Ltd

Main locations: Stonehouse, Woodchester, Wotton-under-Edge

Total employees: 2,151

Charitable donations

2008: £41,000
2007: £64,000
2006: £104,532
2005: £62,541
2004: £49,758

Community involvement

The company gives priority to local appeals (in areas immediate to company locations – Wotton-under-Edge, Stonehouse and Woodchester, involving young people, and to local branches of national charities concerned with children/ youth. Other preferred causes include: animal welfare, the arts, education, older people, enterprise/training, environment/heritage, fundraising events, medical research, religious appeals, science/technology, sickness/disability charities and sport.

The group organises its charitable donations by two methods: firstly, by allocating a fund of money to its charities committee; and secondly, through direct grants decided by the board.

Exclusions

No support for advertising in charity brochures, appeals from individuals, fundraising events for third parties, overseas projects or political appeals. No sponsorship is undertaken.

Applications

Written appeals only, to the chairman of the Charities Committee at the above address. The committee meets at least four times a year to consider all applications for donations from local (Gloucestershire) groups.

Corporate giving

In 2007/08 the company made charitable donations of nearly £41,000 (2006/07: £64,000). The company hs supported Children in Need for a number of years. A further beneficiary during the year was St Werburgh's City Farm – Bristol.

In kind support

In kind support is given by, for example, hosting community/ charitable events at its premises.

Employee-led support

'Renishaw has supported Children in Need for a number of years and in keeping with a long tradition, money raised by Renishaw personnel for Children in Need is matched pound for pound by the company.'

Rentokil Initial plc

Company registration number 5393279

12th Floor, Portland House, Bressenden Place, London SW1E 5BH

020 7592 2700

Website: www.rentokil-initial.com

Correspondent: Paul Griffiths, Director, Group Secretariat

Chairman: B D McGowan

Chief Executive: D Flynn

Year end	Turnover	Pre-tax profit
31/12/2007	£2,203,400,000	£142,000,000

Nature of company business
Principal activity: international company providing services to businesses including, pest control, package delivery, interior landscaping, catering, electronic security, cleaning.

Subsidiaries include: Dudley Industries Ltd

Main locations: East Grinstead, Orpington

Total employees: 76,412

Charitable donations

2007: £107,000
2006: £198,000
2005: £254,000
2004: £130,000
2003: £115,000

Membership: BitC

Community involvement

Previously we were advised that the company is only prepared to consider supporting registered charities or non-profit making organisations which raise funds for charitable causes. Support is given to bodies that aim to 'improve the quality of life in our society, such as the Safer London Foundation'. There exists a local charities budget which supports organisations local to its East Grinstead and Orpington offices. Assistance is also given to employees in their fundraising efforts.

Exclusions

Consideration will not be given to any charity or sponsorship related proposal from any organisation unless a company employee or employees are involved.

Applications

In writing to the correspondent, but note 'exclusions' above.

Other information: The company produces an annual corporate social responsibility report.

Corporate giving

Charitable cash donations amounted to £107,000 in 2007, mostly given as part of the company's match giving scheme.

In kind support

In the UK, Initial catering has developed two websites which provide healthy eating guidelines for schoolchildren (www.coolmeals.co.uk and www.feedyourminds.co.uk), along with healthy eating education packs for teachers to support classroom education and workshops.

Employee-led support

The company operates a staff matched-giving scheme for all its employees worldwide. This means Rentokil Initial will match any amount raised by staff member(s) who take part in an event for a charitable cause. However, only funds raised by employees who actively participate in fundraising events themselves will be matched by the company.

Payroll giving: The company operate the Give As You Earn scheme.

Rexam plc

Company registration number 191285

4 Millbank, London SW1P 3XR

020 7227 4100; Fax: 020 7227 4109

Website: www.rexam.com

Correspondent: The Director of Corporate Communications

Chairman: Rolf Borjesson

Chief Executive: Leslie Van de Walle

Year end	Turnover	Pre-tax profit
31/12/2007	£3,611,000,000	£260,000,000

Nature of company business
Rexam plc is an international consumer packaging company and beverage can maker.

Subsidiaries include: Bowater Security Products Ltd, W H S Halo, Business Printing Group, Staybrite Windows, McCorquodale Card Technology, Cox and Wyman, McCorquodale Engineering Ltd, Cartham Papers, Broadprint Ltd, Bowater Windows Ltd, Bowater Business Forms Ltd, TBS, Laser Image Ltd, Essex Business Forms, Zenith Windows

Main locations: Stevenage, Wakefield, Milton Keynes, Deeside, Luton, London, Tonbridge

Charitable donations	
2007:	£48,000
2006:	£61,000
2005:	£68,000
2004:	£98,000
2003:	£98,000

Community involvement

The community responsibilty section of the company's website states: 'Rexam's plants are usually important citizens in their local communities. They are not only substantial employers in the community, they also contribute in many other ways: through charitable donations; staff volunteering; product donations and any other way in which we can usefully contribute to the strength and well-being of the local societies of which we are proud to be a part.'

Exclusions

Previous information stated that there is no support available for: advertising in charity brochures; animal welfare; appeals from individuals; overseas projects; political appeals; religious appeals; or sport. Sponsorships are not usually undertaken.

Applications

In writing to the correspondent.

Other information: The company produce a corporate environmental and social report. Copies can be downloaded from its website.

Corporate giving

In 2007 the company's UK cash donations amounted to £48,000 (2006: £61,000). The two main recipients were Kidscape and the Children's Safety Education Foundation.

Worldwide donations totalled £320,000 (2006: £589,000).

Employee-led support

The company matches employees' fundraising efforts on behalf of charities of their choice.

Payroll giving: The company operates the Give As You Earn scheme.

Richer Sounds plc

Company registration number 1402643

Unit 3/4, Richer House, Gallery Court, Hankey Place, London SE1 4BB

020 7357 9298; Fax: 020 7357 8685

Website: www.persula.org

Correspondent: Michael Brain, Persula Foundation
Email: info@persula.org

Year end	Turnover	Pre-tax profit
26/04/2008	£84,154,000	£3,704,000

Nature of company business
Hi-fi retail.

Main locations: London

UK employees: 330

Charitable donations
2008: £406,142
2007: £5,731
2005: £216,523

Community involvement

The company's charitable support appears to be routed through the Persula Foundation which was initiated by the founder of Richer Sounds plc. It is a registered charity (Charity Commission no. 1044174), established in 1994 as an independent grant-giving foundation. The Persula Foundation supports any cause which, as a charitable foundation, it feels strongly about. It states that it is always researching new projects and charities to support, but does have core interests, e.g. animal welfare, disabilities, human welfare and human rights.

Exclusions

No support for circular appeals, advertising in charity brochures, appeals from individuals, the arts, education, enterprise/training, fundraising events, medical research, overseas projects, political/religious appeals, science/ technology, sport or large national appeals.

Money for core costs, buildings/building work or to statutory bodies is not given.

Sponsorship is not undertaken.

Applications

In writing to the correspondent.

Corporate giving

In 2007/08, the company made charitable donations of £406,142 which we presume was paid to the foundation.

The Persula Foundation

In 2007, the foundation had an income of £147,589 and made grants totalling £543,906

The following extract is taken from the foundation's latest accounts:

'During the 12 months ended 30 April 2007 the generic research groups of The Persula Foundation continued their work and support of various projects established within the previous year as well as supporting new exciting projects such as support for World Vision with the support for the schools & education programme in Niger; support for the World Society for the Protection of Animals (WSPA) Humane Slaughter World Programme; giving support to the National Autistic Society for their unique befriending project in the UK; we also supported The Shannon Trust with their unique 'Toe to Toe' reading plan which gives literate prisoners the opportunity to teach and mentor illiterate prisoners to read.

'Ongoing projects which continued to run successfully in 2006/2007 included the "On The Right Track Project" providing free touch-screen computerised kiosks for homeless people and young runaways and "Tapesense" our mail-order service which offers subsidised, brand new blank audio cassettes, and popular hifi accessories including the revolutionary Pure Digital Sonus 1XT 'Talking Digital Radio' to Blind and Visually Impaired people (over 5,000 products sent out every week).

'We have continued to develop our "Storytelling Tour" project giving over 400 free sessions of entertaining storytelling and music to visually impaired, disabled children and adults and the elderly throughout the UK.'

Fuller details of some of the wide-ranging projects supported by the foundation are available on its website.

In kind support

The foundation also has access to many resources from the company, such as marketing, design and strategic consultation. It prefers to use these resources to provide an added value aspect to its collaboration with organisations. It also offers support in the form of time and resources. 'Tapesense', the foundation's mail-order service, offers subsidised, brand new blank audio cassettes, and popular hifi accessories to blind and visually impaired people.

Employee-led support

The company supports employee volunteering, allowing paid time off work to volunteers and matching employee fundraising.

Ridgesave Ltd

Company registration number 1745720

141b Upper Clapton Road, London E5 9DB

Correspondent: Mrs H Z Weiss, Trustee

Year end
01/03/2007

Nature of company business
Property investment and trading.

> **Charitable donations**
> 2007: £1,100,000
> 2006: £944,000

Community involvement

This is a somewhat unusual entry in the context of our research into company giving. Ridgesave, although registered as a company limited by guarentee, is also a registered charity (Charity Commission no. 288020).

We have decided to include them here because it has two non-charitable operating subsidiaries – Bullion Properties Ltd (property trading) and Doxit Co. Ltd (property investment). In addition, the bulk of the charity's income is derived from five other companies of which some of the trustees of the charity are also directors. These companies are: Islehurst Ltd; Shirestates Ltd; Urbanhold Ltd; Verehive Ltd; and Englander Co. Ltd.

The main area of charitable activity according to its 2006/07 annual report is: 'To support organisations engaged in education, advancement of religion and the giving of philanthropic aid'. In practice, this support is mainly directed towards Jewish organisations and Judaism.

Applications

In writing to the correspondent.

Corporate giving

In 2006/07, the charity had an income of £1,133,000 of which £1,147,000 resulted from donations from subsidiary and associated undertakings, i.e. the companies named above.

Grants for the year totalled £1,383,744. Unlike the previous year, no beneficiaries were listed in the accounts. In 2005/06, these included BAT (£155,000), UTA (£60,000), Square Foundation Ltd (£50,000), Ateres Yeshua Charitable Trust (£10,000), Side by side (£5,000) and My Dream Time (£1,000).

Rio Tinto plc

Company registration number 719885

5 Aldermanbury Square, London EC2V 7HR

020 7781 2000; Fax: 020 7781 1800

Website: www.riotinto.com

Correspondent: Dominique Cagnetta, External Affairs

Chairman: Paul Skinner

Chief Executive: Tom Albanese

Year end	Turnover	Pre-tax profit
31/12/2007	£16,760,000,000	£4,920,000,000

Nature of company business
Rio Tinto is one of the world's largest mining companies. Based in the UK, Rio Tinto has substantial worldwide interests in metals and industrial minerals with major assets in Australia, South America, Asia, Europe and Southern Africa.

Subsidiaries include: Anglesey Aluminium Ltd

Main locations: London

UK employees: 1,000

Total employees: 47,038

Charitable donations

2007: £1,800,000
2006: £2,500,000
2005: £2,700,000
2004: £2,100,000
2003: £400,000

Membership: BitC, L B Group

Community involvement

Rio Tinto group companies around the world give active support to their local communities, both directly and through independently managed foundations.

The company states the following with regard to its community support:

'Community assistance is the 'value adding' that businesses contribute to the community. These provisions may include enterprise development, training and employment, community-based health, and social and cultural heritage initiatives.

'Our focus in all instances is to ensure such programmes contribute to sustainable development and avoid creating dependency. All our operations update these plans annually as an integral part of the overall operations plan.

'Our community relations programmes are implemented by locally-based practitioners in each of the operations. They receive support from our corporate Community Relations team who co-ordinate their work with specialists from other parts of our company.'

Exclusions

No support is given, directly or indirectly, to any sectarian, religious or political activity. No funding is provided for building projects or general running costs, nor for advertising in charity brochures. Support is not given to individuals, animal welfare or any sporting events.

Applications

In writing to the correspondent.

Corporate giving

The following information is taken from the company's annual report: 'During 2007, the group spent US$107 million on community assistance programmes and payments into benefit receiving trusts set up in directly negotiated community impact benefit agreements. Donations in the UK during 2007 amounted to £1.8 million (2006: £2.5 million) of which £0.2 million (2006: £0.5 million) was for charitable

purposes as defined by the Companies Act 1985 and £1.6 million (2006: £2.0 million) for other community purposes.'

We have no details of the beneficiaries.

RM plc

Company registration number 1749877

New Mill House, 183 Milton Park, Abingdon, Oxfordshire OX14 4SE

01235 826000; Fax: 01235 826999

Website: www.rm.com

Correspondent: Claire Mann, HR Officer

Chairman: John Leighfield

Chief Executive: Tim Pearson

Year end	Turnover	Pre-tax profit
30/09/2007	£270,910,000	£18,435,000

Nature of company business
The main activities are the supply of IT solutions to educational markets, based upon PC technology and incorporating networking, software and services.

Subsidiaries include: Softease, Dacta Ltd, Sentinel Products, TTS (Technology Teaching Systems), Forvus, 3T Productions Ltd

Main locations: Glasgow, Cheadle, Otley, Sheffield, Leeds, Wrexham, Abingdon

UK employees: 2,230

Total employees: 2,230

Charitable donations

2007: £74,000
2006: £26,000
2005: £35,000
2004: £59,000
2003: £35,000

Community involvement

Support is mainly focused on the ten charities chosen by staff, one of which is nominated as the 'Charity of the Year'. Some smaller support is available for locally-based community projects in which staff have a personal interest or involvement. To serve as a focal point for the company's charitable fundraising activities, a foundation has been established.

Charity of the Year: VRH, Seesaw and Helen & Douglas House.

Exclusions

No support for local appeals not in areas of company presence, general or circular appeals and individuals.

Applications

In writing to the correspondent.

Corporate giving

During 2007 the company made various charitable donations totalling £74,000. A further £22,000 was given in locally-based community support projects.

The RM Charitable Foundation

Through the foundation (which is not registered with the Charity Commission), the company supports a number of educational and children-related charities chosen by RM staff: Volunteer Reading Help, an educational charity, with which the company is building a long-term relationship; and two 'charity of the year' (see above). The foundation also 'tops-up' money raised by staff for these charities.

In kind support

In 2005, the Dudley Grid for Learning project replaced 7,000 computers. The RM project team worked in partnership with the charity Digital Links International to send these computers to schools in Africa, playing an important part in improving the life chances of thousands of children across Africa.

Employee-led support

The company adds 33% of any money raised by staff to The RM Charitable Foundation. The foundation runs a community-support programme which allows staff to apply for charitable donations to support causes and projects in which they are personally interested in or involved with.

Every employee can choose to devote a small amount of work time each year to support one of RM's chosen charities.

RM staff are also encouraged to serve as local school governors.

Roche Products Ltd

Company registration number 100674

Hexagon Place, 6 Falcon Way, Shire Park, Welwyn Garden City, Hertfordshire AL7 1TW

01707 366000; Fax: 01707 338297

Website: www.rocheuk.com

Correspondent: Corporate Affairs
Email: welwyn.corporate_affairs@roche.com

Year end	Turnover	Pre-tax profit
31/12/2007	£657,068,000	£34,114,000

Nature of company business
Principal activity: the manufacture and sale of pharmaceutical products used in human health care.

Subsidiaries include: Bohringer Products Ltd

Main locations: Welwyn Garden City, Burgess Hill

Total employees: 2,000

Charitable donations

2007: £101,000
2006: £155,000
2005: £61,000
2004: £99,000
2003: £10,000

Community involvement

'Roche's involvement with charities and the community is ever growing. Each year, Roche in the UK selects a corporate charity to support.'

'We support a wide range of other charities and organisations, both in our local communities and at a national level, to help raise awareness of important health issues.'

Applications

In writing to the correspondent.

Corporate giving

In the year 2007 the company donated £101,000 for charitable purposes (2006: £155,000).

Charity of the Year: the Willow Foundation (2008).

Employee-led support

Employees are encouraged to contribute to their community.

'Roche employees in the UK are committed to improving the lives of those less fortunate and many take part in the annual Aids walk, funds raised from which go to HIV/AIDS projects in Malawi.'

Rolls-Royce plc

Company registration number 1003142

65 Buckingham Gate, London SW1E 6AT

020 7222 9020

Website: www.rolls-royce.com

Correspondent: The Company Secretary

Chairman: Simon Robertson

Chief Executive: Sir John Rose

Year end	Turnover	Pre-tax profit
31/12/2007	£7,435,000,000	£733,000,000

Nature of company business
Rolls-Royce is a global company providing power on land, sea and air.

Subsidiaries include: Vickers plc, NEI Overseas Holdings Ltd, Vickers Engineering plc, Sourcerer Ltd

Main locations: Bristol, Derby, Dounreay, East Kilbride, Hucknall, Hillington, Newcastle, London, Sunderland, Barnoldswick, Ansty

Total employees: 39,500

Charitable donations

2007: £1,100,000
2006: £728,000
2005: £671,000
2003: £397,000

Total community contributions: £3,600,000
Management costs: £430,000

Membership: A & B, BitC, L B Group

Community involvement

The company established the Group Community Investment Committee (Group CIC) in 2003 to oversee the implementation and operation of a new, group-wide policy on charitable donations. The Group CIC is supported by a series of national committees which operate within the policy established by the Group CIC. The policy is as follows:

'The group's charitable donations policy is to 'directly support causes primarily relating to educational, engineering and scientific objectives, as well as social objectives connected with the Group's business and place in the wider community.'

Exclusions

No support for advertising in charity brochures, political appeals, religious appeals, or local appeals not in areas of company presence.

Applications

In writing to the correspondent.

Corporate giving

'The group's charitable donations amounted to £1.8 million, of which £1.1 million were made in the UK. These included support for The Prince's Trust, Community Foundations and Duxford Airspace.'

In kind support

The group offers support in kind to local initiatives including providing places on in-house training programmes; donating surplus computer equipment and furniture; and offering the free use of meeting rooms and premises.

Employee-led support

The company supports employees' volunteering/charitable activities by allowing time off in which to volunteer and through financial support. 'Employee time contributed during 2007 is estimated at a value of at least £2 million, with more than 5,000 employees participating in activities such as community projects and team building activities with societal benefits.'

Payroll giving: The company operates the Sharing the Caring payroll giving scheme. During 2007, employees gave almost £450,000 to more than 350 charitable causes of their choice.

Commercially-led support

Sponsorship: In addition to charitable donations, contributions of £2.5 million were made towards sponsorships and educational programmes, including support for the Smithsonian National Air and Space Museum in North America, the Brandenberg Summer Festival in Germany and the London Symphony Orchestra tour of China.

N M Rothschild & Sons Ltd

Company registration number 925279

New Court, St Swithin's Lane, London EC4P 4DU

020 7280 5000

Website: www.nmrothschild.com

Correspondent: Annette Shepherd, Secretary to the Charities Committee

Chairman: David de Rothschild

Year end	Turnover	Pre-tax profit
29/09/2008	£402,047,000	£72,286,000

Nature of company business
The company and its subsidiaries carry on the business of merchants and bankers. The parent company is Rothschild Continuation Ltd and the ultimate holding company is Rothschild Concordia A G, incorporated in Switzerland.

Main locations: London, Manchester, Leeds, Birmingham

Total employees: 979

Charitable donations
2007: £817,000
2006: £709,000
2005: £862,000
2004: £717,000
2003: £901,000

Membership: BitC, L B Group

Community involvement

The group is committed to supporting charities both in the areas in which it operates and those in the wider community. The Charities Committee was established in 1975 to consider the requests received every year from charities seeking financial support. Typically, the majority of cash donated goes to charities working in the fields of social welfare, young people, and healthcare. Around 50% of the money donated each year is in response to requests from Rothschild employees who have a connection with a particular charity. Applications from small, local charities are particularly welcomed.

The company's subsidiaries around the world support causes in their areas of operation.

Charity of the Year: Little Haven Children's Hospice (2008). The Charity of the Year is chosen by staff in January each year.

Exclusions

No response to circular appeals. No grants for advertising in charity brochures; animal welfare; appeals from individuals; fundraising events; overseas projects; political appeals; religious appeals or sport.

Applications

In writing to the Secretary to the Charities Committee, which meets quarterly to make grant decisions.

Corporate giving

The sum of £817,000 (2006: £709,000) was charged against the profits of the group during the year in respect of gifts for charitable purposes.

Employee-led support

Requests for support from staff in respect of charitable causes with which they are associated, or have an involvement, are actively encouraged.

Apart from making financial donations, the group provides charitable support to local schools in the form of employee volunteers. In London, members of staff attend Bow School weekly to take part in lunchtime literacy and numeracy sessions with those students who need extra support, and a group of volunteers visits South Camden Community School fortnightly to lead mentoring sessions with teenage boys. In Manchester, staff take part in a literacy scheme at Manchester Academy.

A full time member of staff has now been employed to oversee and develop corporate social responsibility initiatives, and further volunteering-based projects are planned.

The group is also a supporter of the Specialist Schools Trust (promoting a dialogue between educators and financial institutions) and has contributed to the achievement of 'specialist' status in maths, science, technology and computing at several schools in the Leeds area.

Payroll giving: The Give As You Earn scheme is in operation.

Commercially-led support

Sponsorship: Proposals should be addressed to the Group Corporate Affairs Department.

Royal & Sun Alliance Insurance Group plc

Company registration number 93792

9th Floor, One Plantation Place, 30 Fenchurch Street, London EC3M 3BD

Website: www.royalsunalliance.com

Correspondent: The Corporate Responsibility Manager

Chairman: John Napier

Chief Executive: Andy Haste

Year end	Turnover	Pre-tax profit
31/12/2007	£6,596,000,000	£670,000,000

Nature of company business
The company's principal activity is the transaction of personal and commercial general insurance business.

Subsidiaries include: Phoenix Assurance plc, Royal Insurance Holdings plc, Swinton (Holdings) Ltd, RSA E-Holdings Ltd, The Marine Insurance Co. Ltd, Sun Insurance Office Ltd, Legal Protection Goup Holdings Ltd, FirstAssist Group Ltd, Royal International Insurance Holdings Ltd, The Globe Insurance Co. Ltd

Main locations: Belfast, Birmingham, Glasgow, Horsham, Leeds, Bristol, Manchester, Liverpool, London

UK employees: 9,626

Total employees: 22,553

Charitable donations

2007: £2,278,661
2005: £530,000
2003: £793,000

Total community contributions: £2,509,241

Membership: L B Group

Community involvement

Royal & Sun Alliance's 2007 annual report stated: 'Over the last few years we have been developing a more targeted and proactive community engagement programme. As a Group, we are focusing on three main areas that are relevant to our business and our interaction with local communities. These are safety, social inclusion and the environment.'

Exclusions

There are few circumstances in which the company is able to provide support outside this policy framework. Therefore, applicants such as political, religious appeals, social or animal welfare, overseas projects or environment/heritage are not considered, nor can charities whose work mainly benefits people overseas or individuals seeking personal or professional sponsorship. Requests received by circular are not actioned.

Applications

Generally applications should be in writing to the correspondent above. However, given the decision to focus on supporting the education of young people through a three year partnership with the Samaritans, successful unsolicited applications are likely to be limited.

Corporate giving

In 2007 overall charitable donations worldwide rose by 13% to £2.3 million, with 8,850 volunteer hours donated.

In kind support

Non-cash support includes staff involvement, gifts in kind, training schemes, nod use of resources (premises and equipment).

Employee-led support

'In 2008, we look forward to our first ever Groupwide volunteer event helping local great causes identified by our employees, and building on the success of the RSA UK National Volunteer Week.' In the National Volunteering Week in 2007, over 800 employees volunteered over 4,500 hours to community activities and raised over £15,000 for local charities.

Payroll giving: Through the company payroll, the Give As You Earn scheme enables staff and pensioners to make tax-efficient donations to any charity of their choice.

The Royal Bank of Scotland Group plc

Company registration number SC045551

Business House F, PO Box 1000, Gogarburn, Edinburgh, United Kingdom EH12 1 HQ

0131 626 3660; Fax: 0131 626 3074

Website: www.rbs.com/community

Correspondent: Stephen Moir, Head of Community Investment
0131 626 4190; Fax: 0131 626 0742
Email: responsibility@rbs.co.uk

Chairman: Sir Tom McKillop

Chief Executive: Sir Fred Goodwin

Year end	Pre-tax profit
31/12/2007	£10,300,000,000

Nature of company business
The Royal Bank of Scotland is one of the world's largest financial services organisations and is engaged in a wide range of banking, insurance and financial services.

Subsidiaries include: Direct Line Insurance Group, RBS Insurance Group Ltd, NatWest Bank plc, Ulster Bank plc

Main locations: Edinburgh

UK employees: 100,704

Charitable donations

2007: £32,173,187
2006: £25,411,211
2005: £24,277,649
2004: £20,100,000
2003: £14,700,000

Total community contributions: £57,700,000
Management costs: £2,000,000

Membership: A & B, L B Group

Community involvement

The group's community investment programme is focused in two areas: business-led activity and employee-led activity.

The business driven programme focuses on issues central to the group's business: helping people to access financial services and money advice, helping people to better understand and effectively manage their money and helping to stimulate and support enterprise.

The employee-led programme supports the group employees who are active in the community as volunteers, fundraisers and payroll givers.

Donations and support of charities, community groups and local organisations are through employee-led involvement.

Exclusions

In backing the fundraising and volunteer efforts of employees the group does not support: charities directly with grants; general funding contributions; core costs, charity advertising; sponsorships of events in aid of charity; or individuals/team fundraising for charities.

Applications

Applications forms are not used. Unsolicited requests are not considered.

Charitable giving is channelled via an employee-led programme.

Corporate giving

In 2007, the group made global community contributions of £57.7 million, of which £38.6 million was in cash, £13.8 million in gifts in kind, £3.3 million in employee time and £2 million in management costs.

It is not known how much of this support was to the benefit of UK-based organisations.

Business-led activity

Money advice programme – £5.5 million partnership with money advice organisations such as Citizens Advice to improve the quality of free, independent money advice for people facing serious problems with debt.

Supergrounds – £6 million community programme helping transform 900 school playgrounds worldwide.

The Prince's Trust – £5 million partnership which helps disadvantaged 14 to 25 years old realise their potential and transform lives by offering training, mentoring and financial assistance.

Money Sense – a unique programme delivers personal finance lessons to young people. Group staff work with teachers to deliver lessons and interactive activities. Since 2004, one and one-half million pupils have benefitted.

In kind support

Group employees are encouraged to get involved in the community. In 2007, over 40,000 employees volunteered in work time, contributing over 173,000 hours.

Employee-led support

Employee-led activity

Charities and community groups are supported through the employee led programme. The programme generated £12 million for 8,500 good causes through the direct involvement of 25,000 employees helping as fundraisers, volunteers or payroll gives.

RBS group is the only employer to double match employees' donations to charity made through Give As You Earn. For every £1 donated directly by staff, from their pay, the group donates a further £2. Over 15,000 employees currently take part in the scheme.

Employees who help good causes with their time, effort and skills can apply for a Community Cashback Award for their organisation. In 2007, the group made 7,000 awards ranging from £100 to £1,000.

Commercially-led support

Sponsorship: The RBS Group has three main areas of sponsorship – sports, the arts and agriculture.

The arts/agriculture – support is usually focused on national, quality non-profit making organisations, such as the Edinburgh International Book Festival. Other events recently sponsored include: Edinburgh Military Tattoo, Royal Highland Show, Kelvingrove Art Gallery and many more.

Sport – The main sports sponsorships are in Rugby (RBS 6 Nations), F1 (AT&T Williams F1), Golf (Jack Nicklaus, Luke Donald, Paula Creamer, Patron of the British Open Championship, Patron of the PGS of America. Support is also given to The Masters and the US Open), Tennis (Andy Murray and Jamie Murray), and Equestrian (Zara Phillips).

For further details of RBS Group sponsorships please look at their website www.RBS.com

Please note that sponsorship is not generally undertaken with respect to: individuals; teams, clubs or societies; fundraising events; publications, videos, films, recordings or website development.

Contact: Proposals should be addressed to David Webb, Head of Sponsorship (tel: 0131 626 3886).

The Royal London Mutual Insurance Society Ltd

Company registration number 99064

Royal London House, Alderley Road, Wilmslow SK9 1PF

08450 502020; Fax: 01625 605406

Website: www.royallondongroup.com

Correspondent: Ms Jo Doyle, Group Internal Communications
Email: jo.doyle@royallondongroup.co.uk

Chairman: Tim Melville-Ross

Group Chief Executive: Mike Yardley

Year end
31/12/2007

Turnover
£1,666,000,000

Nature of company business
Principal activities: the group's businesses offer pensions, life assurance, savings and investment products, protection insurance and provide investment management.

Subsidiaries include: Scottish Life, Bright Grey, Scottish Life International

Main locations: London, Wilmslow, Edinburgh, Douglas

UK employees: 2,624

Charitable donations

2007: £65,400
2006: £63,259
2005: £70,128
2004: £88,803
2003: £46,099

Membership: BitC

Community involvement

Royal London's society and community involvement policy is called 'Helping Hand' and includes an employee volunteering scheme, a national charity, a matched donation scheme and dress down days which take place across the group in aid of charity. As a main employer in the Edinburgh and Wilmslow areas, there is a strong preference for supporting local organisations in these areas.

Royal London has a Corporate Responsibility Committee which meets once a quarter. Its role is to investigate, report, champion and encourage CSR initiatives across the group.

Charity of the Year: Leukaemia Research (2008).

Exclusions

No support for advertising in charity brochures, animal welfare, appeals from individuals, environment/heritage, overseas projects, political appeals, or religious appeals.

Applications

In writing to the correspondent to whom sponsorship proposals should also be addressed. Further information on the company's donations policy and how to apply are available upon request.

Corporate giving

In 2007, the society made donations of £65,400 to charities and community organisations.

£10,000 was donated to the society's charity partner – Leukaemia Research. Some of the other organisations listed as receiving support included: Child Victim Support; Northwest Air Ambulance; Institute for Neuro-physiological Psychology; St Colombas Hospice; The Treloar Trust and Blackfriars Settlement. We note that this list has not changed in the last two years ago which means either, the organisations supported have remained the same or, it is out of date!

Employee-led support

In 2007, the society introduced an employee volunteering scheme – Volunteer 2Day – which enables employees to take up to two days a year of company time to volunteer in the community.

Royal London will match pound for pound the amount an employee raises up to a maximum of £250 per employee, per year. The scheme is open to all employees who help their chosen charity by getting involved in a fundraising activity or event.

In 2007, employees raised approximately £36,134, to which Royal London added approximately £20,000 in matched donations.

Payroll giving: The company operates a payroll giving scheme.

Commercially-led support

Sponsorship: Arts and good-cause sponsorship are undertaken by the company.

Royal Mail Group plc

Company registration number 4074919

148 Old Street, London EC1V 9HQ

Website: www.royalmailgroup.com

Correspondent: The Charities Committee

Chairman: Allan Leighton

Chief Executive: Adam Crozier

Year end
28/03/2008

Turnover
£9,388,000,000

Pre-tax profit
(£221,000,000)

Nature of company business
This is the parent company of Royal Mail, Parcelforce and the Post Office.

Main locations: London

UK employees: 191,757

Charitable donations

2008: £1,800,000
2007: £1,200,000
2005: £2,000,000
2004: £600,000

Membership: BitC, L B Group

Community involvement

'Our social policy is based on five key strategic themes:
- our 'major supported charity' programme
- employee volunteering
- revitalising payroll giving
- recruiting from socially excluded groups
- education & community engagement.'

Applications

In writing to the correspondent. It appears that local organisations can also apply directly to their regional office for support.

Corporate giving

In 2004/05 the company gave £1.8 million in cash donations. A three year partnership – the first of its kind for Royal Mail – between the company and Help the Hospices raised £2 million for the charity. More than 10,000 employees took part in fundraising activities and nearly 6,000 gave payroll donations.

In kind support

Education: Resources have been created to teach primary school children, including educational packs concerning the role of Post Offices and how letters are delivered.

Employee-led support

Staff are encouraged to volunteer and employees are available for secondments. A small financial contribution is made to chosen causes, including for fundraising efforts.

Payroll giving: The company operates a scheme managed on its behalf by the Charities Trust. In 2007/08 more than one in every four employees made donations directly from their wages.

RWE npower

Company registration number 38922782

Trigonos, Windmill Hill Business Park, Whitehill Way, Swindon, Wiltshire SN5 6PB

01793 877777; Fax: 01793 892781

Website: www.rwenpower.com

Correspondent: Carol Hart, Corporate Charity Officer

Chief Executive: Andrew Duff

Year end	Turnover	Pre-tax profit
31/12/2007	£808,000,000	£284,000,000

Nature of company business
Electricity generation and supply; water supply.

Main locations: Worcester, Swindon

UK employees: 2,443

Charitable donations

2007: £666,234
2006: £634,000
2005: £496,000
2003: £280,000

Membership: BitC

Community involvement

RWE npower concentrates its community involvement activities on the support of projects relating to youth work, education and the future.

Exclusions

Support is NOT given to: advertising in charity brochures, animal welfare, appeals from individuals, the arts, heritage, fundraising events, political appeals, religious appeals, science/technology or sport.

Applications

In writing to the correspondent.

Corporate giving

In 2007, the company made worldwide community contributions of €12 million (around £10 million). The company's charitable-giving programme in the UK helps smaller regional charities operating in local communities. Over 90 charities were supported, with company donating over £666,000 in 2007 alone.

In the UK, the company has worked with a range of organisations including the National Trust, Wildlife Trusts and Macmillan Cancer Support, as well as supporting the fuel poor through its Health through Warmth initiative.

In kind support

Education: RWE npower works closely together with schools and universities, seeking to re-kindle the interest of pupils and students in technology and natural sciences and thus contribute to securing future generations of technological experts.

Employee-led support

In 2007, more than 10 percent of the employees of RWE npower were actively involved in some form of voluntary programme. For example, 26 employees helped with the restoration of this historic property in North East England during working hours. This corporate volunteering is part of a partnership with the National Trust that RWE npower entered into in September 2007.

In 2007, the company matched the fundraising efforts of almost 400 employees to the value of £262,000.

Payroll giving: The company operates the Give As You Earn scheme. The company also matched employees' charitable donations to a total of £154,000.

Commercially-led support

Sponsorship: The company undertakes good-cause sponsorship.

Cause-related marketing: November 2003 saw npower and Greenpeace announce the creation of the 'npower Juice Fund', designed to assist the development of projects in other renewable energy fields such as wave and tidal energy. npower will make an annual contribution of £10 for every customer that stays with npower Juice – up to a maximum of £500,000 per year.

Saga Group Ltd

Company registration number 2421829

Saga Building, Enbrook Park, Sandgate, Folkestone, Kent CT20 3SE

Website: www.saga.co.uk

Correspondent: Janice Lee, Director Saga Charitable Trust
01303 771766
Email: contact@sagacharitabletrust.org

Director: J A Goodsell

Director: S M Howard

Year end	Pre-tax profit
31/01/2008	£161,300,000

Nature of company business
Travel, financial services, health and lifestyle.

Subsidiaries include: MetroMail Ltd, MetroMail Ltd

Main locations: Folkstone

Total employees: 395

Charitable donations

2007: £70,000

Membership: A & B, BitC

Community involvement

The Saga Charitable Trust, Charity Commission no. 291991, is constituted by Trust Deed dated 1st May 1985 and is funded by the Saga Group of companies, its customers and staff, with the objective of funding worthy projects at destinations that feature in tour programmes operated by Saga Holidays Ltd.

The trust supports projects that will empower and benefit under-privileged local communities at destinations in developing countries that host Saga holidaymakers. Primarily, this covers the Far East, the Indian sub-continent, South Africa and South America.

Exclusions

No support for advertising in charity brochures; animal welfare; the arts; enterprise/training; fundraising events; medical research; political appeals; religious appeals; science/technology; or sport.

Applications

We are advised that The Saga Charitable Trust will consider small-scale proposals from UK registered charities operating in the developing world. For further information apply in writing to the correspondent.

Corporate giving

No donations were declared by the group in 2007/08 (£70,000: 2006/07).

The Saga Charitable Trust

For the year ending 5th April 2005 the trust had an income of £152,000. During the year £130,000 was expended for direct charitable purposes (www.sagacharitabletrust.org).

In kind support

The Saga Group Ltd has provided donations-in kind of facilities, staff time and the trust's overheads and administrative costs.

Employee-led support

Saga staff support local fundraising events.

J Sainsbury plc

Company registration number 185647

33 Holborn, London EC1N 2HT

020 7695 6000; Fax: 020 7695 7610

Website: www.j-sainsbury.co.uk/cr

Correspondent: Sainsbury's Community Affairs Helpline 0845 074 2618

Chairman: Philip Hampton

Chief Executive: Justin King

Year end	Turnover	Pre-tax profit
22/03/2008	£17,837,000,000	£479,000,000

Nature of company business
The group's principal activities are food retailing, financial services and property development. The group is composed of Sainsbury's Supermarkets, Shaws Supermarkets and Sainsbury's Bank.

Main locations: London

UK employees: 98,600

Charitable donations

2005: £2,340,000
2004: £1,600,000
2002: £5,000,000
2001: £6,000,000

Total community contributions: £7,600,000

Membership: BitC, L B Group

Community involvement

J Sainsbury's community investment focuses on two areas: support for charities and other organisations promoting healthy eating and active living, particularly with children, and donating food to homeless hostels and other charities to provide nutritious meals for people in need, e.g. the Salvation Army, FareShare, Betel of Britain and animal charities.

Exclusions

No response to circulars. No support for advertising in charity brochures, individuals, enterprise/training, environment/heritage, medical research, science/technology, social welfare, restoration/fabric of buildings, National Health projects, overseas projects, local appeals not in areas of company presence, political or religious causes, core or pump priming.

Applications

Appeals to head office should be addressed to the correspondent. Applications can be received at any time, and should include details of aims and objectives, target audience and PR opportunities. Local appeals should be sent to local stores who will then approach the donations committee. This meets quarterly, but a sub-committee meets as and when necessary.

A separate budget exists for small donations to local charities/voluntary groups, administered at store level, in the form of vouchers (see below).

There are also a number of Sainsbury Family Trusts with major grant-making programmes. These are administered separately (see *A Guide to the Major Trusts*), although close contact is maintained with the company's donations programme.

Information available: The company publishes its social report on the 'Responsibility' section of its website.

Advice to applicants: Sainsbury's advises applicants to try to avoid stereotyped circulars. All appeals are responded to, but charities often underestimate the time required for consideration of their appeals. So, applicants should be patient!

Corporate giving

During 2007, cash and in kind donations to charitable organisations and other community projects totalled £7.6 million (2007: £6.6 million). As has become the norm with Sainsbury's reporting, no break down between cash and in kind support was available.

Sainsbury's colleagues, customers and suppliers raised £5.4 million (2007: £12.4 million which included Comic Relief) for charities through events supported by the company, including Sports Relief, Home-Start, which supports families in local communities across the UK, and CLIC Sargent, a charity caring for children with cancer.

Education: *Taste of Success* – Sainsbury's Taste of Success promotes food education in schools with food awards for pupils aged 5–16, teacher training sessions and an educational website. The emphasis is on recognising and rewarding the good work already going on in schools. The initiative is run in partnership with the British Nutrition Foundation and the Design & Technology Association. Sainsbury's provided £100,000 in funding in 2005/06.

Health/sport: Sainsbury's *Active Kids* scheme supports local schools by providing sports and cooking equipment and coaching opportunities. Since the launch of the scheme in 2005, Sainsbury's have donated over £52 million worth of equipment and coaching to over 36,000 UK children's groups, including schools, nurseries, Scouts and Girlguiding UK groups. Nearly 40,000 registrations have been received for this year's scheme.

Top Activity – As part of Sainsbury's partnership with the Youth Sports Trust, it is helping deliver the TOP Activity' programme for teachers. This scheme equips teachers with the training, equipment and resources they need to provide activity options.

Skip2fit – In February 2008, we teamed up with Skip2bfit, a fitness initiative designed to motivate children to exercise.

Future targets

In the coming year (2009), Sainsbury's intends to implement the following:

- 'in 2008/09 we will make available £240,000 to support our 'Local Heroes' (colleagues who volunteer for good causes) by either matching their fundraising or donating to the organisations for whom they volunteer
- 'in early 2008 we trialled the election and support of local charities of the year for 15 of our stores in the North West. Given the strong customer and colleague feedback, we intend to roll out this approach across all our main stores across the country in 2008/09, commencing July 2008.'

In kind support

Sainsbury provides in kind support in a number of ways, including:

Food donations – These are made to charities, such as the Salvation Army, FareShare and the Nehemiah drug rehabilitation project.

Charity donation boxes – All stores have a charity donation box for customers' 'loose change', with the money being given to local registered charities.

Store door collections – Registered charities can hold cash collections outside Sainsbury's stores by applying in writing to the Store Manager.

Gift vouchers – Stores are allocated small budgets for charitable donations. These are usually in the form of gift vouchers for local groups and charities for use as raffle prizes. The vouchers can be used as a prize themselves or exchanged at any Sainsbury's for suitable goods.

Employee-led support

Local heroes: Sainsbury's Local Heroes scheme, now in its seventh year, recognises and rewards the charitable activities of its staff (colleagues). Colleagues who volunteer their time for a good cause can claim an additional £200 through Local Heroes towards their chosen cause.

Local Heroes also provides match funding of up to £500 to support fundraising events at Sainsbury's stores, depots and business centres. Over £230,000 was given in 2007/08.

Payroll giving: The company operates the Give As You Earn payroll giving scheme.

Commercially-led support

Sponsorship: Corporate sponsorship requests should also be addressed to Sainsbury's Marketing Department.

Cause-related marketing: 'Active Kids' is a nationwide initiative launched in 2005 to encourage schoolchildren to take more exercise through non-traditional activities. Customers earn one 'Active Kids' voucher for every £10 spent. These are then collected and redeemed by schools for activity and sports equipment.

Sainsbury's continue to be the national retail partner for Comic Relief's Red Nose Day and is committed to continue its support until at least 2011. Money is raised by selling Red Noses in its stores and through Sainsbury's to You (online shopping). It also works with suppliers to stock products that promote the campaign and include a donation in their price.

Samsung Electronics (UK) Ltd

Company registration number 3086621

1000 Hillswood Drive, Chertsey, Surrey KT16 0PS

01932 455000; Fax: 01932 455400

Website: www.samsung.com/uk

Correspondent: Marketing & Communications Dept

Year end	Turnover	Pre-tax profit
31/12/2007	£2,561,730	£73,821,000

Nature of company business
Samsung Electronics manufacture and distribute electronic and electrical goods. In the UK it manufactures fax machines and colour televisions and designs and develops microwave ovens.

Main locations: Yateley, London, Telford, Chertsey, Wynard

UK employees: 778

Charitable donations

2007: £24,066
2006: £50,700

Community involvement

Although the company's global website is quite comprehensive in its reporting of Samsung's community support programmes, coverage is mainly restricted to Korea and the US.

In general, the company supports causes concerned with: social welfare; culture and the arts; academia and education; sport; and environmental preservation. However, we understand that financial support in the UK tends to be directed towards the charity/charities 'adopted' by the workforce (see breakdown of donations made in 2007).

Applications

In writing to the correspondent.

Corporate giving

In 2007, Samsung made cash donations to charity of £24,066 (2006: £50,700). This was broken down in its annual report and accounts as follows: children's charities (£16,474); Diabetes charities (£3,486); National Autistic Society (£1,922); and others (£2,184). No further information was available.

Employee-led support

According to the company's website, it has set up more than 300 central offices for Samsung community relations worldwide. Strong encouragement and support is given to employees to actively volunteer for social improvement projects. No UK examples were available.

Savills plc

Company registration number 2122174

20 Grosvenor Hill, Berkeley Square, London W1K 3HQ

020 7499 8644; Fax: 020 7495 3773

Website: www.savills.co.k

Correspondent: Ruth Michelson-Carr, Company Secretary
Email: rmcarr@savills.com

Chairman: Peter Smith

Chief Executive: Aubrey Adams

Year end	Turnover	Pre-tax profit
31/12/2007	£650,500,000	£85,900,000

Nature of company business
Savills plc is a holding company. Its principal subsidiaries' activities are advising on matters affecting commercial, agricultural and residential property, and providing corporate finance advice, property and venture capital funding and a range of property related financial services.

Subsidiaries include: NetMortgage Ltd, CMI Project Services Ltd, GHV (Sale) Ltd, Batley Mills Ltd, Grosvenor Hill Ventures Ltd, Grosvenor Hill Properties Ltd, Grosvenor Hill (Southampton) Ltd

Main locations: Banbury, Birmingham, Bishop's Storford, Bath, Perth, Salisbury, Solihull, Sevenoaks, Stamford, Southampton, Windsor, Winchester, Wimbourne, Wilmslow, Esher, Harpenden, Cirencester, Canford Cliffs, Beaconsfield, York, London, Manchester, Oxford, Norwich, Nottingham, Chelmsford, Cranbrook, Bristol, Brechin, Cambridge, Telford, Ipswich, Henley, Lincoln, Glasgow, Exeter, Farnham, Edinburgh, Guildford, Sunningdale

UK employees: 2,637

Charitable donations

2006: £59,525
2005: £64,007
2004: £77,000
2003: £41,669
2002: £62,370

Membership: BitC

Community involvement

Previous information has suggested the company has a preference for local charities in the areas of operation, appeals relevant to company business and charities in which a member of staff is involved. National and local charities are supported, although the final choice is made by the employees.

Exclusions

Unsolicited appeals are unlikely to be successful as all charitable choices are made by the firm's employees.

Applications

In writing to the correspondent who is based at Savills plc, 4th Floor, Landsdowne Road East, 27 Berkeley Square, London W1J 6ER. Local appeals should be addressed to the nearest Savills office, not the head office.

Corporate giving

In 2006, the group made UK cash donations totalling £59,528 (2005: £64,000). No information regarding the beneficiaries was available. However, past beneficiaries have included Mencap, British Heart Foundation, Macmillan Cancer Relief, NSPCC, British Red Cross and Haven Trust.

In kind support

Gifts in kind, joint promotions, training schemes and giving staff time off in which to volunteer are the main sources of support other than cash.

Employee-led support

The group offers a bonus waiver whereby employees may elect to waive an element of annual bonus to registered charities of their own choice upon which the group augments the donation to the chosen charity by 10%.

Employee fundraising is matched by the company up to a maximum of £250.

Payroll giving: The group operates the Give As You Earn (GAYE) payroll scheme.

Commercially-led support

sponsorship: The company undertake arts and good-cause sponsorship.

Schroders plc

Company registration number 637264

31 Gresham Street, London EC2V 7QA

020 7658 6000; Fax: 020 7658 6965

Website: www.schroders.com

Correspondent: Caroline Davis, Charity Co-ordinator
020 7658 6676
Email: caroline.davis@schroders.com

Chairman: Michael Miles

Chief Executive: Michael Dobson

Year end	Turnover	Pre-tax profit
31/12/2007	£1,191,800,000	£392,500,000

Nature of company business
Schroders plc is the holding company of an international asset management group. The group is organised into three principal operating divisions on a worldwide basis: Institutional, Retail/ Unit Trusts and Private Banking.

Subsidiaries include: Milk Street Investments Ltd

Main locations: London

UK employees: 1,233

Charitable donations

2007: £1,252,090
2006: £616,000
2005: £271,000
2004: £543,000
2003: £290,000

Community involvement

Schroders annual report and accounts for 2007 noted the following change to the company's charitable giving policy:

'Our charitable giving has in recent years focused on employee choice with the group matching staff donations and sponsorship. In 2007, the board agreed to increase our charitable giving to include discretionary donations, doubling our donations ...

'A new charity committee was established to receive nominations from staff for potential donations, targeted at specific projects in the areas of education, development and health.'

Exclusions

No support for advertising in charity brochures, animal welfare, appeals from individuals, the arts, children/youth, elderly people, environment, fundraising events, heritage, medical research, political appeals, religious appeals, science/ technology, sickness/disability, social welfare, or sport.

Applications for 'charity of the year' status are not considered.

Applications

In writing to the correspondent.

Information available: The company can provide policy guidelines to those seeking support. It also produces an annual corporate responsibility report.

Corporate giving

In 2007, the company made worldwide charitable donations of £1,252,090 (2006: £616,000). Although we were not given a separate figure for the UK, we understand that the charity committee received 52 applications for consideration before five donations of between £50,000 and £100,000 were made. The beneficiaries were: Childs Dream; Farleigh Hospice; Muscular Dystrophy Campaign; Western Parishes Youth Community Centre Trust; and Whizz- Kidz.

Employee-led support

Employees are encouraged to volunteer, with financial rewards being given to the charity they are involved with. From June 2005, every employee has been given the opportunity to take up to 15 hours paid leave per year to provide volunteer services to the community.

Schroders is a significant corporate supporter of the Hackney Schools Mentoring Programme, with its staff continuing to help mentor 14 and 15 year old students in the London borough.

The company matches employee fundraising up to a maximum of £2,000 per person, per year and employee giving up to a maximum of £2,400 per person, per year.

Payroll giving: The company operates the Give As You Earn scheme. By the end of 2007, nearly 16% of staff were participating in the scheme, donating over £197,000.

Commercially-led support

Sponsorship: Neither arts nor good-cause sponsorship is undertaken.

Scott Bader Company Ltd

Company registration number 189141

Wollaston Hall, Wollaston, Wellingborough, Northamptonshire NN29 7RL

01933 663100; Fax: 01933 666608

Website: www.scottbader.com

Correspondent: Sue Carter, Commonwealth Secretary
01933 663676
Email: sue.carter@scottbader.com

Chairman: Bob Coxon

Year end	Turnover	Pre-tax profit
31/12/2007	£160,000,000	£5,700,000

Nature of company business
The company manufactures and distributes synthetic resins and chemical intermediates.

Main locations: Fareham, Brierley Hill, Leeds, Stockport, Plymouth, Wollaston

UK employees: 270

Charitable donations

2007: £135,000
2006: £125,000
2005: £163,022
2004: £104,691
2003: £122,826

Community involvement

The company was given into common ownership by its founder Ernest Bader in 1951 and is now a leading member of the common ownership movement. Its large philanthropic expenditure reflects the ethos of the company. The Scott Bader Company is wholly owned by the Scott Bader Commonwealth Ltd, a company limited by guarantee and a registered charity (Charity Commission no. 206391). The Commonwealth's income comes almost exclusively from distributions of profit made to it by the Scott Bader Company.

The company supports projects which respond to the needs of those who are most underprivileged. They aim to help people to help themselves based on community based projects. National and local charities are supported, with preference being given to those within a 25-mile radius of Scott Bader locations in the UK.

Criteria

The board is guided by the following criteria in determining whether to recommend a project to members of the community:

- is the project within the commonwealth's specified areas of focus?
- does the project enable people to help themselves?
- does the amount of money and assistance given by the Commonwealth make a significant difference?
- are others involved in the project by way of contributing funds or in other ways?
- is the project adopted by a member of the Commonwealth who will stay in contact with the project and keep members informed on progress?

In trying to decide rationally where to offer support, board members will look for evidence of:

1. clear, relevant and realistic objectives

2. the competence to achieve them

3. potential for replication of the innovative aspects of a project

4. the effect that a Commonwealth grant is likely to have on other potential funding sources

5. where necessary, a medium/long-term funding strategy

6. projects, activities or charities which find difficulty raising funds

7. projects, activities or charities which are innovative, imaginative or pioneering

8. projects which are initiated and/or supported by local people and which will improve the self-respect and self-reliance of those involved.

There were no geographical restrictions put upon the international funds during the year 2005 and the overall policy continued to focus on those groups of people, or communities, to which an injection of finance would give an opportunity to become self sufficient in the long term. The board also gave priority to those organisations that have found it difficult to raise money from other sources and in particular for pump priming projects.

At an Extraordinary General meeting held on 17 March 2005 members agreed to the introduction of a Group Charitable Fund, whereby 50% of the fund made available by Scott Bader Company Ltd will be available to fund projects sourced and supported by the Commonwealth Board of Management. The remaining 50% will be made available to companies within the Group of Scott Bader Co. Ltd, to fund charities that they wish to support, subject to approval of the Directors/Trustees of the Commonwealth Board of Management. This is to encourage greater involvement by members worldwide in the charitable work and to ensure that donations made have an impact in all the countries where Scott Bader has a presence, UK, France, South Africa, Dubai, USA, Czech Republic, Sweden, Germany, Croatia and Spain.

Exclusions

There is no support available for individuals in need, animal welfare, travel & adventure schemes, construction, renovation or maintenance of buildings, arts projects or sports. Political, religious appeals or sponsorship proposals will not be considered.

Applications

In writing to the correspondent. Applications for donations can be made at any time.

There is no application form, but the following points should be taken into account in applying for a grant:

- applications should be no longer than four A4 sides
- supporting material may be sent, but is unlikely to be seen by board members.

The following should be included:

- a short general description of the project and its aims
- a budget broken down under different expenditure headings, indicating what part of the budget is requested from the trust and if the grant is for more than one year
- the names of any other agencies likely to contribute to the cost, and an indication of where money will come from when any funding from the Commonwealth runs out
- information on how the project is to be monitored and, if possible, evaluated and made known to others
- for on-going projects a set of audited accounts.

All applications received are reviewed by the Commonwealth Secretary and, if the criteria are met, the application will be considered at quarterly meetings of the Commonwealth Board of Management. Members in a general meeting have the final decision on grants of over £5,000.

General meetings are held in February, May, August and November each year. Only those who work within the Scott Bader Company Ltd are able to become members of The Scott Bader Commonwealth, and to participate in the charitable and philanthropic work of the Commonwealth.

Corporate giving

In 2007, the company donated £135,000 to the Scott Bader Commonwealth Ltd, a registered charity. At the time of writing (July 2008) the charity's accounts for that year were not available. However, we do know that a major award of £25,000 was given to the following UK charity:

Tools for Self Reliance – aims to enable disadvantaged people living both, in and around Milton Keynes and in developing countries, to use their own efforts to improve themselves, and to play a more active part in the society in which they live. It achieves this by operating a workshop where practical work refurbishing unwanted hand tools is carried out. These are then sent to people in developing countries who use them to earn a living.

Employee-led support

Scott Bader matches employees' fundraising to a maximum of £5,000. Groups of members raised £7,789 for a charity of their choice and this was matched by the company. Volunteering is encouraged and examples of staff support are:

- employees arranged for a Fun Fair to be opened for special needs children and then acted as helpers
- local children were invited to enjoy the use of the swimming pool at the Head Office of Scott Bader
- a group of employees designed and constructed a Christmas grotto for the enjoyment of local children
- volunteers also helped at a youth project which teaches them to recycle and maintain bicycles.

Commercially-led support

Sponsorship is not undertaken.

Scottish & Newcastle UK Ltd

Company registration number SC065527

2-4 Broadway Park, South Gyle, Ediburgh EH12 9JZ

0131 528 1000

Website: www.scottish-newcastle.com

Correspondent: (see 'Sponsorship')

Email: corporate.responsibility@s-n.com

Chairman: Sir Brian Stewart

Year end	Turnover	Pre-tax profit
31/12/2007	£3,260,000,000	£280,000,000

Nature of company business
The group's principal activity is the operation of breweries in 14 countries in Europe and Central Asia.

Main locations: Tadcaster, Manchester, Reading, Hereford, Avonmouth, Dunston

UK employees: 2,932

Charitable donations

2007: £1,300,000
2006: £1,400,000
2005: £1,061,648
2004: £528,000
2003: £536,000

Total community contributions: £4,300,000

Membership: BitC, L B Group

Community involvement

From April 2008 Scottish & Newcastle became part of Heineken NV (Netherlands), the world's most international brewer – www.heinekeninternational.com. S&N UK is now the UK operating company within Heineken's Western European region.

'Scottish & Newcastle has a long history of commitment to local communities. We implement community investment initiatives that enable us to:

- encourage alcohol responsibility and increase consumer awareness of responsible drinking strategies
- work strategically with targeted community organisations so that we can contribute more than funds to community investment initiatives
- work in partnership with relevant local stakeholders such as government, local authorities, community organisations and our customers to deliver integrated, sustainable programmes
- deliver both business and community value by defining clear objectives, measures and targets and reporting outcomes
- encourage employee participation in community activities and recognise their contributions to community activities.'

Exclusions

Previously, no grants for advertising in charity brochures, appeals from individuals, under-18 age group, fundraising events, medical research, political appeals, religious appeals, or local appeals not in areas of company presence.

Sponsorship of individuals, other than company employees, is not undertaken.

Corporate giving

According to the London Benchmarking Group, in 2007 the company made total community contributions of £4.3 million. Of this, and as stated in its annual report and accounts, £1.3 million (2006: £1.4 million) was donated to UK charities. We have no information regarding the beneficiaries.

Commercially-led support

Sponsorship: 'Scottish & Newcastle UK works with local community foundations to support local projects. We focus on projects that:

- encourage health, well-being, self esteem and self-confidence especially through education and training and/or physical activity
- encourage community pride, strengthen networks or bring different parts of the community together.'

'To apply, contact the S&N UK supported foundation in your local community.

'**Newcastle Brown Ale Fund:** supporting projects in Newcastle'www.communityfoundation.org.uk'

'**S&N Fund:** supporting projects in Scotland, especially in Edinburgh, the Lothians and Fife'www.scottishcf.org'

'**Newcastle Breweries Endowment Fund:** supporting projects in County Durham and Darlington'www.countydurhamfoundation.co.uk'

Scottish and Southern Energy plc

Company registration number SC117119

Inveralmond House, 200 Dunkeld Road, Perth PH1 3AQ

Website: www.scottish-southern.co.uk

Correspondent: The Director of Corporate Communications

Chairman: Sir Robert Smith

Chief Executive: Ian Marchant

Year end	Turnover	Pre-tax profit
31/03/2008	£15,256,300,000	£1,182,700,000

Nature of company business
The group's main business is: the generation, transmission, distribution and supply of electricity to industrial, commercial and domestic customers; electrical and utility contracting; and gas marketing. The group holds the generation, transmission

and public supply licence for the north of Scotland, and, through its subsidiary Southern Electric plc, the public supply licence for the south of England, as well as a Gas Supplier's licence.

Subsidiaries include: Scottish Hydro Electricity, SSE Services plc, Airtricity Holdings Ltd, Keadby Generation Ltd, SSE Generation Ltd, Southern Electric Contracting Ltd, Medway Power Ltd, Neos, hienergyshop, SSE Telecom

Main locations: Perth

UK employees: 16,892

Charitable donations

2008: £873,000
2007: £685,000
2006: £496,000
2005: £400,000
2004: £300,000

Membership: BitC

Community involvement

This company was formed by the merger at the end of 1998 of Scottish Hydro-Electric and Southern Electric. Its website included the following:

'We are undertaking a major programme of capital investment in England and Scotland. At all stages in the developments, we are committed to open and honest communication with local communities on which these developments have an impact, including undertaking voluntary pre-planning consultations to determine local views and address local concerns.

'We maintain an active programme of engagement with stakeholders such as local authorities, MPs, MSPs, Ministers, officials and agencies. We have a separate Community Benefit Fund for such projects. Where possible, community benefit programmes are agreed in conjunction with local stakeholders, including local Councillors, MSPs and other elected representatives.'

Exclusions

The company does not support individuals, teams or organisations which have political affiliations. It also excludes advertising in charity brochures, research projects including medical research, overseas projects, animal welfare and religious appeals.

Applications

In writing to the correspondent.

Application forms for The Scottish Hydro-Electric Community Trust can be downloaded from the company's website.

Corporate giving

In 2007/08 the company made charitable donations totalling £873,000. The company quoted its total charitable donations and community benefit figure as almost £1.8 million.

The Scottish Hydro-Electric Community Trust

The trust (Scottish Registered Charity Number SC027243) has an income of around £80,000 per year.

'The Scottish Hydro-Electric Community Trust is an independent charitable trust offering help to customers faced with high charges for an electricity connection within the North of Scotland distribution area, particularly those in rural areas.'

In kind support

'We support educational initiatives through the provision of materials aimed at 7–11 year-olds. These comprise a comic and associated activity sheet, and an interactive website which cover topics including safety and energy efficiency.'

'We also have a Museum of Electricity in Christchurch, Dorset, and Visitors' Centres at our Fiddler's Ferry Power Station and at Pitlochry Dam and Power Station in Perthshire. These facilities are free to schools organising visits.'

Employee-led support

'Into Action Fund – we set aside funds to support staff who are either raising money for, or giving their time to, a UK-based registered charity, or who are involved in running local community or youth sports groups.'

'From time to time, we select a 'partner' charity or charities (currently a number of children's hospices) which we will encourage staff to support through payroll giving. Under the 'Quids In' scheme 20% of the money raised by staff is used to fund a prize draw. The balance – which is matched by the company – is donated to the 'partner' charity.'

In 2008 a total of 1,375 employees participated in 'Quids In' and 502 in 'Into Action'.

ScottishPower plc

Company registration number 2366937

1 Atlantic Key, Glasgow C2 8ST

0141 248 8200

Website: www.scottishpower.com

Correspondent: Ann Loughrey, Head of Corporate Responsibility

Chief Executive: Nick Horler

Year end	Turnover	Pre-tax profit
31/03/2006	£5,446,100,000	£625,100,000

Nature of company business
Principal activities: the generation, transmission, distribution and supply of electricity in the UK and USA.

Main locations: Warrington, Glasgow, Rhostylien

UK employees: 8,892

Total employees: 9,793

Charitable donations

2006: £2,610,000
2002: £3,500,000

Total community contributions: £3,330,000
Management costs: £500,000

Membership: A & B, BitC, L B Group

Community involvement

Since ScottishPower's integration with the Spanish company Iberdrola in 2007, we have been unable to update the company's financial and community investment figures.

However, the company still appears to be concentrating its community support in the UK in the following main programme areas:

- public safety
- science
- energy efficiency
- arts sponsorship.

In addition to this, there is still the long established ScottishPower Learning programme, which is split between school-based, community-based and work-based programmes.

Exclusions

No support is given to appeals from individuals, national charities (unless the fund is used solely for a local project), preservation of historic buildings, research, expeditions, political or military organisations, circular appeals, advertising in charity brochures, animal welfare charities, religious appeals, local appeals not in areas of company presence or overseas projects.

Sponsorship for sporting events and advertisements in publications, etc., will normally only be considered commercially, in terms of potential advertising benefits.

Applications

In writing to the correspondent.

Corporate giving

In 2005/06, the company made UK total community contributions of £33,830,000. Of this amount, cash donations comprised £2,610,000, in kind support £720,000, and management costs £500,000.

Further information about ScottishPower's range of community investment is available on its website.

Employee-led support

The company matches fundraising by employees and employee giving.

Payroll giving: The company operate the Give As You Earn scheme in the UK.

Commercially-led support

Sponsorship: *The arts* – Sponsorship is limited and planned well in advance. Recent beneficiaries of ScottishPower's support include: Celtic Connections; ScottishPower Pipe Band; Edinburgh International Book Festival; National Theatre for Scotland; and Citizen's Theatre Peter Pan.

The company also undertakes good cause sponsorship.

SEGRO plc

Company registration number 167591

234 Bath Road, Slough, Berkshire SL1 4EE

01753 537171; Fax: 01753 820585

Website: www.sloughestates.com

Correspondent: Air Commodore N Hamilton (Retired), Manager External Affairs
Email: nick.hamilton@segro.com

Chairman: Nigel Rich

Chief Executive: Ian Coull

Year end	Pre-tax profit
31/12/2007	£242,900,000

Nature of company business
Industrial and commercial property development, construction and investment, supply of utility services and the provision of services associated with such activities.

Subsidiaries include: HelioSlough Ltd, Cambridge Research Park Ltd, Bilton plc, Kingswood Ascot Properties Investments Ltd, Shopping Centres Ltd, Howard Centre Properties Ltd, The Buchanan Partnership, The Bishop Centre Ltd, Allnatt London Properties plc, Farnborough Business Park Ltd

Main locations: Slough

UK employees: 454

Charitable donations

2007: £363,188
2006: £617,290
2005: £627,914
2004: £525,000
2003: £539,557

Total community contributions: £630,558

Membership: A & B, BitC, L B Group

Community involvement

The company's objective is to: 'To remain actively engaged in the communities in which we operate, and contribute to community vitality through employee time as well as financial contributions'.

'Everyone at SEGRO believes that forging strong links between business and society supports vibrant, healthy and sustainable communities.'

'Donations are made to a variety of community and social charities and in particular to charities connected to localities in which the Group is represented. Slough Social Fund is a charity which provides financial support to local charities in the Slough and South Bucks area. The benefit in kind provided to Corporate Health includes the provision of a rentfree building which Corporate Health (a registered charity) uses to provide occupational health services to the Slough Trading Estate.'

'An important development in relation to our charitable giving has been the devolution of decision making over charitable budget allocation to Regional Directors and Country Heads. This was undertaken to increase the regional ownership and responsibility over community matters with the long-term aim of creating closer links with charities in the regions where we work.'

Exclusions

No grants for non-charities, circular appeals, local appeals not in areas of company presence, appeals from individuals, or overseas projects.

Applications

Decisions are made by a committee which meets quarterly. Air Commodore Nick Hamilton should be contacted for donations.

Corporate giving

In 2007 charitable donations made by the company totalled £630,558. Beneficiaries included: Diabetes UK; Shelter; Slough District Scouts; and Acorns Children's Hospice.

In kind support

In addition to donations to charities, the main area of support is gifts in kind. Equipment and material, professional services and the use of in-house facilities have been donated free of charge for specific purposes.

Employee-led support

The company allows each staff member one day of company time to participate in a community project or a company-wide community initiative.

'Employee volunteering has grown in popularity since last year with an impressive 76 per cent increase in the number of employee volunteer days, from 71.5 in 2006 to 126 in 2007. The Executive Board were keen participants in a series of volunteering events organised as part of Business in the Community's 'Seeing is Believing' campaign which aims to engage Board members in community activity.

Payroll giving: The company operates a payroll giving scheme.

Serco Group plc

Company registration number 2048608

Serco House, 16 Bartley Wood Business Park, Bartley Way, Hook, Hampshire RG27 9UY

01256 745900; Fax: 01256 744111

Website: www.serco.com

Correspondent: Gail Johnson, Head of Corporate Responsibilities and Charities

Chairman: Kevin Beeston

Chief Executive: Christopher Hyman

Year end	Turnover	Pre-tax profit
08/12/2007	£2,800,000,000	£123,000,000

Nature of company business
The provision of a range of facilities management and systems engineering services.

Subsidiaries include: Community Leisure Management Ltd, NPL Management Ltd, Rakmulti Technology Ltd

Main locations: London, Oldbury, Sunbury-on-Thames, Southampton, Wolverhampton, Hook, Glasgow, Lincoln, Leicester

UK employees: 48,000

Charitable donations

2007: £556,000
2005: £586,324
2004: £333,965
2003: £322,349

Total community contributions: £911,000
Management costs: £156,000

Membership: BitC, L B Group

Community involvement

The company prefers to support local appeals relevant to the business. As such, requests for support should be made to the local operating site. Support is given with a preference for children and youth, education, and sport.

Applications

In writing to the correspondent.

Corporate giving

Following a review in 2003 of its charitable giving policy, Serco decided to place more of an emphasis on supporting local charities and communities. Subsequent to this the Serco Foundation was launched which, although mot a registered charity, provides additional financial support for the company's community activities.

In 2007, worldwide community contributions totalled £911,000 of which cash donations accounted for £556,000. Although we do not know what proportion of this was donated in the UK, we were advised that the major beneficiaries were the Duke of Edinburgh's Award and Africa Foundation.

In kind support

Gifts in kind and staff secondments are the main forms of in kind support provided by Serco.

Employee-led support

Serco encourages employee volunteering and allows company time off in which to do so.

Payroll giving: The company operates the CAF scheme.

Commercially-led support

Neither arts, nor good-cause sponsorship are undertaken.

Severn Trent plc

Company registration number 2366619

2297 Coventry Road, Birmingham B26 3PU

0121 722 4000; Fax: 0121 722 4800

Website: www.severn-trent.com

Correspondent: Corporate Community Affairs Manager
0121 722 4000; Fax: 0121 722 4800
Email: corporateresponsibilty@stplc.com

Chairman: Sir John Egan

Year end	Turnover	Pre-tax profit
31/03/2008	£1,552,400,000	£192,400,000

Nature of company business
The group's principal activities are the supply of water and sewerage services, waste management and the provision of environmental services.

Subsidiaries include: UK Waste Management Ltd, Derwent Insurance Ltd, C2C Services Ltd

Main locations: Birmingham

Total employees: 8,707

Charitable donations

2008: £412,471
2007: £277,476
2006: £487,422
2005: £378,825
2004: £276,121

Management costs: £110,000

Membership: BitC, L B Group

Community involvement

The company's 2008 annual report stated: 'The group focuses on the development of long term partnerships with charities close to its major sites which reflect the three core aims of promoting the natural environment, education and building communities. The group is also committed to supporting WaterAid, the UK's only major charity dedicated to providing safe domestic water and sanitation to the world's poorest people.'

The corporate responsibility section of the company's website stated: 'Each year, Severn Trent Water selects partner charities that work within the focus areas of our community strategy. We provide a financial donation and also offer employee time and skills to support their work. This year, through consultation with our employees and other stakeholders, we have reviewed our strategy and approach to the selection of charitable partners. From April 2009 onwards we will direct our support projects taking place in our region that are focussed on issues related to water and waste water.'

The company has made significant contributions to The Severn Trent Trust Fund. This charity was established in 1997 (Charity Commission no. 1108278).

Exclusions

No support for advertising in charity brochures, appeals from individuals, local appeals not in areas of company presence, medical research, fundraising events, political or religious appeals, expeditions, study tours and cultural exchanges or third party organisations fundraising on behalf of national charities.

Applications

In writing to the correspondent. Your application to the company should include:

- a summary of the aims and objectives of your charity
- a summary of the project for which the donation is required
- an explanation of how the money will be spent
- a copy of your latest annual report and accounts.

For more information on how to apply to the Severn Trent Trust Fund website, visit www.sttf.org.uk.

Corporate giving

Donations to charitable organisations during the year amounted to £412,471 (2007: £277,476). In addition, in response to the floods of July 2007 Severn Trent Water established a £3.5 million recovery fund for Gloucestershire. Of the £1.6 million paid during the financial year, approximately £1.1 million was paid to charitable organisations in the Gloucestershire area.

The Severn Trent Trust Fund

'The independent trustees have adopted a policy of giving grants to individuals and families to (a) help them overcome immediate crisis and (b) to encourage financial stability. The majority of grants provide help toward insurmountable water debt but, in addition, help is given with other priority urgent bills and household needs.

The trust supports money advice and debt counselling work and has funded advice work in agencies spread throughout the region.

In kind support

The company receives many requests for a charitable donation in order that a vital piece of equipment can be purchased. In such cases, attempts are made to locate similar surplus equipment within the group of companies and then to donate it as a gift in kind.

Employee-led support

'In 2007/08 Severn Trent Water donated over 5,500 hours of staff time to community projects, compared to almost 5,200 the previous year. Over 480 staff took part in volunteering activities in company time in 2007/8, and the value of staff time (including Education Centre staff) donated was almost £75,773.'

The Community Involvement Fund (CIF) exists to match employee charitable activities pound for pound (up to a maximum of £250).

Payroll giving: The Give As You Earn scheme is promoted throughout the group companies.

Commercially-led support

The 'Be Smart Award' to recognise schools that demonstrate a commitment to the wise use of water. Schools are assigned a Severn Trent Water mentor to support them throughout the scheme which has been designed to meet the organisational and curriculum needs of schools.

The company also encourages suppliers and contractors in their volunteering initiatives.

Shell

Company registration number 140141

Shell Centre, York Road, Waterloo, London SE1 7NA

020 7934 1234

Website: www.shell.co.uk

Correspondent: Sally Gold, Head of Social Investment
020 7934 3199; Fax: 020 7934 7039
Email: sally.gold@shell.com

Chairman: Jorma Ollila

Chief Executive: Jeroen van der Veer

Year end	Turnover	Pre-tax profit
31/12/2007	£178,731,000,000	£25,407,000,000

Nature of company business
Shell is a global group of energy and petrochemicals companies. Most people know Shell for its retail stations, and its exploration and production of oil and natural gas. However, its activities also include: marketing, transporting and trading oil and gas; generating electricity (including wind power);

providing oil products for industrial uses; producing petrochemicals used for plastics, coatings and detergents; and developing technology for hydrogen vehicles.

Main locations: Aberdeen, Fife, Ellesmere Port, London, Lowestoft, Stanlow (Merseyside), Wythenshawe

UK employees: 8,000

Total employees: 104000

Charitable donations

2007: £13,000,000
2005: £7,730,000

Membership: A & B, BitC, L B Group

Community involvement

Shell's community contributions in the UK are channelled in two ways.

Firstly, Shell provides support for causes in the communities who neighbour its places of operation through its regional offices. Examples of activities supported at this level include engineering training colleges, arts events, local schools (mentoring and literacy schemes) and business mentoring amongst others.

Secondly, Shell manages and delivers four of its own nationwide social investment programmes. These focus on entrepreneurship, skills and training, science education and innovation:

Shell Education Service – provides practical, interactive science workshops to over 50,000 primary school children every year, in addition to after-school science clubs and family science days.

Shell LiveWIRE – offers year-round help and advice to young entrepreneurs and runs a web service to provide them with information and support.

Shell Technology Enterprise Programme (STEP) – matches over 600 penultimate year university students each summer with SMEs for a managed eight week project placement, for the benefit of both the student and the company.

Shell Springboard – a national competition offering a no-strings payment of £20–40,000 to companies who have a product or service that reduces carbon emissions.

The majority of resources Shell invests are channelled in these two ways. Hence, Shell does not commonly award grants at UK level to charities or voluntary organisations.

Charity of the Year: Kids Company (2008 – London).

Exclusions

Shell is unable to support animal welfare appeals.

Applications

In writing to the community relations teams at Shell plants or offices for enquiries about local support.

Shell does not commonly award grants outside neighbourhoods surrounding Shell plants and offices. However, applications may be addressed to: UK Social Investment, Shell Centre, York Road, London, SE1 7NA.

Corporate giving

In the UK, Shell donated $26 million (£13 million) in 2007 to charitable causes. Of this, around £8 million was given to the Shell Foundation (Charity Commission no. 1080999) which funds programmes worldwide. Please see the Shell Foundation website for its areas of focus, themes covered and positioning (www.shellfoundation.org).

In kind support

Shell in the UK offers its facilities at key UK plants and offices to community organisations by prior arrangement. Please contact your nearest local community relations team to discuss this.

Employee-led support

Shell employees and pensioners in the UK are very active in their local communities. Many employees get involved in local community activities through initiatives run by local Shell sites. For example, Shell's North West plant runs the Save 'n' Score scheme, linking safe workplace operations by employees to the size of a monthly grant to local good causes. While in London, Shell employees take part in volunteer reading and mentoring at local secondary schools. Shell supports its employees and pensioners in their work with local organisations by making small grants available.

The Project Better World volunteering programme was initiated by Shell employees. Employees volunteer to develop and maintain local initiatives that work towards sustainable development.

Shell matches employee fundraising up to a maximum of £500 per person per year.

Payroll giving: Shell operates the Give as You Earn scheme.

Shepherd Building Group Ltd

Company registration number 653663

Huntington House, Jockey Lane, York YO32 9XW

01904 650700; Fax: 01904 650701

Website: www.shepherd-group.com

Correspondent: Chris Mason, Corporate Relations Manager
01904 650721; Fax: 01904 650746
Email: chris.mason@shepherd-group.com

Chairman: Alan T Fletcher

Year end 30/06/2007	Turnover £684,781,000	Pre-tax profit £42,235,000

Nature of company business
The company is a holding company with subsidiaries engaged in building and ancillary activities.

Subsidiaries include: Portasilo Ltd, Yorkon Ltd, Mechplant Ltd, Portakabin Ltd, Paton Plant Ltd, Computer Skills Ltd

Main locations: York, Manchester, London, Northampton, Langley, Leeds, Darlington, Birmingham

UK employees: 3,400

Charitable donations

2007: £195,000
2005: £98,000

Community involvement

The company made the following statement regarding its community support:

'Shepherd Group is a substantial family-owned business with its headquarters and a high proportion of its shareholders and staff based in and around York. The group benefits from being based in a healthy local environment for business, and is keen to put something back into the community.

'Shepherd has a flexible community support policy that directs available resources to support people and organisations mainly where the business operates.

'Support is principally given in the York area, but initiatives that relate to the group's operations and staff elsewhere are also considered.

'The extent and high profile of the group's operations prompts a large number of requests for help, more than available resources allow. Support is, therefore, weighted towards initiatives that fulfil one or more criteria that have been a feature of the group's practice for many years successful requests tend to relate to the following:

- education and training
- backing local business, inward investment and employment
- healthcare
- the arts
- sport
- employee involvement.

'Charitable and non-profit making organisations are given priority.'

Exclusions

No support for animal welfare, appeals from individuals, purely denominational (religious) appeals, political appeals, local appeals not in areas of company presence, large national appeals or overseas projects.

Applications

In writing to the correspondent.

Corporate giving

In 2006/07, the company made cash donations to charity totalling £195,000. Major beneficiaries were: York Minster Restoration Fund (£25,000); BA Festival of Science at the University of York and York City Knights Foundation (£15,000 each); and Shepherd Group Brass band and York Museum Trust – 'Fingerprints of Time' (£10,000 each).

Employee-led support

Employees are given company time off to volunteer on behalf of the York Cares scheme.

Payroll giving: The company operates the Charity Service scheme.

Commercially-led support

Sponsorship: Arts and good-cause sponsorship are undertaken.

Contact: Chris Mason – Corporate Relations Manager (Tel: 01904 650721).

Shire Pharmaceuticals plc

Company registration number 2883758

Hampshire International Business Park, Chineham, Basingstoke, Hampshire RG24 8EP

01256 894000; Fax: 01256 894708

Website: www.shire.com

Correspondent: Sonia Whyte, Charity Committee

Chairman: Matthew Emmens

Chief Executive: Angus Russell

Year end	Turnover	Pre-tax profit
31/12/2007	£1,220,000,000	£15,700,000

Nature of company business
Speciality pharmaceutical company.

Main locations: Basingstoke

Total employees: 3,436

Charitable donations

2007: £243,000
2006: £303,000
2005: £154,933
2004: £42,319
2003: £66,627

Membership: BitC

Community involvement

Shire's website contains comprehensive policy documents which outline the company's approach to supporting charitable and community organisations. The extract below covers the most salient points.

Management of Community Programmes

The corporate giving programme is also led by corporate communications and funded from the corporate communications budget; however, a charity committee or activities committee involving representative employees is usually involved to ensure that nomination of a 'Charity of the Year' or dissemination of major matched donations is agreed with input from all parts of Shire's organisation.

A number of components make up Shire's giving programme. These include:

- corporate donations (to include both cash and in kind giving) to local, national or international organisations that support Shire's community and/or disease in its therapeutic focus area
- contribution to employee's own raised amount for events that are in support of a charitable non-profit organisation, and where the employee is actively participating in the event or the organisation
- employee volunteering
- payroll giving
- corporate fundraising campaigns – launched at global and local levels, Shire invites employees to make personal one-off donations to a topical high-profile cause; the company agrees to make a matching donation to the total raised by all employees

annual nominated charity – Shire does not send seasonal greetings cards to customers or suppliers. Instead, a group of employees at each site nominates a not-for-profit beneficiary and a one-off donation is made. This organisation is then publicised via Shire's outgoing emails during the month of December.

Besides its employees, other key stakeholders in Shire's communities are patient groups and medical/healthcare education bodies as well as established not-for-profit organisations that are linked with its therapy areas of focus (for example CHADD, Alzheimer's Society, MPS Society) and related research bodies.

As well as these medical related groups, Shire connect with and support local schools and support groups that offer advice to young people who experience behaviour disorders, learning difficulties or social problems. It also targets its support to organisations and community initiatives that provide help for senior citizens.

Exclusions

Shire do not give to appeals from individuals for student study tours, academic bursaries, sports training or other such projects unless there is a specific relationship with the company or its business.

Applications

In writing to the correspondent.

The company aims to acknowledge all approaches in writing, including refusals

Corporate giving

UK charitable donations for 2007 were £243,000 (2006: £303,000) and wee made primarily to charitable medical foundations. support was also given to Kids Company and the British Heart Foundation.

In kind support

Shire does not send seasonal greetings cards to customers or suppliers. Instead, a group of employees at each site nominates a not-for-profit beneficiary and a one-off donation is made. This organisation is then publicized via Shire's outgoing emails during the month of December.

Employee-led support

Contributions to employee's own fundraising – Shire will consider providing a donation to the employee's own raised amount for events that are in support of a charitable non-profit organisation, and where the employee is actively participating in the event or the organisation.

Volunteer schemes – Shire provides one fully paid day off per year to spend working for a not-for-profit organisation. In addition, the company supports community-related activities by its employees including involvement in helping schools, homes for senior citizens and counselling services through the provision of paid time off.

Payroll giving: where possible, Shire provides a payroll deduction programme for its employees to enable ongoing individual donations to a charity of their choice.

Shoe Zone Ltd

Company registration number 148038

Haramead Business Centre, Humberstone Road, Leicester LE1 2LH

0116 222 3000; Fax: 0116 222 3001

Website: www.shoezone.net

Correspondent: Charles Smith, Trustee, The Shoe Zone Trust
Email: info@shoezone.net

Chief Executive: Anthony Smith

Year end	Turnover	Pre-tax profit
29/12/2007	£124,161,000	£7,301,000

Nature of company business
Footwear retailing.

UK employees: 2,871

Charitable donations
2007: £100,000
2006: £80,000

Community involvement

All the money donated to charity by the company is disbursed via The Shoe Zone Charitable Trust (Charity Commission no. 1112972), which was established in January 2005 with the aim of helping disadvantaged children both in the United Kingdom and internationally. The income of the trust is donated from the profits of Shoe Zone Ltd.

In addition to the above, the company facilitates the raising of funds for a number of nominated charities which in 2007 in the UK included: The Caron Keating Foundation; The Variety Club; and the Meningitis Trust.

Support is also given to local charities and community groups and school sin the Leicestershire area.

Shoe Zone staff are encouraged in their volunteering and fundraising activities by the company.

Applications

In writing to the correspondent.

Corporate giving

In 2007 the company made charitable donations in the UK of £100,000 (2006: £80,000), all of which went to the Shoe Zone Trust.

The Shoe Zone Trust

'The objects of the Charity are to make grants and donations to other charities to relieve financial hardship and poverty and/or advancement of education, mainly for children and young persons under age 18 particularly in Leicestershire and Rutland and for certain charities operating in the Philippines and other countries.'

In 2007, the trust made grants totalling £72,204. Beneficiaries included: CORD Vehicle (£21,100); Ministries without Boundaries (£12,024); Wishes4Kids (£2.004); Leicester Charity Link (£2,000); Hope Foundation (£1,000); and Kidsense (£511).

Employee-led support

Shoe staff participated in a number of volunteering and fundraising events including those on behalf of Leicestershire Cares and Mencap.

Education – During the 2006/07 academic year volunteers from head office visited Charnwood Primary School to take part in the Right to Read scheme which helps children to learn to read.

Commercially-led support

Sponsorship: *Sport* – Through the trust the company has 'sponsored' a local youth football team and a young participant at the 2007 World Karate Championship.

Siemens plc

Company registration number 727817

Sir William Siemens Square, Frimley, Camberley, Surrey GU16 8QD

01276 696000

Website: www.siemens.co.uk

Correspondent: Marcus Hall, Communities Support Fund

Chief Executive: Tom White

Guenter Dombrowe

Year end	Turnover	Pre-tax profit
30/12/2007	£3,592,000	£171,800,000

Nature of company business
Siemen's principal activities in the UK cover: information & communication, automation & control, transportation, power, and medical businesses. The company are also engaged in the supply of lighting, commercial research and development, and financial services.

Main locations: Birmingham, Banbury, Basildon, Frimley, Swindon, Telford, Wellingborough, Worcester, Congelton, Cirencester, Manchester, London, Newcastle, Milton Keynes, Nottingham, Oxford, Reading, Poole, Harrogate, Harrow, Ipswich, Hayes, Langley, Hitchin, Hinckley, Lincoln, Crawley, Staines, Ramsey, Walton on Thames

UK employees: 20,387

Charitable donations

2007: £62,516
2006: £90,970

Membership: BitC

Community involvement

Siemens businesses and employees alike support their local communities through charity fundraising events and sponsorship of various educational and community programmes. In particular, the company's community activities concentrate on building stronger local communities and helping young people take advantage of the educational opportunities available to then.

In support of these activities Siemens has developed two programmes – Siemens Generation21, which is committed to education and Siemens Caring Hands, which aims to create stronger communities. Further details on these areas of support can be found on the company's UK website.

Applications

In writing to the correspondent.

Corporate giving

In 2007, Siemens plc declared charitable donations in the UK of £62,516 (2006: £90,970). We are unsure, however, if this covers donations from all 27 group operating companies. Although we have no details of the beneficiaries, in support of education the company has worked closely with schools in Manchester and Nottingham.

Employee-led support

Siemens encourages and supports its employees to be active on behalf of their local communities, whether this is through volunteering or fundraising. Charities recently benefiting from this include: British Heart Foundation and the Motor Neurone Disease Association.

Every month, through the Employee in the Community Award scheme, a cheque for £500 is given to an employee on behalf of the charity/organisation they support.

The company's three main sites in Manchester, Poole and Frimley have a community fund to which employees can choose to make monthly donations. These are then matched by the company. An employees charity committee meets monthly to decide how to allocate the donations to local charities and community groups.

Commercially-led support

Sponsorship: *Sport* – From July 2006 to the end of 2012, Siemens are sponsoring the British Rowing Team to the tune of £3.2 million.

SIG plc

Company registration number 998314

Hillsborough Works, Langsett Road, Sheffield, South Yorkshire S6 2LW

0114 285 6300; Fax: 0114 285 6385

Website: www.sigplc.co.uk

Correspondent: Les Tench, Chairman
Email: info@sigplc.co.uk

Chairman: Leslie Tench

Chief Executive: David Williams

Year end	Turnover	Pre-tax profit
31/12/2007	£2,455,000,000	£140,100,000

Nature of company business
International multi-site distributor. It has four core business sectors: insulation, roofing, commercial interiors, and specialist construction and safety products.

Subsidiaries include: Miller Pattison Ltd, Leaderflush and Shapland Ltd

Main locations: Sheffield, Southampton, Barking, Littleborough, Leominster, Leicester, London, Maidstone, Crawley, Cardiff, Wednesbury, Hyde, St Ives

UK employees: 7,000

Charitable donations

2007: £162,000
2006: £100,000
2005: £98,000
2004: £53,000
2003: £47,000
Membership: BitC

Community involvement

'The group endeavours to contribute to the communities in which it operates. SIG is a member of Business in the Community in the UK and has worked with that organisation to help to develop its approach and practices. This is mainly achieved through charitable donations and other initiatives that help the community. Wherever possible employees are encouraged to get involved with their community.'

In addition to supporting local causes where SIG employees are involved, there exists a policy to provide support for three main charities for a period of three years. This commenced in November 2004, but we have not been given detail of the charities currently being supported. We do know, however, that there is a preference for causes involving children/youth and education. Furthermore, there is a preference for charities working in Yorkshire.

Exclusions

No political donations are made.

Applications

In writing to the correspondent.

Corporate giving

In 2007, cash donations totalled £162,000. No further information was available.

In kind support

This takes the form of gifts in kind.

Employee-led support

The company encourages employees to take an interest in social and community activities outside the workplace. It also provides financial support for employees undertaking charity work overseas.

Payroll giving: The company has a scheme in place.

Commercially-led support

Neither arts nor good-cause sponsorship is undertaken.

Simmons & Simmons

Company registration number 2092142

Citypoint, 1 Ropemaker Street, London EC2Y 9SS

020 7628 2020

Website: www.simmons-simmons.co.uk

Correspondent: Belinda Lodge

Nature of company business
Law firm.

Main locations: London

Community involvement

Simmons & Simmons undertakes pro bono and community work within the communities in which it operates, actively encouraging its staff to become involved in the provision of legal and non-legal services.

Charity of the Year: Kids Company (2008).

Applications

In writing to the correspondent.

Corporate giving

The most up-to-date contributions total is from 2000, when giving totalled £171,436.

In kind support

A variety of schemes are organised by the firm's pro bono coordinator, including mentoring under-privileged children at two Inner London primary schools, and giving free legal advice at an evening surgery at the Battersea Legal Advice Centre.

As members of Lawyers in the Community, a number of the firm's solicitors sit on the management boards of charities and charitable organisations, providing their expertise and advice. The firm also provides help through the ProHelp scheme assisting, for example, the Borough Community Centre, a Southwark-based charity.

Through the British Executive Overseas, the firm sponsors individual legal specialists to travel to developing countries requiring law-related assistance.

Employee-led support

Employees are encouraged to volunteer, in tasks not connected with the legal profession, including mentoring schemes.

In recent years the company has taken part in Stepney Children's Fund's scheme to purchase and wrap gifts of around £10 each to young children in disadvantaged areas of London's East End. Over 200 staff donated to this cause.

In 2007 the company won the Payroll Giving Silver Quality Mark Award.

Slaughter and May

One Bunhill Row, London EC1Y 8YY

020 7600 1200; Fax: 020 7090 5000

Website: www.slaughterandmay.com

Correspondent: Jacquelyn Collins, Community Affairs Manager

Chairman: Chris Saul (Senior Partner)

Chief Executive: Graham White (Executive Partner)

Managing Director: Paul Olney (Practice Partner)

Nature of company business
Leading law firm.

Total employees: 2,130

Charitable donations

2008: £328,500

Community involvement

The firm contributes to the wider community through donations from the Slaughter and May Charitable Trust (Charity Commission no. 1082765) and by encouraging its staff to join the various projects run with community partners in its local area.

The charitable trust supports a range of legal, educational and community projects, which vary from law centres to mentoring projects and the regeneration of local green spaces.

Exclusions

No support for individuals, local appeals not in areas of company presence or political appeals.

Applications

In writing to the correspondent at: Slaughter and May Charitable Trust, 2 Lambs Passage, London EC1Y 8YY.

Corporate giving

In 2007/08, the firm donated £333,000 (including £4,500 in gifts in kind, i.e. audit fees) to its charitable trust. The trust made grants during the year totalling £320,337, some of the beneficiaries of which included: Educational Charity of City of London Solicitors (£48,000); Legal Advice Centre – Bethnal Green (£15,000); National Literacy Trust (£10,000); Hackney schools mentoring programme (£5,000); The Food Chain (£4,000); Islington Play Association (£2,500); Ragged School Museum (£1,650); and Wellbeing of Women (£1,000).

In kind support

'[Slaughter and May] have a long history of providing free legal advice to those who might otherwise be unable to access it. Examples of ongoing legal or 'pro bono' work include:

- Islington Law Centre and Battersea Law Centre – helping to staff evening clinics advising on small claims
- LawWorks for Community Groups – advising local community groups on commercial real estate matters
- Free Representation Unit – serving as advocates on employment or social security tribunals
- Royal Courts of Justice Advice Bureau – providing a weekly rota of qualified litigators to litigants-in-person, as shown in our case study.'

No value appears to be attributed to the above work which, given figures quoted by other legal firms, would be quite substantial.

Employee-led support

'[Slaughter and May's] volunteering programmes go beyond pro bono. We encourage all employees to get involved in our projects and underpin these efforts with financial support. Examples of our non-legal volunteering opportunities include:

- Primary Partners – various initiatives with our local schools, as shown in our case study
- Hackney Schools' Mentoring Programme – attending fortnightly programmes with Year 10 students to improve their self-confidence, academic performance and aspirations

- Citizenship Foundation Twinning – attending workshops with a local class of Year 10 students to help the pupils understand the citizenship curriculum and learn about life as a City lawyer.'

It is important to the partners that employee philanthropy is supported and encouraged and there are two main ways in which this is done:

- Payroll giving – which allows employees to make regular charitable donations direct from their salary payments
- Funds for Fundraisers – Slaughter and May's home-grown matched funding programme.

Smith & Nephew plc

Company registration number 324357

15 Adam Street, London WC2R 6LA

Website: www.smith-nephew.com

Correspondent: Corporate Affairs

Chairman: John Buchanan

Chief Executive: David Illingworth

Year end	Turnover	Pre-tax profit
31/12/2007	£1,684,500,000	£234,500,000

Nature of company business
A global medical devices company manufacturing and marketing clinical products principally in orthopaedics, endoscopy, wound management and rehabilitation.

Main locations: Cambridge, Hull, Huntingdon, Gilberdyke, York

UK employees: 1,735

Total employees: 9,190

Charitable donations

2007: £250,000
2005: £325,000
2003: £470,000

Membership: A & B, BitC

Community involvement

Most of the company's UK charitable donations are channelled through the Smith & Nephew Foundation (Charity Commission no. 267061), which supports education and research for individuals in the medical and nursing professions. The funding policy is to invite individuals to apply to advertisements (see 'Applications' section).

Exclusions

All awards are advertised in the relevant medical and nursing journals and are posted on the foundation's website (www.snfoundation.org.uk). Applications are not considered at any other time. Physicians and/or surgeons must be resident and working in the UK. Nurses, midwives and health visitors must hold an active UKCC number.

Applications

All awards are advertised in relevant medical or nursing journals. Any correspondence should be addressed to the Foundation Administrator, Smith & Nephew Foundation.

Applications are not considered except in response to advertisements for the various awards.

Corporate giving

In 2005, Smith & Nephew made total community contributions worldwide of £801,500 of which £250,000 was given to the Smith & Nephew Foundation.

Doctoral Nursing Research Fellowship

This is offered once a year to nurses, midwives and health visitors, working in the UK, who are at the beginning of their career. 'It provides financial support to work with an established UK research team, based in a university, school/ faculty or department of nursing, which has a proven track record of research and development in the field of skin or tissue damage and vulnerability.' The award is worth up to £90,000 over three years.

Post-Doctoral Nursing Research Fellowships

These are offered once a year to nurses, midwives and health visitors, working in the UK, who are undertaking research as part of a PhD programme. 'This award will support an outstanding career nurse researcher and seeks to enhance nursing post-doctoral research capacity. It provides financial support to work with an established UK research team, based in a University School/Faculty or Department of Nursing, which has a proven track record of research and development in the field of skin or tissue damage and vulnerability. The award is open to members of the nursing and midwifery professions, working in the United Kingdom, who hold active registration with the Nursing & Midwifery Council.' The award is worth up to £120,000 over three years.

Applicants should check that the focus of their research meets the criteria as it may change each year.

In kind support

In addition to support given through the foundation, the company supports links with educational facilities in areas where its main operations are situated, provides gifts in kind and seconds staff.

Employee-led support

The company supports employees' volunteering/charitable activities by allowing time off in which to volunteer, and matching employee fundraising and giving.

D S Smith Holdings plc

Company registration number 1377658

4–16 Artillery Row, London SW1P 1RZ

020 7932 5000; Fax: 020 7932 5003

Website: www.dssmith.uk.com

Correspondent: Peter Aubusson, Group Communications Manager

Chairman: Peter Johnson

Chief Executive: A D Thorne

Year end	Turnover	Pre-tax profit
30/04/2008	£1,967,500,000	£109,100,000

Nature of company business
Production of corrugated and plastic packaging, primarily from recycled waste, and the distribution of office products.

Subsidiaries include: St Regis Paper Company Ltd, Spicers Ltd, A A Griggs & Co. Ltd

Main locations: London, Maidenhead, Rugby, Windsor, Cambridge

UK employees: 6,900

Charitable donations

2008: £72,000
2007: £71,000
2006: £84,000
2005: £128,000
2004: £109,000

Community involvement

The corporate social responsibility review contained in the company's annual report 2008 states: 'We seek to develop and maintain good relations in the local communities in which we operate. As well as providing significant employment opportunities, we aim to make positive contributions to these communities and build a reputation as a good neighbour and employer. Our businesses work closely with local schools and colleges providing training, mentoring, work experience placements and other opportunities for pupils to learn about industry and business. The group is involved in a wide range of other local community activities including sponsorship of community projects or sports teams and provision of adult skills training.

'The group supports charitable fundraising activities through cash contributions and in the form of products and services or staff time. The majority of the modest amount of money donated by the group is given by individual operating units, principally to good causes in their local communities. Donations by the group headquarters are principally focused on helping young disadvantaged people become involved in business and working life.'

Exclusions

No support for advertising in charity brochures, animal welfare, appeals from individuals, the arts, fundraising events, overseas projects, political or religious appeals.

Applications

In writing to the correspondent.

Information available: The company includes a social responsibility report as part of its annual report and accounts.

Corporate giving

In 2007/08, the company made charitable donations totalling £72,000 (2006/07: £71,000). We have no details of the beneficiaries.

In kind support

In addition to cash donations, the company provides gifts in kind.

Employee-led support

Donations made through employee fundraising and giving is matched by the company.

Payroll giving: The company operates the Charities Trust scheme.

WH Smith plc

Company registration number 471941

Greenbridge Road, Swindon, Wiltshire SN3 3RX

01793 616161; Fax: 01793 562560

Website: www.whsmithplc.com

Correspondent: Sarah Heath, Head of Communications

Chairman: Mike Ellis

Chief Executive: Kate Swann

Year end	Turnover	Pre-tax profit
31/08/2008	£1,352,000,000	£76,000,000

Nature of company business
The group's principal activities are the retail, publishing and news distribution.

Subsidiaries include: Hodder Headline Ltd

Main locations: London

UK employees: 17,891

Charitable donations

2008: £671,420
2007: £600,335
2005: £781,000

Total community contributions: £927,340

Membership: BitC

Community involvement

As a member of Business in the Community, WH Smith is committed to investing a minimum of one percent of its UK pre-tax profits in support of the community. Over the last few years it has refocused its efforts towards education and life-long learning, with particular emphasis on improving young people's literacy skills.

Charitable donations, as opposed to community investment, are mainly channelled through the WH Smith Group Charitable Trust (Charity Commission no. 1013782).

The company's donations programme is entirely proactive.

Exclusions

Unsolicited requests are not supported. No support for advertising in charity brochures, animal welfare, appeals from individuals, the arts, older people, enterprise/training, environment/heritage, fundraising events, medical research, overseas projects, political appeals, religious appeals, science/technology, sickness/disability, social welfare or sport.

Applications

The group is proactive in identifying potential partners for its community programme. Unsolicited requests, therefore, are not considered.

Corporate giving

In 2007/08, the company made total community contributions in the UK of £927,340. This comprised cash donations of £671,420, gifts in kind of £115.200 and staff time/management costs of £140,720.

During the year the company collaborated with its independent charitable trust and the National Literacy Trust to fund the WH Smith Summer Read. Around 3,600 children across 18 UK locations were given help.

Employee-led support

The company encourages employee volunteering, matching the time committed by staff volunteers to 'reading initiatives'. It also actively encourages staff to raise funds for its own trust – The WH Smith Group Charitable Trust (Charity Commission no. 1013782).

The funds raised each year are split, with two-thirds of the net proceeds going to the staff's chosen charity of the year. The remaining third is allocated to support the efforts of employees who are directly involved in local charities or schools. In addition, support is provided to a smaller number of selected trade/allied charities such as the Newsvendors Benevolent Fund. Grants can be for up to £3,000.

Employees volunteering efforts may also be recognised under the WH Smith Community Award scheme. In 2008, 20 teams received awards of £500 each towards supporting their local charities.

Payroll giving: During 2008, the company launched a new voluntary payroll giving scheme to raise awareness of the trust amongst employees and enable them to contribute to its work. Called 'Pennies from Heaven', the scheme works by rounding up the pennies on employees' salary to form a monthly donation.

Commercially-led support

Sponsorship: The group does not undertake sponsorship.

Smiths Group plc

Company registration number 137013

765 Finchley Road, Childs Hill, London NW11 8DS

020 8458 3232; Fax: 020 8458 0680

Website: www.smiths-group.com

Correspondent: Charitable Donations Committee

Chairman: Donald Brydon

Chief Executive: Philip Bowman

Year end	Turnover	Pre-tax profit
31/07/2007	£2,160,900,000	£256,000,000

Nature of company business
The company is involved in the medical, industrial, aerospace and sealing solutions industries.

Subsidiaries include: Hypertac Ltd, John Crane, Chartco Ltd, Specac Ltd, Dowty Propellors, Graseby Medical Ltd, Hamble Structures, Microcircuit Engineering, Beagle Aircraft, Kelvin Hughes Ltd, Trak Microwave, Portex Ltd, Reynolds Rings Ltd, Flexible Ducting Ltd, Pneupac Ltd, Mixing Solutions Ltd, Performance Plus

Main locations: Birmingham, Dundee, Eastleigh, Gloucester, Hounslow, Burnley, Crawley, Tewkesbury, Watford, Croyden, Christchhurch, Glalsgow, Wolverhampton, Hythe, Ilford, Orpington, Nelson, Onchan, Newmarket, Newbury, Manchester, Luton, Slough, Southampton

UK employees: 29,068

Charitable donations

2007: £389,000
2005: £625,000
2004: £602,000
2003: £708,000

Membership: BitC

Community involvement

Smiths seek to contribute to the communities in which it operates by participation in, and support for, community and charitable initiatives. The company's support of charities is wide-ranging covering everything from the local village fete to national causes. Appeals are considered on their merits and their relevance to the company's business (i.e. medical, industrial, aerospace and sealing solutions) and geographical interests.

Smiths make donations, in cash and kind, to schools, community institutions and projects.

Individual group businesses review and approve local requests, while a charity & donations committee administers a central budget supporting national and international charitable organisations.

Exclusions

No support for advertising in charity brochures, animal welfare, appeals from individuals, the arts, fundraising events, overseas projects, political appeals, religious appeals or sport.

Applications

In writing to the correspondent. Charities should give their appeals reasonable time to be processed as the company receives about 10 appeals a week and all are considered. A donations committee decides appeals and meets fairly regularly. Applications should be concise, not too scruffy or glossy, and should briefly set out what is wanted and why.

Corporate giving

In 2006/07, the company made donations of £389,000 for charitable purposes including payments totalling £150,000 for the Smiths Medical Chair of Anaesthesia and Critical Care and other donations made by the company's businesses worldwide to miscellaneous charities.

In kind support

Support such as gifts in kind and secondments may be provided at a local level by subsidiaries. Education and enterprise initiative support is also carried out at a local level.

Employee-led support

Smiths employees take an active role in the community, in hospitals, schools, universities and through charitable projects. These are often small but significant interventions involving people's time rather than large corporate donations.

In the UK, employees have recently supported the following organisations: Comic Relief; Paula Carr Diabetes Trust; St Mungo's; and The Science Museum.

Payroll giving: A number of schemes are operated by the company.

Commercially-led support

Sponsorship: The subsidiary Portex Ltd sponsor the Chair of Paediatric Anaesthesia at the Institute of Child Health at Great Ormond Street Hospital.

Sodexo Ltd

Company registration number 842846

Communications Department, Capital House, 2nd Floor, 25 Chapel Street, London NW1 5DH

020 7535 7400; Fax: 020 7535 7401

Website: www.sodexho.co.uk

Correspondent: Thomas Jelley, Corporate Cittizenship Manager Email: thomas.jelley@sodexo.com

Chief Executive: Yann Coleou

Managing Director: Chris John

Year end	Turnover	Pre-tax profit
31/08/2007	£387,782,000	£14,233,000

Nature of company business
The provision of catering management services to clients in commercial, industrial, educational, healthcare and other establishments. Activities also include catering at special events, sporting, leisure and public locations, vending services, supply of catering equipment, facilities management, design and allied services.

Subsidiaries include: Town & County Catering Ltd, Kelvin International Services Ltd, Gilmour & Pether Ltd, Ring & Brymer Holdings Ltd, Wheatsheaf Catering Ltd

Main locations: Kenley, Hitchin, Abertillery, Aberdeen, Alperton, Aldershot

UK employees: 43,000

Charitable donations

2007: £33,617
2006: £40,254
2005: £55,229
2004: £145,875
2003: £100,000

Membership: BitC

Community involvement

In 2005, the company launched the STOP Hunger campaign in the UK and Ireland, with clear aims to both combat poor nutrition in its local communities and provide a central focus for community related activities. The campaign is managed through the Sodexo Foundation (Charity Commission no. 1110266). Its objectives are to educate and provide relief from financial hardship in relation to health, nutrition and well-being through the provision of grants, goods and services.

STOP Hunger supports a number of charities but is insistent that each are involved in one or more of the following activities:

▷ healthy eating and healthy lifestyle education
▷ healthy food provision to those in need

basic life skills education to those in need, for example cooking on a budget, basic cooking skills, basic food hygiene and health and safety.

Sodexo are currently committed to a three year strategic partnership with FareShare, a charity that seeks to minimise food waste through practical solutions that ensure the maximum amount of 'fit for purpose' food is properly distributed to those in need.

Charity of the year: FareShare.

Applications

In writing to the correspondent.

If you are a charity and wish to apply for funding or become a charity partner for the STOP Hunger campaign, please email a one page summary to: stophunger@sodexo.com

Information available: The company publishes an annual corporate citizenship report.

Corporate giving

In 2006/07, the group made charitable donation totalling £33,617. However, it is not wholly clear from either the company's website or its CR report what this money went in support of. Some £10,300 was given by Sodexo Services Group Ltd to cover the running costs of the Sodexo Foundation, whilst a further portion may have been used to support the 'Healthy Matters' programme being run in Scottish schools in partnership with Scottish Business in the Community. No other information was available.

Sodexo Foundation

In 2006/07, the foundation had an income of £166,000 of which the majority (£155,000) came from the fundraising efforts of Sodexo employees. Grants totalled £96,000. Beneficiaries included: FareShare (£66,000 – including £6,000 sponsorship of a FareShare vehicle); and NCH (£30,000).

Note: In addition to supporting FareShare and a number of smaller charities that meet the STOP Hunger objectives, the trustees receive from time to time requests from employees to support a local cause. In such cases the following policy will apply:

- requests should be submitted by employees and should relate to a project or cause with which they are personally involved
- such grants are limited to a maximum of £500 per applicant
- such grants are only made to registered charities.

Employee-led support

'Sodexo employees are involved in the following three ways; financial donations through employee fundraising, employee volunteering and the sharing of Sodexo knowledge and expertise with charity partners (beneficiary charities).'

Payroll giving: The company operates a giving scheme and will match this in 2008 up to a total of £10,000.

Commercially-led support

Sponsorship: *Sport* – Sodexo sponsors the Professional Cricketers Association (PCA) Masters team. The PCA Masters brings together stars from county and international cricket, both current and past players, to play in showcase matches across the country.

Sodexo's support allows the PCA to offer local school children valuable coaching sessions on Masters match days.

Sony United Kingdom Ltd

Company registration number 2422874

The Heights, Brooklands, Weybridge, Surrey KT13 0XW

01932 816000; Fax: 01932 817000

Website: www.sony.net

Correspondent: The Charity Department

Year end	Turnover	Pre-tax profit
31/03/2007	£4,572,810,000	(£135,118,000)

Nature of company business

The company is the distributor in the United Kingdom of Sony branded products which are principally electronic goods for the domestic, leisure, business and professional markets. The company distributes Sony branded video and audio systems for commercial and professional use, and computer peripheral and component products, including semiconductor products, for use throughout Europe, Africa and the Middle East. Sony colour televisions, television tubes and other key components for the domestic and export markets are manufactured at factories which are operated by the company in South Wales.

Subsidiaries include: Specialized Electonics Services (Glasgow) Ltd

Main locations: Bridgend, Thatcham, Pencoed, Weybridge, Basingstoke

UK employees: 1,763

Charitable donations

2007: £83,646
2006: £70,750
2005: £94,385
2004: £154,056

Community involvement

Sony prefers to support local charities in areas of company presence (Weybridge, Basingstoke, Thatcham, Pencoed and Bridgend), appeals relevant to company business, and charities in which a member of staff is involved.

The Sony Group publish an annual corporate social responsibility report. The report states "Sony undertakes a wide variety of social contribution activities in fields in which it is best able to do so, to help address the needs of communities in regions around the world where Sony conducts business.'

Donations in the UK were made in support of: Community (66%); Health (17%); Sport (14%); and Environment (3%).

Exclusions

No support for advertising in charity brochures.

Applications

Appeals should be addressed to the correspondent and are considered monthly.

Corporate giving

In 2007, donations to charitable organisations totalled £83,646 (2006: £70,750). These donations relate primarily to support for local charities and events. We have no information regarding the recipient organisations.

Employee-led support

Employees of Sony Computer Entertainment Europe Ltd (SCEE) in London took part in conservation activities at a local park. The main goals of the park are to preserve a valuable habitat for threatened species, provide an educational resource for local schools and community groups, and provide a peaceful and tranquil site for members of the local community. Work was carried out by two groups of SCEE employees.

Payroll giving: Sony operates the Give As You Earn scheme.

Commercially-led support

Sponsorship: *The arts* – Local organisations to have received support include Brooklands Museum and the Newbury Spring Festival.

Southern Co-operatives Ltd

Company registration number 1591R

44 High Street, Fareham, Hampshire PO16 7BN

01329 223000; Fax: 01329 223022

Website: www.southern.coop

Correspondent: Clerk of the Trustees

Email: foundation@southern.coop

Chairman: D J Blowe

Chief Executive: G R Bennett

Year end	Turnover	Pre-tax profit
26/01/2008	£198,100,000	£10,024,000

Nature of company business
Independent consumer co-operative society.

UK employees: 2,866

Charitable donations
2008: £68,960
2007: £76,790

Community involvement

Supported by funding from Southern Co-operatives Ltd, the Southern Co-operative Foundation (Charity Commission no. 1107270) was established in 2004.

Major grants – The foundation invites applications from organisations, groups and individuals for projects which are charitable and demonstrate and reinforce co-operation or mutuality. Project details are sought in a specific format and applications reviewed against agreed criteria.

Other schemes – In addition, the charity operates four schemes in conjunction with Southern Co-operatives Ltd (SCL). All applications under these schemes must meet the criteria of demonstrating co-operation or mutuality. Briefly, these are:

- small grants distributed via SCL stores to community groups, charities and organisations which are holding events or have small projects
- matched funding where two or more employees of SCL carry out fundraising activity for charitable or community purposes

- Co-operative Community Councils Awards for community organisations and charities within SCL's six regional areas
- Customer nominated local charities or organisations to benefit from a community support scheme operated by a specific SCL store.

Full details of the size of grant/award available under each of these schemes are available on the co-operative's website.

Applications

The Co-operatives website contains full details of how to apply to each of the schemes available. For example, for major grants guidance notes are provided on how to complete the required application form.

Potential applicants for grants are advised to regularly revisit the Southern Co-operative's web pages (look under 'Foundation') as new schemes may be added as well as currently 'closed' schemes re-open for new applications.

Corporate giving

In 2007/08, the Southern Co-operative donated £68,960 (2006/07: £76,790) to the foundation, which in turn made charitable awards and donations totalling £86,198.

Beneficiaries included: The Rixon Playground Co-operative (£10,000); The Art and Soul Traders Ltd (£5,000); Emsworth Community Responders (£4,800); and The Stockbridge Evergreen Club (2,000).

Donations through the four schemes already described were broken down as follows:

- stores small donations (748 groups) – £24,310
- stores large donations (18 groups) – £2,375
- community awards (18 groups) – £4,500
- matched funding (36 groups) – £6,879.

Spar (UK) Ltd

Company registration number 634226

Mezzanine Floor, Hygeia Building, 66–68 College Road, Harrow HA3 1BE

020 8426 3700; Fax: 020 8426 3701

Website: www.spar.co.uk

Correspondent: Susan Darbyshire, Marketing Director

Managing Director: Jerry Marwood

Year end	Turnover	Pre-tax profit
28/04/2007	£159,823,307	£299,000

Nature of company business
Independently-owned nationwide convenience stores operating under the SPAR banner.

UK employees: 50,000

Charitable donations

Membership: BitC

Community involvement

SPAR sees its role within the community as an integral part of the way it does business and because of this is a subscribed member of Business in the Community (BitC). As part of this involvement, SPAR is developing a framework in which it can support those issues that are important to the communities' local to its stores.

In addition to the above, national organisations can also receive support with those involved with children and sport being particularly favoured.

SPAR also has an associated charitable trust – The SPAR Charitable Fund (Charity Commission no.236252) administered from the address given above.

Exclusions

No support for political or religious causes.

Applications

Please contact your local store manager, unless stated otherwise.

Corporate giving

Quantifying SPAR's community investment in monetary terms has proved, and continues to prove, elusive. No general charitable donations were declared in the company's latest annual report and accounts, whilst those for the associated trust are equally bereft of any details of a donation being received directly from the company.

Despite this, it is clear that SPAR does engage with its local communities and national charity partners. On this basis we believe an entry here is still warranted.

From 2006 until 2008 SPAR is sponsoring the NSPCC, ChildLine and the NSPCC's sister organisation in Scotland, Children 1st. Whilst SPAR facilitates fundraising on behalf of these charities, through its own staff and customers, it is not clear if any cash donations are made directly by the company. Those funds that are raised are deposited as 'restricted funds' with the SPAR Charitable Trust before being passed on to the nominated charities.

The SPAR Charitable Trust

In 2007, the trust had income of £111,000 and made donations of £120,000 to related trade benevolent funds, the British Heart Foundation, Childline and the NSPCC.

In kind support

Sport – Local SPAR stores are donating special athletics kits to local schools and youth sports teams (over 70% of SPAR retailers already support their local schools in some way or another). If you haven't been approached yet please DON'T contact your local store directly, but send an email to: sportsdaykits@spar.co.uk expressing your interest.

SPAR will then ask your local store if they would like to donate a kit to your school and you will be contacted.

Environment – SPAR has teamed up with the Woodland Trust to celebrate 50 years of being 'Rooted in the Community'.

To help secure the future of the countryside the Woodland Trust is planting over 500,000 trees every year. As its contribution towards this, SPAR is dedicating 2,700 trees throughout the UK – one for every SPAR store.

Spirax Sarco Engineering plc

Company registration number 596337

Charlton House, Cirencester Road, Cheltenham, Gloucestershire GL53 8ER

01242 521361; Fax: 01242 581470

Website: www.spiraxsarcoengineering.com

Correspondent: Jane Husband, Secretary to the Chief Executive

Chairman: M Townsend

Chief Executive: Mark Vernon

Year end	Turnover	Pre-tax profit
31/12/2007	£417,317,000	£72,163,000

Nature of company business
The provision of knowledge, service and products worldwide for the control and efficient use of steam and other industrial fluids.

Subsidiaries include: Watson-Marlow Ltd

Main locations: Glasgow, Cheltenham

UK employees: 1,133

Total employees: 3,899

Charitable donations

2007: £72,387
2006: £62,424
2005: £59,400
2004: £47,982
2003: £49,910

Community involvement

The company's 2005 Annual Report states: 'The group has a charitable trust which donates to registered charities and additional donations are made to appropriate requests for support from bodies which are not registered charities'.

'The operating companies in the group are encouraged to provide support to local communities through company donations, employee organised charitable activities, donation of equipment no longer required and through the provision of information.'

Exclusions

Previous information collated suggested that the company will make no response to circular appeals, and no grants for advertising in charity brochures, religious appeals, local appeals not in areas of company presence and large national appeals.

Applications

In writing to the correspondent.

Corporate giving

In 2007, the company made cash donations totalling £72,387 primarily through the Spirax-Sarco Engineering plc Group Charitable Trust (Charity Commission no. 1082534). Beneficiaries have included: British Red Cross – Tsunami Appeal (£10,000); National Star Centre (£3,000); Lillian Faithful Homes (£2,000); Seven Springs Play and Support

Centre (£1,000); Gloucestershire Wildlife Fund (£750); and SS Great Britain (£500).

In kind support
In addition to cash donations, the company donates equipment that is no longer required to the local community.

Employee-led support
Employees are encouraged to organise charitable activities.

Spirent plc

Company registration number 470893

Spirent Communications plc, Northwood Park, Gatwick Road, Crawley, West Sussex RH10 9XN

01293 767676; Fax: 01293 767677

Website: www.spirent.com

Correspondent: Company Secretary

Chairman: Edward Bramson

Chief Executive: Willian Burns

Year end	Turnover	Pre-tax profit
31/12/2007	£237,000,000	£17,800,000

Nature of company business
An international technology group focused on the design, development, manufacture and marketing of specialist electronic products.

Subsidiaries include: PG Drives Technology Ltd

Main locations: Crawley, Devon, Bedfordshire

UK employees: 1,661

Charitable donations
2007: £40,000
2006: £32,000
2005: £96,000
2004: £63,000
2003: £63,000

Community involvement
The company made the following statement in its 2007 annual report. 'Spirent strives to be a responsible partner in the communities in which we operate, and we recognise the significance of local communities through our Charitable Donations Policy. Our businesses are encouraged to support the particular needs of their population by contributing to local charities and participating in community initiatives. Support takes the form of employee time and skills, gifts in kind and cash donations.'

Exclusions
No support for appeals from individuals, or for local appeals not in areas of company presence.

Applications
In writing to the correspondent.

Corporate giving
In 2007, Spirent made charitable cash donations of £40,000 (2006: £32,000).

In kind support
In 2007, continued support was given to education by offering internships and work experience programmes. The company also donate materials and equipment to local causes throughout the world.

Employee-led support
Staff are involved in fund raising activities for local concerns and community initiatives, such as 'food drives', collections and sponsored events that help organisations provide food, clothing and children's toys to people around the world.

'Spirent continues to support all of our employees and businesses in finding new ways of becoming involved to help their communities.'

Sportech plc

Company registration number SC69140

Walton House, 55 Charnock Road, Walton, Liverpool L67 1AA

0151 525 3677

Website: www.sportechplc.com

Correspondent: Cathy Lee

Email: enquiries@sportech.com

Chairman: Piers Pottinger

Chief Executive: Ian Penrose

Year end	Pre-tax profit
31/12/2007	£11,600,000

Nature of company business
The principal activities of the Group are those of Football Gaming and e-Gaming.

Main locations: Liverpool, London

UK employees: 287

Charitable donations
2007: £1,300,000
2006: £1,300,000
2005: £1,700,000

Community involvement
Between 2000 and 2007, Sportech plc acquired Littlewoods Gaming, Zetters Football Pools and Vernons Football Pools. In 2008, it launched 'The New Football Pools' and established The Football Pools Trust which will address the needs of community football.

'During 2007, the company reviewed the basis of its long-standing support for communities across the United Kingdom and re-established its status as a major supporter of the national game. In addition to the annual multi-million pound donations of the Foundation for Sport and the Arts (www.thefsa.net), with which it maintains its close links, the company struck an agreement with the four English and Scottish professional football leagues which will see £5.9m directed into football charities over the next four years. This funding will be managed by a committee of league and company representatives.

'The company actively promotes GamCare, the national association for gambling care educational resources, to its customers and has contributed to the Responsibility in Gambling Trust and its predecessor body over recent years.'

Applications

Applications should be made in writing to the correspondent.

Corporate giving

In 2007, through its lottery operations, £1.3 million (2006: £1.3 million) was generated for good causes and charities. Some small specific charitable donations were made to a small number of charitable causes and totalled £5,600 (2005: £75,000). We have no details of the beneficiaries.

SSL International plc

Company registration number 388828

35 New Bridge Street, London EC4V 6BW

020 7367 5760; Fax: 020 7367 5790

Website: www.ssl-international.com

Correspondent: Garry Watts, Chief Executive

Chairman: Gerald Corbett

Chief Executive: Garry Watts

Year end	Turnover	Pre-tax profit
31/03/2008	£533,900,000	£10,900,000

Nature of company business
The manufacture and distribution of healthcare products.

Subsidiaries include: London International Group plc, Scholl Consumer Products Ltd, Scholl Ltd, LRC Products Ltd

Main locations: Manchester, London

Total employees: 5,095

Charitable donations
2008: £200,000
2007: £100,000
2006: £100,000
2005: £100,000
2004: £100,000

Community involvement

SSL International look to support the local communities in which its employees live and work by investing resources through charitable donations and employees' time and skills.

Exclusions

No support for local appeals not in areas of company presence.

Applications

In writing to the correspondent.

Corporate giving

In 2007/08, charitable donations doubled to £200,000. It is not clear from the accounts whether this is a UK or worldwide figure.

No list of beneficiaries was available. However, SSL is a patron company member of The Outward Bounds Trust so we assume some financial support will have been given here.

Employee-led support

The company's website states that employees engage with their local communities.

St James's Place plc

Company registration number 3183415

1 Tetbury Road, Cirencester, Gloucestershire GL7 1FP

01285 640302

Website: www.sjp.co.uk

Correspondent: The Secretary, St James's Place Foundation

Chairman: Mike Wilson

Chief Executive: David Bellamy

Year end	Pre-tax profit
31/12/2007	£103,200,000

Nature of company business
St James's Place plc is a financial services group involved in the provision of wealth management services.

Subsidiaries include: J Rothschild Assurance plc

Main locations: London

Total employees: 635

Charitable donations
2007: £1,200,000
2006: £950,000
2005: £765,380
2003: £500,000

Membership: BitC

Community involvement

St James's Place channels its cash contributions to charity through the St James's Place Foundation (Charity Commission no. 1031456). All administrative and management costs are met by St James's Place plc.

The objective of the foundation is to raise money for distribution to organisations that meet its main current theme of 'Cherishing the Children'. This theme is aimed at children and young people who are mentally and/or physically disabled, or have a life threatening or degenerative illness up to the age of 25. The foundation now also supports the Hospice Movement.

Exclusions

No response to circular appeals, and no grants for advertising in charity brochures sponsorship or individuals.

Applications

The foundation will only consider applications from established charities or special needs schools for projects that meet the funding criteria.

The management committee of the St James's Place Foundation considers applications at its quarterly meetings. Application forms can be requested from the secretary.

Corporate giving

St James's Place plc matches, on a pound for pound basis, all the money raised by the foundation. During 2007 the foundation raised a total of £2.4 million.

The corporate donation is distributed differently from the other funds raised. It was agreed between the management committee and the trustees, that the corporate donation should be used to fund larger projects not necessarily in keeping with the foundation's theme.

Stagecoach Group plc

Company registration number SC100764

10 Dunkeld Road, Perth PH1 5TW

01738 442111; Fax: 01738 643648

Website: www.stagecoachgroup.com

Correspondent: Stagecoach Group Community Fund 01738 442111

Chairman: Robert Speirs

Chief Executive: Brian Souter

Year end	Turnover	Pre-tax profit
30/04/2008	£1,763,600,000	£167,300,000

Nature of company business
Principal activity: The provision of public transport services in the UK and North America.

Subsidiaries include: East Kent Road Car Co. Ltd, East London Bus & Coach Co. Ltd, National Transport Tokens Ltd, Stagecoach Scotland Ltd, PSV Claims Bureau Ltd, Cleveland Transit Ltd, South East London & Kent Bus Co. Ltd, Greater Manchester Buses South Ltd, East Midland Motor Services Ltd, Busways Travel Services Ltd, Cambus Ltd

Main locations: Ilford, Chichester, Isle of Wight, Exeter, Gwent, Norhampton, Perth, Sheffield, Rugby, Sunderland, Oxford, Manchester, London, Liverpool, Cowdenbeath, Cambridge, Chesterfield, Carlisle, Gloucester, Ayr

UK employees: 24,986

Total employees: 29,548

Charitable donations

2008: £700,000
2007: £700,000
2006: £600,000
2005: £300,000
2004: £300,000

Community involvement

The company referred us to its website from where the following information was taken.

'[Stagecoach] helps local people share in our success by funding the vital work of local, national and international charities ... [donations were made to] many worthwhile causes, including many health charities and local community projects in areas where Stagecoach provides lifeline bus and rail services.'

Applications

In writing to the Stagecoach Group Community Fund at the above address.

Corporate giving

In 2007/08, the company made charitable donations totalling £700,000. Some of the organisations supported included:

- contributions to several homeless shelters, providing funds for equipment and new dormitories. South West Trains is a regular supporter of the Railway Children, a charity which helps runaway youngsters, and also helps Dorset Voluntary Search and Rescue.

- continuing support for the UK educational charity businessdynamics, which provides courses designed to build the skills and confidence of young people as they prepare to enter the worlds of work and further education.

In kind support

Stagecoach has a national agreement with Guide Dogs for the Blind that allows the dog trainers free travel on its buses and trains.

Employee-led support

The company also supports employees' volunteering/ charitable activities by considering, where appropriate, financial help, allowing time off to volunteer, and matching employee fundraising.

Payroll giving: The Give As You Earn scheme is in operation.

Commercially-led support

Sponsorship: *The Arts* – Stagecoach continues to support a number of arts initiatives.

Education – Stagecoach is providing £500,000 through a major four-year sponsorship to fund a gym at the new Oasis Academy in Grimsby. The academy, which will have around 1,100 students, is a partnership between the Oasis Trust, North East Lincolnshire Council and the Department for Education and Skills to improve choice for parents and raise the overall standard of education in the local area. The Grimsby curriculum will be enhanced by a specialism in sports and health.

Standard Chartered plc

Company registration number 966425

1 Basinghall Avenue, London EC2V 5DD

020 7885 8888

Website: www.standardchartered.com/uk/

Correspondent: The Community Relations Manager

Chairman: E Mervyn Davies

Chief Executive: Peter Sands

Year end	Pre-tax profit
31/12/2007	£4,035,000,000

Nature of company business
The group's principal activity is the provision of banking and other financial services.

Main locations: London

UK employees: 1,400

Total employees: 70,000

Charitable donations

2007: £2,250,000
2005: £71,448
2003: £780,000

Total community contributions: £2,250,000

Membership: L B Group

Community involvement

The group's donations policy is focused on those countries in Asia, Africa, the Middle East and Latin America where it has operations.

'In addition to many initiatives at a global, regional and local level the Group operates four major programmes; Living with HIV, Seeing is Believing, Empowering Women and Employee Volunteering.'

Note: Although some support is given to UK registered charities, this is only given to those focusing on supporting work outside the United Kingdom.

Exclusions

Generally no support for charities working to the benefit of communities in the UK, circular appeals, advertising in charity brochures, appeals from individuals, purely denominational (religious) appeals, local appeals not in areas of company presence or large national appeals. Donations are not made to political parties.

Applications

Please note the following points:

- Ensure that the project for which you are seeking support fits the criteria set out.
- Write a short summary of the project (not more than one page of A4 paper). It should then be sent to the Standard Chartered corporate affairs manager of the country where the project is taking place. Should the group then be able to consider supporting the project a more detailed proposal will be required. The company has operations in over 40 countries in Africa, Asia, the Middle East, and Latin America.
- As donation plans for the year are usually agreed at the end of the year, it is advisable to submit a proposal no later than the third quarter of a given year.
- It is group practice to support a limited number of charities and, where possible, to support them for a period of up to three years. The opportunity for involvement of Standard Chartered and direct support by its people is a key element in gaining funding.

Corporate giving

In 2007, the group gave £2.25 million to fund the work of registered charities in the UK (focusing on supporting their work outside the UK).

In kind support

The company also supports a range of fundraising events, provides advice, secondments and scholarships.

Employee-led support

Standard Chartered encourages its people to become involved in the communities in which they work. Many participate in a wide range of charitable and community support programmes.

Standard Life

Company registration number SA000038

Standard Life House, 30 Lothian Road, Edinburgh EH1 2DH

0131 225 2552

Website: www.standardlife.com

Correspondent: The Corporate Social Responsibility Manager

Chairman: Gerry Grimstone

Chief Executive: Sandy Crombie

Year end	Pre-tax profit
31/12/2007	£620,000,000

Nature of company business
Life assurance, pensions, health insurance, investment management and banking.

Subsidiaries include: STLM Ltd

Main locations: Edinburgh

UK employees: 7,278

Total employees: 9,998

Charitable donations

2007: £263,253
2005: £342,364
2003: £267,328

Total community contributions: £263,353

Membership: A & B, BitC, L B Group

Community involvement

'Our business has an impact on the communities we work in and they provide us with key resources that help us succeed as a business. We have been committed to supporting a wide range of initiatives in our community for over fifteen years. In 2007, three areas came to the fore – developing financial capability, building employment skills and supporting health and wellbeing.'

Exclusions

In order for the company to concentrate its energies on the five main areas stated above, the following are excluded: political or religious activities, animal welfare, buildings and heritage, or sports clubs.

Further, the group does not sponsor individuals, nor get involved with third party funding activities, nor buy charity advertising space.

Applications

In writing to the correspondent.

Corporate giving

In 2007 payments for charitable purposes by the group totalled £263,252 of which £197,271 was given to UK resident charities, mainly to Cancer Research UK and NCH.

In kind support

Services provided to charities have included use of its design, print and copying facilities, meeting room space in its buildings, provision of old computer equipment and even the donation of an unused forklift truck.

Secondments: The group seconds its people to community groups and charities to do specific projects over a period of 3–12 months. Two of the seven we helped in 2007 were The Rock Trust and The Scottish Social Enterprise Coalition.

Employee-led support

'Our people also raise money for charity, with the incentive that the Group matches every penny donated. The main recipients in 2007 were Cancer Research UK who received £261,557 for the Colorectal Cancer Unit at the Western General Hospital in Edinburgh and NCH The Children's Charity, who received £123,085 for their Young Carers Project in Motherwell. In addition, Standard Life Healthcare supported three hospices, donating a total of £13,866.'

Payroll giving: The Give As You Earn scheme is in operation.

Commercially-led support

Sponsorship: Standard Life undertakes arts sponsorship. It has also sponsored the printing of publicity materials and helped to publicise those events.

Good cause sponsorship: 'We are sponsoring the Royal National Institute for Deaf People's Volunteer Resource project. The aim of this project is to pay for training in organisations like the Samaritans and Citizens Advice Bureaux, that will help them communicate with people who are deaf and hard of hearing. Alongside this the project encourages deaf and hard of hearing people to volunteer themselves with these organisations.'

Starbucks Coffee Company (UK) Ltd

Company registration number 2959325

Chiswick Park, 566 Chiswick High Road, London W4 5YE

020 8834 5000

Website: www.starbucks.co.uk

Correspondent: Jim Curtis, Community Affairs Specialist

Year end	Turnover	Pre-tax profit
30/09/2007	£328,160,137	(£1,399,057)

Nature of company business
The retail and wholesale of gourmet coffee, tea and related products in the United Kingdom. There are currently 580 Starbucks stores in the UK.

Main locations: London

UK employees: 7,771

Charitable donations

2007: £60,000

Membership: BitC

Community involvement

The company provides support under three themes: Partners in Education; Bringing People Together; and Programmes in Coffee Origin Countries.

Some information about each of these is given below.

Applications

In writing to the correspondent.

Corporate giving

Although the company clearly makes cash donations in the UK (see the example below), no such declaration was made in its 2007 annual report and accounts. However, we believe around £60,000 to be a fair (if under) estimate.

Partners in education

'Starbucks and the National Literacy Trust have been proud partners since 2001, over that that time we have dedicated funds and partner (employee) time to positively affect the lives of over 10,000 children and their families. Our customers and partners have also donated almost half a million books to our Starbucks Bookdrive and these have been distributed to primary schools in need of a reading boost.

'Literacy has a huge impact on happiness and success. We know that supporting young people through literacy in local communities will empower them to achieve their full potential. 2008 is the National Year of Reading that's why we're launching a renewed five year partnership with the National Literacy Trust.

'We will commit funds and partner time to support the National Literacy Trust Reading is Fundamental programme and over the next five years it will help over 23,000 young people to develop a natural love of reading.'

Bringing people together

Through its established association with the Royal Society for the Arts and the 'Coffee House Challenge', Starbucks invited local communities to debates and discussions across the country. Over 190 events were held in 2007, to find realistic solutions to local challenges. As a result, 45 local projects have received seed funding from Starbucks (up to £1,500 each).

Programmes in coffee origin countries

'Starbucks and CARE International have for many years worked together on development and aid programmes in coffee growing communities in South America, Indonesia and Africa. Over the next three years, Starbucks UK and Ireland will provide further support to a rural Ethiopian farming community. With our partners and customers in the UK and Ireland, we're supporting water projects for the Gewgew Dingete community in West Harrarghe, Ethiopia. This project builds on a number of programmes in this region over recent years.'

In kind support

The company can donate its products to coffee mornings and so on. It has also allowed its premises to be used for similar activities.

Employee-led support

Staff (partners) are encouraged to volunteer, either for voluntary organisations of their own selection or through initiatives supported by the company such as Timebank, the national volunteering charity.

In some circumstances, cash donations have been linked to volunteering, as with the Gewgew Dingete community project. For every 30 minutes they pledge. Starbucks will donate £5 to the project which is overseen by CARE International.

Stemcor Holdings Ltd

Company registration number 1038435

Level 27, CityPoint, 1 Ropemaker Street, London EC2Y 9ST

020 7775 3600; Fax: 020 7775 3679

Website: www.stemcor.com

Correspondent: The Charity Committee

Email: info@stemcor.com

Chairman: Ralph Oppenheimer

Managing Director: David Faktor

Managing Director: Julian Verden

Year end	Turnover	Pre-tax profit
31/12/2007	£4,176,362,000	£65,443,000

Nature of company business
The principal activity of the group is international trading in both steel products and raw materials for the production of steel.

UK employees: 1,089

Charitable donations
2007: £650,000
2006: £464,000

Community involvement

The company sets aside 1% of pre-tax profits for distribution to charitable causes. Decisions regarding this are taken by Stemcor's charity committee, which comprises three board members who consider suggestions submitted by staff and external parties before deciding where to direct support.

Further to this, 'The bulk of funding is used to support a select few global charities, the aim being to achieve far-reaching impact and sustainable progress, but we also fund smaller charities in countries where we have a presence. Key themes supported by Stemcor are education, health, housing and disaster relief'.

'The selection process includes an analysis of the track record of a charity, its international presence, its size and its financial effectiveness. The Charity Committee also expects to see measurable progress reports demonstrating the impacts and outputs of the work we support.'

Applications
In writing to the correspondent.

Corporate giving

In 2007, the company made charitable donations of £650,000 (2006: £464,000). The following extract is taken from its annual report and accounts for the year.

'During the year, Stemcor's largest charitable donations were to:
- Save the Children – to support their "Reading for Children" programme in Vietnam and Bhutan, giving disadvantaged children access to education
- MAGE – to rebuild educational facilities destroyed by the tsunami in Sri Lanka, particularly a hostel for medical students
- CARE – to fund an education project for girls in Uttar Pradesh, India.

'A Stemcor team took part in the annual Empire State Building run-up in New York, raising a total of £35,000 (including matched funds) for Save the Children. A further £17,000 was raised when Stemcor matched funds raised at the International Steel Trade Association's annual lunch in London.

'Donations of, or exceeding, £10,000 were made to the following charities: The Citizens Foundation (Pakistan), Doctors Without Borders (Kurdish region of Iraq), The Hunger Project (Ghana/ Bangladesh), Magic Bus (India), Practical Action (Bangladesh), Pratham (India), The Red Cross (Peru), Save the Children (Iraqi refugees in Jordan) and World Vision (Dominican Republic).

'Many smaller donations were also made, including matching grants for the individual fundraising efforts of Stemcor staff around the world.'

Steria Ltd

Company registration number 4077975

Three Cherry Trees Lane, Hemel Hempstead, Hertfordshire HP2 7AH

08702 416181; Fax: 08702 426282

Website: www.xansa.com

Correspondent: Sarah Massingham, Corporate Relations

Chairman: Bill Alexander

Chief Executive: John Torrie

Year end	Turnover	Pre-tax profit
30/04/2007	£379,700,000	£16,400,000

Nature of company business
Formerly trading as the Xansa Group, the company is now part of the Steria Group. Principal activities are as an outsourcing and technology company.

Subsidiaries include: Druid Group plc, First Banking Systems Ltd, ASL Information Services Ltd, OSI Group Holdings Ltd

Main locations: Bedford, Birminham, Manchester, Northampton, Southampton, Reading, Edinburgh, Leeds, Holborn

UK employees: 3,039

Total employees: 7,654

Community involvement

Formerly included here under Xansa Group plc, the company became part of the French headquartered Steria Group in October 2007. At this point in time (November 2008) it appears that there are two community investment programmes running in parallel, although the contact remains that previously given for the Xansa Group. It is likely, however, that these will be brought together in the future.

The following information regarding each company's community support policy is taken from their respective websites.

Xansa in the community

'Investing in the local community is the right thing to do. But it's also right for our business. We have made a decision to proactively work in partnership with like minded clients, local governments and charities to contribute to the development and growth of the communities in which we operate.'

Xansa therefore focuses its community programme on the things it feels it does best and so gives support in the following areas:

▹ basic education and mentorship

▹ educational infrastructure and IT skills

▹ entrepreneurship skills.

Directors are authorised to spend up to 1% of pre-tax profit each year in support of the group's community investment.

Steria in the community

'Steria supports three charities as part of our commitment to invest in community development and to reduce our impact on the environment.

'Active engagement and involvement with community groups and charities, also enables Steria people to gain a greater understanding of new and emerging markets, particularly in relation to education and the criminal justice arena.'

Reference to the parent company's website (www.steria.com) reveals the existence of a foundation – Foundation Steria. Although information is available in English, it is not clear if application is open to UK-based organisations.

Please note: All financial and donation figures quoted refer, at present, to the former Xansa Group.

Applications

In writing to the correspondent at: Steria Ltd, 420 Thames Valley Park, Thames Valley Park Drive, Reading RG6 1PU.

For further information on how to get involved with the company's community support programmes, contact community@xansa.com or telephone: 08702 416181.

Information available: The company produce an annual community report.

Corporate giving

In 2007, the company made worldwide community contributions of £154,064 (2006: £98,970) of which 374,105 (2006: £68,307) was in cash donations. We do not know what proportion of this went to UK organisations.

In kind support

Mentorship: 'In the UK, Xansa volunteers based on a client site in Chesterfield have forged successful relationships with four local schools. Programmes include interview skills development at the Springwell School and mentors at Parkside, Brookfield and Newbold School where volunteers have committed to mentor a child, over the course of three years.

'An additional 16 Xansa volunteers participate in a 'buddy reading' scheme with the Parkside School, committing to working with individual children weekly over the entire school year.'

Employee-led support

Through the use of enabling grants and matching funds, employees are encouraged to contribute to their local community by volunteering their skills, experience and energies as well as fundraising on behalf of charitable causes.

In 2007, matching funds and enabling grants totalled £43,000.

December 2007 marked the launch of 'Do More Day,' a new annual event to raise awareness amongst its employees and clients of Xansa's community activities. 'Do More Day' involves fundraising and volunteering events across the UK and India on an annual basis.

During 'Do More Day' 2006, the company raised £21,000 in 24 hours for educational and charitable organisations. These included schools for the disadvantaged in India, The Prince's Trust, Segal House Nursery for children with special needs, and Pathways Centre for the Homeless.

J Stobart and Sons Ltd

Company registration number 783738

Newlands Mill, Hesket Newmarket, Wigton, Cumbria CA7 8HP

01697 478261

Correspondent: (See 'Applications')

Managing Director: P J Stobart

Year end	Pre-tax profit
31/12/2006	£705,907

Nature of company business
The manufacture and retail of animal feeding stuffs.

Main locations: Carlisle

UK employees: 21

Community involvement

No doubt much to the chagrin of Eddie Stobart 'spotters', we have decided to replace that company's entry with information about a perhaps less well known Stobart family business. The main reason for this is that despite the company having a high and recognisable profile, information about what it did in support of local charities and good causes has remained very sketchy. The company's acquisition by W A Developments Ltd has further muddied the water, although according to the 2006 accounts, it does still make very limited charitable donations.

On the other hand, J Stobart and Sons Ltd provide substantial charitable support through the Stobart Newlands Charitable Trust (Charity Commission no. 328464), although this is mainly in aid of Christian causes.

Exclusions

No grants for individuals.

Applications

In writing to: Mrs M Stobart, Trustee, The Stobart Newlands Charitable Trust, Mill Croft, Newlands, Hesket Newmarket, Wigton, Cumbria CA7 8HP. Please note, however, that unsolicited causes are unlikely to succeed.

Corporate giving

In 2006 the company made charitable donations of £700,000 (2005: £700,000), all of which went to the associated family trust of which the directors of the company are also trustees.

The Stobart Newlands Charitable Trust

For the year ended 31 December 2006, the trust made around 50 grants to various charities totalling nearly £1.12 million, the majority to Christian, religious and missionary bodies. The major beneficiaries were: Operation Mobilisation (£270,000); World Vision (£230,000); Mission Aviation Fellowship (£200,000); Moorlands College (£40,000); and Spurgeons and Tear Fund (£35,000 each).

Levi Strauss (UK) Ltd

Company registration number 892419

Swann Valley, Northampton NN4 9BA

01604 581501; Fax: 01604 599815

Website: www.levistrauss.com

Correspondent: Vanessa Ashton, Facilities Supervisor

Year end	Turnover	Pre-tax profit
30/11/2007	£63,753,000	£3,538,000

Nature of company business
Clothing marketing and sales under the Levi's brand.

Main locations: Northampton

UK employees: 100

Total employees: 10,000

Charitable donations

2007: £465
2006: £56
2005: £161,300

Community involvement

Donations from the Levi Strauss Company in the UK have fallen significantly in the last couple of years (see 'Community contributions'). However, as support is still given to qualifying UK-based organisations through the Levi Strauss Foundation, we continue to include the company here.

Levi Strauss Foundation

'The company's website states that: The Levi Strauss Foundation has prioritised its funding areas after carefully considering research findings, examining the gaps in funding by other foundations and governments, and looking at the legacy of philanthropic focus and leadership by the foundation and the company.

'We have identified three specific program areas where we seek to have the most significant impact to alleviate poverty among women and youth. These are building assets; preventing the spread of HIV/AIDS by addressing stigma and discrimination and funding education and harm-reduction programs such as syringe access; and improving the working and living standards of garment workers through a global workers' rights initiative.

'We seek to collaborate with other institutions and to fund innovative programs that will foster positive, long-term social change.

'We fund organisations in communities around the world where our employees and contractors' employees live and work.

'We strive for focus and effectiveness in our grant making. Our programme staff adopt a proactive, 'hands on' approach in identifying partnerships that advance our strategic goals within each of the issue areas we support.'

Exclusions

No support is given to: individuals; capital or endowment campaigns; building work; sports teams or competitions; advertising; event sponsorship; sectarian or religious activities; or political campaigns or causes.

Applications

In writing to the correspondent.

Due to the proactive stance taken by the Levi Strauss Foundation in finding organisations to support, unsolicited grant requests, product donation requests or charitable sponsorship requests are not accepted.

Corporate giving

In 2007, the Levi Strauss Foundation made grants to UK organisations totalling £458,000 (around £230,000). The beneficiaries were: Accountability; London Rebuilding Trust; Motorvations Project; National AIDS Trust; New Economics Foundation; and Toynbee Hall.

In kind support

The company may occasionally make some of their products (jeans) available to charitable organisations. Donations of furniture, machines, and the like that are no longer in use may also be made to support the work of an organisation.

Employee-led support

Staff are allowed time off for activity of community benefit and encouraged to become volunteers in their own time. The company operates a matching scheme for employee fundraising.

STV Group plc

Company registration number SC042391

Pacific Quay, Glasgow G51 1PQ

Website: www.smg.plc.uk

Correspondent: Director of Corporate Affairs

Chairman: Richard Findlay

Year end	Turnover	Pre-tax profit
31/12/2007	£119,000,000	(£22,700,000)

Nature of company business
Formerly Scottish Media Group plc, STV Group plc is a Scottish media company.

Subsidiaries include: Pearl & Dean Cinemas Ltd, Ginger Television Productions Ltd, Grampian Television Ltd, Scottish Television Ltd, Scottish Television Enterprises Ltd, Caledonian Publishing Ltd

Main locations: Glasgow

UK employees: 728

Charitable donations

2007: £29,000
2006: £293,000
2005: £328,000
2004: £307,000
2003: £346,000

Community involvement

The group has a policy of providing assistance to professional, community and amateur organisations and individuals concerned with theatrical and musical performances. It will also consider charitable or social organisations undertaking new or special activities. There is a preference for Scottish-based appeals, especially local charities in central Scotland and particularly those providing an element of training. In kind support is also given.

Exclusions

Sponsorship is not undertaken. No support for fundraising events, advertising in charity brochures, purely denominational (religious) appeals, local appeals not in areas of company presence, large national appeals or overseas projects.

Applications

In writing to the correspondent. The Community Programmes Co-ordinator should be contacted regarding Social Action broadcasting.

Corporate giving

In 2007 the group made cash donations of £29,000. Major recipients in previous years have included Scottish Opera, Scottish Ballet, Edinburgh International Television Festival, Drambuie Edinburgh Film Festival, Celtic Film Festival, Museum of Scotland Projects, National Television Archive, various community festivals, support for young trainee film-makers and Comunn Na Gaidhlig.

In kind support

Support may be given in the form of equipment and the use of facilities free of charge.

Employee-led support

Staff are allowed time off for activities of community benefit and are encouraged to become volunteers in their own time.

Staff supported Breast Cancer Awareness month by taking part in 'Wear it Pink' Day.

SMG has launched a match funding initiative called Charity Challenge which matches donations raised by staff pound for pound.

Commercially-led support

Sponsorship: In 2007 STV was the media partner for ChildLine Scotland's annual charity five-a-side tournament, World Footie.

Pearl & Dean, along with Vodafone and Bliss Magazine supported the Anti-Bullying campaign by sponsoring people to make a short film about anti-bullying, with the winning film being screened on digital.

Swann-Morton Ltd

Owlerton Green, Sheffield S6 2BJ

0114 234 4231; Fax: 0114 231 4966

Website: www.swann-morton.com

Correspondent: Michael Hirst, Trustee, Swann-Mortion Foundation

Year end	Turnover	Pre-tax profit
31/10/2007	£21,902,299	£621,106

Nature of company business
The manufacture of fine edge blades for both surgical and industrial purposes.

UK employees: 323

Charitable donations

2007: £53,593

Community involvement

Founded in Sheffield during 1932, Swann-Morton has become a world leader in the manufacture of surgical blades, scalpels and handles. Its business activities, to some extent, shape its charitable support. This is mainly channelled through the Swann-Morton Foundation (Charity Commission no. 271925), the aims and objectives of which are as follows:

- the purchase of medical instruments or equipment for the use by or for patients with infirmity
- the promotion of education and research in medicine and surgery aimed at the relief of suffering or handicap
- for the encouragement of scholarship at schools, colleges and universities.

Applications

In writing to the correspondent.

Corporate giving

In 2007, the company made charitable donations totalling £53,593 of which £35,500 was gift-aided to the foundation.

Swann-Morton Foundation

In 2006/07, the foundation had an income of £45,489 and made grants totalling £45,944. Beneficiaries included: Student grants and electives (£5,000); Sheffield Children's Hospital and St Luke's Hospice (£3,500 each); Jessop Hospital for Women (£3,000); and Crown Hill Workshops and Woodseats Baptist Church (£2,000 each).

John Swire & Sons Ltd

Company registration number 133143

Swire House, 59 Buckingham Gate, London SW1E 6AJ

020 7834 7717; Fax: 020 7630 03

Website: www.swire.com

Correspondent: J R Adams, Secretary

Chairman: J W J Hughes-Hallett

Year end	Turnover	Pre-tax profit
31/12/2007	£2,512,000,000	£829,000,000

Nature of company business
Principal activities: marine including shipowning and operating, aviation (via Cathay Pacific Airways which is 44% owned by Swire Pacific), cold storage and road transport, industrial and trading activities, plantations and property. The company owns a 30% stake in the tea trader, James Finlay.

Subsidiaries include: James Finlay, Cathay Pacific

Main locations: London

Total employees: 61,823

Charitable donations

2007: £635,000
2006: £634,000
2005: £508,000
2004: £1,187,000

Community involvement

In the UK, John Swire & Sons provide support for a variety of charities, particularly those in the medical and educational fields.

Although there are several trusts with connections to the company – John Swire (1989) Charitable Trust (Charity Commission no. 802142), the Swire Educational Trust (Charity Commission no. 328366) and the Swire Charitable Trust (Charity Commission no. 270726) – as the latter receives almost all of its income from the company it is to this that we refer.

Applications

In writing to the correspondent saying how the funds could be used and what would be achieved.

Corporate giving

In 2007, the company made charitable donations in the UK of £635,000 (2006: £634,000) of which £450,000 was paid to the Swire Charitable Trust. We have no details of the organisations which received support directly from the company.

The Swire Charitable Trust

The trust made grants totalling nearly £390,000 in 2007 including those to: Mentor Foundation (£2,500); Dystonia Society (£2,000); Royal Hospital for Neuro-disability (£1,800); Hand in Hand (£1,500); and Paintings in Hospitals and Voices Foundation (£1,000 each),

Tate & Lyle plc

Company registration number 76535

Sugar Quay, Lower Thames Street, London EC3R 6DQ

020 7626 6525; Fax: 020 7623 5213

Website: www.tate-lyle.co.uk

Correspondent: The Corporate Social Responsibility Manager

Chairman: Sir David Lees

Chief Executive: Iain Ferguson

Year end	Turnover	Pre-tax profit
31/03/2008	£3,424,000,000	£173,000,000

Nature of company business
Principal activities are: the processing of carbohydrates to provide a range of sweetener and starch products and animal feed; and bulk storage. The company's UK sugar refinery is in London.

Subsidiaries include: G C Hahn & Co. Ltd, Cesalpinia UK Ltd, Orsan SA Ltd, The Molasses Trading Company Ltd

Main locations: Burton-on-Trent, Hull, Newham, Merseyside, Selby

Total employees: 6,488

Charitable donations

2008: £642,000
2007: £687,000
2006: £386,000
2005: £317,000
2004: £297,000

Membership: BitC

Community involvement

Tate & Lyle's main areas of charitable support are education and causes close to where the company operates or those in which an employee is involved. Main locations are Newham, Merseyside, Avonmouth, Hull, Burton-on-Trent and Selby.

The company aims to contribute to the following sectors:

- education and youth 50%
- civic and environment 25%
- health and welfare 15%
- arts 10%

'Tate & Lyle aims to play a positive role in all the communities in which we operate. Over the years we have developed a Group-wide community involvement policy that forms one of the core components underpinning our ethical behaviour. Our programme involves building long-term relationships with local partners to deliver a shared objective: establishing strong, safe and healthy communities by investing time and resources into projects that directly address local needs.

Overview

'Our community partnerships are well supported by employees, many of whom take part in our programmes. Tate & Lyle's community involvement benefits our employees by enhancing their own local community, offering significant personal development opportunities and making Tate & Lyle a company they are proud to work for.

'Each year we support around 300 organisations, ranging from long-established charities to fledgling community organisations. Community support takes many forms, depending on the needs of the organisation, and includes funding, employee volunteering, consultancy, donation of products and equipment and, for selected partners, free use of the Company's warehousing, office accommodation and meeting room facilities.

'We were delighted to win a silver 'Big Tick' award at the UK's Business in the Community's 2007 Jubilee Awards in recognition of our long-term partnerships with local organisations. These stretch back 30 years in the case of Community Links and are aimed at supporting the regeneration of the local community around Thames Refinery.'

Exclusions

No support is given to circular appeals, advertising in charity brochures, individuals, purely denominational (religious) appeals, local appeals not in areas of company presence, animal welfare, political appeals, sport or large national appeals.

Applications

In writing to the correspondent.

Corporate giving

In 2007/08 worldwide charitable donations totalled £642,000

In the UK organisation to benefit 2007/08 included VerbalEyes, Community Links, Community Food Enterprise, Eastside Young Leaders Academy and Hoops4Health.

In kind support

Education: The company's main education activities are the major literacy programmes, Reading is Fundamental and the Newham Literacy Programme.

Non-cash support has also been given to education business partnerships.

Enterprise: The company supports Business in the Community and the East London Partnership.

Secondments: Applications for secondments to enterprise agencies are considered, and executives throughout the group are encouraged to participate in local educational systems.

Employee-led support

The company operates an employee volunteering scheme.

Education: Links are developed with local schools and colleges offering work experience and work shadowing.

Payroll giving: The company operates the Give As You Earn scheme.

Commercially-led support

Sponsorship: Arts and good cause sponsorship are undertaken.

Taylor Woodrow Construction

Company registration number 296805

4143 Clarendon Road, Watford, Hertfordshire WD17 1TR

01923 478400; Fax: 01923 478401

Website: www.taylorwoodrow.com

Correspondent: Corporate Social Responsibility Manager

Year end	Turnover	Pre-tax profit
31/12/2007	£639,823,000	(£513,000)

Nature of company business
The group is engaged in construction, property, housing and trading activities.

Main locations: Solihull, Manchester, Leighton Buzzard, Livingston, Welwyn Garden City, Newbury, Darlington, Watford

UK employees: 1,431

Total employees: 3,639

Charitable donations

2007: £13,180
2006: £9,281
2005: £96,000
2004: £113,000
2003: £98,000

Community involvement

'**Community support** – in addition to financial support we also sustain communities by sharing expertise or knowledge; bringing benefits to both Taylor Woodrow and the local communities that we engage with.

'On all our projects, we are working hard to be good neighbours not only by being considerate but also by taking part in and supporting local activities.'

Exclusions

No support for appeals from individuals, fundraising events, political or religious appeals.

Applications

In writing to the correspondent.

Corporate giving

During 2007 group companies donated £13,180 (2006: £9,281). This represents a significant drop from the £96,000 given in 2005.

Employee-led support

The company matches employee fundraising activities.

Payroll giving: Employees are encourage to participate in 'give as you earn' programmes.

TDG plc

Company registration number 469605

4–5 Grosvenor Place, London SW1X 7HU

020 838 7775

Website: www.tdg.eu.com

Correspondent: The Group Secretary

Chairman: Charles Mackay

Chief Executive: David Garman

Year end	Turnover	Pre-tax profit
31/12/2007	£669,500,000	£15,800,000

Nature of company business
Road transport, warehousing and logistics.

Subsidiaries include: Scio Solutions Ltd

Main locations: London

Total employees: 7,200

Charitable donations
2007: £33,337
2006: £32,243
2005: £32,856
2003: £36,500

Community involvement

TDG have chosen to partner with charitable organisations that work in the field of road safety and logistics: Brake and Transaid.

In addition, many of its employees give up their own time to support charities and local organisations that mean something to them.

Exclusions

No donations for political, circular or general appeals. No assistance is given to individuals.

Applications

Although not clear from the information available, it would appear that unsolicited applications will not be considered.

Corporate giving

In the 2007, the company made charitable donations totalling £33,337 (2006: £32,243). We presume this was given in support of its chosen charities.

Employee-led support

Employees volunteering in their own time or raising money through donations or sponsorship, have the first £250 of any funds collected matched by the company.

Telefonica O2 Europe plc

Company registration number 5300128

Wellington Street, Slough SL1 1YP

0113 272 2000

Website: www.o2.com

Correspondent: Corporate Responsibility

Email: cr@o2.com

Chairman: Matthew Key

Year end	Turnover	Pre-tax profit
31/03/2007	£5,872,000,000	£827,000,000

Nature of company business
Part of Telefonica, a world leader in the telecommunication sector, O2 is a group of companies providing mobile phones and other mobile communication equipment throughout Europe.

Main locations: Braddan, Bury, Hammersmith, Douglas, Leeds, Runcorn, Slough

UK employees: 11,732

Total employees: 18,240

Charitable donations
2007: £675,000
2006: £264,000
2005: £636,266
2004: £427,000
2003: £444,000

Total community contributions: £1,037,060

Membership: BitC, L B Group

Community involvement

Telefonica O2 launched its new community awards programme – It's Your Community – with the Conservation Foundation in July 2006. The programme gives members of the public access to funding for projects they want to develop that will improve their local communities.

It's Your Community

It's Your Community encourages local initiatives with the tag line 'If you could change one thing about where you live, what would it be?' The application process is straightforward and award decisions are made within 28 days.

'What kind of projects do you support?

'We support projects that bring people together and benefit your community; here are some examples in our four categories that we supported recently. This list is by no means exhaustive – we are always open to new, ground breaking ideas.

- rebuild and restore
- cultural
- active
- green and clean.'

The awards are independently judged and administered by The Conservation Foundation on behalf of O2.

Charity Partnerships

Telefonica O2's charity partnerships focus on local community needs through social, environmental and educational initiatives. Current partners are Childnet International and Prison, Me – No Way!

Employee involvement

Telefonica O2's employee involvement revolves around three programmes:

- volunteering
- charity top-up
- payroll giving.

Exclusions

No support for religious organisations; political organisations; individuals; expeditions; general appeals; and those intending to buy advertising or promotion.

Applications

It's Your Community award

Here's what you need to do:

First, download the application guide which will give you all the information you need to fill in the application form. Also have a read of the criteria to ensure that your project is the kind of thing Telefonica O2 support.

Basically your idea needs to:

- bring together and benefit your community
- have long lasting effects – that will keep going once the money has been spent
- have real, tangible results that you can see
- demonstrate fresh, bold thinking, which is innovative enough to inspire others.

Now you need to create an account and then complete the application form.

Finally, your application will be judged within a month and you can see if you were successful by logging back in to the site (http://www.itsyourcommunity.co.uk/ApplyForAnAward.aspx) after the 10th of the following month.

Corporate giving

Telefonica O2's website states that in 2007, total community contributions were £1,031,494. This was broken down as follows: cash donations (£1,031,494); in kind donations (£4,100); and time in paid hours (£1,466). However, the company's annual report for the year notes that £675,000 of the cash donations was made from UK-based companies, which is the figure we have used.

During 2007 the Its Your Community scheme supported over 500 local initiatives with awards between £100 and £1,000. Projects ranged from helping to create community gardens to repairing old donated bicycles and supporting a youth angling club.

For example, 'in East London a young group undertook one project that defines the fund's scope to involve people in improving their surroundings. Fed up with the graffiti covering their estate, 20 young volunteers set out to clear up some of the worst affected areas. They used an It's Your Community award to buy cleaning materials and a jet powered hose to assist them.'

In kind support

Equipment is available which would be of use to voluntary projects. It has looked at integrating its technology with disability access equipment (with DisabledGo!) and asthma monitors.

Employee-led support

Employee involvement

Volunteering: During the year a total of 547 employees volunteered their time to social causes, equating to £1,466 in paid hours at a rate of £20 an hour.

Charity Top-up: The company encourage employees to give time and imagination to their own fundraising efforts too.

Charity Top-up supports all of the company's fundraising activities, including those personally supported by individuals or teams.

O2 UK matches funds raised by up to a total of £350 for an individual or £1,500 for a team.

The total amount raised through Charity Top-Up during the financial year was £165,313. This includes employee donations and Telefónica O2 UK matched funds.

Payroll Giving: In December 2007 around three per cent of all employees subscribed to this scheme. In total, Telefónica O2 UK employees gave £90,958 (Jan-Dec '07) through the payroll giving scheme. This compares with £85,753 in 2006. Contributions are exempt from tax and include a further 20 per cent donation from Telefónica Europe plc.

In 2006, a new way for employees to give to charity was introduced through the Pennies from Heaven scheme. An individual's monthly salary is rounded down to the nearest pound and the spare pennies donated to Telefonica O2 UK's chosen charity. During the year, £2,302 was raised.

Telegraph Media Group Ltd

Company registration number 451593

111 Buckingham Palace Road, London SW1W 0DT

020 7931 5000

Website: www.telegraph.co.uk

Chairman: A S Barclay

Chief Executive: Murdoch MacLennan

Year end	Turnover	Pre-tax profit
30/12/2007	£354,900,000	£9,900,000

Nature of company business
Publication of national newspapers. Within the UK the company publishes the Daily Telegraph, Sunday Telegraph, Weekly Telegraph, Electronic Telegraph and the Spectator.

Subsidiaries include: The Spectator Ltd

Main locations: London

UK employees: 996

Charitable donations

2007: £116,245
2006: £76,083
2005: £164,375
2004: £162,520

Community involvement

Support is principally given to charities associated with the group's newspapers and employees.

Applications

We were unable to obtain the name of the contact to whom applications for support should be addressed.

Although previously we were advised that an appeal committee usually met quarterly to decide on donations, we do not know if this is still the case. Furthermore, support for organisations unconnected with the newspaper industry appears to be very limited.

Corporate giving

In 2007, charitable donations were made by the group of £116,245, principally to charities associated with the newspapers and their employees.

Employee-led support

Payroll giving: The Give As You Earn scheme is operated by the company.

Tesco plc

Company registration number 445790

Tesco House, Delamare Road, Cheshunt, Hertfordshire EN8 9SL

01992 632222

Website: www.tescoplc.com

Correspondent: Ruth Girardet, CSR Director
Email: ruth.girardet@uk.tesco.com

Chairman: David Reid

Chief Executive: Sir Terry Leahy

Year end	Turnover	Pre-tax profit
23/02/2008	£47,928,000,000	£2,803,000,000

Nature of company business
Tesco is a multiple retailer with superstores and supermarkets in England, Scotland, Wales and Northern Ireland.

Subsidiaries include: Spen Hill Properties Ltd

Main locations: Cheshunt

UK employees: 282,868

Total employees: 444,127

Charitable donations

2008: £22,655,173
2007: £17,698,393
2006: £15,047,768
2005: £4,576,210
2004: £3,953,582

Total community contributions: £77,198,086
Management costs: £360,000

Membership: L B Group

Community involvement

Tesco's community involvement varies from country to country, but typically support is given to environmental action, healthy lifestyles and children and the nominated 'Charity of the Year'. The latter becomes the main focus for staff fundraising and receives a 20% 'top up' from the Tesco Charity Trust.

There is a central committee team in head office who manage national charity and sponsorship activity and set the guidelines for the company's community support. Community Co-ordinators have responsibility for coordinating and managing the community awards and sponsorship funds for the Tesco stores in their region.

The company differentiates between donations and sponsorship (although not between donations and cause-related marketing). The former are made through the Tesco Charity Trust (Charity Commission no. 297126), which supports registered charities only, or organisations recognised by the Inland Revenue as having charitable status.

Charity of the Year: Marie Curie (2008).

Exclusions

No support for circular appeals, advertising in charity brochures, animal welfare, appeals from individuals, the arts, enterprise/training, environment/heritage, fundraising events, medical research, overseas projects (outside of help given through the British Red Cross), political appeals, religious appeals, science/technology, or sport.

The trust will not give grants to other trusts or charities acting as intermediaries.

Applications

In writing to the correspondent.

Other information: The company's Retired Staff Association maintains links with retired employees and through it can offer support and assistance to those in retirement who need it.

Details of the company's community support is given in the text of its annual report and on its website at: www.tesco.com/everylittlehelps

Corporate giving

In 2007/08, the company made total contributions to community projects and to charities worldwide of £77,198,086 (including management costs) of which cash donations to charities amounted to £22,655,173. We do not know how much of this support was given in the UK.

Tesco Charitable Trust

The Tesco Charity Trust was set up on 1 June 1987 to support both national and local community charities, and to add a 20% top up to staff fundraising. It is run by a board of trustees recommended by the main board of Tesco plc.

In the year ended February 2008, the Tesco Charity Trust made cash grants of £1,726,243 to local and national charities in the UK. This figure includes:

- community award donations to local community charities totalling £582,687
- donations to other charities totalling £501,140
- £642,416 in 20% top up on staff fundraising for Tesco Charities of the Year, Cancer Research UK and other charities.

For Community Awards criteria and application form, go to www.tescocharitytrustcommunityawards-applications.co.uk

We recommend you click on 'Questions' before completing the online application. This may help you to prepare any information you need in advance of completing the form online.

Guidelines for the Tesco Charity Trust Community Award Scheme can be downloaded from the company's website, or obtained by writing to Tesco Charity Trust, Tesco Stores Ltd, Delamare Road, Cheshunt EN8 9SL.

Community vouchers

In addition to the above, stores receive an allocation of community vouchers to support requests for raffle prizes and so on. The vouchers may be redeemed at checkouts in the store. A maximum donation of £50 can be made to local organisations through this scheme. Over £600,000 is donated in this way.

In kind support

Education: Local schools are supported through visits and work experience placements for pupils. Training schemes are also set up where new stores are built in regeneration areas.

Facilitated giving: Charity collections at stores are balanced between national charities and local community appeals. One two-day collection is allocated each month.

For further details email:
community.sponsorship@uk.tesco.com

Employee-led support

A considerable amount of staff fundraising is organised in company time, with the Tesco Charity Trust adding 20% to all money raised for charity by Tesco employees.

Through the Tesco Time to Care Appeal, staff, customers and supporters aim to raise £3 million on behalf of the 2004 'Charity of the Year' – Help the Hospices.

Payroll giving: The company operates the Give As You Earn and Sharing the Caring payroll giving schemes. Around 12,250 employees have donated over £1,520,000 in the past two years.

Commercially-led support

Sponsorship: *Sport* – As part of its healthy lifestyles campaign, Tesco launched the FA Tesco Skills programme in 2007. This is a three-year partnership with the National Sports Foundation and the Football Association. The aim is to get a million children active and involved by 2010, providing them with top-quality skills coaching.

Cause-related marketing: – Computers for Schools ran for the 16th year in 2007 – making it the UK's longest running schools' programme. Since 1992, Tescop has donated approximately £118 million worth of computer equipment to over 30,000 schools. In 2007, around 20,000 schools received equipment worth £7.5 million, including more than 1,600 computers.

Thales UK Ltd

Company registration number 868273

2 Dashwood Lang Road, The Bourne Business Park, Addlestone, Surrey KT15 2NX

01932 824800; Fax: 01932 824887

Website: www.thalesgroup.co.uk

Correspondent: Mike Seabrook, Thales Charitable Trust
Email: mike.seabrook@thalesgroup.com

Chairman: The Rt Hon. Lord Freeman

Chief Executive Officer: A Dorrian

Vice Chairman: J Howe

Year end	Turnover	Pre-tax profit
31/12/2007	£326,280,000	£14,756,000

Nature of company business
Principal activities: The design, manufacture and sale of defence electronic products, encompassing electronic warfare, radar, displays, defence radio and command information systems.

Main locations: Belfast, Birmingham, Bury St Edmunds, Glasgow, Doncaster, Stockport, Addlestone

UK employees: 2,019

Charitable donations

2007: £166,000
2006: £167,070
2005: £130,000
2004: £130,000
2003: £131,000

Membership: BitC

Community involvement

The company state on its website that: 'Thales UK conducts its business in a responsible and ethical manner. We are committed to equal opportunities, the conservation of natural resources and the support of selected charities'.

Donations by the company are primarily made through the Thales Charitable Trust (Charity Commission no. 1000162). The trust's policy is to relieve poor, needy, sick and disabled people, and to support those who are engaged in work, including research, to this end. Thus 70% of the budget is spent on health and medical care, 20% on social welfare and 5% on community services.

Exclusions

No support for circulars, individuals, expeditions, advertising in charity brochures, fundraising events or small purely local events in areas of company presence. Unless there are exceptional reasons the trustees prefer to deal directly with a charity rather than with intermediaries.

Applications

All appeals for charitable donations should be sent in writing to the correspondent. Grant decisions are made by a donations committee which meets quarterly. No appeals are considered independently of head office as subsidiaries have no authority to respond.

The company has previously stated that it welcomes appeals from charities, but that the volume of mail is getting too large to handle. Thus, applicants should consider the nature and relevance of their appeal and the following advice from the charitable trust. Applicants are advised to apply at the same time every year. No reply is sent to unsuccessful applicants, and it is seldom worth repeating an appeal regularly if it has been rejected.

Corporate giving

The financial information included here refers to Thales UK Ltd, which in 2007 declared charitable donations of £16,000. However, group funding of the Thales Charitable Trust comes via Thales Corporate Services which in 2006 and 2007 provided around £150,000. According to the Charity Commission's website all of this appears to have been given away in grants, although no details of the beneficiaries are available due to the latest full accounts being for 2005.

In 2005, major beneficiaries included: Childnet International (£40,000); National Deaf Children's Society (£20,000); Armed Forces Memorial Trust and Richard House Trust (£10,000 each); and grants of £5,000 each to 10 organisations including, EDT Headstart and Young Engineers.

Commercially-led support

Sponsorship: *Education* – Thales sponsors the annual Schools Aerospace Challenge.

Thomson Reuters plc

Company registration number 1796065

The Thomson Reuters Building, 30 South Colonnade, Canary Wharf, London E14 5EP

020 7542 8599

Website: www.thomsonreuters.com

Correspondent: Julia Fuller, Corporate Responsibility Manager
Email: foundation@reuters.com

Chairman: David Thomson

Chief Executive: Thomas Glocer

Year end
31/12/2008

Nature of company business
Thomson Reuters principal activity is the provision of intelligent information for businesses and individuals in the financial, legal, tax and accounting, scientific, healthcare and media markets.

Main locations: London, Edinburgh

UK employees: 7,000

Total employees: 50,000

Membership: BitC

Community involvement

As of 17 April 2008, The Thomson Corporation and Reuters Group plc combined to form Thomson Reuters. The following information was provided by the new business as an interim statement on it community support policy:

'Thomson Reuters operates to a policy of corporate responsibility which commits us to underlying responsibilities in the way we deliver our business. Inherent in this policy is a commitment to deliver a robust programme of community and societal support.

'This commitment is delivered through Thomson Reuters Foundation, the company's UK and US registered charity and by line management and staff throughout Thomson Reuters.

'Thomson Reuters addresses societal needs not only by the sharing of core skills through the foundation's programmes but through a programme of philanthropy, supporting the giving of staff time, cash grants and supporting staff cash giving.

'Support is delivered in accordance with the community support policy approved by the Thomson Reuters Executive Committee in November 2008.

'At the international level, Thomson Reuters is primarily concerned with causes that are relevant to Thomson Reuters business as a global information organization. At the national level, Thomson Reuters aims to support the social and business communities in which the company operates.

'As we integrate the Thomson and Reuters businesses we are working on a series of new initiatives for 2009 which will draw on the strengths of both heritages providing a robust programme of support through which we can address specific needs in our communities.'

Applications

Thomson Reuters Foundation does not give cash grants to community-based charities or concerns outside the range of core programmes described herein.

Thomson Reuters Foundation does not consider unsolicited requests for support.

Corporate giving

The following information was provided by the new business in November 2008:

Thomson Reuters Foundation

'Following the merger of Thomson Corporation and Reuters Group plc, The Thomson Reuters Foundation has been created and founded on the legacy of the Reuters Foundation, itself established in 1982 to promote high standards of journalism through training and scholarships. Since Reuters Foundation was established, over 600 journalists each year from around the world have been educated to the highest global standards, and there is now alumni of over 5,000 Reuters Foundation trained journalists located around the world. The foundation has also created global initiatives as the AlertNet forum ("www.alertnet.org") which brings together relief workers around the world and the international media to provide timely and accurate information on humanitarian crisis.

'At the heart of the Thomson Reuters Foundation is a commitment to providing trusted, reliable, powerful, concise information around the world, where it is most needed, to those who most need it – at times of catastrophic disaster and greatest hardship.

'Addition recent initiatives have also included:

- the establishment of Aswat-al-Iraq, in 2004 – an independent news agency set up in Iraq to support the early steps towards democracy
- and in 2006, we created The Reuters Institute for the Study of Journalism – in partnership with Oxford University – to build a successful program for research and leadership in international journalism.'

'The Thomson Reuters Foundation is building on the legacy programmes it inherited – not just to combine them but to develop them, to enhance them and to leverage the expertise and skills they have. The new Foundation will roll out ambitious new projects around the world, whilst continuing to develop and enhance existing programmes.

'The first will be our EMERGENCY NEWS AGENCY, or ENA. When disasters strike, good information can spell the difference between life and death for ordinary people. Timely, accurate, concise, up-to-date information is one of the most powerful forms of aid itself.

'Taking ENA one step further, the second project for the Thomson Reuters Foundation is to expand our existing AIDFUND programme.

'AIDFUND was established in 2001 to provide rapid funding to the AlertNet aid community in the critical immediacy of the first few days of major emergencies. It allows a very quick response to the need for humanitarian aid – one of the big criticism's of many aid programmes is that the funding takes too long to reach those in need.

'AIDFUND has, to date, provided financial assistance to agencies around the globe in response to natural disasters and sudden crises. From the Gujarat earthquake in 2001 and Mozambique floods to the Asian tsunami and Myanmar cyclone, we have so far made 14 significant grants to NGO partners who will help save lives.

'AIDFUND offers members of the global community the opportunity to respond efficiently and effectively with financial aid on the heels of a natural disaster. It allows big business to give responsibly as well getting maximum benefit from their funds for those in need.

'At the heart of the foundation's work is our journalistic heritage and specifically journalism training for those who need it – from countries where there is no history of these values, or from places where there is no strong legacy of professional journalism.

'The Thomson Reuters Foundation will continue to develop and build its journalism training programme around the world.

'There are many places we can look to expand this training and are increasing the variety of courses we offer as well as the number of languages we train in.

'We will also grow the training programmes to expand into areas of excellence brought by the legacy Thomson businesses – for instance, how to better report on science and health issues.'

Daniel Thwaites plc

Company registration number 51702

PO Box 50, Star Brewery, Blackburn, Lancashire BB1 5BU

01254 686868; Fax: 01254 681439

Website: www.thwaites.co.uk

Correspondent: Susan Woodward, Secretary and Trustee
Email: susanwoodward@thwaites.co.uk

Chairman: Mrs Ann Yerburgh

Managing Director: P A Morris and I A H Spencer

Year end	Turnover	Pre-tax profit
31/03/2008	£161,400,000	£9,900,000

Nature of company business
Principal activities are the brewing and canning of beer, the distribution of wines and spirits and the operation of hotels and public houses.

Main locations: Blackburn

UK employees: 1,366

Total employees: 1,366

Charitable donations

2008: £16,600
2006: £27,000
2005: £28,000
2004: £25,893

Community involvement

The company operates The Daniel Thwaites Charitable Trust (Charity Commission no. 1038097). The trust states that 'emphasis is placed on giving tangible, physical help, be that wheelchairs, computers, musical instruments, beds or other specialist equipment for helping improve interaction, or items such as bingo machines and televisions that improve the quality of life for groups of people'. Support is given across the UK, although there is a preference for appeals from within a 50 mile radius of Blackburn.

Applications

In writing to the correspondent.

Corporate giving

In 2007/08, the company made charitable donations of £16,600 (2006/07: £27,000) through its charitable trust. Grants to organisations totalled nearly £26,000. No list of beneficiaries was included.

The Daniel Thwaites Travel Scholarship

The aim of the scholarship is to enable students to experience life in a different culture, not as a tourist, but as part of a local family. The students take part in community work, visit local attractions and interact with their host family.

The scholarship is arranged every year with the help of EIL (Experiment in International Living). EIL provide a list of suggested countries and the choice is made by Thwaites.

The students are not chosen specifically for their academic prowess, but more for their ability to communicate and work as a team with the other students. They are usually aged 17–19.

The trips usually take place in July and the students relate their experiences at a presentation evening held in September

TJX UK (formerly TK Maxx)

Company registration number 3094828

50 Clarendon Road, Watford, Hertfordshire WD17 1TX

01923 473000

Website: www.tkmaxx.com

Correspondent: Marketing Department

Year end	Turnover	Pre-tax profit
28/01/2008	£1,028,247,500	£36,405,300

Nature of company business
A nationwide chain of stores selling clothing, gifts and homeware below recommended retail prices.

Main locations: Watford

UK employees: 13,235

Charitable donations

2007: £897,520
2006: £750,824
2005: £590,161
2003: £350,000

Community involvement

Although a name change took place in 2007, the company still trades under the TK Maxx brand. The company has five nominated charities which receive cash support. These are Cancer Research UK, Comic Relief, The Woodland Trust, Northern Ireland Hospice Care and NCH Action for Children.

Applications

In writing to the correspondent.

Corporate giving

In 2007/08, donations made directly to the nominated charities by the company totalled £897,520 (2006/07: £788,775); this figure includes administration costs.

No further information was available.

T-Mobile (UK) Ltd

Company registration number 2382161

Hatfield Business Park, Hatfield AL10 9BW

01707 315000; Fax: 01707 319001

Website: www.t-mobile.co.uk

Correspondent: Community Affairs Team

Managing Director: J Hyde

Year end	Turnover	Pre-tax profit
31/12/2006	£3,063,069	£165,575,000

Nature of company business
The principal activities of the company are the design, development, construction, installation, ownership, operation, running, maintenance and marketing of a mobile telecommunications network.

UK employees: 5,864

Charitable donations

2006: £30,000

Community involvement

T-Mobile supports the local community through its corporate and social responsibility programme which focuses on encouraging youth volunteering through the Youth Action Network and TimeBank charities.

Exclusions

No support for political appeals.

Applications

In writing to the correspondent.

Corporate giving

In 2006, the company made cash donations in the UK totalling £30,000. Although no specific details of the beneficiaries were provided, we assume the majority was given in support of youth organisations.

Commercially-led support

Sponsorship: T-Mobile's sponsorship programme is in place for 2008 and covers music and football. Unfortunately, they aren't in a position to consider any further requests at the moment.

TNT UK Ltd

Company registration number 1628530

TNT Express House, Holly Lane Industrial Estate, Atherstone CV9 2RY

01827 303030; Fax: 01827 720215

Website: www.tnt.co.uk

Correspondent: Steve Doig, Marketing Director
Email: steve.doig@tnt.co.uk

Managing Director: Tom Bell

Year end	Turnover
31/12/2007	£819,652,000

Nature of company business
Transportation and logistics holding company./p>

Main locations: Atherstone, Bury, Stubbins

Total employees: 11,500

Charitable donations

2007: £529,000
2005: £160,000
2004: £148,000

Total community contributions: £550,000

Membership: BitC

Community involvement

The company's strategy is ' ... to develop mutually beneficial partnerships with charitable organisations that focus on the personal development of young people whose success depends on efficient transport networks'.

It also stated that: 'All TNT Express sites across the UK are actively involved with initiatives in their local communities. TNT has consistently supported a range of projects in the areas of education, health, sport and the environment.'

Exclusions

No support for advertising in charity brochures; animal welfare; appeals from individuals; the arts; elderly people; enterprise/training; heritage; medical research; political appeals; religious appeals; science/technology; sickness/ disability; or, social welfare.

Applications

In writing to the correspondent.

Information available: The company can provide policy guidelines, an application form and such like for potential applicants.

Corporate giving

In 2007, TNT UK Ltd advised that its total community contributions in the UK amounted to £550,000. Of this, cash donations accounted for £529,000.

Although we were not given any specific details as to how this money was distributed, the company's website gave the following examples:

Education

- provided £10,000 worth of equipment and expertise to set up an IT suite at Racemeadow Primary School in Atherstone and supported the Manor Park Community School in Nuneaton via initiatives under Business in the Community
- donated £400 to buy new equipment for the Atherstone Army Cadet Force
- £750 donation to the South Gloucestershire Cycling Proficiency scheme for children.

Health

- sponsorship of a vehicle operated by the George Eliot Hospital in Nuneaton which visits companies and towns to give advice on healthy living
- support for the charity Mencap in Warwickshire.

Environment

- TNT is the main sponsor of the North & South Warwickshire Cycleways which take cyclists on a route through country lanes around Birmingham, Sutton Coldfield, Coventry, Tamworth, Nuneaton, Kenilworth, Warwick, Rugby, Stratford-upon-Avon, Coventry, Kingsbury Water Park, Atherstone, Hinckley, Leamington Spa and Daventry.

Sport

- support of numerous junior and school sports clubs.

In kind support

TNT provides in kind support to Wooden Spoon events across the UK through distribution and transport services and also supports Crucial Crew events, raising road safety awareness. TNT supports Transaid, an organisation which contributes transport and logistics support to help the development of poorer countries.

Employee-led support

TNT fully encourages staff at all levels to become involved in the support of local community and charitable projects. Towards this end, it provides financial support and allows employees company time off in which to volunteer.

Payroll giving: The company operates the Pennies from Heaven scheme.

Tomkins plc

Company registration number 203531

East Putney House, 84 Upper Richmond Road, London SW15 2ST

020 8871 4544; Fax: 020 8877 5055

Website: www.tomkins.co.uk

Correspondent: Charitable Fund Administrator

Chairman: David Newlands

Chief Executive: James Nicol

Year end	Turnover	Pre-tax profit
29/12/2007	£2,941,900,000	£262,600,000

Nature of company business
Tomkins plc is an international engineering business. The company is organised into two business segments – Industrial & Automotive and Building Products, consisting of various business areas which operate in a variety of end markets.

Subsidiaries include: Gates (UK) Ltd, Schrader Electronics Ltd

Main locations: London

Total employees: 35,894

Charitable donations
2007: £97,979
2006: £155,939
2005: £165,483
2004: £68,424
2003: £110,090

Community involvement

Tomkins provided the following statement regarding its community support policy: 'Tomkins has well-established guidelines that determine the nature of organisations to which support is given. The charities given assistance cover a wide range of activities including health and welfare, education, civic and community projects, culture and the arts. Tomkins prefers to spread its charitable giving across many smaller local charities that usually do not have the organisation, structure or resources to compete with the marketing skills of the larger, high-profile charitable bodies. Tomkins makes further donations through advertising, products for prizes and volunteers or other in kind support.

'In the UK, applications are normally made to Tomkins' corporate office in London. Requests for donations are made from a variety of charities and Tomkins tries to respond positively to as many requests as possible, provided they come from smaller local charities and are registered with the Charity Commission.

'Each year, upon the initiative of the board of Tomkins, consideration is given to making a single donation to a registered charity of an amount exceptional to Tomkins' normal level of giving. Normally, such single donation is made in response to an appeal with a special purpose and the board, in its absolute discretion, determines whether or not such appeal is eligible for consideration and the amount of the donation.'

Exclusions

No support for overseas projects.

Applications

Applications should be made in writing to the correspondent.

Corporate giving

In 2007, Tomkins donated £424,904 for community and charitable purposes, of which £97,979 was in the UK. No information regarding the beneficiaries was available.

Employee-led support

'In addition to their charitable giving activities, Tomkins' businesses run a range of initiatives for the benefit of local communities. Many members of our staff and management serve their local community through work on boards, committees and other bodies covering a wide range of activities, giving their time and expertise free to the local community – something Tomkins encourages and supports. These include allowing employees time off to participate in community activities and other charitable support.'

Topps Tiles plc

Company registration number 3213782

Thorpe Way, Grove Park, Enderby, Leicestershire LE19 1SU

0116 282 8000; Fax. 0116 282 8170

Website: www.toppstiles.co.uk

Correspondent: Janet Burgess

Email: jburgess@toppstiles.co.uk

Chairman: B F J Bester

Chief Executive: M Williams

Year end	Turnover	Pre-tax profit
29/09/2007	£207,898,000	£37,833,000

Nature of company business
The principal activity of the company is the retail and wholesale distribution of ceramic tiles, wood flooring and related products.

Main locations: Enderby

UK employees: 1,722

Charitable donations

2007: £10,000
2006: £10,000
2005: £20,000
2003: £32,000

Community involvement

Each year support is given to a particular cause such as asthma charities (to which the company has a long-term commitment), and appeals from areas in which the company has a presence. Only a limited number of appeals can be assisted in any one year.

Charity of the Year: Asthma UK.

Exclusions

The company does not make political contributions.

Applications
In writing to the correspondent.

Corporate giving

In 2006/07 the company made charitable donations of £10,000 to Asthma UK. However, it provides significant in kind support to youth football.

Commercially-led support

Sponsorship: *Sport* – 'Topps is one of the biggest supporters of youth football in the UK, providing new kits and equipment to junior teams local to our stores. Whenever we open a new store we make a point of selecting a local team to support. This is a simple and effective way of reaching out to the local community wherever we decide to trade. This makes us one of the biggest supporters of youth football in the UK and we currently support over 300 teams.'

Toshiba Information Systems (UK) Ltd

Company registration number 918861

Toshiba Court, Weybridge Business Park, Addlestone Road, Weybridge, Surrey KT15 2UL

01932 841600; Fax: 01932 847240

Website: www.toshiba.co.uk

Correspondent: Stephen Beresford, Corporate Sponsorship
Email: communications@toshiba.co.uk

Managing Director: Andy Bass

Year end	Turnover	Pre-tax profit
31/03/2007	£744,550,665	£10,415,693

Nature of company business
The sale, marketing and distribution of computers and telephone systems, consumer products and mobile phones.

Main locations: Weybridge

UK employees: 654

Charitable donations

2007: £40,000
2005: £37,406

CRM figure: £20,000

Community involvement

'Toshiba has been committed to supporting the local community for over 18 years and focuses its attention in the areas of youth, elderly, disabled, and education. In addition to providing significant sums annually for one major charitable partnership (Disability Challengers 2005, Duke of Edinburgh 2006, Sam Beare 2007 and Reed School 2008); they also provide one-off donations or gifts in kind to local schools and colleges. Additionally, they sponsor the Surrey Herald Sports Awards and the Weybridge Male Voice Choir.'

Charity of the Year: Sam Beare Hospice (2007/08).

Exclusions

The company does not support appeals from individuals, medical research, purely denominational appeals, political appeals, local appeals not in areas of company presence, large national appeals, overseas projects, or science/technology.

Applications

In writing to the correspondent. Policy guidelines and an application form are available to those seeking support.

Information available: The company produces a corporate social responsibility report.

Corporate giving

In 2007, Toshiba made total UK community contributions of £40,000 all of which was in cash donations. Organisations benefiting from this included: Weybridge Male Voice Choir;

Surrey Herald Sports Awards; Sam Beare Hospice; and local schools.

In kind support

The main areas of non-cash support are gifts in kind, training schemes, joint promotions and mentoring.

Employee-led support

Depending on the activity, the company may match by up to 50% employees fundraising on behalf of charitable causes. Company time may also be given off for volunteering activities.

Payroll giving: The Give As You Earn scheme is in operation.

Commercially-led support

Sponsorship: *Sport* – Toshiba sponsor the Surrey Herald Sports Award to the sum of £1,500 a year.

Total UK Ltd

Company registration number 553535

33 Cavendish Square, London W1G 0PW

020 7416 4377; Fax: 020 7416 4497

Website: www.total.co.uk

Correspondent: Brian O'Neill, Public Affairs and Corporate Communications Manager 020 7416 4376; Fax: 020 7416 4497

Year end	Turnover	Pre-tax profit
31/12/2007	£6,930,000,000	£264,000,000

Nature of company business

The refining, distribution and sale of petroleum products and lubricants.

Main locations: Milford Haven, London, Watford, Redhill, Immingham, Stalybridge, Aberdeen

UK employees: 4,185

Charitable donations

2007: £540,000
2006: £536,000
2005: £280,000

Membership: A & B, BitC

Community involvement

Formerly having entries under Total Oil Marine plc and Elf Exploration UK plc, the company was formed through the merger of Total, Petrofina and Elf. The company supports national charities (see below), while at a local level, regional offices, refineries and service stations organise 'Fun Days' on behalf of a chosen charity.

We were previously advised that the company had a preference for local charities in areas of company presence (i.e. Aberdeen, Watford, Immingham, Milford Haven, Redhill and Stalybridge), appeals relevant to company business, or those which have a member of company staff involved. Preferred areas of support are: the arts, youth, education, enterprise/training, environment/heritage, medical research and science/technology.

Charity of the Year: CLIC Sargent (2008).

Exclusions

No support for circular appeals, advertising in charity brochures, animal welfare, appeals from individuals, elderly people, fundraising events, overseas projects, political appeals, religious appeals, sickness/disability, social welfare or sport.

Applications

In writing only to the correspondent for those organisations located near to Total refining and marketing facilities (please refer to the list of 'preferred locations'). For organisations based near to Total's exploration and production facilities in Aberdeen, please contact: Sandra McIntosh, Public Affairs & Communications Department, Total E&P plc, Crawpeel Road, Altens, Aberdeen AB12 3FG.

Information available: The company produce a Corporate Social Responsibility Report.

Corporate giving

Charitable donations in 2007 amounted to £540,000 (2006: £536,000). Past beneficiaries have included: Royal Scottish National Orchestra; National Galleries of Scotland; Young People's Trust for the Environment; and Disaster Emergency Committee. The national charity CLIC Sargent appears to receive yearly support from the company.

Education: Through the Total Bursary Awards Scheme awards of £1,000 each are available to up to six local students who will be taking up a university course immediately after their A-levels. Some bursaries are reserved for students with disabilities, for those who have suffered illness or experienced a family bereavement, or for whom English is not their first language. Gap year students are not eligible to apply. Application forms are available from the schools in the scheme (we do not have a list) or from: Eleanor Brooks, TOTAL UK, 40 Clarendon Road, Watford WD17 1TQ (email: eleanor.brooks@total.co.uk). Applications must be submitted before the end of January in the year in which the student will be commencing university.

In kind support

The company provides the use of facilities such as postage/photocopying.

Employee-led support

Payroll giving: The company operates the Give As You Earn Scheme.

Commercially-led support

Sponsorship: *The arts* – sponsorship is undertaken.

Toyota Motor Manufacturing (UK) Ltd

Company registration number 2352348

Burnaston, Derbyshire DE1 9TA

01332 282121

Website: www.toyotauk.com

Correspondent: Susan Wilkinson, External Affairs Department

Chairman: T Agata

Year end	Turnover	Pre-tax profit
31/03/2008	£2,773,783,000	£9,254,000

Nature of company business
Car and engine manufacture.

Main locations: Burnaston, Deeside

UK employees: 3,933

Charitable donations

2008: £349,330
2007: £256,541

Membership: BitC

Community involvement

Since the start of production in 1992 Toyota has contributed to a variety of local and national community causes. The focus of support is based around four main areas – environment, children, education, and health. In addition, employee involvement in the community is encouraged and, where suitable, we will financial support is given to employee fundraising activities or to local community organisations in which employees play an active role. Local charitable events are regularly supported through the donation of raffle prizes and vehicles.

Exclusions

No support for advertising in charity brochures, animal welfare, appeals from individuals, the arts, enterprise/training, fundraising events, overseas projects, political or religious appeals, science/technology, social welfare, sport, or local appeals not in areas of company presence. No response to circular appeals.

Applications

A self-screening eligibility form and an application form are posted on the company's website. If your organisation meets the eligibility criteria, please forward your completed application form to the correspondent.

All applications submitted are fully assessed on a monthly basis and a reply is forwarded to the applicant.

Corporate giving

In 2007/08, the company made charitable donations of £349,330 (2006/07: £256,541). These donations comprised:

- £40,102 to charities involved in conserving the environment and promoting environmental preservation and awareness
- £17,733 to charities involved in medical research
- £291,495 was donated to local charities involved in a range of activities in the communities surrounding Burnaston and Deeeside.

Toyota Manufacturing UK provides grants of up to £1,000 for successful projects in the fields of the environment, children, education and health within its local communities.

These grants are intended for the purchase of long-term tangible equipment and resources up to the value of £1,000.

In kind support

Toyota engineers visit four secondary schools in Derbyshire, Staffordshire and Flintshire each week to work alongside pupils on a variety of real-life engineering challenges. Toyota has supported the national Young Engineers programme since 2000. The programme runs clubs in schools and colleges across the UK and aims to inspire young people to recognise the importance and excitement of a future career in engineering.

Employee-led support

Employee involvement in the community is encouraged and, where suitable, financial support given.

Employee fundraising efforts are matched by the company up to a maximum of £250 per activity.

Payroll giving: A payroll giving scheme is in operation.

Travelex Holdings Ltd

Company registration number 5356574

65 Kingsway, London WC2B 6TD

020 7400 4000; Fax: 020 7400 4001

Website: www.travelex.co.uk

Correspondent: PA to the Chairman 020 7400 4000

Chairman: Lloyd Dorfman

Chief Executive: Ian Meakins

Year end	Turnover	Pre-tax profit
31/12/2007	£536,200,000	£14,400,000

Nature of company business
The group's principal activities are the provision of travel money services, funds transfer services, issuance of travellers' cheques, dealing in foreign bank notes and the provision of other travel and financial related services. The Group operates through its subsidiaries in the United Kingdom, North America, Asia Pacific, Continental Europe and Africa.

UK employees: 5,700

Charitable donations

2007: £17,000
2006: £85,000
2004: £103,000
2003: £105,000

Community involvement

The group currently supports young people, medical research and the arts. No further information was available.

Exclusions

No support for advertising in charity brochures, local appeals not in areas of company presence.

Applications

In writing to the correspondent.

Corporate giving

In 2007, the group made donations in the UK for charitable purposes amounting to £17,000 (2006: £85,000) in support of cancer research, the development of young people, and the arts.

Employee-led support

The group encourages its employees worldwide to become involved with local initiatives in the wider community in which it operates.

Commercially-led support

Sponsorship: *The arts* – Travelex have sponsored the 'Travelex £10 Season' at the National Theatre and following its success have launched 'Travelex £10 Mondays' at London's Royal Opera House.

Travis Perkins plc

Company registration number 824821

Lodge Way House, Harlestone Road, Northampton NN5 7UG

01604 752424; Fax: 01604 758718

Website: www.travisperkins.co.uk

Correspondent: Linda Doughty, Marketing Director
Email: linda-doughty@travisperkins.co.uk

Chairman: Tim E P Stevenson

Chief Executive: Geoff Cooper

Year end	Turnover	Pre-tax profit
31/12/2007	£3,186,700,000	£261,400,000

Nature of company business
The marketing and distribution of timber, building and plumbing materials and the hiring of tools to the building trade and industry generally.

Subsidiaries include: Keyline Builders Merchants Ltd, D W Archer Ltd

Main locations: Northampton

UK employees: 14,725

> ### Charitable donations
> 2007: £153,656
> 2006: £203,996
> 2005: £281,000
> 2004: £312,000
> 2003: £105,310

Community involvement

With 1,000 branches throughout the UK, the group encourages each branch to support their local community through involvement in local affairs such as by sponsoring organisations or donating materials to projects. Local appeals should be made to the appropriate regional office.

Charity of the Year: Action for Children, Enable (Scotland), Leukaemia Research and Mencap.

Exclusions

No support for advertising in charity brochures, animal welfare, appeals from individuals, the arts, children/youth, education, elderly people, enterprise/training, environment, heritage, medical research, overseas projects, political appeals, religious appeals science/technology, sickness/disability, social welfare, sport, local appeals not in areas of company presence or large national appeals.

Applications

In writing to the correspondent.

Corporate giving

In 2007, the company made charitable donations of £153,656 (2006: £203,996).

'Four main charities benefited from the company's donations and fundraising activities – NCH The Children's Charity, Mencap, ENABLE Scotland and Leukaemia Research. A charity committee helps to steer a variety of fundraising activities at branches and stores nationwide throughout the year. Past events have included family fun days, carnival floats, dress up/dress down days, '3 Peaks' and '4 Peaks' Challenges, Dragon Boat racing, Car Washes and much more.'

In kind support

The company may occasionally donate materials.

Employee-led support

Payroll giving: In 2007, staff raised £40,254 (2006: £33,585) on behalf of charity through a payroll-giving scheme.

Trinity Mirror plc

Company registration number 82548

One Canada Square, Canary Wharf, London E14 5AP

020 7293 3000; Fax: 020 7510 3405

Website: www.trinitymirror.com

Correspondent: Paul Vickers, Secretary & Group Legal Director

Chairman: Sir Ian Gibson

Chief Executive: Sly Bailey

Year end	Turnover	Pre-tax profit
30/12/2007	£1,009,000,000	£203,000,000

Nature of company business
The main activity of the group is the publication and printing of newspapers both in the UK and overseas.

Subsidiaries include: Century Press and Publishing Ltd, Midland Newspapers Ltd, Inside Communications Ltd, Examiner News & Information Ltd, The Derry Journal Ltd, Southnews plc, Western Mail & Echo Ltd, The Chester Chronicle and Associated Newpapers Ltd, Ethnic Media Group Ltd, Gazette Media Co. Ltd, Scottish Daily Record and Sunday Mail Ltd, Yellow Advertiser Newspaper Group Ltd, Newcastle Chronicle and Journal Ltd, Middlesex County Press Ltd, Raceform Ltd, Midland Independent Newspapers Ltd, The Liverpool Daily Post and Echo Ltd, Mediaserve Ltd, Scottish and Universal Newspapers Ltd, MGN Ltd

Main locations: Chester, Liverpool

Total employees: 800

> ### Charitable donations
> 2007: £80,000
> 2005: £60,000
> 2004: £287,000
> 2003: £181,000
>
> Membership: BitC

Community involvement

The company's policy with regard to charitable donations is as follows:

'Trinity Mirror believes that it can best support charities through the pages of its newspapers. This support will either be through appeals to readers for donations or through editorial content, describing the aims and activities of various charities. In every case the decision as to whether or not to support a charity appeal, or whether to run an editorial comment, will be one for the editor of each newspaper.

'Trinity Mirror plc will make direct cash donations to charities in certain limited circumstances. The company will, at a group level, support various charities connected or associated with the newspaper, printing or advertising industries.

'A second category of direct cash support will be to charities operating in the communities immediately surrounding Trinity Mirror's offices and print sites. The charities that are likely to receive support are smaller community-based charities where a modest donation will make a big impact. It is unlikely that a major national charity that just happens to be based very close to one of our offices will receive a donation.

'There will be a further limited general pool of funds out of which donations will be made to legitimate and supportable causes that fall outside the above two criteria. There will, however, need in each case to be a demonstrable business/commercial reason why such support should be given.

'Each of our regional newspaper companies will have a small budget out of which they will make direct cash donations to charities working in the community in which the newspaper is based. Scottish Daily Record and Sunday Mail Ltd will similarly make a number of donations to appropriate charities based in Scotland.

'The national titles of The Mirror, Sunday Mirror and Sunday People are most unlikely to make direct cash donations. They will do so only where they are asked to make a payment to a charity in lieu of a fee for an interview or some form of support. Any "corporate donations requested from the national titles are likely to be redirected to the group, as the company's headquarters share the same location as that of the national titles.'

Exclusions

No support for local appeals not in areas of company presence.

Applications

Applications at group level should be made in writing to the correspondent, but only where one of the following applies:
- charities connected with or associated with the newspaper, printing or advertising industries
- charities operating in the communities immediately surrounding Trinity Mirror's offices and print sites
- legitimate and supportable causes falling outside the above two criteria, but with a demonstrable business/commercial reason why such support should be given.

Applications at regional level should be addressed to the editor or manager of the newspaper/print site based in your community. Prior agreement of the relevant managing director will be required before a donation can be made.

Corporate giving

In 20007, cash donations to charities totalled £80,000. The following examples of beneficiaries were given on the company's website:

In July 2007 the Newcastle Evening Chronicle launched the Give Tilly A Hand Appeal to raise the money to help the youngster live as normal a life as possible after the 21-month-old lost both her hands and toes to meningitis. The appeal was started with £5,000 from the newspaper's own Sunshine Fund.

On the 17 August 2007 the Daily Mirror, donated 2p for every copy sold to the children's charity ChildLine. The paper also included a four-page editorial feature on ChildLine. This was part of wider support where all the group's national titles as well as a number of websites and regional newspapers, including The Birmingham Mail, Liverpool Echo, Newcastle Chronicle and the South Wales Echo, also promoted the campaign.

In kind support

In addition to cash donations, the company is active in making donations in kind, in the form of used computer equipment, furniture, books and so on. Through its community involvement programmes the company makes available members of its staff for volunteering and mentoring programmes.

Employee-led support

The company has an established employee volunteering policy which enables all of its employees to volunteer to work for a day to support a good cause in their area. This is backed up with unspecified financial support.

Payroll giving: 'The company is actively investigating the introduction of a payroll giving programme.'

TT Electronics plc

Company registration number 87249

Clive House, 12–18 Queens Road, Weybridge, Surrey KT13 9XB

01932 841310; Fax: 01932 836450

Website: www.ttelectronicsplc.com

Correspondent: John Newman, Chairman

Chairman: John W Newman

Chief Executive: Geraint Anderson

Year end	Turnover	Pre-tax profit
31/12/2007	£544,900,000	£33,300,000

Nature of company business
The main activities of the company are in two business divisions: electronic components and industrial engineering.

Subsidiaries include: AEI Compounds Ltd, Welwyn Components limited, AB Connectors Ltd, Prestwick Circuits Ltd, Erskine Systems Ltd, MMG Neosid Ltd, BAS Components Ltd, Welwyn Systems Ltd, Linton and Hirst Ltd, BI Technologies, AB Automotive Electronics Ltd, W T Henley Ltd, Genergy plc, Houchin Aerospace Ltd, AEI Cables Ltd, AB Electronic Assemblies Ltd

Main locations: Havant, Edenbridge, Gravesend, Filey, Letchworth, Hinckley, Haverhill, Lancing, Cardiff, Cowes,

Colnbrook, Coalville, Cleckheaton, Chester-le-Street, Tipton, Swindon, Wolverhampton, Mountain Ash, Newport, Manchester, Skelmersdale, Sevenoaks, Scarborough, Rotherham, Romford, Ramsbottom, Bedlington, Ashford, Blyth, Bootle

Total employees: 8,430

Charitable donations

2007: £50,000
2006: £50,000
2005: £50,000
2004: £50,000
2003: £50,000

Community involvement

We currently have no information on the charitable donations policy of the company.

Exclusions

The company does not make political contributions.

Applications

In writing to the correspondent.

Corporate giving

In 2007, the company made cash donations to charity of £50,000. No breakdown of this amount was available.

TUI UK Ltd

Company registration number 2830117

TUI Travel House, Crawley Business Quarter, Fleming Way, Crawley, West Sussex RH10 9QL

Website: www.tui-group.com

Year end	Turnover	Pre-tax profit
30/09/2007	£1,718,912,000	(£86,953,000)

Nature of company business
The principal activities of the company comprise the provision of inclusive holidays and the sale of other related travel services, including the sale of foreign currencies.

Subsidiaries include: Simply Travel Ltd, Crystal International Travel Group Ltd, TTG Independent Holidays Group Ltd, Manchester Flights Ltd, Port Philip Group Ltd, Robert Sibbald Travel Agents Ltd, Britannia Airways Ltd, The Original Travel House Ltd, Digital Travel Group Ltd, Team Lincoln Ltd, Magic Travel Group Ltd, Lunn Poly Ltd

Main locations: London

UK employees: 7,584

Charitable donations

2005: £87,499
2004: £65,245

Total community contributions: £87,499

Community involvement

In March 2007, TUI UK Ltd (along with the majority of TUI AG's other tourism businesses) were combined with that of First Choice Holidays plc to form TUI Travel plc. The company was admitted to the London Stock Exchange listings in September 2007, but has not yet issued its first report and accounts.

As a result, the accounts for TUI UK Ltd are for a nine-month period only and declare no charitable donations for the period. However, reference to its parent company's website (www.tui-group.com) and to that for Thomson in the UK (www.thomson.co.uk) provide a number of examples of the group's charitable support. We assume that this support will continue under the new company and hope that fuller details of its policy will be made available once the new plc's first annual report is available.

Currently support is direccted towards health/ill health, medical research and projects in developing countries.

Applications

Previously, we had been given the contact name of Phil White – Operations Manager based at Columbus House, Westwood Way, Westwood Business Park, Coventry CV4 8TT (Tel: 024 7628 2828). However, given the changes the company has undergone, we have not been able to confirm whether this remains the case.

Corporate giving

In 2005 the company made cash donations of £87,499 to charities (2004: £65,245). Although we have been unable to obtain current figures, organisations listed as having received support from the company are: Born Free; McMillan Cancer Care and the Travel Foundation.

Thomson und Thomsonfly have supported Help a Hallam Child initiative which helps underprivileged children in the Yorkshire/North Midlands region. Whilst Thomson has been cooperating for over three years with the Great Ormond Street Hospital Children's Charity.

Employee-led support

Staff fundraising efforts are acknowledged by the company through matched funding, on which there is a relatively low cap.

Tullis Russell Group Ltd

Company registration number SC150075

Rothersfield, Markinch Glenrothes, Fife KY7 6PB

01592 753311; Fax: 01592 755872

Website: www.trg.co.uk

Correspondent: Mandy Cooper, Secretary, Charities Committee

Year end	Turnover	Pre-tax profit
31/03/2008	£144,364,000	£7,188,000

Nature of company business
Tullis Russell Group Ltd is an employee-owned industrial holding company, providing management services. The principal subsidiary companies are involved in the manufacture of papers and boards for clients world-wide.

Main locations: Bollington, Hanley, Glenrothes

UK employees: 751

Charitable donations

2008: £17,000
2007: £18,000
2006: £29,000
2005: £37,000

Community involvement

Past information suggested that the company decides how to distribute funds via a charity/donations committee and that support is only given to local appeals in areas of company presence, covering a wide range of causes.

Exclusions

No grants for local appeals not in areas of company presence, large national appeals, enterprise/training, medical research, overseas projects, political appeals, science/technology or sport.

Applications

In writing to the correspondent.

Corporate giving

In 2007/08, the company made cash donations to 'charitable and public organisations' of £17,000 (2006/07: £18,000). We have no information regarding specific recipient public organisations/charities.

In kind support

The main area of non-cash support is gifts in kind such as donations of paper to schools and local organisations. Larger amounts have also been supplied for the production of posters, guides and catalogues for arts events.

Employee-led support

Group companies are involved in local schools, colleges and universities through individual employees and the Confederation of Paper Industries schools resources programme.

UBS

Company registration number 2035362

100 Liverpool Street, London EC2M 2RH

020 7568 2365; Fax: 020 7567 3364

Website: www.ubs.com

Correspondent: Nick Wright, Managing Director, Community Affairs

Year end
31/12/2007

Nature of company business
International banking.

Main locations: Taunton, Brighton, Edinburgh, Manchester, London, Newcastle, Edinburgh, Birmingham

Charitable donations

2005: £2,000,000

Membership: A & B, BitC, L B Group

Community involvement

UBS is a leading international bank, and states: 'Successful companies need successful communities. A truly successful company is sensitive to the concerns of all those on whom it depends and that's why UBS Warburg is committed to being a good corporate citizen.'

UBS also enables its clients the opportunity of engaging in charitable causes. The UBS Optimus Foundation invests donations from clients into a number of programmes and organisations that focus particularly on children.

Applications

In writing to the correspondent.

Corporate giving

Although we were unable to obtain a figure for the company's community support, the breadth of its work in the community suggests substantial investment in terms of time and money.

UBS was the first financial firm to sponsor a new secondary school under the UK government's 'Academy' programme, making a financial contribution of £2 million to the project.

One of the key charity partnerships is with Brokerage, a small, proactive charity working in the City of London to promote local recruitment. It was established to widen access to quality, sustainable job opportunities in the City for people living in impoverished inner-city areas. Whilst another is with Circus Space, one of Europe's top three training facilities for aspiring and professional performers, providing participatory programmes for local residents and degree-level education.

In addition, since 1999 UBS has supported Community Links, an innovative inner-city charity that runs community-based projects in East London.

In kind support

Support is given in kind, especially through the recycling of unwanted goods. This is a useful way of helping organisations with little money to spare. Items such as mobile phones, business clothes, foreign coins, spectacles, office equipment and toys are all collected to aid those in need.

Employee-led support

Employees of UBS are active fundraisers and, in many cases, volunteer their own time and efforts to these and other organisations. Staff are strongly encouraged to participate in volunteering projects and are given two days a year to do so. Current initiatives, in which employees are currently participating, include business mentoring, student mentoring, community challenges, and work experience projects.

By way of further encouragement the bank has put in place a number of schemes to facilitate employees' community and charitable involvement. These include matched giving with the firm matching donations up to $2,500 around £1,500) a year for most registered charities.

Payroll giving The Give As You Earn scheme is in operation, which in most instances is matched by the company £ for £.

Commercially-led support

Sponsorship: *The arts* – UBS has recently established a three-year partnership with Tate Modern and supports the London Symphony Orchestra through its Soundscapes collaboration.

UIA (Insurance) Ltd

Company registration number AC000532

Kings Court, London Road, Stevenage, Hertfordshire SG1 2TP

01438 761761; Fax: 01438 761762

Website: www.uia.co.uk

Correspondent: Andrew Gay, Charity Administrator, UIA Charitable Foundation
Email: info@uia.co.uk

Chairman: Malcolm Cantello

Managing Director: Ian Templeton

Year end	Pre-tax profit
31/12/2007	(£3,150,000)

Nature of company business
Insurance company.

Main locations: Stevenage

Charitable donations

2007: £23,000
2006: £30,000
2005: £28,000
2004: £28,000
2003: £74,000

Community involvement

UIA is a mutual insurance company that provides services to UNISON, other trade unions and similar organisations. Its community support programme is directed through a charitable foundation, details of which are given below.

UIA Charitable Foundation

Set up in 1999, the UIA Charitable Foundation (Charity Commission no. 1079982) funds registered charities working to help 'the disadvantaged in society'. Funded entirely by donations from UIA (Insurance) Ltd, UNISON's insurance company, the foundation focuses its support on lesser known groups that take positive action on important social issues that might not otherwise be addressed.

Support is given to small organisations or groups where a modest grant will make a real difference and which deal with:

- victims of domestic abuse
- victims of drug and alcohol addiction
- rehabilitation of offenders
- Third World poverty
- Third World human rights.

Exclusions

The foundation does not make grants for the following:

- organisations that are not registered charities or formally constituted voluntary organisations
- organisations that are not based in the UK
- charities whose combined grant-related support costs and governance costs are greater than 10% of their turnover
- work that we believe should be, or is, publicly funded
- national charities that have an established constituency of supporters
- funding for information/advice-giving or newsletters
- conferences or training courses

- personal support of individuals
- the arts
- work in mainstream education, including schools, nurseries, playschools, 'out of hours' clubs and academic research
- environment, conservation, animal welfare, heritage or sporting projects
- work with a bias towards a particular religion.

This list may be amended at any time.

Applications

Committee meetings are usually held twice a year, in March and September. The trustees will only consider applications submitted on the foundation's application form and operate on a first come first served basis. In order to keep costs down and avoid postage, we ask applicants to download the form from this website and post eight copies and their annual accounts to the named correspondent.

Applications should reach the company no later than the beginning of February or August, but please note that receipt of an application does not guarantee that it will be considered at the next meeting. The committee may ask for more information and may take up references. This helps the committee to learn more about your work, but such a request does not guarantee that a grant will be made. It is unlikely that the committee will want to meet with you directly.

Corporate giving

In 2007, the company donated £23,000 (2006: £30,000) to the UIA Charitable Foundation.

In 2006 (the latest year for which accounts are available), the foundation made 41 grants totalling £24,971. These were broken down as follows:

- children and families (two grants totalling £1,350)
- disability (13 grants totalling £6,657)
- drug and alcohol addiction (two grants totalling £1,000)
- elderly (two grants totalling £1,250)
- humanitarian aid (one grant of £3,000)
- overseas development (four grants totalling £2,540)
- poverty (eight grants totalling £4,788).

UK Coal plc

Company registration number 2649340

Harworth Park, Blyth Road, Harworth, Doncaster, South Yorkshire DN11 8DB

01302 751751; Fax: 01302 752420

Website: www.ukcoal.com

Correspondent: Laura Heath, PA to the Chief Executive

Chairman: David Jones

Chief Executive: Jon LLoyd

Year end	Turnover	Pre-tax profit
31/12/2007	£328,485,000	£69,023,000

Nature of company business
The principal activities of the group are coal mining, opencast and underground, and associated activities.

Subsidiaries include: CIM Resources Ltd, Harworth Insurance Co. Ltd, Harworth Power Ltd, The Monckton Coke & Chemical Co. Ltd, Coal Supplies (UK) Ltd

Main locations: Doncaster

UK employees: 3,285

Charitable donations

2007: £24,200
2006: £5,300
2005: £30,000
2004: £39,000
2003: £27,000

Membership: BitC

Community involvement

The company has a preference for supporting charities and associations involved with the coal industry and local communities.

Exclusions

No support for local appeals outside areas of company presence.

Applications

In writing to the correspondent.

Corporate giving

Although the company's declared charitable donations have dropped quite dramatically in recent years (down to £4,200 in 2007), its in kind support, as evidenced below, is appears substantial. Furthermore, for some reason it has not included its pound-for-pound matching of awards made by the Miners Welfare National Educational Fund (see below). Our figures do include this, however.

The following examples of UK Coal's community support are taken from its website:

'We have maintained our philosophy of supporting suitable community projects focused on the surface and deep mines and also on major property developments operating at the heart of the communities in which they are based.

'In Derbyshire, as a community project, we are now completing the stabilisation of a medieval stronghold, the Codnor Castle and Monument which dates back to shortly after the Norman Conquest. By the time the work is completed this summer, around £1.5 million will have been spent on stabilising the castle and the nearby Jessop Monument Tower and Hall.

'In 2007 we agreed to match awards made by the Miners Welfare National Educational Fund pound-for-pound to the family members of former and current employees studying full-time at a university or college or on a designated course of higher education. Each year, the fund provides grants of around £50,000 in total. UK COAL's financial commitment to these schemes cannot be fully quantified at this time as the scheme for the current educational year is open to applicants until 31 March 2008. We, however, estimate approximately £20,000 per annum will be distributed to qualifying applicants. This initiative has been warmly welcomed by the communities in which we work and by the individuals who have received the support.'

In kind support

Environment: 'We typically plant up to 500,000 young trees a year on our restored surface mine sites and other land. In the last decade, we planted around 4 million trees 1 million in the North East, 1 million in Yorkshire, 1.6 million in the Midlands and around 0.4 million in Scotland and the North West.'

Unilever UK

Company registration number 41424

Unilever House, Springfield Drive, Leatherhead KT22 7GR

01372 945000

Website: www.unilever.co.uk

Correspondent: Community Affairs Team

Chairman: Michael Treschow

Chief Executive: Patrick Cescau

Year end	Turnover	Pre-tax profit
31/12/2007	£32,149,600,000	£4,147,200,000

Nature of company business
Unilever is one of the world's leading suppliers of fast moving consumer goods in foods, household and personal care products. Its brands include Knorr, Hellmans, PG Tips, Birds Eye, Wall's Ice Cream, Sure, Persil, Comfort, Cif, Dove, Lynx and Colman's.

Unilever UK is based in a number of sites around the UK. The head office is in Walton on Thames, and it is from here that UK Community Involvement is managed.

Subsidiaries include: Diversey Lever, Ben & Jerry's Ice Cream, Birds Eye Wall's, Lever Fabergé, Slimfast, Unipath

Main locations: Bedford, Walton on Thames, Lowestoft, Purfleet, London, Manchester, Port Sunlight, Windsor, Kingston on Thames, Burton on Trent, Crumlin, Bebington, Warrington, Crawley, Leeds, Hull, Ipswich, Gloucester

UK employees: 11,000

Total employees: 212,000

Charitable donations

2007: £1,000,000
2005: £2,800,000
2003: £7,600,000

Total community contributions: £6,340,000
Management costs: £250,000

Membership: A & B, BitC, L B Group

Community involvement

Community involvement takes place in many forms, from direct funding for national projects to employee volunteering support for local community initiatives.

Unilever is increasingly focusing on longer term partnerships, in some cases lasting up to 25 years. This means that while Unilever invests a great deal in community involvement, budgets are often fully committed years in advance, with funding for major projects only becoming available when an existing project comes to an end.

In order to maximise the impact of Unilever UK's community investment programme its efforts are focused on the following key areas:

- education – in the form of school governance and leadership
- sustainable development – in the areas of water, agriculture and fisheries
- the arts – focused on visual arts
- health – focused on nutrition and healthy lifestyles.

Note: Most of the projects in the Unilever Community Investment Programme are researched and identified by its in-house community investment team. Unsolicited funding applications are not, therefore, normally encouraged.

Exclusions

Under no circumstances is support given to political parties or to organisations with primarily political aims. Unilever makes a declaration to this effect in the Annual Report and Accounts that binds Unilever and all its operating units. Support is not given to churches or denominational charities. This does not exclude support for charities with a religious connection whose work is ecumenical. Support is not given to individuals to undertake studies, gap year trips, social work or for any other purposes.

Applications

Projects supported by Unilever's community investment programme are mostly researched and identified by its in-house community investment team.

Unsolicited applications are not therefore encouraged as less than 1% of unsolicited applications sent to the UK head office generally receive support.

Unilever asks that you use the 'Contact Us' section of the Unilever UK website to ensure that your request is directed to the correct person.

Information Available: Unilever UK has an internet site www.unilever.co.uk which contains information about its community involvement activities as well as more general information on its approach to managing corporate responsibility issues.

Corporate giving

Unilever UK measures the cost of its community involvement using the London Benchmarking Group (LBG) model. Unilever helped to develop this model and are represented on the LBG's steering group.

In 2007, Unilever made total community contributions in the UK of £6.6 million. Usefully, and in line with the LBG recommendations, this was broken down as follows:

- charitable donations: £1.0 million
- community investment: £1.24 million
- commercial initiatives in the community: £4.1 million
- management costs: £0.25 million.

The projects and organisations Unilever support include the following:

- British Nutrition Foundation
- British Skin Foundation
- Forum for the Future
- Business in the Community
- Re-Solv (solvent abuse prevention)
- East Leeds Family Learning Centre
- Mersey Basin Campaign.

In kind support

The main areas of non-cash support are secondments, employee time and occasional donations of stock (although these are normally made to In-Kind Direct, please see the 'Sponsorship' section, below).

Education: Education is a key area of support, particularly for employee volunteering, and a number of sites participate in reading and number partner schemes. Unilever has moved away from the funding and provision of curriculum based educational resources, although selected resources such as From Field to Fork (a KS 3&4 resource focused on plant science, nutrition and sustainability) continue to be funded on an ongoing basis. Unilever also invests heavily in supporting current and retired staff who volunteer as school governors, with a monthly email briefing, regional seminars and a high profile annual conference which attracts leading figures from the world of education.

Sustainable development: Unilever is committed to sustainable development and this is reflected in the UK by the significant support provided to a number of key organisations and campaigns. Unilever has a 25 year commitment to providing support to the Mersey Basin Campaign and is a Foundation Corporate Partner of the Forum for the Future, the UK's leading sustainable development charity.

Health & nutrition: Unilever provides significant funding to both the British Nutrition Foundation and the British Skin Foundation. It has also worked with the Anaphylaxis Campaign to raise the awareness of food allergy issues.

Employee-led support

Numerous Unilever employees give time in assisting local schoolchildren with their reading and writing skills. Whilst since 1990, through the Unilever Governors' network, support has been given to employees who volunteer to be school governors.

Payroll giving: The company operates the Give As You Earn scheme.

Commercially-led support

Sponsorship: *The arts* – The company sponsors 'The Unilever Series at Tate Modern'. Unilever began this sponsorship in 2000 and has extended its support to 2012.

Locally, Unilever has a number of local sites around the UK. Each of these sites are encouraged to develop partnerships with key local organisations to address local issues. Again, many of these partnerships are with long term established community partners. Decisions about local programmes are made locally at the relevant site.

Requests for product donations, advertising or brand sponsorship (e.g. Flora London Marathon) should be addressed directly to the brand concerned at the following address: Freepost RRHS-XXKK-LKAE, Consumerlink Unilever, London W4 5QB.

Alternatively, email: sponsorshipenquiries@unileverconsumerlink.co.uk

Unipart Group of Companies Ltd

Company registration number 1994997

Unipart House, Garsington Road, Cowley, Oxford OX4 2PG

01865 778966

Correspondent: Communications Department

Chairman: Lord Shepherd

Chief Executive: J M Neill

Year end	Turnover	Pre-tax profit
31/12/2007	£1,143,000,000	£19,200,000

Nature of company business
Unipart develops, implements and operates supply chain solutions in the logistics market in partnership with its customers in a wide range of automotive technology, rail retail and consumer industries.

Subsidiaries include: Surestock Health Services Ltd, Advanced Engineering Systems Ltd, H Burden Ltd, Partco International Ltd, Partco Group Ltd, Surepart Ltd, Railpart (UK) Ltd, EW (Holdings) Ltd, Serck Ltd, Partco Ltd, SVG Ltd

Main locations: Oxford, Paddockwood (Kent), Coventry, Birmingham

UK employees: 8,712

Charitable donations

2006: £12,200
2005: £11,300

Total community contributions: £150,000

Membership: BitC

Community involvement

Unipart's policy on corporate community investment is to encourage and support its employees in participating in activities which benefit the community at large. In addition, it will 'Endeavour to contribute 1% or more of its pre-tax profits to the community, such contributions to include cash donations, management and employee time as well as gifts in kind'.

Organisations/projects that may be considered for support are:

» charities
» not-for-profit organisations representing economically and socially disadvantaged groups
» schools and youth organisations
» environmental, developmental and cultural organisations which aid economic or social regeneration
» campaigns addressing specific community needs.

Exclusions

Unipart will not support an activity whose purpose is to benefit a political or morally corrupt cause.

Applications

In writing to the correspondent.

Corporate giving

During 2007, Unipart provided cash and in kind services totalling £150,000. Although no indication of the cash element

was given, we believe it to have been around £12,000 as in previous years.

Some of the initiatives supported by the company included: blood donor sessions; the provision of dedicated facilities for Sea Scouts; staff from Unipart Logistics working with Oxford Community School to develop new business courses; the InspireEd project at Cowley which provided educational and vocational training to permanently excluded Year 11 students from the Oxford area; and sponsorship for BitC's 'Ready for Work' programme which saw five homeless people brought back to work in the Cowley Distribution Centre.

In kind support

In addition to cash donations the company contributes through gifts in kind, management and employee time and expertise, and the free use of company facilities and premises.

Employee-led support

Unipart actively encourages all employees to become involved in community service and charitable activity. The company provides matched funding for employees' fundraising efforts.

Uniq plc

Company registration number 3912506

No 1 Chalfont Park, Gerrards Cross, Buckinghamshire SL9 0UN

01753 276000; Fax: 01753 276071

Website: www.uniq.com

Correspondent: The Company Secretary

Chairman: Ross Warburton

Chief Executive: Geoff Eaton

Year end	Turnover	Pre-tax profit
31/12/2007	£736,100,000	(£44,100,000)

Nature of company business
Uniq is a European chilled and frozen food producer. It makes predominantly fresh chilled desserts, salads, sandwiches, fish, dips and dressings and ready meals for sale in the UK and continental Europe. It is a major supplier to leading supermarket groups in Europe on a branded and customer own label basis.

Subsidiaries include: Wincanton Holdings Ltd, Toft Foods Ltd

Main locations: Gerrards Cross, Annan, Evercreech, Minsterley, Paighton, Northampton, Spalding

Total employees: 6,551

Charitable donations

2007: £6,000
2006: £15,000
2005: £52,000
2004: £30,000

Community involvement

Support is given to a limited range of charitable causes on a selective basis with most donations committed long-term to national charities.

In addition, there is a strong preference for local charities in areas of company presence and appeals relevant to the company's business. We were previously advised that areas likely to be considered for support include the arts, children/youth, education and elderly people.

Exclusions

No support for brochure advertising, individuals, local appeals not in areas of company presence, overseas projects or political appeals.

Applications

Appeals, where relevant, should be addressed to the correspondent. However, unsolicited requests outside the criteria listed will not succeed.

Corporate giving

In 2006/07, the company made donations to charitable causes totalling £6,000 (2005/06: £15,000). Although this is below the minimum threshold for inclusion here, the drop appears to have been due to the company's recent poor economic performance. We shall continue to monitor the situation.

We have no details of the beneficiaries, but previously, support was focused primarily on Caravan, the grocery industry charity.

In kind support

Non-cash support is given in the form of gifts in kind, secretarial and administrative support, and advice and consultation.

Employee-led support

The company encourages employees to contribute directly to community initiatives; allowing them time away from work to serve as magistrates, school governors, local councillors, trade union officials or representatives of professional bodies.

Many Uniq employees serve on charitable committees or have worked together to organise and participate in fundraising events. These have included sponsored mountain climbs, rowing events and other activities.

Unisys Ltd

Company registration number 103709

Bakers Court, Bakers Road, Uxbridge UB8 1RG

01895 237137; Fax: 01895 862093

Website: www.unisys.co.uk

Correspondent: Human Resources Department

Managing Director: Duncan Tait

Year end	Turnover	Pre-tax profit
31/12/2007	£2,190,630,000	£14,289,000

Nature of company business
The development, manufacture, supply and maintenance of information technology systems and related services and supplies.

Main locations: Altrincham, Birmingham, Bristol, Glasgow, Leeds, Slough, Milton Keynes, Liverpool, Uxbridge

UK employees: 1,120

Charitable donations

2007: £48,471
2006: £32,370
2005: £101,036
2004: £166,404
Membership: BitC

Community involvement

We were previously advised that Unisys prefers to invest in those communities in which it has a presence. These investments take the form of:

- technology and business education
- health and human services
- arts, cultural and civic organisations
- global diversity.

Exclusions

Charitable causes operating outside of community focused employee-led initiatives.

Applications

In writing to the correspondent, but in view of support being directed towards matching employee fundraising initiatives, unsolicited applications are unlikely to be successful.

Corporate giving

In 2007, Unisys Ltd made cash donations to charitable organisations amounting to £48,471 (2006: £32,370). We have no details of the beneficiaries, but were previously advised that the company no longer makes cash donations directly to charitable organisations. Instead, it channels financial help towards supporting employee initiatives (see Employee-led support).

In kind support

This mainly comprises of gifts in kind.

Employee-led support

Staff are encouraged to become involved in the local community through becoming volunteers and school governors and through fundraising which the company matches pound for pound up to a maximum of £500.

United Airlines

Company registration number BR001592

United House Building, 451 Southern Perimeter Road, Hounslow, Middlesex TW6 3LP

020 8276 6000

Website: www.unitedairlines.co.uk

Nature of company business
Airline.

Main locations: Hounslow

Community involvement

The company states on its UK website that: 'Our commitment to corporate social investment extends around the globe.

Many of these activities take advantage of our unique capabilities as a global airline and involve both our employees and our customers. Our philanthropic wing, the United Airlines Foundation, provides much of this support.

'The foundation states that: Our mission is to develop, implement and communicate United's commitment to community service by sponsoring and supporting charitable organisations, as well as programmes and activities that improve the communities where our customers and employees live and work.

'The foundation's current philanthropic focus is on education, health, arts and culture, volunteerism and diversity.

'Be aware that the foundation concentrates the majority of its resources in United's US hubs.'

Exclusions

No support for matching gifts, air transportation for fundraising events or individuals. No philanthropic support for the following: capital and building grants, development campaigns, individuals, political or fraternal organisations, religious institutions, or individual public or private schools.

Applications

As at November 2008, the foundation was no longer accepting new or unsolicited proposals at the present time. However, examples of the information typically required for an application to be considered are still available on the company's website.

Corporate giving

Past beneficiaries have included Habitat for Humanity, towards building affordable subsidised homes in Banbury, Eastbourne, Liverpool and Southwark.

Employee-led support

The company has created a United We Care scheme which both encourages payroll giving and matches employees with volunteer opportunities.

United Biscuits Ltd

Company registration number 3877866

Hayes Park, Hayes End Road, Hayes, Middlesex UB4 8EE

020 8234 5000; Fax: 020 8234 5555

Website: www.unitedbiscuits.co.uk

Correspondent: Alison Harper, Communications Department

Chairman: David Fish

Chief Executive: Jeff van der Eems

Managing Director: Benoit Testard

Year end	Turnover	Pre-tax profit
29/12/2007	£1,142,300,000	(£11,200,000)

Nature of company business
The principal activity of the group is the manufacture and sale of a wide range of food products, including biscuits and savoury snacks.

In October 2006, an agreement was reached to sell United Biscuits in its entirety to a consortium comprising The Blackstone Group and PAI. No further details were available at the time.

Subsidiaries include: McVities Group, KP Snacks, UK Foods

Main locations: Glasgow, Harlesden, Halifax, Hayes, High Wycombe, Carlisle, Manchester, Liverpool, Consett, Rotherham, Ashby-de-la-Zouch

Total employees: 8,726

Charitable donations
2007: £40,000
2005: £50,000
2004: £30,000

Membership: BitC

Community involvement

United Biscuits' (UB) community affairs programme seeks to build partnerships with schools, further education establishments and local communities.

The company launched its 'Building our Community Manifesto' in 2007 which sets out its specific goals and commitments in this respect.

Exclusions

No response to circular appeals. No grants for animal charities, political appeals, or religious appeals.

Applications

For appeals from organisations local to Hayes Park, please apply in writing to the correspondent.

Please note that there is no central charitable budget. The charitable policy across the company is operated on the basis of decentralisation. Individual sites are therefore responsible for decisions regarding the budget they allocate to charitable causes and the charities they support (within the guidelines already noted).

Other information available: The company publish an annual 'Community Affairs Review'.

Corporate giving

In 2007, the group made total community contributions of around £100,000 of which cash donations amounted to £40,000. We have no details of the beneficiaries, but around 120 organisations in all benefited.

In kind support
Education: Support is given to employees who are school governors and the company works in partnership with the School Governors' One Stop Shop to encourage more employees to become governors with inner city schools.

Employee-led support
United Biscuits provide a day of additional paid leave to employees supporting community activities and contribute 25% to the funds raised by employees for any 'well-being' charity.

Payroll giving: The group is registered with the Give As You Earn scheme. In 2007, employees donated £30,000 to good causes through the scheme.

Commercially-led support
Sponsorship: Requests regarding sponsorship, or use of a particular brand (such as Penguin or Hula Hoops), should be forwarded to the relevant brand managers. United Biscuits

does not have a central sponsorship budget as all sponsorship should be done by a brand recognised by consumers.

United Business Media Ltd

Company registration number 152298

Ludgate House, 245 Blackfriars Road, London SE1 9UY

020 7921 5000; Fax: 020 7928 2728

Website: www.unm.com

Correspondent: Nigel Main, Head of Marketing

Chairman: John Botts

Chief Executive: David Levin

Year end	Turnover	Pre-tax profit
31/12/2007	£801,600,000	£129,500,000

Nature of company business
UBM is an international media and business information company.

Subsidiaries include: NOP Research Group Ltd, CMP Europe Ltd, PR Newswire Europe Ltd, United Advertising Publications plc

Main locations: London

UK employees: 1,544

Total employees: 6,476

Charitable donations

2007: £543,372
2006: £600,138
2005: £434,300
2004: £240,200

Membership: A & B

Community involvement

The following information is taken from the company's 2007 annual report and accounts:

'During 2007 we continued to develop our charitable donations policy. This is administered by a central charity committee which allocates funds to each division to be expended in line with established guidelines. As a media and information group, United Business Media (UBM) particularly supports projects which promote education and literacy, and media and communications. Whilst UBM is keen to maintain this important legacy we are also eager to assist in relieving poverty and homelessness, and promoting healthcare both in the markets we operate and in society more widely.

'With the involvement of our employees UBM supports charities and not-for-profit organisations around the globe; from smaller grassroots donations, to large long-term international projects.'

Support is also provided through donations in kind.

Exclusions

No support is given to circular appeals, fundraising events, purely denominational (religious) appeals, local appeals not in areas of company presence or overseas projects.

Applications

In writing to the correspondent.

Corporate giving

In 2007, worldwide charitable donations totalled £543,372 and went to over 80 charities recommended by employees. In line with United Business Media's development of its 'offshoring' activity, a significant proportion of this support was given to UK organisations working overseas, particularly in India. Examples include: £150,000 to an Oxfam education programme in the Democratic Republic of Congo; £50,000 to CARE International UK for their Girls' Education Programme in India; and £10,000 to Agents of Change for the building of a respite care home in Romania.

In kind support

In 2007, the CMPi Leadership Development Programme worked with four UK charities – The Bridge Trust in Tonbridge, The Aquarius Community Centre in Manchester, CRASH in London and Thames Hospice Care in Ascot – whereby four groups of four participants worked on projects which took three months to complete. CMPi (a subsidiary company) gave each group time off work to complete the projects, giving the participants the opportunity to bring business and commercial skills to help the charities concerned.

Employee-led support

United Business Media (UBM) encourages employees to support the community through employee volunteering programmes.

Payroll giving: UBM operates a payroll giving scheme in the UK, whereby regular donations by employees are matched by the company. A separate matched giving scheme through which fundraising efforts by UBM's employees are matched on a one-off basis also exists.

United Utilities Group plc

Company registration number 2366616

Haweswater House, Lingley Mere Business Park, Great Sankey, Warrington WA5 3LP

01925 237 000; Fax: 01925 237 066

Website: www.unitedutilities.com

Correspondent: Jan Potter

Email: jan.potter@uuplc.co.uk

Chairman: Dr John McAdam

Chief Executive: Phillip Green

Year end	Turnover	Pre-tax profit
31/03/2008	£2,363,000,000	£478,000,000

Nature of company business
A multi-utility supplying water/waste water services, electricity, gas and telecommunications worldwide.

Subsidiaries include: Norweb Gas Ltd, NORWEB plc, Vertex Data Science Ltd, Norweb Telecom Ltd

Main locations: Warrington

UK employees: 8,673

> **Charitable donations**
>
> 2007: £3,080,070
> 2005: £1,432,000
> 2004: £1,335,759
> 2003: £1,015,310
>
> Total community contributions: £3,790,569
>
> Membership: BitC, L B Group

Community involvement

The following is taken from the 'Supporting the Community' section of the company's website:

'Over the last year [2007/08], we have conducted a wide ranging review of our approach to corporate responsibility. The review covered everything from our corporate responsibility strategy down to the partnerships we have developed with community organisations.'

'As a result, we are placing greater emphasis on two particular areas:

> climate change, where the water sector faces tougher challenges than most other industries

> developing and attracting the skills we need to successfully meet the future challenges of running our business.

'We continue to support our employees' activities by providing volunteering opportunities, match-funding and community grants for those that volunteer in their own time.'

Exclusions

No support for appeals from individuals, religious appeals or political appeals.

Applications

In writing to the correspondent.

Information available: The group publishes a social and environmental impact report.

Corporate giving

We did not receive a reply to our request for updated information about the company's community investment, which is unfortunate, as the annual report and accounts quotes conflicting figures.

The section on corporate responsibility states that: 'We invested around £2.5 million in the communities in which we operate last year, including cash, time and in kind help', whilst that in the director's report section quotes a figure of £3,790,569. In view of the preciseness of the latter, and the fact that it is given as part of statutory reporting requirements, we have used this figure as that for total community contributions. As we do not know the cash element of this amount, we do not quote a figure for this.

The majority of the UK donations went towards supporting the company's official community partners; Groundwork and the Mersey Basin Campaign.

Support is also given through the United Utilities Trust Fund (Charity Commission no. 1108296). This 'independent' grant-making trust was established in 2005 to help people out of poverty and debt. Funded by United Utilities, the day to day management and administration is carried out by Auriga Services Ltd in line with the policy set by the trustees.

As with similar trusts established by other utility companies, the people it primarily assists are customers of United Utilities who are unable to pay their water bills.

Further details on how to apply are available at: www.uutf.org.uk

In kind support

Education: United Utilities have a range of free teaching packs and videos, which support the National Curriculum, developed jointly with teachers and its community partners. The company provide teacher inset days and are involved with a number of new education initiatives.

For general information, please contact the Education Liaison Service (01257 425550; Fax: 01257 423364; email: education@ uuplc.co.uk).

Employee-led support

United Utilities match funds employees fundraising efforts on behalf of charitable organisations up to a maximum of £250 per application.

Payroll giving: The company offer its employees the Charities Trust payroll giving scheme.

Unum

Company registration number 4661006

Milton Court, Dorking, Surrey RH4 3LZ

01306 887766; Fax: 01306 881394

Website: www.unum.co.uk

Correspondent: Inderpal Sokhy, Head of Community Affairs
Email: inderpal.sokhy@unum.co.uk

Chairman: Thomas Watjen

Chief Executive: Susan Ring

Year end	Turnover	Pre-tax profit
31/12/2006	£468,000,000	£131,600,000

Nature of company business
Income protection insurance.

Main locations: Dorking

UK employees: 914

> **Charitable donations**
>
> 2006: £704,713
> 2005: £400,000
> 2004: £499,118
> 2003: £427,427
> 2002: £611,548
>
> Total community contributions: £735,393
> Management costs: £49,372
>
> Membership: BitC, L B Group

Community involvement

'Unum's corporate responsibility programme seeks to ensure that we achieve high standards in how the business is led and in our behaviour in the marketplace, among our workforce, in the communities where we have a presence and in the environment more widely.'

Exclusions

No support for advertising in charity brochures, animal welfare, appeals from individuals, enterprise/training, local appeals outside areas of company presence, medical research, overseas projects, political/religious appeals, or science/technology.

Applications

In writing to the correspondent.

Corporate giving

In 2006, total community contributions were £735,393 of which £704,713 was in cash donations. Beneficiaries during the year included: Surrey Care Trust; Business in the Community; EFD; Radar; and Seeability.

In kind support

Gifts in kind may be given in support of appropriate causes.

Employee-led support

Employees are encouraged and supported in their volunteering activities.

Payroll giving: A scheme is in operation.

Commercially-led support

Sponsorship: Neither arts nor good-cause sponsorship is undertaken.

UPS

Company registration number 1933173

Forest Road, Feltham, Middlesex TW13 7DY

08457 877877; Fax: 020 8844 2815

Website: www.ups.com

Correspondent: Marketing & Communications

Email: marketinguk@ups.com

Managing Director: Jim Barber

Year end
31/12/2007

Nature of company business
Carrier and package delivery company providing specialist transportation, logistics, capital and e-commerce services.

Main locations: Feltham

UK employees: 8,000

Charitable donations
2007: £148,469
2004: £148,600
2003: £34,450

Community involvement

Grants in the UK are made through the US-based UPS Foundation (Federal Tax ID No. 13–6099176). However, these are initiated by the company proactively seeking potential beneficiaries whose work ties in with the interests of the foundation. National and local charities UKwide can be supported.

The foundation has five current focus areas, namely: Economic and global literacy; Environmental sustainability; Non-profit effectiveness; Diversity; and Community safety.

Exclusions

The UPS Foundation does not award grants to individuals, religious organisations or theological functions, or church-sponsored programmes limited to church members.

Grants supporting capital campaigns, endowments or operating expenses are seldom approved.

Applications

As of 1 June 2007, The UPS Foundation no longer accepts or responds to unsolicited proposals.

Information available: UPS's sustainability report can be accessed at: www.sustainability.ups.com

Further information about its community support programme is avaialble at: www.community.ups.com

Corporate giving

In 2007, the foundation made donations in the UK totalling £148,469. Major beneficiaries were: RNID; RNIB; 1st Bury St Edmunds Scout Troop; Children's Adventure Farm Trust; and Business Dynamics.

Employee-led support

The company has an established employee volunteering scheme with a total of 2,300 hours being 'donated' by the staff to good causes in 2007. Around 9% of the workforce participated in volunteer activities.

No value appears to be put on this form of support by UPS.

Commercially-led support

Sponsorship: Neither arts nor good-cause sponsorship is undertaken.

Vodafone Group plc

Company registration number 1833679

Vodafone House, The Connection, Newbury, Berkshire RG14 2FN

01635 33251; Fax: 01635 45713

Website: www.vodafone.com

Correspondent: Andrew Dunnett, Head of Vodafone UK Foundation

Chairman: Sir John Bond

Chief Executive: Vittorio Colao

Year end	Turnover	Pre-tax profit
31/03/2008	£35,478,000,000	£9,001,000,000

Nature of company business
Mobile telecommunications.

Main locations: Banbury, Gloucester, Warrington, Welwyn Garden City, Theale, Trowbridge, Croydon, Newbury, Abingdon

UK employees: 10,620

Community involvement

Much of the company's support in the UK is given through the Vodafone UK Foundation (Charity Commission no. 1013850), although substantial donations are made to the Vodafone Group Foundation (see below).

The company states that:

'Our foundations make social investments that help the people of the world to lead fuller lives by:

- sharing the benefits of developments in mobile communications technology as widely as possible
- supporting the local communities in which Vodafone operates
- helping to alleviate suffering in disaster areas
- supporting sport and music projects to benefit young people and their communities
- promoting the health and well-being of young people
- protecting the natural environment.'

Applications

An application form can be downloaded from the Vodafone UK Foundation's website (www.vodafoneukfoundation.org). Alternatively, email a proposal to thevodafoneukfoundation@vodafone.co.uk

Corporate giving

Unfortunately, the company's annual report and accounts is not very clear about exactly how much Vodafone Group plc donated in the UK in 2007/08.

Although it declares a donation of £24 million to the Vodafone Group Foundation (Charity Commission no. 1089625), the majority of foundation funds are distributed in grants through operating company foundations (of which there is a network of 21 local operating company and associate foundations around the world).

In addition, the report states that operating companies donated a further £12.9 million to their foundations and a further £4.2 million directly to a variety of causes. However, there is no indication of which operating companies gave how much or where.

Nevertheless, some clarity regarding Vodafone's UK community investment is to be found in the accounts of The Vodafone UK Foundation. Here it clearly states its income of over £6.7 million to have come from The Vodafone Group Foundation (£2.9 million) and Vodafone Ltd (£3.8 million). Given that the £6.7 million is company money paid either directly to the UK foundation or via the group foundation, this is the figure we have used to indicate Vodafone's level of support in the UK.

The Vodafone UK Foundation

During the year ended 31 March 2007 the Foundation made grant awards totalling £6,433,295 (2006: £4,872,939). Grants approved by the trustees were to projects within the following categories, with a particular emphasis on those that are communications-based:

- partner charities ('Flagships')
- national projects and donations
- local communities and schools
- employee fundraising programmes.

The trustees give preference to projects focusing on the 16–25 year old range, the digital divide and access to technologies, with particular emphasis on preventing exclusion.

Grants are also made from the foundation to local projects and local formally constituted voluntary organisations. The criteria for support of local projects and voluntary organisations are based more broadly around the benefit to that community. Substantial grants to projects with a local benefit are confined largely to Banbury, Newark, Warrington, Trowbridge, West Berkshire, Stoke and Northern Ireland, namely UK locations where the Vodafone Group has a significant staff presence.

Employee-led support

Payroll giving: Vodafone employees in the UK are able to donate through this method if they choose to do so.

Employees can claim up to 24 hours paid leave per year for volunteering activities in the local community.

VT Group plc

Company registration number 1915771

V T House, Grange Drive, Hedge End, Southampton SO30 2DQ

023 8083 9001; Fax: 023 8083 9002

Website: www.vvtplc.com

Correspondent: M Jowett, Company Secretary

Chairman: M Jefferies

Chief Executive: P Lester

Year end	Turnover	Pre-tax profit
31/03/2007	£852,528,000	£59,818,000

Nature of company business
Support services, shipbuilding and marine products, communications services, and schools support services.

Subsidiaries include: Flagship Training Ltd, Airwork Ltd, Fleet Support Ltd, Careers Enterprise Ltd

Main locations: Bournemouth, Chichester, Bordon, Watford, Portsmouth, Reading, Southampton, London, Hove, Leatherhead

UK employees: 14,100

Community involvement

The company has a central group charity committee made up of employees' representative of the main areas of the group. The committee meets regularly throughout the year and distributes funds to charities with preference given to those local to the group's principal places of business and which relate to education, health, community and the arts.

The company is currently reviewing its approach to community interaction and charitable giving. At group level the aim is to move towards more long-term partnerships with fewer charities, whilst still allowing business units at a local level the autonomy to support organisations of importance to employees/the community.

Exclusions

No support for advertising in charity brochures, animal welfare, appeals from individuals, the arts, enterprise/training, environment/heritage, overseas projects, political appeals, social welfare or sport.

Applications

In writing to the correspondent.

Corporate giving

In 2006/07, the group contributed a total of £93,000 (2005/06: £112,000) to charitable organisations. In response to employee nominations, some 38 charities received support from VT Group Services charities committee. The largest donation was to Southampton Hospital for the refurbishment of the family room in the Special Care Baby Unit.

Other charities supported during the year included: SSAFA Forces Help, Action for ME, and LEAP (Local Employment Access Projects).

In kind support

In addition to cash donations, the company provides in kind support to its local communities in the form of manual work for schools and old people's residences providing members for charitable fundraising committees, school bodies and local authorities.

Employee-led support

Employees are positively encouraged to undertake fundraising activities for their chosen charity and are assisted in this by financial support from the company.

Warburtons Ltd

Company registration number 178711

Back o'th Bank House, Hereford Road, Bolton, Lancashire BL1 8HJ

0800 243 684

Website: www.warburtons.co.uk

Correspondent: Jill Kippax, Corporate Affairs Manager

Chairman: Jonathan Warburton

Managing Director: Robert Higginson

Year end	Turnover	Pre-tax profit
29/09/2007	£414,227,000	£48,997,000

Nature of company business
The production and distribution of bakery products.

Main locations: Wakefield, Bolton, Enfield, North London

UK employees: 4,494

Charitable donations

2007: £191,000
2006: £232,000
2005: £219,000
2004: £149,000
2003: £15,625

Membership: BitC

Community involvement

Warburton's provide informative and accessible information regarding its community support via its website (www.trustwarburtons.co.uk), from which the following information is taken:

'Warburtons is committed to operating in a socially responsible manner within its local communities. As a family business, the company has a strong track record of charitable giving and active involvement and recognises the positive effect of community partnerships.

'Family members spearhead Warburtons community giving programme and the company is a member of Business in the Community. Warburtons provides support in three ways: financial support, product donations and the personal involvement of individuals (both employees and family members).

'The Community Giving Programme focuses on charities, organisations and initiatives that improve the quality of family life. Therefore, the programme supports projects that have a positive impact on the health and wellbeing of the whole family, especially in the areas of diet, fitness, safety and education, as well as caring initiatives that improve the quality of life for the sick, elderly or disabled.'

Warburtons has 13 bakeries and 12 distribution depots across the UK. The location of each of these is given on the company's website.

Exclusions

Warburton's community support programme does not support charities, organisations, initiatives or individuals in the following areas:

- 'those that are of a political or religious nature
- involve animal welfare – except where they positively improve the quality of life of a sick, elderly or disabled person, such as guide dogs
- associated with addiction or criminal rehabilitation
- individuals seeking personal funding for academic fees
- professional sportsmen/women or organisations. However, the programme does support amateur sportsmen/women and organisations in sports that are accessible to a majority audience
- third party fundraisers. That is, the programme aims to provide direct support to charities, organisations, individuals or initiatives as opposed to individuals fundraising on their behalf (with the exception of Warburtons employees, customers or suppliers).'

Applications

Applications should be made via the online form. Providing each application fulfils the criteria stated in the 'Policy and Guidelines' (also available online), a charity or organisation will not be precluded from making an additional application in a successive year, whether or not the initial application has been successful.

Please note: Where a financial donation is being applied for, the company requests that the money is used to fund a specific need or project. Financial support will not be awarded to assist ongoing fundraising activity.

Corporate giving

In 2007, the company made charitable donations totalling £191,000 (2006: £232,000). Besides its two long-standing commitments to Bolton Lads' and Girls' Club and to its own School Visitor programme, the following organisations have also recently received support:

The New Children's Hospital Appeal (Manchester); CANtreat; Royal Agricultural Benevolent Institution (RABI); Oldham and Rochdale Brownie and Scouts; Mr Sunbeam Playgroup – Crosshouse; and Spofforth FC.

In kind support

Help is given in time, and donations of products and equipment.

Employee-led support

A matched funding scheme is operated for employees' fundraising.

Commercially-led support

Sponsorship: Consideration is given to sponsorship requests which fall within the criteria stated in the 'Policy and Guidelines' document.

Wates Group Ltd

Company registration number 1824828

Wates House, Station Approach, Leatherhead, Surrey KT22 7SW

01372 861000

Website: www.wates.co.uk

Correspondent: Director of the Foundation Team

Chairman: Paul Drechsler

Chief Executiive: Paul Drechsler

Year end	Turnover	Pre-tax profit
31/12/2007	£973,982,000	£37,661,000

Nature of company business
Construction services and residential development.

UK employees: 2,212

> ### Charitable donations
>
> 2007: £58,000
>
> Membership: BitC, L B Group

Community involvement

Wates state in its annual report and accounts for 2007 that: 'Our community investment will concentrate on boosting skills and employability in deprived communities, primarily through our Building Futures programme'. (See 'In kind support' for further details).

Employees are encouraged to undertake voluntary work, particularly on the annual 'Community Day'.

There is a major trust associated with the Wates family – The Wates Foundation (Charity Commission no. 247941). However, it appears not to receive any direct financial support from the company.

Further information is available in *A Guide to the Major Trusts – Vol. 1*, published by the Directory of Social Change.

Applications

In writing to the correspondent.

Corporate giving

In 2007, the company made charitable donations totalling £58,000. We have no information regarding the beneficiaries.

In kind support

Employability/training: 'Building Futures provides practical training and a valuable insight into the construction industry, with its wide range of roles. Participants focus on areas such as interviewing skills, raising self esteem and first aid training. They undertake trade taster sessions at local skills centres in trades such as joinery, bricklaying and plastering. They also participate in training and sit for the test to obtain the health and safety component of the CSCS card, which is crucial to work on sites.

'In 2007, we delivered ten two-week training programmes with local partners in London, Birmingham, Glasgow, Cardiff and Merthyr Tydfil. In Wates' 110th year of trading, we were pleased to achieve our goal of providing places to 110 individuals of whom 65% are in employment.'

Employee-led support

Volunteering: Employees, supply chain partners and customers volunteered in excess of 8,000 hours and donated materials for the company's annual 'community day'.

Weetabix Ltd

Company registration number 267687

Weetabix Mills, Burton Latimer, Kettering, Northamptonshire NN15 5JR

01536 722181; Fax: 01536 726148

Website: www.weetabix.co.uk

Correspondent: Pat Reay, Marketing Assistant

Year end	Turnover	Pre-tax profit
29/12/2007	£374,877,000	(£13,052,000)

Nature of company business
The manufacture, marketing and sale of ready to eat cereal foods.

Subsidiaries include: Ryecroft Foods Ltd, Vibixa Ltd, B L Marketing Ltd

Main locations: Ashton under Lyne, Burton Latimer, Hastings, Corby

UK employees: 1,738

Total employees: 2,306

Community involvement

Weetabix Ltd is now wholly owned by the Latimer Group Ltd, a company incorporated by Lion Capital. The financial information contained herein refers to the Latimer Group.

Specific information about the company's community support proved non-existent (on both the Latimer Group and the Weetabix websites). We therefore repeat the last information we received:

'The company has supported a wide range of groups and activities in the county of Northamptonshire. These have ranged from making donations to local schools, to sponsoring a variety of projects involving local charities. The company has also been keen to support local sports groups.'

Although there exists an associated company trust – The Weetabix Charitable Trust (Charity Commission no. 1044949), this no longer appears to receive money from the company.

Exclusions

No support for local appeals not in areas of company presence, or appeals from individuals.

Applications

In writing to the correspondent.

Information available: Weetabix published a new corporate social responsibility report in July 2008. Unfortunately, it contains no information about its community support.

Corporate giving

In 2007, the company made charitable donations in the UK amounting to £87,000 (2006: £159,368). This principally consisted of amounts paid to the National Grocers Benevolent Fund and local charities.

Commercially-led support

Sponsorship: *Sport* – The company appears to still sponsor the Weetabix Youth Football League in Northamptonshire.

The Weir Group plc

Company registration number SC002934

Clydesdale Bank Exchange, 20 Waterloo Street, Glasgow G2 6DB

0141 637 7111; Fax: 0141 221 9789

Website: www.weir.co.uk

Correspondent: Alan Mitchelson, Company Secretary
Email: alan.mitchelson@weir.co.uk

Chairman: The Lord Smith of Kelvin

Chief Executive: Mark Selway

Year end	Turnover	Pre-tax profit
30/12/2007	£1,060,600,000	£114,000,000

Nature of company business
Principal activities: engineering services and specialist engineering products.

Subsidiaries include: Neyrfor-Weir Ltd, Tooling Products Holdings Ltd, Hopkinsons Ltd, Girdlestone Pumps Ltd, Liquid Gas Equipment Ltd, Flowguard Ltd, Strachan & Henshaw Ltd, G Perry & Sons Ltd, Warman International Ltd

Main locations: Aylestone, Altens, Bristol, Cathcart, Glasgow, Newton Heath, Huddersfield, Stockton on Tees, South Gyle, Petersfield

Total employees: 8,359

Community involvement

Previously we were advised that, 'Causes, events and charities are often nominated and driven by our employees, reflecting their own interests and social engagement.'

The company is a member of Scottish Business in the Community.

Applications

In writing to the correspondent. The main decisions are made by a board committee.

Corporate giving

In 2007, worldwide charitable donations (being specifically for health, heritage, educational and community purposes) totalled £252,227 (2006: £169,218). We have no details of the beneficiaries.

Employee-led support

During 2007 employees in Scotland helped raise money on behalf of Maggie's Cancer Centres, Chest, Heart and Stroke Scotland and White Settlement Community Services.

Wessex Water Services Ltd

Company registration number 2366633

Claverton Down Road, Claverton Down, Bath BA2 7WW

01225 526000; Fax: 01225 528000

Website: www.wessexwater.co.uk

Correspondent: Marilyn Smith, Head of Stakeholder Relations
Email: info@wessexwater.co.uk

Chairman: Colin Skellett

Year end	Turnover	Pre-tax profit
31/03/2008	£394,400,000	£124,500,000

Nature of company business
Principal activity: water and sewerage services.

Main locations: Bath

UK employees: 1,719

Community involvement

Grants are given to registered charities operating in the area administered by Wessex Water, i.e. South Gloucestershire, Wiltshire, Dorset, and Somerset.

Conservation grants are available through the Watermark Award. In kind support is mainly given in connection with schools education programmes.

Exclusions

No support for national charities, advertising in charity brochures, animal welfare, the arts, enterprise/training, political appeals, religious appeals or science/technology.

Applications

In writing to the correspondent. The community involvement committee meets monthly.

Corporate giving

In 2007/08, the company donated a total of £150,000 (2006/07: £93,000) to UK charitable and community groups.

Launched in 1993, Wessex Watermark is a grant scheme set up by the company to help fund environmental projects in the region. Organised by the Conservation Foundation, grants from £100 to £2,500 were awarded to numerous environmental projects throughout the region.

Local charities based within the region also receive support through the company's community involvement committee which awards small grants every month.

Since its creation in 1981, Wessex Water has supported WaterAid, the international water and sanitation charity by organising fundraising events and raising money through customers and staff. In 2008, in recognition of the UN international year of sanitation, Wessex Water launched a new campaign working with WaterAid called 'Wessex for West Africa'.

In kind support

Education: Wessex Water offers an education service catering for 5 to 15 year olds. There are now nine education centres in the Wessex Water region. Services include:

- primary and secondary education packs
- education advisers
- visits to schools
- tailor-made lessons (water cycle, river & pond studies, WaterAid and practical sessions)
- education centres (nine in total – details on website)
- site visits.

Special needs: Customer Care Plus is a special programme for those customers with special needs, including older and disabled people. A register of such customers is held, in order that the company can identify and respond to their requirements.

Help includes: a text telephone service for people with impaired hearing; Braille or audio bills; a doorstep security password system; and advance warning of interruptions to water supply.

Employee-led support

Payroll giving: The company operates the Give As You Earn scheme.

Commercially-led support

Sponsorship: *The environment* – The company sponsors local, environmental and water-related activities.

West Bromwich Building Society

Company registration number 651B

374 High Street, West Bromwich, West Midlands B70 8LR

0121 525 7070; Fax: 0121 500 5961

Website: www.westbrom.co.uk

Correspondent: Brian Seymour-Smith, Public Relations Manager

Chairman: Brian Woods-Scarwen

Chief Executive: Stephen Karle

Year end	Turnover	Pre-tax profit
31/03/2008	£102,600,000	£41,100,000

Nature of company business
Building society.

Main locations: West Bromwich

UK employees: 800

Community involvement

Although the society does not make direct contributions to charitable causes, it supports in kind many community-based activities and local projects, especially those involving small-scale grassroots organisations and young people.

Exclusions

No support for local appeals not in areas of company presence.

Applications

In writing to the correspondent.

Corporate giving

In 2007/08, the society, through good-cause sponsorship and in kind donations made contributions to its local communities of £750,000. Some examples of this support are given below.

The Mercian Trust – the society continued its partnership with the Diocese of Lichfield (the Mercian Trust Partnership) which is now in its tenth year. With support from the society an extensive community campaign was undertaken to reach those small-scale grassroots organisations which can have a real impact in their immediate area but, all too often, are overlooked by funding bodies.

AweSum Challenge – launched this year, the challenge is a free online game, available to every school in the UK, and was devised in conjunction with the Mercian Trust and education specialists to enhance the mathematical aptitude and financial literacy of primary school children.

Other individual good causes, such as Wolverhampton Link Line, the Big Issue Foundation, Outward Bound, Rotary Club Walsall Fun Run and the Severn Valley Railway Flood Damage Appeal have also benefited from the Society's support.

In kind support

Sport – Ongoing support has been provided for the Football in the Community programmes of West Bromwich Albion, Walsall and Shrewsbury Town football clubs. These programmes provide both sporting and educational opportunities for children, invariably within more socially deprived areas.

Employee-led support

The society encourages its staff to fundraise.

Commercially-led support

Cause-related marketing: The society runs an affinity savings account for local charities and a Community Counts scheme which gives new mortgage customers the chance to donate £100 to a local charity or good cause of their choice. We have no figure regarding how much this raised on behalf of local charities.

The society has been a key supporter of Birmingham Children's Hospital's Red Balloon Appeal, which is geared to making the Hospital's Burn Unit a world-leader in the treatment of children with severe burns. This is supported at a corporate level by the society's Red Balloon Affinity Account.

Western Power Distribution

Company registration number OC303753

Avonbank, Feeder Road, Bristol BS2 0TB

0117 933 2005; Fax: 0117 933 2366

Website: www.westernpower.co.uk

Correspondent: Sharon Cross, Corporate Communications
0117 933 2005
Email: scross@westernpower.co.uk

Chief Executive: R A Symons

Year end	Turnover	Pre-tax profit
31/03/2008	£458,100,000	£223,000,000

Nature of company business
Distribution of electricity.

Main locations: Bristol

UK employees: 2,356

Charitable donations

2008: £154,000
2006: £55,000
2004: £186,000

Community involvement

Each year the company sets a community support policy. In 2008, the themes are education, safety and environment. The company will consider offering support to projects or events in its region that fall under these banners.

The company has also set up a charitable foundation, under which registered charities may receive grants from the company. The foundation enables WPD to support those good causes, which may otherwise fall outside the company's sponsorship activities. The foundation's grant making was previously administered by the Charities Aid Foundation, but it is not clear from the information provided by the company whether this is still the case.

Exclusions

No support for local appeals not in areas of company presence, advertising in charity brochures, animal welfare, appeals from individuals, overseas appeals, religious appeals, political appeals, or sport.

Applications

In writing to the correspondent.

Corporate giving

In 2007/08, the company made cash donations of £154,000, of which £28,000 went to registered charities. In addition to this, the WPD Foundation donated £56,000. We have no details of the beneficiaries other than that the donations were made to organisations in the South West.

Employee-led support

The company encourages its employees to support their communities in practical as well as monetary terms. This may be through the Leading Lights initiative – an employee volunteer scheme – or by fundraising for their favourite charity, which WPD acknowledges by matching the funds raised £ for £.

Commercially-led support

Sponsorship: Good cause sponsorship may be undertaken.

J D Wetherspoon plc

Company registration number 1709784

Wetherspoon House, Central Park, Reeds Crescent, Watford WD24 4QL

01923 477777; Fax: 01923 219810

Website: www.jdwetherspoon.co.uk

Correspondent: Alex Bull

Email: abull@jdwetherspoon.co.uk

Chairman: Tim Martin

Chief Executive: John Hutson

Year end	Turnover	Pre-tax profit
25/07/2007	£888,473,000	£62,024,000

Nature of company business
The development and management of public houses.

UK employees: 16,966

> ## Charitable donations
> 2007: £45,736
> 2006: £44,127

Community involvement

J D Wetherspoon state that it aims to make a valuable contribution to society through a number of areas, with special attention being paid to:

> environment
> community
> charities
> people
> ethics.

In addition to encouraging each of its pubs to support a local charity, J D Wetherspoon also has a nominated charity – CLIC Sargent – which it has supported for the past two years through donations and various fundraising events. The policy of having a nominated charity may, however, be reviewed during 2008.

Applications

In writing to the correspondent

Corporate giving

In 2006/07, the company made charitable donations amounting to nearly £46,000 (2005/06: £44,000). Although not explicitly stated, we assume that the majority of this was given in support of CLIC Sargent, with further small donations being given via a charity committee to local causes.

No value appears to have been attributed to the company's in kind support even though it states that: 'Currently, we sponsor around 30 local sports teams, through monetary contributions for kit or equipment. Teams are from the world of rugby, football and netball: we proudly support the University of Portsmouth's women's football team, The Robert Shaw netball team in Bolton and Derecharra United in Enniskillen'.

In kind support

The company has provided support in a number of ways, including: raffle prizes; computers to schools; and unwanted furniture to local institutions.

Employee-led support

Employees are encouraged to fundraise on behalf of the company's chosen charity and to facilitate fundraising amongst customers for charities at a local level.

Commercially-led support

Sponsorship: The company's website makes reference to the fact that they 'sponsor' a number of sports teams. However, we do not believe this to mean sponsorship in its fullest business sense (see under 'Community contributions').

Whitbread plc

Company registration number 29423

Whitbread Court, Houghton Hall Business Park, Porz Avenue, Dunstable LU5 5XE

01582 424200

Website: www.whitbread.co.uk

Correspondent: The Community Investment Director

Email: communityinvestment@whitbread.com

Chairman: A Habgood

Chief Executive: A Parker

Year end	Turnover	Pre-tax profit
28/02/2008	£1,206,700,000	£134,600,000

Nature of company business
The company's principal activities are the operation of hotels, restaurants and racquets, health and fitness clubs.

Subsidiaries include: David Lloyd Leisure plc, The Pelican Group plc

Main locations: London

UK employees: 27,041

> ## Charitable donations
> 2008: £0
> 2007: £0
> 2006: £41,366
> 2004: £1,380,000
>
> Membership: BitC

Community involvement

Although Whitbread can rightly claim to have been actively involved in the community for many years, its monetary contribution appears to be on a downward slope (no in kind contribution figure was made available).

'Today, according to the company's website, Whitbread's community investment programme focuses on:

> providing financial and in kind support to employees and to the charities which are close to their hearts
> investing in countries and communities that are an integral part of Whitbread's business
> building strong and mutually beneficial charity partnerships.'

Within this, there is a strong preference towards enabling young people (14–28) to achieve their potential, with financial support coming from the Whitbread 1988 Charitable Trust (Charity Commission no. 800501).

In addition to the above, group company Costa Coffee has set up the Costa Foundation; a charity which seeks to put something back into coffee-growing communities. Further details of the work of the foundation are available on Whitbread's website under 'corporate responsibility'.

Exclusions

The following are not usually supported: advertising in charity brochures, animal welfare, the arts, elderly people, enterprise/training, ticket purchases for charity events, appeals from religious bodies (unless for the benefit of the community as a whole), political organisations, medical research, charitable organisations operating overseas, science/technology, sickness/disability, social welfare or appeals from individuals.

Applications

In writing to the correspondent.

Corporate giving

For the last two financial years the company has made no direct charitable donations, but refers in its annual report and accounts to those made by the associated trust. However, we wonder about the usefulness of this as the last time the trust received a donation from the company was in 2006. Even then the quoted donation of £41,366 was reduced to around £17,000 due to nearly £24,000 being 'tax irrecoverable'. We are uncertain what this means exactly, but we thought charities were supposed to benefit fully from any donations received!

Employee-led support

Whitbread engages its employees in volunteering and fundraising activities through its match-funding and payroll giving schemes.

All Whitbread employees can apply to the Whitbread Charitable Trust for an award of up to £750 for any charity or good cause to which they regularly commit their time and energy. Over £100,000 was generated through the Raise & Match scheme in 2007.

Payroll giving: 13% of employees donate to good causes through the group's scheme. This generates over £200,000 of charitable donations each year.

Wilkinson Hardware Stores Ltd

Company registration number 365335

J K House, Roebuck Way, Manton Wood, Worksop, Nottinghamshire S80 3YY

01909 505505; Fax: 01909 505777

Website: www.wilkonsonplus.com

Correspondent: Jean Guiliatt, Charity Coordinator

Chief Executive: Stuart Mitchell

Joint Chair: Karen Swann

Joint Chair: Lisa Wilkinson

Year end	Turnover	Pre-tax profit
02/02/2007	£1,246,022,000	£48,364,000

Nature of company business
Principal activity: sale of domestic hardware and other related goods.

Subsidiaries include: L M Cooper & Co. Ltd, Wilkinson Bros (Handsworth) Ltd, S C Hardwares Ltd

Main locations: Worksop

UK employees: 21,836

Charitable donations

2007: £367,378
2005: £565,290
2003: £426,432
Membership: BitC

Community involvement

The company has over 200 stores throughout the UK and tends to support charities local to those stores. Each year a contribution is made from company profits to community initiatives within the company's trading areas and usually supporting education, the family, sports and arts.

For many years the company has been a core supporter and sponsor of DARE (Drug Abuse Resistance Education). DARE works within schools to raise awareness of drug abuse and teach self-confidence. There is a dedicated committee to consider applications from groups for charitable donations.

Charity of the Year: NSPCC (2007).

Exclusions

No support for local appeals not in areas of company presence.

Applications

In writing to the correspondent.

Corporate giving

The company made cash donations to charitable organisations in 2007 of £367,378. We have no specific details of the beneficiaries other than the information given above.

In kind support

The company's Helping Hand scheme offers vouchers and financial support to local groups, charities and organisations within the store's catchment area.

Recently help was given to the Fenland Association for Community Transport in Cambridgeshire to buy paint, brushes and weed killer to brighten up their premises and Watergall Primary School in Peterborough to develop a garden and vegetable plot.

Employee-led support

Each year team members select a national charity to fund-raise for. Team members chose to fund raise for the NSPCC in the year 2006/07 and collected a total of £241,000 on behalf of the charity.

Staff are actively encouraged to raise funds for the year's national charity and for annual events such as Comic Relief and Children in Need.

Willmott Dixon Ltd

Company registration number 198032

Spirella 2, Icknield Way, Letchworth, Hertfordshire SG6 4GY

01462 671852; Fax: 01462 681852

Website: www.willmottdixon.co.uk

Correspondent: Rick Willmott, Chairman

Chairman: Rick Willmott

Chief Executive: John Frankiewicz

Year end	Turnover	Pre-tax profit
31/12/2007	£380,393,000	£10,415,000

Nature of company business
The provision of major capital works construction to non-housing clients, including building fabric maintenance and care, interior design and fit-out, plus sustainable consultancy.

Subsidiaries include: Widacre Homes, Inspace, Camtec

Main locations: Letchworth

UK employees: 704

Charitable donations

2007: £23,267
2006: £17,508
2005: £52,750
2003: £72,041

Membership: BitC

Community involvement

Previous information has suggested that strong emphasis is placed on involvement by staff with their favoured charities, coupled with a commitment to support clients' preferred causes wherever possible. We have been informed that the directors choose one charity per year to donate to.

Exclusions

General and unsolicited appeals are not considered. No grants for local appeals not in areas of company presence or for overseas projects.

Applications

In writing to the correspondent.

Corporate giving

In 2007, the company made cash donations to charity of £23,267 (2006: £17,508). We have no details of the beneficiaries.

Robert Wiseman Dairies plc

Company registration number SC146494

159 Glasgow Road, East Kilbride, Glasgow G74 4PA

01355 244261; Fax: 01355 230352

Website: www.wiseman-dairies.co.uk

Correspondent: Joanne Rae, Marketing Manager
Email: care@wiseman-dairies.co.uk

Chairman: Alan W Wiseman

Chief Executive: Robert T Wiseman

Year end	Turnover	Pre-tax profit
29/03/2008	£721,983,000	£29,184,000

Nature of company business
The processing and distribution of milk and associated products.

Main locations: Glasgow

UK employees: 3,340

Charitable donations

2008: £12,000
2007: £0
2006: £10,000
2005: £10,000
2004: £32,000

Community involvement

Robert Wiseman Dairies has believes that it has a responsibility to get involved with local communities, in particular where it has dairies and distribution centres. As such, in 2008 it launched 'Wiseman In the Community'. This comprises of small groups of people who work for Wiseman and who are representative of parts of the country where the company operate. Various initiatives are undertaken throughout the year guided by the three principal elements of its community investment programme, namely: education, designated charity and community involvement.

Charity of the Year: The Variety Club (currently receives year on year support from the company as its 'designated' charity).

Exclusions

Local appeals not in areas of company presence. No support for appeals from individuals.

Applications

In writing to the correspondent.

Corporate giving

In 2007/08, the company declared UK cash donations of £12,000 principally to the benefit of local charities serving the communities in which it operates. Although this figure in below the threshold for inclusion here, we consider the company's education bursaries, good-cause sponsorship and in kind support to be at a level which justifies this. Furthermore, it is hoped that the recently launched 'Wiseman in the Community' initiative will add focus to this. Some examples of the company's recent support are given below.

Education: Recently the company has become involved with the Manufacturing Institute in the North West of England who run an initiative, 'Make It', which aims to get GCSE level children involved with the manufacturing sector.

Designated charity: A successful partnership with The Variety Club continues with the company pledging its seventh Robert Wiseman Dairies Sunshine Coach to Wren Spinney School in Kettering, near to its new depot in Northampton.

Community involvement: Locally, support has been given to the Vale of Athol Pipe Band, Young Farmers and the freshnlo Great Scottish Run.

Employee-led support

Employees are encouraged to fundraise on behalf of the company's designated charity.

Commercially-led support

Sponsorship: *The Arts* – The company has agreed to sponsor the Vale of Athol Pipe Band over a three-year period. This will enable the band to attend events and competitions throughout the year.

Cause-related marketing: Wiseman has sought to use its product to support numerous events and good causes throughout the year via on pack promotions; this includes

Macmillan Cancer Support's 'World's Biggest Coffee Morning' Fundraiser, the Sufi Festival and the Year of Food and Farming.

John Wood Group plc

Company registration number SC036219

John Wood House, Greenwell Road, East Tullos, Aberdeen AB12 3AX

01224 851000; Fax: 01224 851474

Website: www.woodgroup.com

Correspondent: Carolyn Smith, Corporate Communications Director 01224 851099
Email: carolyn.smith@woodgroup.com

Chairman: Sir I C Wood

Chief Executive: Allister G Langlands

Year end	Turnover	Pre-tax profit
31/12/2007	£4,432,700,000	£259,900,000

Nature of company business
Engineering services to the oil and gas, petrochemical and power-related industries.

Subsidiaries include: Frontier Engineering Solutions Ltd, IONIK Consulting, J P Kenny Engineering Ltd, Mustang Engineering Ltd, ODL, Sulzer Wood Ltd, TransCanada Turbines UK Ltd, Woodhill Frontier, Northern Integrated Services Ltd, Rolls Wood Group Ltd

Main locations: Staines, Surrey, Ellon, Glasgow, Liverpool, Dundee, Aberdeen

Total employees: 21,613

Charitable donations

2007: £395,000
2006: £320,235
2005: £184,000
2003: £45,000

Community involvement

Unfortunately, we did not receive a reply from the Wood Group in response to our request for information. Furthermore, there is very little on the company's website regarding its community support in the UK. We therefore repeat the last information we published.

The Wood Group believes in supporting the communities in which it operates. In particular, the company supports projects involving the young, older people, medical research, education, the arts and the disabled. The Wood Group recognises the importance of providing in kind support as well as financial help. Each company within the Wood Group has the freedom to choose which charities and projects they would like to support.

The company only supports local community projects in areas of company presence and projects in which employees are directly involved. National charities are generally not supported except in special circumstances, in which case the donation must receive approval from Sir Ian Wood. Unlike many major companies, the Wood Group does not select one charity each year, but prefers to distribute their budget across as many worthwhile causes as possible.

Exclusions

The following causes are not likely to receive support: specific religious groups, political organisations, sports organisations with no Wood Group employee involvement, and organisations without charitable status.

Applications

In writing to the correspondent. All requests for donations are reviewed monthly by the charity and community relations committee.

Corporate giving

In 2007, charitable donations worldwide amounted to around £395,000. Other than that the company has supported NHS Grampian's ' Give Kids a Chance' for many years, we have no details of donations made to other UK-based charitable organisations.

The company offers support to Scottish Business in the Community (SBC), of which it is a member.

Employee-led support

The company runs an Employee Community Fund to encourage employees to support a charity/sponsorship of their choice, up to a maximum of £250 per employee. The group gives an average of £10,000 a year through the scheme. Organisations supported have included Roxburghe House Support Group, Denman Preschool Playgroup, Aberdeen University Rollerhockey Club, Stonehaven and District Lions Club, Culter Boys Club and Millie's Campaign.

WPP Group plc

Company registration number 1003653

27 Farm Street, London W1J 5RJ

020 7408 2204; Fax: 020 7493 6819

Website: www.wpp.com

Correspondent: Janet Smith, Executive PA
Email: jsmith@wpp.com

Chairman: Philip Lader

Chief Executive: Sir Martin Sorrell

Year end	Turnover	Pre-tax profit
31/12/2007	£31,666,000,000	£719,400,000

Nature of company business
Principal activity: the provision of communications services worldwide.

Subsidiaries include: The Gepetto Group, Banner MacBride, Goldfarb Consultants, IMRB International, PRISM Group, Tempus Group plc, Carl Byoir & Associates, The Food Group, Management Ventures, A Eicoff & Co, Mando Marketing, The Farm, RTCdirect, Walker Group/CNI, MindShare, Coley Porter Bell, Millward Brown, SCPF, Pace, The Henley Centre, Portland Outdoor, BDG McColl, International Presentations, The Market Segment Group, Lambie-Nairn, Buchanan Communications, EWA, Addison, P Four Consultancy, The Grass Roots Group, Ogilvy Public Relations, CommonHealth, RMG International, The Wexler Group, Y & R Advertising, Clever Media, Research International, Shire Hall Group, Savatar, Einson Freeman, J Walter Thompson, The Media Partnership, Timmons and Company, Ogilvy & Mather, Oakley Young, Metro Group, Media

Insight/Maximize, Brierley & Partners, Chime Communications plc, ROCQM, Equus, Quadra Advisory, Enterprise IG

Main locations: London

Total employees: 100,000

Charitable donations

2007: £3,500,000
2006: £3,900,000
2005: £3,400,000
2003: £120,000

Total community contributions: £16,300,000

Membership: BitC

Community involvement

The following policy relates to donations and support provided by the UK parent company. Support is also provided by the operating companies, particularly from the UK advertising agencies, J Walter Thompson and Ogilvy & Mather.

The company focuses its support on education, the arts and young people. Other areas supported included health, local community, environment and drugs/alcohol. No geographical area is given preference; each application is considered on merit.

Applications

In writing to the correspondent.

Information available: Further details of the company's charitable support can be found in its annual Corporate Social Responsibility Report.

Corporate giving

In 2007, the group made worldwide community contributions of £16.3 million, much of which was given through pro bono work, and made cash donations totaling £3.5 million. Although we do not know what proportion of this went to UK organisations, the company stated in its 2007 annual report and accounts that support in the UK was given to:

- Education Africa UK
- Gambian Education Development Trust
- International Business Leaders Forum
- INSEAD Trust for European Management Education
- NABS, a charity which offers financial, practical and emotional support to those in the advertising industry
- The London Business School
- The National Portrait Gallery
- The Natural History Museum
- The Royal Opera House
- University of Cambridge
- University of Oxford.

In kind support

Assistance may be given in the form of gifts in kind, joint promotions and pro bono marketing and communication support.

Employee-led support

This varies between operating companies.

Commercially-led support

Sponsorship: *Arts and education* – sponsorship is undertaken. In the UK, WWP sponsorship support includes that to Charles Edward Brooke Girls' School, which specialises in media arts; the Royal College of Art; and two bursary awards for D&AD, the professional association for design and advertising. The company is the corporate patron of the National Portrait Gallery in London.

Wragge & Co. LLP

Company registration number OC304378

55 Colmore Row, Birmingham B3 2AS

0121 903 1000; Fax: 0121 904 1099

Website: www.wragge.com

Correspondent: Lee Nuttall, Trustee

Managing Partner: Ian Metcalfe

Senior Partner: Quentin Poole

Year end	Turnover
30/12/2007	£125,500,000

Nature of company business
Legal firm.

Main locations: London, Birmingham

UK employees: 1.184

Total employees: 1,184

Charitable donations

2007: £45,000
2004: £64,000

Membership: BitC, L B Group

Community involvement

The firm's community investment policy, is, quote, 'All about pro bono, volunteering and charitable donations. Our priorities are homelessness, education and mentoring, and inner city needs'.

Most of the firm's cash support appears to be channelled through The Wragge & Co. Charitable Trust (Charity Commission no, 803009) which receives a gift aid donation each year. Support is given across the West Midlands to registered charities only, with some preference for health related issues.

Charity of the year: KidsOut (2008).

Exclusions

No grants for individuals or for local appeals not in the area of company presence.

Applications

For the trust, applications should be made in writing to the correspondent, enclosing a copy of the most recent accounts.

Enquiries regarding the corporate responsibility work of the firm should be sent by email to the head of corporate responsibility, Lorna Gavin (lorna_gavin@wragge.com).

Corporate giving

Although the firm provides a significant amount of in kind support, we have been unable to obtain a figure for this. A gift aid donation of £45,000 was, however, made to the associated charitable trust during 2007.

The Wragge & Co. Charitable Trust

In 2006/07 the trust had a total income of £58,000 and made grants amounting to £46,522. Major beneficiaries included: University of Warwick Foundation (£6,000); KES Foundation (£5,385); Sense (£3,500); Birmingham Women's Aid (£3,060); Second City Second Chance (£3,000); and Cancer Research UK (£2,375).

In kind support

Wragge state that, 'Free legal advice is at the heart of our community work. Pro bono clients range from large non-governmental organisations (NGOs) to small charities and community organisations'.

Support is also given, for example, to homeless people to help them back into employment. This includes the use of staff skills around drafting CVs, preparing for interviews and giving homeless people practical work experience.

WSP Group plc

Company registration number 2136404

Buchanan House, 24–30 Holborn, London EC1N 2HS

020 7314 5000; Fax: 020 7314 5111

Website: www.wspgroup.com

Correspondent: Human Resources

Email: info@wspgroup.com

Chairman: David Turner

Chief Executive: Christopher Cole

Year end	Turnover	Pre-tax profit
31/12/2007	£539,000,000	£37,400,000

Nature of company business
An international business supplying specialist management and integrated services in the built and natural environment.

Main locations: London

Total employees: 8,179

Charitable donations

2007: £26,902
2006: £12,232
2005: £237,556
2004: £31,127

Community involvement

The company's policy is to contribute to the economic, social and sustainable development of the communities in which it operates.

Exclusions

No support for general or circular appeals, individuals, political or religious causes, or local appeals not in areas of company presence.

Applications

In writing to the correspondent.

Corporate giving

In 2007, the company declared worldwide charitable donations of £126,184 (2006: £89,754). Of this amount, £26,902 (2006: £12,232) was given in the UK. Note: these figures do not include pro-bono and volunteering contributions.

We have no details of the beneficiaries, although in the UK the company has started to work closely in educational development.

Employee-led support

On an informal basis the company makes donations to support charities with which its staff are involved.

Payroll giving: A wider reaching Give As You Earn scheme was rolled out in April 2008.

Wyevale Garden Centres Ltd

Company registration number 1972554

258 Bath Road, Slough, Berkshire SL1 4DX

Website: www.wyevale.co.uk

Chairman: James Hodkinson

Chief Executive: Barry Stevenson

Year end	Turnover	Pre-tax profit
31/12/2006	£185,072,000	£4,229,000

Nature of company business
Garden centres.

Subsidiaries include: Wyevale (Leisure Centres) Ltd, Great Gardens of England Investments Ltd, Country Gardens plc

Main locations: Hereford

UK employees: 3,917

Charitable donations

2006: £5,000
2005: £96,000
2003: £109,000
2002: £94,000

Community involvement

Wyevale Garden Centres plc was acquired in 2006 by WCC Hortis, a takeover company promoted by millionaire retail entrepreneur Tom Hunter's TBH Trading and Icelandic investment group Baugur. As a result, it has been delisted from the Stock Exchange and is now a privately-owned company.

Previously, we were advised that there was a preference for supporting causes local to its garden centres (which are throughout England and Wales), such as schools, gardening related organisations and sports associations. We do not know at present if this will continue under the new owners.

Exclusions

No support for local appeals not in areas of company presence.

Applications

Due to the recent change in company ownership, no clear community support policy was available.

For small scale donations at a local level, it is suggested contact is made with the nearest Wyevale Garden Centre rather than head office.

Corporate giving

In 2006, the company made donations to charity of £5,000 (2005: £96,000). Although this is below the minimum normally required for inclusion, we shall wait and see if this is a one-off or develops into a trend.

Xerox (UK) Ltd

Company registration number 330754

Bridge House, Oxford Road, Uxbridge UB8 1HS

01895 251133; Fax: 01895 254095

Website: www.xerox.com

Correspondent: Mrs Jacqueline Robertson, Xerox (UK) Trust

Managing Director: A P Charnley

Year end	Turnover	Pre-tax profit
31/12/2007	£479,100,000	£57,200,000

Nature of company business
The principal activity of the group during the year was the marketing and financing of xerographic and electronic printing equipment, document managing systems and ancillary supplies in the UK.

Main locations: Mitcheldean, Cambridge, Welwyn Garden City

UK employees: 3,348

Charitable donations

2007: £0
2006: £0
2005: £0
2004: £60,000
2003: £60,000

Community involvement

The company previously made donations through an associated trust – The Xerox (UK) Trust (Charity Commission no. 284698). However, since 2005 the company has suspended its yearly donation under deed of covenant. This was originally supposed to be for 2005 and 2006 only, but looking at the company's 2007 accounts shows that no charitable donations were made in that year either.

We have contacted the company and trust for clarification of the situation, but as at November 2008 still await a reply.

Exclusions

Strictly no support for non-registered charities, or charities concerned with 'non-UK' activities or causes.

Applications for overseas projects, and such like, MUST be addressed to the local Rank Xerox operation in the country concerned.

Applications

Information about the trust's grantmaking criteria were previously made available via a telephone helpline on: 01895 843 288. However, this no longer seems to be the case.

However, as the trust is still making grants from its reserve funds, we suggest you contact the correspondent for further information.

Please note that there is no application form and that you should not try ringing the company to check on your application's progress.

Corporate giving

The Xerox (UK) Trust

The latest set of accounts available at the Charity Commission were those for year ending 31 December 2004. During the period, the trust generated an income of £63,540 and made charitable donations totalling £64,240. Beneficiaries included: The Free Spirit Trust and Maggie's Centre (£5,000 each); The Mulberry Centre (£4,000); St Raphael's Hospice (£3,000); The Panathlan Charity (£2,500); Music Alive (£2,000); and Get Kids Going (£1,000).

In kind support

Please note that the company does NOT make donations of equipment or consumables no matter how worthy the cause.

Yattendon Investment Trust plc

Company registration number 288238

Barn Close, Yattendon, Thatcham, Berkshire RG18 0UX

01635 203929; Fax: 01635 203921

Website: www.yattendoninvestmenttrust.co.uk

Correspondent: George Bremner, The Ilffe Family Chariytable Trust

Chairman: Lord Iliffe

Year end	Turnover	Pre-tax profit
31/12/2007	£117,003,000	£20,328,000

Nature of company business
Yattendon Investment Trust is a private company owned by the Iliffe family, with operations in the UK and Canada, and interests in newspaper publishing, television, electronic media, marinas and property.

Subsidiaries include: Hartridge Investments Ltd, Stafforshire Newsletter Ltd, Dean & Dyball Ltd, MDL Management plc, Staffordshire Newspapers Ltd, The Advertiser, Herts & Essex Newspapers Ltd, Cambridge Newspapers Ltd, Marina Developments Ltd, Burton Daily Mail Ltd

Main locations: Thatcham

UK employees: 1,276

Charitable donations

2007: £150,000
2006: £150,000
2005: £150,000
2004: £120,000

Community involvement

Charitable giving is made through The Iliffe Family Charitable Trust (Charity Commission no. 273437). The trust was established in February 1977 for 'such exclusively charitable objects and purposes in the United Kingdom or in any other part of the world as the trustees ... think fit'. The trust generally, however, donates funds to charities operating in the areas of education, medicine, welfare, religion, conservation and heritage.

Applications

The trust is administered from the same address as the company. Applications should be addressed to the charity correspondent, Mr G A Bremner. Only successful applications are acknowledged.

Corporate giving

In 2007, The Iliffe Family Charitable Trust received a total income of £195,250 of which £150,000 was gift-aided by the company. Grants were awarded totalling £254,141. Some of the beneficiaries included:

Yattendon PCC (£40,000); Marine Society and Sea Cadets (£25,000); St Bride's Appeal (£20,000); Berkshire Community Foundation (£15,000); Royal Horticultural Society (£10,000); Prior's Court Foundation (5,000); and North Atlantic Salmon Fund (£1,000).

Yorkshire Building Society

Company registration number 66B

Yorkshire House, Yorkshire Drive, Bradford BD5 8LJ

01274 472512

Website: www.ybs.co.uk

Correspondent: Mrs A L Fitzpatrick, Trust Secretary
Email: charitable@ybs.co.uk

Chairman: Ed Anderson

Chief Executive: Iain Cornish

Year end	Pre-tax profit
31/12/2007	£54,600,000

Nature of company business
Building society.

Subsidiaries include: Yorkshire Gurnsey, Accord Mortgages

Main locations: Bradford

UK employees: 2,364

Charitable donations

2008: £75,000
2007: £50,000
2006: £75,000
2005: £75,000
2004: £75,000

Community involvement

Yorkshire Building Society channels its charitable donations through The Yorkshire Building Society Charitable Foundation (Charity Commission no. 1069082). Its purpose is to support good causes where the society's members and staff live and work.

The foundation's priorities are to support registered charities or good causes involving anyone who is vulnerable (particularly children, the elderly or those with physical/mental/communication disabilities) or people suffering hardship. The trustees also extend these priorities to registered charities working to relieve suffering in animals and will consider other locally-based charities and good causes.

All requests made to the society are referred to the foundation (which is based at the same address). There are five trustees, three of which are independent of the society.

Exclusions

The society does not support any activity which is not carried out by a registered charity or which does not otherwise count as being a good cause. Additionally, there may be projects or activities which could be considered as registered charities or good causes but which the society feels do not fall within its priorities or meet other criteria. Examples of these are:

- fundraising for the purposes of pursuing political or propagandist activities
- the support of religious activities or the advancement of religion (although this would not prevent consideration for support to members of a group or community that was otherwise in need)
- any fundraising or activity under which those organising the fundraising activity would or could have a personal benefit
- provision of support for a person or people who do not come within the priority of the foundation or are not in genuine need
- applications from national charitable organisations for general ongoing funding (although this would not prevent consideration of specific items for local initiatives/branches)
- any organisation considered to be illegal or which may act illegally, or where funds are raised from, or for immoral purposes
- provision of sport generally or seeking to achieve excellence or professionalism in sport. For example this would exclude any sponsorship activities, or the provision of equipment for sports teams. The only exception to this would be, for example, some sporting activity for children who are in need, or disabled people, or other people suffering hardship
- support for individuals or groups engaged in expeditions or projects requiring them to raise funds to enable them to participate
- proposals which are purely concerned with raising funds for other organisations or charities and/or where such funds are likely to go to the administration expenses of such organisations e.g. provision of sponsorship to an individual or individuals participating in another charitable or good cause event
- carnivals or shows which are concerned with mainly entertaining the public and where there is no control over the eventual destination of funds raised
- any purposes concerned with the promotion of friendship or international friendship e.g. town twining associations
- support for a person or persons who do not come within the priority of the Foundation, or are not thought to be in genuine need

support of activities in or equipment for mainstream schools. The only exception to this would be activities or equipment to help children with special needs

provision of equipment for hospitals or other health establishments which are the responsibility of a statutory body. Equipment to be provided by a charity or good cause supporting a hospital/establishment may be considered.

Applications

Applications are usually received from members of the society or through the society's branches or head office departments. This helps ensure support is given to local charities and good causes in areas important to members and staff.

To apply, contact your local branch to discuss your application. Staff there will be pleased to help and provide you with a copy of the foundation guidelines. If you don't have a local branch, apply in writing to the above named correspondent.

Corporate giving

In 2007, the Yorkshire Building Society made a cash donation of £75,000 (2006: £50,000) to the foundation. During the year the foundation donated over £340,000 to 1,350 causes, of which 1,148 were suggested by members, maintaining the trustees' desire to support causes across the UK with the assistance of member nominations.

The Yorkshire Building Society Charitable Foundation

In 2007/08, the charity made donations of £378,447 to charitable institutions. The major grant giving activity each year has been a national appeal in support of one or more charities. Beneficiaries receiving over £1,500 each included: Macmillan Cancer Support (£110,000); Hospice of the Good Shepherd (£3,250); Just for Kids (£3,100); Redbridge Action Against Domestic Abuse, Dales Care and Bristol Music Space (£2,000 each); Second Chances (£1,950); Isle of Wight Society for the Blind (£1,875); Freshfield Animal Rescue Centre (£1,645); and Alder Hey Children's Hospital (£1,600).

The majority of the foundation's income comes from the society's Small Change, Big Difference scheme. Promoted by the Yorkshire Building Society, holders of society savings or loan accounts agree to the transfer to the foundation of an amount equivalent to the pence earned (or charged) on their accounts. In 2007/08, this amounted to £257,953.

Employee-led support

In 2007, the society launched its staff volunteers programme 'Actioneering'. So far, over 350 members of staff have signed up to get involved in activities such as business mentoring, school governorships, helping a child to read, or working with colleagues in the community on a team or individual basis.

All members of staff are entitled to take up to one day's paid leave per year to help in the local community.

Donations made by staff through fundraising are matched by the foundation to a maximum of £2,000.

Payroll giving: The Charities Trust, 'Caring Together', payroll giving scheme is in operation.

Yule Catto & Co. plc

Company registration number 98381

Central Road, Temple Fields, Harlow, Essex CM20 2BH

01279 442791; Fax: 01279 641360

Website: www.yulecatto.com

Correspondent: Richard Atkinson, Company Secretary

Chairman: A E Richmond-Watson

Chief Executive: A M Whitfield

Year end	Turnover	Pre-tax profit
31/12/2007	£565,595,000	£21,524,000

Nature of company business
The principal activities of the company are in the areas of speciality chemicals, pharmaceuticals and building products.

Subsidiaries include: Autoclenz Ltd, William Blythe Ltd, Oxford Chemicals Ltd, Arrow Direct, Reabrook Ltd, Uquifa, Synthomer Ltd, Revertex Finewaters, PFW, Holliday Pigments Ltd, Arrow Chemicals, James Robinson Ltd, Brencliffe Ltd, Nielsen Chemical

Main locations: Harlow

UK employees: 2,672

Charitable donations
2007: £54,000
2006: £92,000
2005: £93,000
2004: £116,000
2003: £78,000

Community involvement

The company supports an established list of charities, mainly in the fields of children and youth, elderly people, medical research, and sickness/disability charities. Both local and national charities (in the Harlow area) are supported.

Exclusions

No support for overseas projects, political appeals, or religious appeals.

Applications

In writing to the correspondent, but please note that as the company has charities which it supports regularly, unsolicited applications are unlikely to be successful.

Corporate giving

In 2007, the company made cash donations of £54,000. We have no details of the recipients, but know that support has been given in the past to: Harlow Community Trust, St Clare Hospice Care Trust, Help the Aged, Age Concern – England, and Barnardo's.

Zurich Financial Services (UKISA) Ltd

Company registration number 865292

PO Box 1288, Swindon, Wiltshire SN1 1FL

01793 514514

Website: www.zurich.co.uk

Correspondent: Kate Hodges, Community Affairs 01793 514514
Email: communityaffairs@uk.zurich.com

Chief Executive: David Sims

Year end
31/12/2007

Nature of company business
Zurich Financial Services (UKISA) is part of the Zurich Financial Services Group and comprises the group's operations in the UK, Ireland and South Africa.

Main locations: Swindon

UK employees: 13,500

Total employees: 55,000

Charitable donations

2007: £1,900,000
2006: £1,900,000
2005: £1,900,000

Membership: BitC, L B Group

Community involvement

Zurich states that it is: 'Committed to be good corporate citizens, and in doing so to encourage and support its employees to do their part to make a better world'. In striving to achieve this goal, the Zurich Community Trust (Charity Commission no. 266983) provides the umbrella for all the company's community work in the UK.

'The main objective of the trust is to give money, skills and time donated from Zurich together with money and time leveraged from employees of Zurich and advisors and employees of Openwork to help disadvantaged people achieve an independent future for themselves.

'The focus is on disadvantaged local communities, on issues that are often overlooked and where we can have the biggest impact.

'The trust fulfils this objective through:

- long term transformation programmes focusing on particular areas of social need
- charity partnerships and grant programmes through the Zurich Cares programme
- charity partnerships and grant programmes through the Openwork Foundation
- an employee volunteering programme through the Zurich Cares programme'

'As well as making charitable grants, a significant amount of Zurich staff time is committed to the community through working in partnership with charity partners and by brokering the volunteering needs of the voluntary sector with time and skills available from employees within the Zurich business.

'There are two strands to the Zurich Community Trust:

'**Transformation programmes**

'These work in partnership with charities to deliver transformational change over a minimum five year period. The current programmes are focusing on:

- helping non-governmental organisations(NGO's) in Southern India build their capacity (' India Programme')
- supporting vulnerable older people ('Call In Time');
- breaking the generational cycle of drug misuse ('Breaking The Cycle')
- supporting families experiencing mental health issues. ('Mental Health and Families Programme')'

'*Zurich only accept applications from those who are invited to apply.*

'**The 'Zurich Cares' employee involvement programme**

'The trust uses some of the financial donation from the Zurich UK business to match the financial donations from Zurich employees. Zurich also provides business time to enable employees to volunteer in the community and get involved in organising and managing fundraising events, volunteering schemes and local grant programmes. A great deal of employee personal time is also leveraged through this programme. This is all managed by members of the Zurich Community Trust Team.

'The six national partnerships with Canine Partners, The Calvert Trust, The Foundation for Conductive Education, Marie Curie, NSPCC (Childline) and Hope and Homes for Children supported a range of people in the UK with disabilities through the provision of trained assistance dogs, specialist outdoor activities and improved mobility. They also enabled skilled nursing time to support the terminally ill, telephone counselling to help vulnerable children and new family homes to support orphaned children in the Ukraine.

'The charity partnerships and regional and local grants from the Zurich Cares programme reached over 64,000 disadvantaged people in 2007. The feedback from stakeholders who had received grants through the Zurich Cares programme showed that 60% of them had been able to attract further funds due to our support.'

Exclusions

No grants to individuals, research, animal welfare, emergency or disaster appeals or to political, religious or mainstream educational institutions – unless directly benefiting people with disabilities, political or religious organisations.

Applications

Trust programmes – potential partners are researched, identified and selected by the Community Affairs team.

Zurich Cares – you can check your eligibility for these grants by looking at the Zurich Cares section of the company's website.

Openwork Foundation – further advice can be obtained about this scheme by calling 0870 608 2550.

Corporate giving

In 2007, Zurich UK businesses donated £1.9 million (2006: £1.9 million) to the Zurich Community Trust.

Zurich Community Trust

In 2007, the trust made grants totalling £1,951,000. The trust's policy is to focus on areas that are less popular issues and where support can be difficult to obtain. Typically, the trust allocates large amounts of money to a limited number of issues.

Within the charitable activities already identified, the total given in grants was broken down as follows: Transformation (£547,000); Zurich Cares (£939,000) and Open work Foundation (£465,000).

Employee-led support

Staff are encouraged to support charitable causes through contributions of time as well as money. Two funds exist to facilitate this:

Zurich Cares

Supported by staff of the UK businesses, sharing time and money with local communities. They do this through:

- payroll giving scheme
- active volunteering
- challenge programmes
- matching schemes for staff and their children for fundraising for charity (50% to £500 maximum per event)
- donation of gifts – for example, at Christmas and Easter time
- partnerships with 17 local, national and overseas voluntary
- a local grant programme awarding grants to local and overseas projects – all selected by employees

Local grant programmes are active in Wiltshire, Hampshire, Gloucestershire and a few other locations where Zurich have large offices. Grants range from £100 – £10,000 and support disadvantaged people to live a more independent lifestyle. Support has also been given for carers, special needs children, people with disabilities, counselling, homeless people, teenage pregnancy, and ethnic minorities.

Grants are sometimes given for core costs such as salaries, premises, transport and food costs, whilst a number of one-off purchases e.g. IT equipment, training, access and equipment for people with disabilities, have also been made.

Openwork Foundation

This is funded by employees and members of Openwork. The objective of the Openwork Foundation is to help disadvantaged children under a theme of 'Cares 4 Kids'.

The Openwork Foundation currently works in partnership to help disadvantaged children with: the Association of Children's Hospices (ACH); Winston's Wish and The Philippines Community Trust.

Through the partnerships and grant programmes during 2007 the Openwork Foundation reached 13,533 disadvantaged children. During 2007 £465,000 (2006: £435,000) was donated, support costs were £95,000 (2006: £73,000).

Payroll giving: The company runs the Give As You Earn scheme. Employees' giving is matched in full by the company, without limit.

20% of employees donate to the Zurich community Trust through this scheme.

Commercially-led support

Sponsorship: Arts and good-cause sponsorship is undertaken.

Arts & Business aims to build the knowledge and capacity of the arts and cultural sectors by supporting organisations to engage with the private sector and to stimulate personal philanthropy.

The organisation's principal focus is within the areas of not-for-profit performing and visual arts, but it also actively supports the activities of museums, libraries, archives, literary and heritage organisations. To achieve its aims, Arts & Business works in partnership with stakeholders across the UK, including Arts Council England and the governments of Scotland, Wales and Northern Ireland.

If you are involved with an arts or cultural organisation based in England, Scotland, Wales or Northern Ireland and would like information about building your fundraising potential or recruiting members for your board from the business sector, please visit the website of the appropriate regional Arts & Business office listed below.

In November 2008, Arts & Business launched The Prince of Wales Medal for Arts Philanthropy. The medal celebrates individuals who support the arts and recognises the contribution of the most inspiring philanthropists in the UK.

Arts & Business also produces a number of guides giving advice on topics such as sponsorship and tax. These are available online at: www.aandb.org.uk.

Contacts

Arts & Business Head Office (London)
Nutmeg House
60 Gainsford Street
Butlers Wharf
London
SE1 2NY
Tel: 020 7378 8143
Email: london@aandb.org.uk

Northern Ireland
Bridge House
Paulett Avenue
Belfast
BT5 4HD
Northern Ireland
Tel: 028 9073 5150
Email: northern.ireland@aandb.org.uk

Scotland
11 Abercromby Place
Edinburgh
EH3 6LB
Tel: 0131 556 3353
Email: scotland@aandb.org.uk

Wales (north)
Room 40
The Town Hall
Lloyd Street
Llandudno
LL30 2UP
Tel: 01492 574 003
Email: morth.wales@aandb.org.uk

Wales (south)
16 Museum Place
Cardiff
CF10 3BH
Tel: 029 2030 3023
Email: cymru@aandb.org.uk

East
First Floor
St Andrew's House
59 St Andrew's Street
Cambridge
CB2 3BZ
Tel: 01223 321 421
Email: east@aandb.org.uk

London (see 'Head Office')

Midlands
Suite 16–18
21 Bennetts Hill
Birmingham
B2 5QP
Tel: 0121 248 1200
Email: midlands@aandb.org.uk

North East
9th Floor, Cale Cross
156 Pilgrim Street
Newcastle upon Tyne
NE1 6SU
Tel: 0191 222 0945
Email: rr@communityfoundation.org.uk

North West
Portland Buildings
127–129 Portland Street
Manchester
M1 4PZ
Tel: 0161 236 2058
Email: north.west@aandb.org.uk

North West – Cumbria
C/o Community Foundation
Dovenby Hall
Dovenby
Cockermouth
Cumbria
CA13 0PN
Tel: 01900 825760
Email: north.west@aandb.org.uk

South East
4 Frederick Terrace
Frederick Place
Brighton
East Sussex
BN1 1AX
Tel: 01273 738 333
Email: south.east@aandb.org.uk

South West – Bristol
61 Park Street
Bristol
BS1 5NU
Tel: 0117 929 0522
Email: south.west@aandb.org.uk

South West – Cornwall
Hall for Cornwall
Back Quay, Truro
Cornwall
TR1 2LL
Tel: 01872 321979
Email: south.west@aandb.org.uk

South West – Exeter
2nd Floor Senate Court
Southernhay Gardens
Exeter
EX1 1UG
Tel: 01392 434272
Email: south.west@aandb.org.uk

Yorkshire
Dean Clough
Halifax
West Yorkshire
HX3 5AX
Tel: 01422 367 860
Email: yorkshire@aandb.org.uk

Corporate Members

NORTHERN IRELAND

Allianz Northern Ireland
Angela Connolly
Apple Recruitment
Arthur Cox
ARUP
Autoline Insurance Group
Barclays
Barnabas Venture Ltd
Bank of Ireland Ltd
being
Belfast Media Group
Belfast Visitor & Convention Bureau
Blu Zebra Ltd
Bluewater Financial Planning
Bombardier Aerospace
Botanic Inns Ltd
BT Northern Ireland
Business in the Community
Carson McDowell
Cathy Law Communications
CBS Outdoor
Cleaver Fulton Rankin
Coca Cola Bottlers (Ulster) Ltd
Consarc Design
CRN
Cunningham Coates, Stockbrokers
Davy
Design Ethos
Diageo Northern Ireland
Donelly Neary & Donnelly, Solicitors
Finbrook Investments
First Trust Bank plc
Frank McGlone Consulting
HPA Architecture
IAS SMARTS
Irwin Donaghey Stockman
JPR
James Street South
Kearney Consulting
KPMG
Lagan Boat Company
Legal & General Partnership Services Ltd
L'Estrange & Brett
Mailroom Ltd
Marsh UK Ltd
MCI, Belfast
Millar McCall Wylie, Solicitors
McKinty and Wright, Solicitors
Nicholson & Bass Ltd
Northern Bank
Octave Music Solutions
P&O Irish Sea
Parker Green International
Patterson Donnelly Solicitors
PricewaterhouseCoopers
Project Planning International
Queen's University
Robinson McIlwaine
Robinson Patterson Partnership
Royal Mail Group plc
Sheridan Group
Spirit Marketing Group
Stratagem
Tandem Design
Templeton Robinson
The Independent Mortgage Shop
The Merchant Hotel
The Outlet

The Patton Group
Think Creative
Translink
Tughans Solictors
Ulster Bank Ltd
Ulster Journals Ltd
Unicorn Consulting
University of Ulster
WJR Consulting
Weber Shandwick worldwide

SCOTLAND

664 Productions
AAMCI Consulting
Aberdeen and Grampian Chamber of Commerce
Aberdeen City Council
Aberdeenshire Council
Aeolus Group
Apollo Capital Projects Ltd
Black Light
BP
Capital Solutions
CB Richard Ellis
Chevron Upstream Europe
City Inn
City of Edinburgh Council
Clydesdale Bank
Cowan & Partners
Creative Entrepreneurs Club
Culture & Sport Glasgow
D8 Design
Davis Duncan Architects
Deloitte
Dundee City Council Leisure and Communities Department
Dunfermline Building Society
Edinburgh Chamber of Commerce
Elphinstone Group Ltd
Eskmills
Freight Design
Gillespie Macandrew LLP
Glasgow Chamber of Commerce
Hand Up Media Ltd
HBOS
Henzteeth
Institute of Directors
Inverarity Vaults Ltd
Inver House Distillers Ltd
Inverness Chamber of Commerce
Kingscavil Consulting
Kynesis
Liddell Thomson
LifeScan Scotland
Lloyds TSB Commercial Finance
Lloyds TSB Scotland
Marque Creative
Material Marketing & Communications Ltd
McFadden Associates Ltd
Mearns & Gill
Metro Ecosse
Morris & Spottiswood
Murray Beith Murray WS
MRUK
Navyblue Design Group
Peoplematters
Peopletree
Pinsent Masons
Pointsize Wolffe and Co
PricewaterhouseCoopers LLP
Print 2000

Prudential
Quirk & Co
Redding Park Developments Company Ltd
Ritchie Neill Solicitors and Estate Agents
Royal Bank of Scotland
Royal Institution of Chartered Surveyors
Royal Mail Group
SATV
Scotch Malt Whisky Society
Scottish Borders Chamber of Commerce
Scottish Council for Development and Industry
Scottish Enterprise
Scottish Government Health Department
Scottish Leadership Foundation
Scottish & Newcastle
ScottishPower
Scottish Retail Consortium
Scottish Widows
Shell UK
Standard Life
Strathclyde Fire & Rescue
Summerhall Press
Sundial Properties
Talisman Energy (UK) Ltd
The List
The Town House Company
Tods Murray LLP
TOTAL E&P UK PLC
Tullibardine Distillery
Turcan Connell
VisitScotland
Weber Shandwick
Whitespace
William Anderson & Sons
Wm Grant & Sons Distillers Ltd
YSC Scotland

WALES

33 Park Place
Aaron & Partners
Admiral Group
Alchemy Wealth Management Ltd
Arts Council of Wales
Arup
Atradius
Barclays Bank plc
BHP Billiton
Black Sheep
Carmarthenshire County Council
Carrick Design & Print
CBI Wales
Chandler KBS
Child & Child Chartered Accountants
City & County of Swansea
Coastal Housing Group Ltd
Confused.com
Conwy County Borough Council
Daily Post
Deloitte
Denbighshire County Council
DeVine Personalised Gifts
Dwr Cymru Welsh Water
Ethnic Business Support Programme
Eversheds
Faenol Festival
Fulcrum Direct
Glyndwr University
Grant Thornton UK LLP
Gravells
Group 4 Securicor
G W Consulting

Heritage Hardwood Conservatories Ltd
Hugh James Solicitors
ITV Wales
Legal & General Ltd
Leo Abse & Cohen
Live Nation – Cardiff International Arena
March Hare Music
Maskreys Ltd
Milford Haven Port Authority
Newport City Council
Newport School of Art, Media and Design
Nolan uPVC
Raytheon Systems Ltd
Royal Mail Group plc
Royal Oak Hotel
S4C
Silver Star Coach Holidays Ltd.
South Wales Chamber of Commerce
Stride Treglown Davies
Tipyn Bach Chocolate Company
University of Glamorgan
University of Wales Bangor
University of Wales Institute Cardiff
View Creative
Warwick International
West Coast Energy
West Wales Chamber of Commerce
Willmott Dixon Construction

EAST

Anglian Water Services
Ashwell Property Group
BAA Stansted
BT Research & Venturing
Cambridge University Press
Chelmsford Borough Council
Colchester Borough Council
Deloitte
Ernst & Young
Essex & Suffolk Water
Essex County Council
James Blake Associates
Jarrold & Sons
John Lewis
Kodak
Land Securities (The Hatfield Galleria)
Land Securities (The Howard Centre)
Marsh UK Ltd
May Gurney
MLA East of England
National Express East Anglia
Savills
Smith Ltd
South Cambridgeshire District Council
Stevenage Borough Council
Targetfollow
Thurrock Council
The Technology Partnership plc
University of Bedfordshire
Wrenbridge Land

LONDON

agnès b. UK
Artwise
Aviva plc
AXA Art Insurance Ltd
BAFTA
Bank of America
Barclays Bank plc
Bloomberg
BMW
BNP Paribas

BOX
BP plc
brandRapport
British Airways London Eye
British Airways plc
British Council
British Land Company plc
British Sky Broadcasting Group plc
BT
Business in the Community
Cadwalader, Wickersham & Taft
Capitalize
Carat Sponsorship
Channel 4
Circle Anglia
City Inn Ltd
CMR (Corporate Mobile Recycling)
Coca Cola
Coutts & Co
Confederation of British Industry
Conran Design Group
Deloitte
Deutsche Bank
Diageo plc
DMW
EDF Energy
Ernst & Young
Execucare
Exposure Promotions
Four Communications
GlaxoSmithKline plc
Gordon's Gin
Great Eastern Hotel
Habitat
Hamptons International
Haringey Council
Herbert Smith
Hermes
HIT Entertainment
The Holborn Partnership
The Hospital
HSBC Holdings
HS Projects
Icon Display
innocent drinks
Institute of Physics
JPMorgan
Kallaway Ltd
Kaupthing Singer & Friedlander Ltd.
Land Securities Properties Ltd
Legal & General Group plc
Lehman Brothers
Live Nation – Apollo Victoria
Live Nation – Dominion Theatre
Live Nation – Lyceum Theatre
Live Nation – Wembley Arena
Lloyd Northover
Lloyds of London
Lloyds TSB (Commercial finance)
London Borough of Lambeth/arts
London Borough of Southwark
London Calling Arts Ltd
London Underground Ltd
Man Group plc
Marsh & McLennan Companies
nabCapital
Ogilvy & Mather Ltd
Orange plc
Parker Harris Partnership
Pentland Group plc
Pretzel Films

PricewaterhouseCoopers
ProbusBNW Ltd
Prudential Ltd
Resolve
Richard Lynam Partnership
Richemont Holdings (UK) Ltd
Royal Bank of Scotland
Russell-Cooke Solicitors
SAGE Publications
Sevil Peach Gence Associates
Shell International Ltd
Shiseido Co. Ltd
Sponsorship Consulting Ltd
Strategic Real Estate Advisors Ltd
Talent Staffing
The Phoenix Consultancy
TPP Not For Profit
The World Famous
Turner Broadcasting System Europe
UBS
Unilever Ice Cream & Frozen Food
Unilever UK
UNISON
United Business Media plc
Wates Construction London
Wolff Olins

MIDLANDS

Acme Whistles
Advantage West Midlands
Arts Council England West Midlands
Aston Business School AstraZeneca
Bee Bee Developments Ltd
BioCity
Birmingham City Council
Birmingham Heartlands & Solihull NHS
Trust
Birmingham & Solihull Chamber of
Commerce and Industry
Birmingham City University
British Waterways
Business Link West Midlands
Calthorpe Estates
Clarke Associates
Complex Development Projects Ltd.
City Inn, Birmingham
Deloitte
EDS
Egg Banking plc
Ernst & Young
Experian Ltd
Geldards LLP
Hammonds
Hart Hambleton plc
Hortons' Estate Ltd
Howes Percival Solicitors
Ikano
Irwin Mitchell
Jaguar Cars
Land Rover
Leicestershire County Council
Like Minds
Live Nation – Alexandra Theatre
MADE
Marketing Birmingham
MLA East Midlands
Opus Developments Ltd
Ortus Professional Search
Parenthesis Design & Media
Communications Ltd
Pinsent Masons LLP
PMD Group Ltd

Pro Active Accounting
Prudential
Rolls-Royce plc
RO St Bernards Ltd
Grant Thornton UK Llp.
Rubery Owen Holdings Ltd
Shrewsbury & Atcham Borough Council
Smith of Derby Ltd
Spot Marketing
Telford & Wrekin Council
University of Northampton
University of Worcester
Worcester City Council

NORTH EAST

Admast Advertising
Blue River Design
Browne Smith Baker
Community Foundation (serving Tyne &
Wear and Northumberland)
Dickinson Dees
EDF Energy
Eversheds
ITV Tyne Tees
ncj Media Ltd
Newcastle Building Society
Newcastle College
North East Museums, Libraries and
Archives Council
North East Times
Northern Rock
Northumbria University
Northumbrian Water Group
One North East
Orange
Parabola Estates
Polar Productions
Procter & Gamble
Robert Muckle LLP
Ryder HKS
Samuel Philips
Silverlink Holdings Ltd
SLMO
The Gate
The UK Postcode Lottery
UBS Wealth Management
UK Land Estates
Universal Building Society
University of Durham
University of Newcastle
Ward Hadaway

NORTH WEST

Abode Manchester
Addleshaw Goddard
Annabel Williams Studio
Argent Estates
Arrk Ltd
AstraZeneca
Axa Art Insurance Ltd
Blackburn with Darwen Borough Council
BP
Bruntwood Estates Ltd
BT
Castle Hotels Group
CBI
Channel 4
City Inn Manchester
Clydesdale Bank
Consort Healthcare
Coutts & Co
Creative Lancashire

Cumbria Community Foundation
Cumbria County Council
Delineo
Deloitte
DLA Piper LLP
DWF Solicitors
EDF Energy
Ernst & Young
Experian
Frogmore Northern Ltd
Gifford
Gilbraith (TS) Ltd
Gunwharf Quays Management Ltd
Haden Freeman Ltd
HBOS
Iggesund Paperboard (A member of The
Holman Group)
Institute of Directors
John Lewis Partnership
Land Securities Properties Ltd
Lanternhouse International
Legal & General Assurance Society Ltd
Legal & General Group plc
Lloyds TSB Development Capital Ltd
Lloyds TSB Commercial Finance Ltd
Marsh UK Ltd
Manchester Airports Group plc
Manchester College of Art & Technology
Mawdsleys
MLA North West
National Australia Bank
Ogilvy
Pinsent Masons
Pricewaterhousecoopers
Prudential
Royal Bank of Scotland
Showing off Ltd
St Helens Borough Council
SEGRO
T-Shirts and Suits Ltd
The Co-operative Group (CWS) Ltd
The Creative Branch
The Howard Centre
The Mersey Partnership
The Piccadilly Partnership (Manchester)
Ltd
Tiger Tiger Manchester
Unilever UK
Wild in Art Ltd
Yorkshire Bank plc

SOUTH EAST

Abbott Laboratories Ltd
Advanced Media Associates
American Express Technologies Division
Arora International Hotel
AXA PPP Healthcare
BAA Southampton
BDO Stoy Hayward LLP
Bees Marquees
BMW Group Plant Oxford
Buss Murton LLP
CADIA
Conran & Partners Ltd
The Concorde Club & Hotel
Crawley & Gatwick Chamber of Commerce
Denplan Ltd
DMH Stallard
Eastbourne & District Chamber of
Commerce
EDF Energy
EEF South

Gifford and Partners Ltd
Gunwharf Quays Management Ltd
Hot Horse Ltd
iCrossing
John Packer Associates
Kingston Smith Chartered Accountants
Legal & General Assurance Society Ltd
Liberty Property Trust UK Ltd
MDL Marinas
MLA South East
Moore & Blatch
RLF Brighton
RPM Print & Design
SEGRO
Star Syringe
Surrey Chambers of Commerce
Thames Valley Chamber of Commerce
The Pensions Regulator
Thomas Eggar
Toshiba Information Systems UK Ltd
University of Brighton
Unilever Ice Cream & Frozen Food
Unilever UK
Varian Medical Systems
Wessex Group
West Sussex County Council Library
Wilson & Scott (Highways) Ltd
Wolseley plc
Women in Business Crawley
Yamaha-Kemble Music (UK) Ltd

SOUTH WEST

Aardman Animations
A4E Plymouth
Aedas
Arts Council England South West
Barclays Wealth (Bournemouth)
Bart Spices Ltd
Bath Spa University
Beachcroft LLP
Blackman Advertising, Marketing & Design
Burges Salmon LLP
Chelsea Building Society
City Inn Contemporary Hotel Bristol
Clydesdale Bank plc
Cornwall Chamber of Commerce &
Industry
Coutts UK
Deloitte
Devon & Cornwall Business Council
Dirty Design
Dorset Business
Dorset County Council
Dorset Echo
EDF Energy
Edis International Ltd
Feilden Clegg Bradley Architects
GWE Business West
H W Chartered Accountants
Humphries Kirk
Institute of Physics Publishing
Integria Ltd
J P Morgan (Bournemouth)
Lloyds TSB Commercial Finance
Lyons Davidson
Midas Construction Ltd
Minster Press
Morgan Cole
Northcroft
Opus Classical Exeter
Peoples Republic of South Devon
Pinsent Masons

Poundbury Systems Ltd
Plymouth Gin Ltd
QinetiQ
RAC
Roper Rhodes Ltd
Royal Bank of Scotland
RWE npower
Smith & Williamson
Southwell Business Park Ltd
Swindon Borough Council
TLT Solicitors
Target Consulting Group
Terence O'Rourke
The Loop Communication Agency
Tuffin Ferraby Taylor
Thring Townsend Lee & Pembertons
University College Falmouth
University College Plymouth St Mark & St John
University of the West of England
Urban Splash (South West)
Wessex Water
Willmott Dixon Construction
Wilsons

Withy King Solicitors
Wooden Tiger Furniture Company Ltd
Wootton Basset School

YORKSHIRE

Balance Consulting
Bradford & Bingley plc
Bradford Urban Regeneration Company
Brahm
Broker Network
Bruntwood
Calderdale MBC
Cobbetts
Dean Clough Ltd
Deloitte
designSmiths
Elspeth Consulting
Ernst & Young
HBOS
IT Help & Training
Jackson Coles
Leeds City Council
Lloyds TSB
KBC Bank NV

Last Cawthra Feather
Lilian Black
Lupton Fawcett LLP
Pinsent Mason
Provident Financial plc
Reclaim Creative
Richmonds Solicitors
Savills (L&P) Ltd
Sheffield City Council
Skipton Building Society
SMC Gower Architects
Smith & Nephew plc
St James Securities
Stephen Mason Solicitors
Tennants Auctioneers
The Firm Consultancy
The Osmosis Agency
Walker Morris
Wakefield Metropolitan District Council
York City Council
Yorkshire Bank
Yorkshire Building Society
Yorkshire Forward

Business in the Community

Business in the Community aims to make community involvement a natural part of successful business practice, and to increase the quality and extent of business activity in the community. It exists to work with companies to mobilise resources (skills, expertise, influence, products and profits) to promote social and economic regeneration. ProHelp (see separate listings in this guide) is an initiative of Business in the Community.

Contacts

Business in the Community Head Office
(covering London and South East)
137 Shepherdess Walk
London
N1 7RQ
Tel: 020 7566 8650
Web: www.bitc.org.uk
Email: london@bitc.org.uk

Northern Ireland
Bridge House
Paulett Avenue
Belfast
BT5 4HD
Tel: 028 9046 0606
Email: info@bitcni.org.uk

Wales
4th Floor, Empire House
Mount Stuart Sq
Cardiff
CF10 5FN
Tel: 029 2048 3348
Email: wales@bitc.org.uk

North East
4 & 6 Kingsway House
Kingsway
Team Valley Trading Estate
Gateshead
NE11 0HW
Tel: 0191 487 7799
Email: northeast@bitc.org.uk

North West
2nd Floor
Amazon House
3 Brazil Street
Manchester
M1 3PJ
Tel: 0161 233 7750
Email: northwest@bitc.org.uk

Yorkshire & Humberside
44–60 Richardshaw Lane
Pudsey
Leeds
West Yorkshire
LS28 7UR
Tel: 0113 205 8200
Email: yorkshire@bitc.org.uk

East Midlands
3rd Floor
30–34 Hounds Gate
Nottingham
NG1 7AB
Tel: 0115 924 7400
Email: eastmidlands@bitc.org.uk

West Midlands
83 Bournville Lane
Birmingham
B30 2HP
Tel: 0121 451 2227
Email: westmidlands@bitc.org.uk

East
Bank House
58 High Street
P O Box 93
Newmarket
CB8 8ZN
Tel: 01638 663 272
Email: eastern@bitc.org.uk

South East
Organisations based in Kent, Surrey, Sussex, Buckinghamshire, Hampshire, Oxfordshire and the Isle of Wight should contact head office above.

West
ITV West
Bath Road
Brislington
Bristol
BS4 3HG
Tel: 0117 972 2111
Email: southwest@bitc.org.uk

South West
Second Floor
Alliance House
161 Armada Way
Plymouth
PL1 1HZ
Tel: 01752 510410
Email: southwest@bitc.org.uk

Members

3i Group
3M UK
4Delivery
A&L Goodbody (NI)

ABB
Abbey
Abbott Mead Vickers
Accenture
Access Bank
Accord Housing Group
Action Renewables (NI)
Addleshaw Goddard
Adidas UK
Adnams
Advance Performance
Advantage West Midlands
AES Kilroot Power (NI)
AF Blakemore
Affinity Sutton Group
Aggregate Industries
Aircelle
Airporter (NI)
Airtricity (NI)
Allen & Overy
Alliance & Leicester
Alliance Boots
Alliance Boots (NI)
Allianz (NI)
Allied Bakeries (NI)
Allstate Northern Ireland (NI)
Almac Group (NI)
Almanac Gallery
Amaryllis
AMEC
American Express Services Europe
Amey
Amey (NI)
Amey Business Services (NI)
Andor Technology (NI)
Anglian Water Group
Anglo American
Anglo Beef Processors
Anglo Irish Bank Corporation
Anglo Irish Bank Corporation (NI)
Apax Partners
Aramark
Archant
Arco
Arena Coventry
Argent Group
Arthur Cox Solicitors (NI)
Arts & Business (NI)
Arup Group
Ascent Media
ASDA Stores
ASD Metal Services

Asidua (NI)
Associated British Foods
Associated British Ports
Atisreal UK
Atkins
Audi UK
AVIVA
Avon Cosmetics
AXA UK
Axis Europe

B.P. McKeefry (NI)
B9 Energy O&M (NI)
BAA
Babcock International Group
Bacardi Martini
BAE SYSTEMS
Bain & Company UK
Bain Capital
Baker & McKenzie
Baker Tilly
Balfour Beatty
Ballymore Properties
BAM Construct UK
Bank of America
Bank of England
Bank of Ireland
Barclays Bank
Barratt Developments
BBC
BBC (NI)
BDO Stoy Hayward
BDO Stoy Hayward (NI)
Beachcroft
Beaverbrooks the Jewellers
Bedeck (NI)
Belfast Harbour Commissioners (NI)
Belfast Health and Social Care Trust (NI)
Belfast Metropolitan College (NI)
Belfast Telegraph (NI)
BemroseBooth
Berkeley Group, The
Betfair
Bettys & Taylors of Harrogate
BHP Billiton
BIH Housing Association (NI)
Birmingham City University
Birmingham International Airport
Bishop Grosseteste University College
Lincoln
Biwater Services
Blackstone Group
Bloomberg
BluePrint (NI)
BNP Paribas
BOC
Botanic Inns (NI)
BP
BP Oil UK (NI)
Bradford & Bingley
BrightHouse
Bristol Zoo Gardens
Britannia Building Society
British Airways
British American Tobacco
British Energy Group
British Gas Wales
British Horseracing Authority

British Land Company
British Sky Broadcasting Group
British Transport Police
Broadgate Homes
Brooks Belfast (NI)
Brother UK
Brown-Forman
Bruntwood
BT
BT (NI)
Bunzl
BUPA
Burges Salmon
Buro Happold

Cadbury
Cadbury Trebor Bassett (NI)
Calico Housing
Calor Gas
Cambridge University Press
Camelot Group
Canary Wharf Group
Candover
Canon (NI)
Capgemini (UK)
Capital One
Cardiff City Transport Services
Carillion
Carphone Warehouse
Carson McDowell (Solicitors) (NI)
Castlebeck Group
Castlecourt Shopping Centre (NI)
Castleoak Care Partnerships
Cattles
Cavanagh Kelly (NI)
CE Electric UK
CEMEX
Centrica
Channel 4 Television
Chesapeake Belfast (NI)
Cheshire Building Society
Child Support Agency (NI)
Chime Communications
Chiswick Park Estate Management
Cinven
Circe (NI)
Cirque du Soleil
Citigroup (NI)
Citi United Kingdom
City College Norwich
City of Bristol College
City of London
Clanmill Housing Association (NI)
Clarehill Plastics (NI)
Clarendon Executive (NI)
Cleaver Fulton Rankin (NI)
Clifford Chance
Close Brothers Group
Clugston Group
Cluttons LLP
Clydesdale & Yorkshire Bank
CMWORKS (NI)
Coca-Cola
Coca Cola Bottlers (NI)
COLT Telecom Group S A
Compass Group
Compass Group (NI)
Connswater Shopping Centre (NI)

Consarc Design Group (NI)
Consilium Technologies (NI)
Cooper Parry
Corporate Culture
Corporate Express UK
Corus Group
Costain group
Council for the Curriculum Examinations
& Assessment (NI)
Coventry Building Society
Crane Stockham Valve (NI)
Credit 360
Credit Suisse
Croda International
Crossrail
Crown Estate, The
CSC Computer Sciences
Cummins Engine Company
Cundall Johnston & Partners
Cushman & Wakefield

Dairy Crest Group
Danone Dairies UK & Ireland
Davis Langdon
Davy (NI)
DCC Energy (NI)
Debenhams Retail
Deloitte
Deloitte (NI)
Delta Print & Packaging (NI)
Derbyshire Building Society
Deutsche Bank AG London
Diageo
Dillon Bass (NI)
Direct Rail Services
DLA Piper UK
Dollond & Aitchison
Dove Nest Group
Drax Power
Dresdner Kleinwort
Driving and Vehicle Agency (NI)
DSG International
DTZ
Duchy of Cornwall
Dunbia (NI)
DuPont UK (NI)
DVLA

E.ON UK
Ecclesiastical Insurance Group
EDF Energy
EDS
E H Booth & Co
Energia (NI)
Enterprise Rent-A-Car
Enterprise Rent-A-Car (NI)
Environ
EOL IT Services
Ernst & Young
Esh Group
Eversheds
Everyclick
Evron Foods (NI)
Exitoso (NI)
Experian
ExxonMobil

F&C Asset Management

Fabrick Housing Group
FGS McClure Watters (NI)
FG Wilson (Engineering) (NI)
Financial Services Authority
Firmus Energy (NI)
First Trust Bank (Head Office) (NI)
Fitzpatrick Contractors
Fleet Support
Fold Housing Association (NI)
Foyle Meats (NI)
FPM Accountants (NI)
FremantleMedia
Freshfields Bruckhaus Deringer
Friends Provident
Fujitsu Services
Fujitsu Services (NI)
Funeral Services (NI)

G4S
Gala Coral Group
Gallaher
Gallaher (NI)
GAM Fund Management
Gardiner & Theobald
GCap Media
Genesis Breads (NI)
Gentoo
George Best Belfast City Airport (NI)
Gilbert-Ash (NI)
GlaxoSmithKline
Gleeds
Goldblatt McGuigan (NI)
Grafton Recruitment (NI)
Grainger
Grant Thornton
Grant Thornton UK (NI)
Greggs
Grimsby Institute of Further & Higher
Education
Grosvenor
Groupama Insurances
GSH Group
GSL Ireland (NI)
Guardian Media Group

Habinteg Housing Association (NI)
Hadley Group
Haldane Fisher (NI)
Halliwells
Hallmark Cards
Hamilton Shipping (NI)
Hammerson
Hammonds
Harper Adams University College
Harvey Ingram
HBOS
HBOS (NI)
HCL BPO Services (NI)
HEAT (NI)
Heidrick & Struggles International
Hendre Housing Association
Henry Denny & Sons (NI)
Herbert Smith
Hewlett Packard (NI)
Hill & Smith Holdings
Hivolt Capacitors (NI)
HJ Banks
HLN Architects

HM Revenue and Customs
Holder Mathias Architects
Holiday Inn Hotel (NI)
Home Group
Homeloan Management
Home Retail Group
Homeserve
Honda Racing F1 Team
Hood Group
HRG
HR Wilson Associates (NI)
HSBC Bank
Hughes Christensen Co (NI)
Huhtamaki (NI)
Hutchinson Home (NI)

IBM UK (NI)
Identity and Passport Service (NI)
IEB Software (NI)
IKEA (NI)
IMI
Impact Development Training Group
Imperial Tobacco Group
International Power
INVISTA Textiles (NI)
Ipsos MORI
Ipsos MORI (NI)
Irish News (NI)
Irwin Mitchell
ISG InteriorExterior
Isles of Scilly Steamship Group
ISS UK
ITS (NI)
ITV

Jackson Building Centres
Jackson Graham Associates (NI)
Jaguar and Land Rover
J D Wetherspoon
JN Bentley
John Laing
John Lewis Partnership
John McKee & Son Solicitors (NI)
Johnson & Johnson
Johnson Matthey
Johnston Press (NI)
John Thompson & Sons (NI)
Jones Lang LaSalle
Jordan's Cereals
JP Corry Group (NI)
JPMorgan
J Sainsbury
J Sainsbury (NI)
JT Group

KCOM Group
Keepmoat
Kelda Group
Kier Group
Kilwaughter Chemical Company (NI)
Kingfisher
King Sturge
Knight Frank
Knowsley Community College
KPMG
KPMG (NI)
Kraft Foods

Lafarge Cement (NI)
Lafarge Cement UK
Laing O'Rourke
Lancaster University
Land Registry
Land Securities
Land Securities Trillium (NI)
Larne Harbour (NI)
Leeds Metropolitan University
Legal & General Group
Lincolnshire Co-operative
Linden Foods (NI)
Lindsay Cars (NI)
Linklaters
Liverpool City Council
Liverpool Daily Post & Echo
Liverpool John Moores University
Lloyds of London
Lloyds TSB Group
LMS Capital
Logistik
Londonderry Port & Harbour
Commissioners (NI)
Loughborough University
Loughborough University
Lovells
LSI Architects
Lubrizol
Lyle Bailie International (NI)

MACE
Macquarie Bank
Magnox North
Manchester Airport
Manchester City Football Club
Manchester Metropolitan University
Man Group
Mapeley Estates
Marks & Spencer
Marks & Spencer (NI)
Marsh
Marsh (NI)
Marshalls
Mars UK
Martineau
Masterlease
Masternaut (UK)
Mazars
McCain Foods (GB)
McDonald's Restaurants
McGrigors Belfast (NI)
McKinsey & Co UK
McMullen Architectural Systems (NI)
Media Wales
MediCare Pharmacy Group (NI)
Merlin Entertainments Group
Merrill Lynch
Merseyside Fire & Rescue Service
Merseytravel
Met Office
Michelin Tyre (NI)
Michelmores
Microsoft
Microsoft (NI)
Midland Heart
Mills & Reeve Solicitors
Ministry of Defence (NI)
MITIE Group

Mivan (NI)
MK Electric
Montupet (UK) (NI)
Moody's Investors Service
Morgan Cole
Morgan Est
Morgan Stanley
Morrison Facilities Services
Mott MacDonald Group
Mott MacDonald Group (NI)
Moy Park (NI)
Multi Development (NI)
Munro & Forster
Munster Simms (NI)
Musgrave Group
Musgrave Retail Partners (NI)
MWH UK

NACCO Materials Handling (NI)
Nambarrie Tea Company (NI)
National Express East Anglia
National Grid
National House-Building Council
Nationwide Building Society
Nationwide Building Society (NI)
NATS
NB Real Estate
Nestle Holdings UK
Network Rail
Next
NFT Distribution
NFU Mutual Insurance Co
NHBC (NI)
NI Ambulance Service Health & Social
Services Trust (NI)
NI Blood Transfusion Service (NI)
NI Chamber of Commerce & Industry (NI)
NI Co-Ownership Housing Association (NI)
NI Court Service (NI)
NIE Energy (NI)
NIE Energy (Woodchester House) (NI)
NIjobs.com (NI)
Nitec Solutions (NI)
N M Rothschild & Sons
Nominet
Norfolk & Waveney Mental Health NHS
Foundation Trust
Norfolk County Services
NORTEL NI (NI)
Northcliffe Media
Northern Bank (NI)
Northern Foods
Northern Rail
Northgate Information Solutions (NI)
Northumbrian Water
Northwest Regional Development Agency
North West Vision
Norton Rose
Norwich & Peterborough Building Society
Nottingham Forest Football Club
NP Aerospace
NPS Group Property Consultants
Nutricia
Nuvia Limited

Odyssey Trust Company (NI)
Office for National Statistics
Old Bushmills Distillery Co (NI)

One NorthEast
Opera North
Oracle Corporation UK
Orange
Ordnance Survey
Osborne

Pardoes Solicitors
Parker Green (NI)
Pattonair
Patton Group (NI)
Pause
Paymentshield
Peabody Trust
Pearson
Pennine Healthcare
PepsiCo UK and Ireland
Permira Advisers
Petrofac Services
Pfizer
Phoenix Natural Gas (NI)
PHS Group
Pinsent Masons
PKF (UK)
Places for People
Police Service of Northern Ireland (NI)
Port of London Authority
Premier Farnell
Premier Power (NI)
PricewaterhouseCoopers
PricewaterhouseCoopers (NI)
Principality Building Society
Pritchitt (NI)
Probation Board for Northern Ireland (NI)
Procter & Gamble UK
Progressive Building Society (NI)
ProLogis Developments
Provident Financial
Prudential UK
PSA Peugeot Citroen
Punch Taverns
Pureprint Group

QinetiQ Group
Queen's University of Belfast (NI)

Rand Group
Random House UK
RCT Homes
Real Radio
Real Radio
Redrow
Reed Elsevier
Reed in Partnership
Reed Smith
Refugee Housing Association
Remploy
Rentokil Initial
Resource (formerly Maybin Property
Support Services (NI)
Resource (NI)
Richmond Centre (NI)
Ricoh UK
Ridgeons
Ringway Group
Rio Tinto
Riverside Group
RKCR/Y&R

Rolls-Royce
Royal & Sun Alliance (NI)
Royal Liver Assurance
Royal London Group
Royal Mail Group
Royal Mail Group (NI)
RPS Consulting Engineers (NI)
RSA Group
Rural Development Council for Northern
Ireland (NI)
RWE npower

SABMiller
S A Brain & Co
Saga Group
Sage UK
Samworth Brothers (Holdings)
Sangers (NI)
SAS Software
SCA Packaging Ireland (NI)
Scottish & Newcastle
Scottish and Southern Energy
Scottish Power
SDC Trailers (NI)
Seagate Technology (NI)
Segro
Sellafield
Serco (NI)
Serco Group
Severn Trent Group plc
Sheffield Hallam University – Faculty of
Organisation and Management
Sheffield Homes
Shell UK
Shine Group
Shire Pharmaceuticals Group
Shoosmiths
Siemens
Siemens Automation and Drives
Siemens Industrial Turbomachinery
Siemens Metering Services
SIG
Simons Group
Singularity (NI)
SITA (NI)
SJ Berwin
Smarts (NI)
Smith & Nephew
Smoke Control Services
Social Security Agency (NI)
Société Générale
Sodexo
Sony United Kingdom
Southampton Solent University
South Eastern Health and Social Care
Trust (NI)
South Eastern Regional College (NI)
South Staffordshire Water
South Wales Police
SPAR
Speedy Hire
Spengler Fox (NI)
Spice Holdings
SP McCaffrey & Co Accountants (NI)
SPP Group
Springfields Fuels Limited
Standard Life
Stanhope

Starbucks Coffee Company
State Street
St David's Hotel
Stevenson Munn (NI)
St George Regeneration
St James's Place
Stradform
Stratagem (NI)
Strategic Investment Board (NI)
Stream (NI)
Styles & Wood
Supreme Group

Targetfollow Group
TATA Consultancy Services
Tate & Lyle
Taylor Wimpey
TD Waterhouse
Telefonica O2
TeleTech UK (NI)
Tesco
Tesco Stores (NI)
Texthelp Systems (NI)
Thales Group
Thames Water
The Apollo Group
The Bennie Group
The Bio Group
The BSS Group
The Care Circle (NI)
The Carvill Group (NI)
The Consortium
The Co-operative Group
The Football League Trust
The Henderson Group (NI)
The Law Society
The Midcounties Cooperative
The Pilkington Group
The Wrigley Company
The Writer
Thomson Reuters Group
Thorntons
Tim Lewis Recruitment (NI)
TLB Properties
TLT Solicitors
T-Mobile (UK)
Tolent
Total UK

Toyota Motor Manufacturing (UK)
Training Services Wales
Translink (NI)
Transport for London
Tribal Group
Trinity Mirror
TR Shipping Services (NI)
TTS Group
Tullow Oil
Turner & Townsend

UBS
UCAS
UFI (Learn Direct)
UK Coal
Ulster Carpets (NI)
Ulster Stores (NI)
Unilever
Unipart Group
Unisys
United Biscuits
United Dairy Farmers (NI)
United Utilities
University of Bradford
University of Bristol
University of Central Lancashire
University of Derby
University of East Anglia
University of Hertfordshire
University of Hull Business School
University of Leeds
University of Lincoln
University of Portsmouth Business School
University of Sheffield Management School
University of the West of England
University of Ulster (NI)
University of Warwick
Unum
USEL (Ulster Supported Employment) (NI)
Utility & Environmental Solutions
UTV Media (NI)

Valuation Office Agency
Veolia Environnement Group
Verity Appointments
Vinci
Virgin Media

Viridian Group (NI)
Vision Capital
VocaLink
Vodafone
Vodafone (NI)
Volker Stevin
VT Group

W5 (NI)
Wales and West Utilities
Walt Disney Company
Warburtons
Ward Hadaway
Warner Estate Holdings
Wates Group
Watford Football Club
Wessex Water
West Bromwich Building Society
Western Health & Social Care Trust (NI)
Westmorland Limited
West Yorkshire Police
Whitbread Group
White Young Green
White Young Green (NI)
WHSmith Retail
WH Stephens & Sons (NI)
Wilkinson
William Hill (NI)
William Reed Publishing
Willmott Dixon
Wiltan
Wincanton
Wolseley
Woolworths
Working Links
Workspace Group
WPP Group
Wragge & Co
Wrengate
Wrightbus (NI)
WSP Group

Yell Group
Yell Group (NI)

Zurich Financial Services

Business in the Community

Scottish Business in the Community (SBC) is a not-for-profit company whose aim is to support, broker and challenge businesses to continually improve their positive impact on society to ensure a successful, sustainable economy and environment.

It is led by its member companies who are committed to the promotion of responsible business practice in Scotland. Key themes include employability, health, education and the economy.

Contact:

Scottish Business in the Community
Livingstone House
First Floor (East)
43a Discovery Terrace
Heriott-Watt Research Park
Edinburgh
EH14 4AP
Tel: 0131 451 1100
Fax: 0131 451 1127
Email: info@sbcscot.com
Web: www.sbcscot.com

Members 2008

Aberdeen College	Goldfish	ScottishPower
AllianceBoots	Greggs	Scottish & Southern Energy
Amey Group	Halcrow	Scottish Enterprise
Anderson Strathern	HBOS plc	Scottish Gas
Aramark	John Lewis	Scottish & Newcastle
BAE Fleet Solutions	Johnson & Johnson	Scottish Water
BT Scotland	Johnston Press	Scottish Widows
BP	KPMG	Shell
Buccleuch Group	Kwik Fit	Sodexho
CALA Group	Laing O'Rourke	SQA
Clydesdale Bank	Lloyds TSB Scotland	Standard Life
D C Thomson	Marks and Spencer	Student Loans Company
Dell Corporation	Maersk Oil	Taylor Wimpey
Diageo	McGrigors	Total
DLA Piper	Norwich Union	Visit Scotland
Dunfermline Building Society	Oracle	Waterfront Edinburgh
Enterprise Rent-a-Car	PricewaterhouseCoopers	Weir Group
Ernst & Young	Prudential	WH Smith
First Group	Royal Mail	Wilson James
GlaxoSmithKline	Sainsbury's	Wood Group

London Benchmarking Group

In 1994 six leading UK-based international companies came together to form the London Benchmarking Group (LBG), to manage, measure and understand corporate community involvement better.

Companies' foremost contribution to society is in providing goods and services and thereby creating wealth, generating jobs and paying taxes. Traditionally many have also made an additional voluntary, usually charitable, contribution. As companies' relationships with the community become more complex, the motivations for involvement are more diverse. These include:

▷ a sense of moral and social responsibility; also responding to expectations from society

▷ a belief that companies have a long-term interest in fostering a healthy community, sometimes known as enlightened self-interest

▷ the knowledge that community interventions involving employees, customers and suppliers can have direct benefits, through increased profitability, stronger company image, reduced costs, better employee morale and improved customer loyalty.

The original members used these three motivations as the basis to understand how each managed and measured its community involvement programmes. Since then, the Group has grown to number over 100, with many more applying the techniques independently.

All members recognise that companies are expected to get involved in the community and are often judged on the amount they contribute. This involvement often goes beyond straightforward donations to charity – and if a comprehensive account is not produced, key groups such as staff, local communities, opinion formers and the media might easily form the wrong impression.

The challenge facing the founding members of the LBG was how to effectively report their community activities to demonstrate that they are indeed responsible corporate citizens. Effective reporting is best based on solid measures of performance, but in the 'soft' area of social reporting hard measures are still in their infancy.

Their solution was to devise a tool with which to manage, measure and compare their relationship with the community – The London Benchmarking Model. Further information about the group and its benchmarking model may be found at www.lbg-online.net.

Members

Abbey	Citi	ISS UK	Royal Mail Group
Accenture	Citi USA	J Sainsbury plc	SABMiller
Airbus UK	City of London	John Lewis Partnership	Scottish and Newcastle
Allen and Overy	Clifford Chance LLP	Johnson Matthey	ScottishPower plc
Anglo American	CMS Cameron McKenna	KPMG	Segro plc
ANZ	Coca-Cola Hellenic Bottling	Laing O'Rourke	Sellafield Ltd
Arab African International	Company	Land Securities	Severn Trent plc
Bank	Deloitte	Legal and General	Shell
AstraZeneca	Deutsche Bank AG London	Liberty Global Europe BV	Standard Chartered Bank
AXA UK	Diageo	Linklaters	Standard Life
BAA plc	DLA Piper	Lloyds TSB	Syngenta
BAE Systems	Dubai International Financial	London Stock Exchange	Telecom Italia
BAM Construct UK Ltd	Centre	LOréal	Telefonica O2 Europe
Bank of America	E.ON	Lovells	Tesco
Barclays	East Midlands Airport	Marks and Spencer	Thames Water
BBC	EDF Energy	Morgan Stanley	The Boots Company
BD	Energias de Portugal	National Grid	The Co-operative Group
Berwin Leighton Paisner	Ernst and Young	Nationwide	The Royal Bank of Scotland
BG Group	ExCeL London	Nestlé UK	Group
Bradford and Bingley	Financial Services Authority	Nokia Corporation	Trader Media Group
Britannia	FirstGroup	Norwich Union	Turner Broadcasting
British Airways	Freshfields Bruckhaus Deringer	npower	UBS AG
British American Tobacco	Friends Provident	Pearson	Unilever
British Land	Gallaher	Philip Morris International	United Utilities
Britvic	GlaxoSmithKline	PricewaterhouseCoopers LLP	Unum
Brown-Forman	Hammerson	Procter and Gamble UK	Virgin Media
BSkyB	HBOS	Provident Financial	Virgin Unite
BT	Herbert Smith	Prudential	Vodafone
BUPA	Home Retail Group	Rabobank	Wates Group
Cadbury	HSBC	Reed Elsevier	Weil Gotshal and Manges
Camelot Group	ING	Rio Tinto	Wragge and Co
Capita Group	International Personal Finance	Rolls-Royce	Yell Group
Caterpillar	Investec plc	Rothschild	Zurich
Centrica	IPC Media	Royal and Sun Alliance	

ProHelp

What is ProHelp?

Formerly the Professional Firms Group, ProHelp is a national network of over 800 firms across the UK who volunteer their time and expertise for the benefit of the local community. It is a Business in the Community initiative whose member firms supported over 1,600 community groups with £2.3 million of free professional advice in 2008. ProHelp was established over 17 years ago.

Participating professional firms include lawyers, accountants, IT consultants, architects, surveyors, marketing specialists and engineers. Community Groups that receive support from ProHelp are non-profit making, locally based and cannot afford to pay for professional services. Firms can contribute towards a single project or give longer-term strategic support such as becoming a trustee.

What help can they provide?

The professional firms undertake short assignments, which include feasibility studies, structural surveys, marketing and business plans, legal and accountancy advice and property valuations.

Will my project be eligible?

You must be a community-based not-for-profit organisation working for the social and economic regeneration of your local area and should fit within the following criteria.

- You must have a track record of working successfully with the local community.
- You must not have the funding for the specific piece of work to be done nor be retaining paid advisors to do the work.
- If you are a branch of a national organisation, you must be locally constituted and prove that neither the expertise nor the funding to pay for the work is available centrally.
- Your project must be realistic and viable.
- Your governing body must authorise the involvement of ProHelp.

When will a project not qualify?

- Applications for assistance with litigation will not be considered.
- Help is generally not given to animal welfare organisations whose primary focus is overseas aid.
- Assistance to religious groups will only be offered if the project benefits the wider community.

What do I do now?

If you have a project in mind which could benefit from support from ProHelp, please get in touch with the relevant regional contact listed below. More local contacts are listed on the website at: www.bitc.org.uk/community/employee_volunteering/prohelp

What will happen then?

If your project is appropriate, you will be asked to fill in a standard questionnaire. It may also be necessary for you to meet with a representative from ProHelp to develop a fuller brief for the assignment. A summary of your project will then be taken to a group who will decide whether your project meets the eligibility criteria and if there is a firm available to do the work. A meeting will then be arranged between yourself and the interested professional firm.

The National ProHelp Manager (employee volunteering)

Gennie Franklin
Tel: 020 7566 8711
Email: gennie.franklin@bitc.org.uk

Regional contacts

Northern Ireland

Jill McCluskey
Bridge House
Paulett Avenue
Belfast
BT5 4HD
Tel: 028 9046 0606

Scotland

Scottish Business in the Community
CARES (Team Challenge)
Livingstone House
First Floor (East)
43a Discovery Terrace
Heriott-Watt Research Park
Edinburgh, EH14 4AP
Tel 0131 451 1100
Fax 0131 451 1127
Email: info@sbcscot.com

Wales

Jill Salter
ProHelp Co-ordinator
Business in the Community
4th Floor Empire House
Mount Stuart Square
Cardiff
CF10 5FN
Tel: 029 2048 3348
Email: jill.slater@bitc.org.uk

East of England

Gary Towers
Deputy Regional Director
Business in the Community
Bank House
PO Box 93
Newmarket
Suffolk
CB8 1ZN
Tel: 01603 508438
Email: gary.towers@bitc.org.uk

East Midlands

Ann Hilton
ProHelp Manager
Business in the Community
3rd Floor
30–34 Hounds Gate
Nottingham
NG1 7AB
Tel: 0115 924 7408
Email: ann.hilton@bitc.org.uk

London and the South East

Anna Springbett
Business in the Community
137 Shepherdess Walk
London
N1 7RQ
Tel: 020 7566 8652
Email: anna.springbett@bitc.org.uk

North East

Business in the Community
Units 4 & 6 Kingsway House
Kingsway
Team Valley Trading Estate
Gateshead
NE11 0HW
Tel: 0191 487 7799

North West

Sadie Tutton
Business in the Community
2nd Floor, Amazon House
3 Brazil Street
Manchester
M1 3PJ
Tel: 0161 233 7761
Email: sadie.tutton@bitc.org.uk

South West

Marie Smith
Business Engagement Manager
Business in the Community
ITV West
Bath Road
Bristol
BS4 3HG
Tel: 0117 972 2111
Email: marie.smith@bitc.org.uk

West Midlands

Birmingham Cares
C/o Cadbury
83 Bournville Lane
Birmingham
B30 2HP
Tel: 0121 451 2227
Email: jennifer.leech@bitc.org.uk

Yorkshire & Humber

Jo Crossley
Regional Campaign Manager
Business in the Community
Kingswood House
80 Richardshaw Lane
Pudsey
Leeds
LS28 6BN
Tel: 0113 205 8202
Email: jo.crossley@bitc.org.uk

This section classifies the companies included in the guide according to their main activities. It should enable charities to target companies for specific appeals or services. Companies which fall into two or more categories are listed under each one, except in the more obvious cases. For example, building companies and property companies, where the categories have been cross-referenced. Retailers have been split into further separate categories due to the variety covered.

Accountants

Accenture UK Ltd
Cooper-Parry LLP
Deloitte
KPMG LLP
Mazars LLP
PKF (UK) LLP
PricewaterhouseCoopers LLP

Advertising/marketing

Abbott Mead Vickers – BBDO Ltd
DDB UK Ltd
WPP Group plc

Aerospace

BAE Systems
Bombardier Aerospace Europe Ltd
Cobham plc
QinetiQ Group plc
Smiths Group plc

Agriculture

Alan Hudson Ltd
Man Group plc
Pfizer Ltd

Airport operators

BAA plc
Birmingham International Airport Ltd
East Midlands Airport
Manchester Airport Group plc

Aviation

British Airways plc
John Swire & Sons Ltd
United Airlines

Banking

Abbey
Alliance & Leicester plc
Bank of England
Bank of Ireland UK Financial Services
Barclays plc
Cazenove Group plc
CIBC World Markets plc
Close Brothers Group plc
Clydesdale Bank plc
Coutts & Co
Credit Suisse

Deutsche Bank
Dresdner Kleinwort Ltd
First Trust Bank
Goldman Sachs International
HBOS plc
HFC Bank Ltd
HSBC Holdings plc
Julian Hodge Bank Ltd
Kaupthing Singer & Friedlander Ltd
Lazard & Co. Ltd
Lloyds TSB Group plc
N M Rothschild & Sons Ltd
Royal Bank of Scotland Group plc
Standard Chartered plc
Standard Life
UBS

Brewers/distillers

Adnams plc
Daniel Thwaites plc
Diageo plc
Scottish & Newcastle UK Ltd

Building material merchants

Focus (DIY) Ltd

Building materials

Aggregate Industries Ltd
Hanson Ltd
SIG plc

Building Society

Bradford & Bingley plc
Britannia Building Society
Chelsea Building Society
Cheshire Building Society
Coventry Building Society
Derbyshire Building Society
Leeds Building Society
Nationwide Building Society
Newcastle Building Society
Norwich & Peterborough Building Society
Nottingham Building Society
Principality Building Society
West Bromwich Building Society
Yorkshire Building Society

Building/construction

AMEC plc
Barrett Developments plc

Bellway plc
Berkeley Group plc
Carillion plc
CEMEX UK Operations
Costain Group plc
Esh Group
Gladedale Holdings Ltd
Miller Group Ltd
Persimmon plc
Redrow Group plc
Robert McAlpine Ltd
Shepherd Building Group Ltd
Taylor Woodrow Construction
Travis Perkins plc
Wates Group Ltd
Willmott Dixon Ltd
Yule Catto & Co plc

Business equipment

Xerox (UK) Ltd

Business services

Bain & Company Inc. UK
Canon (UK) Ltd
Economist Newspaper Ltd
Informa plc
Reed Executive plc
Rentokil Initial plc
Serco Group plc

Cash 'n' Carry

Bestway (Holdings) Ltd
Dhamecha Group Ltd

Catalogue shopping

Findel plc
Littlewoods Shop Direct Home Shopping Ltd
Mothercare plc

Catering services

ARAMARK Ltd
Sodexo Ltd

Chemicals & plastics

3M United Kingdom plc
Akzo Nobel UK Ltd
BASF plc
Bayer plc
Ciba UK plc

Clariant UK Ltd
Dow Chemical Company Ltd
Dow Corning Ltd
Huntsman/Tioxide Europe Ltd
Kodak Ltd
Low & Bonar plc
Pfizer Ltd
Scott Bader Company Ltd
Yule Catto & Co plc

Clothing manufacture

GAP (UK) Ltd
Levi Strauss (UK) Ltd
Pentland Group plc

Commodity traders

Cargill plc
Glencore UK Ltd

Computer software

Adobe Systems UK
CA plc
Microsoft Ltd
Misys plc
Oracle Corporation UK Ltd
RM plc
Steria Ltd

Confectionery

Cadbury plc
Lofthouse of Fleetwood Ltd

Consulting engineers

Arup Group Ltd
Mott MacDonald Ltd

Dairy products

Robert Wiseman Dairies plc

Defence

BAE Systems
HESCO Bastion Ltd
QinetiQ Group plc

Distribution

Bunzl plc
Cargill plc
John Menzies plc
Palmer & Harvey McLane Ltd
SIG plc

Domestic appliances

Dyson Ltd
Hoover Ltd

Drinks manufacture

Coca-Cola Great Britain
Innocent Drinks
Intercontinental Hotels Group plc
Nestlé UK Ltd

Electricity

British Energy Group plc

British Nuclear Fuels plc
C E Electric UK Ltd
E.ON UK plc
EDF Energy plc
National Grid plc
RWE npower
Scottish and Southern Energy plc
ScottishPower plc
United Utilities Group plc
Western Power Distribution

Electronics/computers

CEF Holdings Ltd
Cobham plc
Filtronic plc
Hewlett-Packard Ltd
IBM United Kingdom Ltd
Panasonic UK Ltd
Philips Electronics UK Ltd
Psion plc
RM plc
Samsung Electronics (UK) Ltd
Siemens plc
Sony United Kingdom Ltd
Spirent plc
Toshiba Information Systems (UK) Ltd
Unisys Ltd

Engineering

AEA Technology plc
AMEC plc
Biwater plc
Charter plc
Cummins Ltd
Dyson Ltd
FKI plc
GKN plc
IMI plc
John Wood Group plc
Laird Group plc
Marshall of Cambridge (Holdings) Ltd
Network Rail Infrastructure Ltd
Renishaw plc
Rexam plc
Rolls-Royce plc
Smiths Group plc
Spirax Sarco Engineering plc
TT Electronics plc
Weir Group plc

Exploration services

Hunting plc

Financial services

3i Group plc
Apax Partners LLP
Boyer Allan Investment Investment Management LLP
British Land Company plc
Caledonia Investments
Capital One Holdings Ltd
Cattles plc
Citibank International plc
Close Brothers Group plc
Egg Ltd
Ernst & Young LLP

Execution Ltd
F&C Asset Management plc
Family Assurance Friendly Society Ltd
Fidelity Investment Management Ltd
Financial Services Authority
First Plus Financial Group plc
Henderson Group plc
HSBC Holdings plc
ICAP plc
Invesco Asset Management Ltd
J P Morgan Chase
Julian Hodge Bank Ltd
Legal & General plc
Liberty International plc
Lincoln Financial Group
Liverpool Victoria
Lloyds TSB Group plc
Man Group plc
Marks and Spencer Group plc
Midcounties Co-operative
Morgan Stanley International Ltd
Northern Rock plc
Old Mutual plc
Principality Building Society
Private Equity Foundation
Prudential plc
RAB Capital plc
Royal Bank of Scotland Group plc
Saga Group Ltd
Schroders plc
St James's Place plc
Standard Chartered plc
Travelex Holdings Ltd

Food manufacture

Arla Foods Ltd
Associated British Foods plc
Baxters Food Group Ltd
Bernard Matthews Ltd
Diageo plc
Greencore Group UK
Greggs plc
H J Heinz Company Ltd
Kellogg Company of Great Britain
Kraft Foods UK Ltd
McCain Foods (GB) Ltd
Nestlé UK Ltd
Northern Foods plc
PepsiCo UK
Premier Foods plc
Sara Lee UK Holdings Ltd
Unilever UK
Uniq plc
United Biscuits Ltd
Warburtons Ltd
Weetabix Ltd

Food services

Norbert Dentressangle

Footwear manufacture

Pentland Group plc

Furniture manufacture

Cadogan Group Ltd
Galiform plc

Gaming

Camelot Group plc
Genting Stanley plc
Ladbrokes plc
Sportech plc

Garden centres

Wyevale Garden Centres Ltd

Glass

Pilkington Group Ltd

Health/beauty products

Avon Cosmetics Ltd
Mascolo Ltd

Healthcare

Alliance Boots
Baxter Healthcare Ltd
BUPA Ltd
GE Healthcare
Medtronic Ltd
Pfizer Ltd
Procter & Gamble UK
Smith & Nephew plc
SSL International plc

Hotels

Adnams plc
Daniel Thwaites plc
De Vere Group plc
Intercontinental Hotels Group plc
Ladbrokes plc
Whitbread plc

Household

O⁻ˑ ne & Little Ltd
    ussons plc
    er & Gamble UK
    tt Benckiser plc
    ohnson Ltd
    Lee UK Holdings Ltd
    ːver UK
    ːrford Wedgwood UK plc
Wilkinson Hardware Stores Ltd

Industrial products/services

Du Pont (UK) Ltd

Information management & communication

Communisis plc
Informa plc
WPP Group plc

Information Technology

Agilent Technologies UK Ltd
AOL UK Ltd
CA plc
Data Connection Ltd
Electronic Data Systems Ltd
Fujitsu Services Holdings plc
Lockheed Martin

Medtronic Ltd
Oracle Corporation UK Ltd
W S Atkins plc

Instrumentation

Invensys plc
Unipart Group of Companies Ltd

Insurance

Admiral Group plc
AEGON Scottish Equitable plc
Allianz Insurance plc
Aviva plc
Brit Insurance Holdings plc
BUPA Ltd
Catlin Group Ltd
Congregational & General Insurance plc
Cooper Gay (Holdings) Ltd
Ecclesiastical Insurance Group plc
Fortis Insurance Ltd
Friends Provident plc
HFC Bank Ltd
Hiiscox plc
Jardine Lloyd Thompson Group plc
Liverpool Victoria
Lloyd's
Marsh Ltd
Novae Group plc
Personal Group Holdings plc
Provident Financial plc
Prudential plc
Royal & Sun Alliance Insurance Group plc
Royal Bank of Scotland Group plc
Royal London Mutual Insurance Society Ltd
Standard Life
UIA (Insurance) Ltd
Unum

Legal

Addleshaw Goddard
Allen & Overy LLP
Freshfields Bruuckhaus Deringer LLP
Herbert Smith LLP
Linklaters
Simmons & Simmons
Slaughter and May
Wragge & Co LLP

Leisure

Caledonia Investments
De Vere Group plc
J D Wetherspoon plc
Ladbrokes plc
Northern Trust Group Ltd
Rank Group plc
Saga Group Ltd
Scottish & Newcastle UK Ltd
Thomas Cook Group plc
TUI UK Ltd
Whitbread plc
William Hill plc

Life assurance

Zurich Financial Services (UKISA) Ltd

Logistics

Geopost UK Ltd
John Menzies plc
Norbert Dentressangle
TDG plc
TNT UK Ltd
Uniq plc
UPS

Manufacturing

Caparo Group Ltd
Cookson Group plc
Euro Packaging Ltd
FKI plc
Morgan Crucible Company plc
Robert Bosch Ltd
Swann-Morton Ltd
Tomkins plc

Marine

John Swire & Sons Ltd
QinetiQ Group plc
VT Group plc

Media

Aegis Group plc
AOL UK Ltd
Archant
Bloomsbury Publishing plc
British Sky Broadcasting Group plc
Chrysalis Group plc
Daily Mail and General Trust plc
Economist Newspaper Ltd
Future plc
Guardian Media Group plc
IPC Media Ltd
ITV plc
Johnston Press plc
National Magazine Co Ltd
News International plc
Northern & Shell Network Ltd
Pearson plc
STV Group plc
Telegraph Media Group Ltd
Thomson Reuters plc
Trinity Mirror plc
United Business Media Ltd
Yattendon Investment Trust plc

Metals

Alcoa UK Holdings Ltd
Anglesey Aluminium Metals Ltd
Corus Group plc
Johnson Matthey plc
Stemcor Holdings Ltd

Mining

Anglo American plc
Banks Group
BHP Billiton plc
Celtic Energy Ltd
De Beers
Rio Tinto plc
UK Coal plc

Miscellaneous

Amey UK plc
eaga plc
Johnson Service Group plc
Royal Mail Holdings plc

Motors & accessories

Arriva plc
Avon Rubber plc
BMW UK Ltd
Citroën UK Ltd
Fiat Group Automobiles UK Ltd
Ford Motor Company Ltd
General Motors UK Ltd
Honda of the UK Manufacturing Ltd
Inchcape plc
Jaguar Cars Ltd
Kwik-Fit Group
Michelin Tyre Public Ltd Company
Toyota Motor Manufacturing (UK) Ltd
Unipart Group of Companies Ltd

Music

EMI Group Ltd

Oil & gas/fuel

Air Products Group Ltd
BP p.l.c.
British Nuclear Fuels plc
Calor Gas Ltd
Centrica plc
Chevron Ltd
E.ON UK plc
Esso UK Ltd
Hess Ltd
Shell
Total UK Ltd
United Utilities Group plc

Personal care products

Colgate-Palmolive (UK) Ltd
Mascolo Ltd

Pharmaceuticals

Alliance Boots
AstraZeneca plc
Bristol-Myers Squibb Pharmaceuticals Ltd
Eli Lilly and Company Ltd
GlaxoSmithKline plc
Merck Sharp & Dohme Ltd
P Z Cussons plc
Reckitt Benckiser plc
Roche Products Ltd
Shire Pharmaceuticals plc
Yule Catto & Co plc

Plant equipment

J C Bamford Excavators Ltd

Print/paper/packaging

Bunzl plc
D S Smith Holdings plc
De La Rue plc
LINPAC Group Ltd

Low & Bonar plc
Rexam plc
Tullis Russell Group Ltd

Professional support services

Capita Group plc
Tullis Russell Group Ltd
WSP Group plc

Property

Allied London Properties Ltd
AMEC plc
Berkeley Group plc
British Land Company plc
Brixton plc
Broadland Properties Ltd
Bruntwood Ltd
Cadogan Group Ltd
Caledonia Investments
Canary Wharf Group plc
Crest Nicholson plc
Daejan Holdings plc
Dhamecha Group Ltd
Evans Property Group
Gladedale Holdings Ltd
Great Portland Estates plc
Grosvenor Group
Hammerson plc
John Swire & Sons Ltd
Jones Lang LaSalle Ltd
Kaupthing Singer & Friedlander Ltd
Kingfisher plc
Land Securities Group plc
Miller Group Ltd
Muir Group
Northern Trust Group Ltd
Ravensale Ltd
Redrow Group plc
Ridgesave Ltd
Robert McAlpine Ltd
Savills plc
SEGRO plc
Taylor Woodrow Construction

Quarrying

Aggregate Industries Ltd
Lafarge Aggregates & Concretes UK

Retail – Clothing & footwear

GAP (UK) Ltd
JJB Sports plc
Marks and Spencer Group plc
Next plc
Shoe Zone Ltd
TJX UK (formerly TK Maxx)

Retail – Department & variety stores

Anglia Regional Co-operative Society Ltd
Fenwick Ltd
House of Fraser (Stores) Ltd
John Lewis Partnership plc
Mothercare plc
T.J. Morris Ltd

The Co-operative Group

Retail – DIY/furniture

Galiform plc
Kingfisher plc
Wilkinson Hardware Stores Ltd

Retail – Electrical

DSG International plc
Richer Sounds plc

Retail – Miscellaneous

Body Shop International plc
Carphone Warehouse Group plc
Clinton Cards plc
Greggs plc
Halfords Group plc
N Brown Group plc
Southern Co-operatives Ltd
Starbucks Coffee Company (UK) Ltd
Topps Tiles plc
WH Smith plc

Retail – Restaurants/fast food

Compass Group plc
Diageo plc
J D Wetherspoon plc
McDonald's Restaurants Ltd
Mitchells & Butlers plc
Whitbread plc

Retail – Supermarkets

Anglia Regional Co-operative Society Ltd
ASDA Stores Ltd
Co-operative Group
J Sainsbury plc
John Lewis Partnership plc
Midcounties Co-operative
Southern Co-operatives Ltd
Spar (UK) Ltd
Tesco plc
Wm Morrison Supermarkets plc

Securities/shares

Goldman Sachs International
London Stock Exchange

Security services

QinetiQ Group plc

Services

eaga plc

Shipping

Cargill plc

Sports clothing

adidas (UK) Ltd
JJB Sports plc
Nike (UK) Ltd

Sugar refiners

British Sugar plc
Tate & Lyle plc

Telecommunications

ADC Krone (UK)
AT&T (UK) Ltd
BT Group plc
Cable and Wireless plc
Caudwell Holdings Ltd
Orange PCS Ltd
QinetiQ Group plc
Telefonica O2 Europe plc
Thales UK Ltd
Carphone Warehouse Group plc
T-Mobile (UK) Ltd
Toshiba Information Systems (UK) Ltd
Vodafone Group plc

Textiles

Coats plc
Osborne & Little Ltd
Sara Lee UK Holdings Ltd

Tobacco

British American Tobacco plc
Gallaher Ltd
Imperial Tobacco Group plc

Toy manufacture & distribution

Hasbro UK Ltd

Transport & communications

First plc
G4S plc
Go Ahead Group plc
J Stobart and Sons Ltd
Mersey Docks and Harbour Company
National Express Group plc
Stagecoach Group plc
TDG plc

Transport & shipping services

Associated British Ports Holdings Ltd

Transportation

Network Rail Infrastructure Ltd
TNT UK Ltd
UPS
VT Group plc

Waste management

Biwater plc
Severn Trent plc

Water

Anglian Water Services Ltd
Dwr Cymru Welsh Water
Kelda Group plc
Northumbrian Water Group
Pennon Group plc
Severn Trent plc
United Utilities Group plc
Wessex Water Services Ltd

Geographical listing of head offices

This geographical index is based purely on the head office address given at the start of each company entry. While it is generally the case that companies give some preference to charities local to their operating sites, including the head office, this is not always so. Once this index has been used to produce a preliminary list of potential companies to approach, the individual entries for each company should be read carefully to determine whether or not your particular project falls within the company's criteria.

England

Bedfordshire
Abbey
General Motors UK Ltd
Personal Group Holdings plc
Whitbread plc

Berkshire
3M United Kingdom plc
Baxter Healthcare Ltd
Bayer plc
BMW UK Ltd
CA plc
Centrica plc
Citroën UK Ltd
Costain Group plc
Fiat Group Automobiles UK Ltd
Fujitsu Services Holdings plc
Hanson Ltd
Hewlett-Packard Ltd
HFC Bank Ltd
Microsoft Ltd
Oracle Corporation UK Ltd
Panasonic UK Ltd
PepsiCo UK
Reckitt Benckiser plc
Sara Lee UK Holdings Ltd
SEGRO plc
Telefonica O2 Europe plc
The Morgan Crucible Company plc
The Rank Group Plc
Vodafone Group plc
Wyevale Garden Centres Ltd
Yattendon Investment Trust plc

Bristol
Bank of Ireland UK Financial Services
Imperial Tobacco Group plc
Orange PCS Ltd
Western Power Distribution

Buckinghamshire
GE Healthcare
Intercontinental Hotels Group plc
Uniq plc

Cambridgeshire
Alan Hudson Ltd
Anglian Water Services Ltd
Marshall of Cambridge (Holdings) Ltd

Cheshire
BASF plc
British Nuclear Fuels plc
Cheshire Building Society
Ciba UK plc
Focus (DIY) Ltd
Johnson Service Group plc
Muir Group
Northern Trust Group Ltd
The Royal London Mutual Insurance Society Ltd
United Utilities Group plc

County Durham
C E Electric UK Ltd
Cummins Ltd
Esh Group
Huntsman/Tioxide Europe Ltd
Northumbrian Water Group
The Banks Group

Cumbria
J Stobart and Sons Ltd

Derbyshire
Cooper-Parry LLP
Derbyshire Building Society
East Midlands Airport
Egg Ltd
Greencore Group UK
Toyota Motor Manufacturing (UK) Ltd

Devon
Pennon Group plc

Dorset
Cobham plc
Liverpool Victoria

East Sussex
Family Assurance Friendly Society Ltd
Palmer & Harvey McLane Ltd

Essex
Clinton Cards Plc
Ford Motor Company Ltd
Yule Catto & Co plc

Gloucestershire
ADC Krone (UK)
Chelsea Building Society
Ecclesiastical Insurance Group plc
Kraft Foods UK Ltd
Lincoln Financial Group
Renishaw plc

Spirax Sarco Engineering plc
St James's Place plc

Greater Manchester
Addleshaw Goddard
adidas (UK) Ltd
Bruntwood Ltd
Guardian Media Group plc
Kellogg Company of Great Britain
Kwik-Fit Group
N Brown Group plc
P Z Cussons Plc
The Co-operative Group
The Manchester Airport Group plc

Hampshire
BAE Systems
De La Rue plc
Eli Lilly and Company Ltd
Fortis Insurance Ltd
IBM United Kingdom Ltd
QinetiQ Group plc
Serco Group plc
Shire Pharmaceuticals plc
Southern Co-operatives Ltd

Hertfordshire
Camelot Group plc
DSG International plc
Du Pont (UK) Ltd
J D Wetherspoon plc
Kodak Ltd
Medtronic Ltd
Merck Sharp & Dohme Ltd
Mothercare plc
Premier Foods plc
Robert McAlpine Ltd
Roche Products Ltd
Steria Ltd
Taylor Woodrow Construction
Tesco plc
TJX UK (formerly TK Maxx)
T-Mobile (UK) Ltd
UIA (Insurance) Ltd
Willmott Dixon Ltd

Kent
Fidelity Investment Management Ltd
Saga Group Ltd

Lancashire

Daniel Thwaites plc
JJB Sports plc
Lofthouse of Fleetwood Ltd
Warburtons Ltd

Leicestershire

Aggregate Industries Ltd
Alliance & Leicester plc
Barrett Developments plc
Lafarge Aggregates & Concretes UK
Next plc
Shoe Zone Ltd
Topps Tiles plc

London

3i Group plc
Abbott Mead Vickers - BBDO Ltd
Accenture UK Ltd
Aegis Group Plc
Akzo Nobel UK Ltd
Allen & Overy LLP
Allied London Properties Ltd
AMEC plc
Anglo American plc
AOL UK Ltd
Apax Partners LLP
ARAMARK Ltd
Arup Group Ltd
Associated British Foods plc
Associated British Ports Holdings Ltd
AstraZeneca plc
Aviva plc
BAA plc
Bain & Company Inc. UK
Bank of England
Barclays plc
Bestway (Holdings) Ltd
BHP Billiton Plc
Bloomsbury Publishing Plc
Boyer Allan Investment Investment
Management LLP
BP plc
Brit Insurance Holdings plc
British American Tobacco plc
British Land Company plc
Brixton plc
BT Group plc
Bunzl plc
BUPA Ltd
Cable and Wireless plc
Cadbury plc
Cadogan Group Ltd
Caledonia Investments
Canary Wharf Group plc
Caparo Group Ltd
Capita Group plc
Catlin Group Ltd
Cazenove Group plc
Charter plc
Chevron Ltd
Chrysalis Group plc
CIBC World Markets plc
Citibank International plc
Close Brothers Group plc
Coca-Cola Great Britain
Cookson Group plc
Cooper Gay (Holdings) Ltd

Corus Group plc
Coutts & Co
Credit Suisse
D S Smith Holdings plc
Daejan Holdings plc
Daily Mail and General Trust plc
DDB UK Ltd
De Beers
De Vere Group plc
Deloitte
Deutsche Bank
Diageo plc
Dresdner Kleinwort Ltd
Economist Newspaper Ltd
EDF Energy plc
EMI Group Ltd
Ernst & Young LLP
Execution Ltd
F&C Asset Management plc
Financial Services Authority
Freshfields Bruuckhaus Deringer LLP
Galiform plc
Glencore UK Ltd
Goldman Sachs International
Great Portland Estates plc
Grosvenor Group
Hammerson plc
Henderson Group plc
Herbert Smith LLP
Hess Ltd
Hiiscox plc
HSBC Holdings plc
Hunting plc
ICAP plc
Inchcape plc
Informa plc
Innocent Drinks
Invensys plc
Invesco Asset Management Ltd
IPC Media Ltd
ITV plc
J P Morgan Chase
J Sainsbury plc
Jardine Lloyd Thompson Group plc
John Lewis Partnership plc
John Swire & Sons Ltd
Johnson Matthey plc
Jones Lang LaSalle Ltd
Kaupthing Singer & Friedlander Ltd
Kingfisher plc
KPMG LLP
Land Securities Group plc
Lazard & Co. Ltd
Legal & General plc
Liberty International plc
Linklaters
Lloyd's
Lloyds TSB Group plc
Lockheed Martin
London Stock Exchange
Low & Bonar plc
Man Group plc
Marks and Spencer Group plc
Marsh Ltd
Mascolo Ltd
Mazars LLP
McDonald's Restaurants Ltd
Misys plc

Morgan Stanley International Ltd
N M Rothschild & Sons Ltd
National Express Group plc
National Magazine Co Ltd
Network Rail Infrastructure Ltd
News International plc
Northern & Shell Network Ltd
Novae Group plc
Old Mutual plc
Osborne & Little Ltd
Pearson plc
Pentland Group plc
PKF (UK) LLP
PricewaterhouseCoopers LLP
Private Equity Foundation
Prudential plc
Psion plc
RAB Capital plc
Reed Executive plc
Rentokil Initial plc
Rexam plc
Richer Sounds plc
Ridgesave Ltd
Rio Tinto plc
Rolls-Royce plc
Royal & Sun Alliance Insurance Group
plc
Royal Mail Holdings plc
Savills plc
Schroders plc
Shell
Simmons & Simmons
Slaughter and May
Smith & Nephew plc
Smiths Group plc
Sodexo Ltd
Spar (UK) Ltd
SSL International plc
Standard Chartered plc
Starbucks Coffee Company (UK) Ltd
Stemcor Holdings Ltd
Tate & Lyle plc
TDG plc
Telegraph Media Group Ltd
The Carphone Warehouse Group plc
The Laird Group plc
Thomson Reuters plc
Tomkins plc
Total UK Ltd
Travelex Holdings Ltd
Trinity Mirror plc
UBS
United Business Media Ltd
William Hill plc
WPP Group plc
WSP Group plc

Merseyside

Littlewoods Shop Direct Home
Shopping Ltd
Pilkington Group Ltd
Sportech plc
T.J. Morris Ltd
The Mersey Docks and Harbour
Company

Middlesex

Adobe Systems UK
Bristol-Myers Squibb Pharmaceuticals Ltd
British Airways plc
British Sky Broadcasting Group plc
Coats plc
Compass Group plc
Data Connection Ltd
Dhamecha Group Ltd
Electronic Data Systems Ltd
GlaxoSmithKline plc
H J Heinz Company Ltd
Hasbro UK Ltd
Ladbrokes plc
Ravensale Ltd
Robert Bosch Ltd
Unisys Ltd
United Airlines
United Biscuits Ltd
UPS
Xerox (UK) Ltd

Norfolk

Archant
Bernard Matthews Ltd
Dow Chemical Company Ltd

North Yorkshire

Broadland Properties Ltd
McCain Foods (GB) Ltd
Nestlé UK Ltd
Persimmon plc
Shepherd Building Group Ltd

Northamptonshire

Avon Cosmetics Ltd
Levi Strauss (UK) Ltd
Norbert Dentressangle
Scott Bader Company Ltd
Travis Perkins plc
Weetabix Ltd

Nottinghamshire

Alliance Boots
Capital One Holdings Ltd
Nottingham Building Society
Wilkinson Hardware Stores Ltd

Oxfordshire

AEA Technology plc
Amey UK plc
RM plc
The Midcounties Co-operative
Unipart Group of Companies Ltd

Peterborough

Anglia Regional Co-operative Society Ltd
British Sugar plc
Norwich & Peterborough Building Society
Thomas Cook Group plc

Somerset

Future plc
Wessex Water Services Ltd

South Yorkshire

SIG plc
Swann-Morton Ltd
UK Coal plc
Southampton
VT Group plc

Staffordshire

Britannia Building Society
Caudwell Holdings Ltd
J C Bamford Excavators Ltd
Michelin Tyre Public Ltd Company
Waterford Wedgwood UK plc

Suffolk

Adnams plc

Surrey

Air Products Group Ltd
Allianz Insurance plc
Berkeley Group plc
Biwater Plc
Canon (UK) Ltd
Cargill plc
CEMEX UK Operations
Colgate-Palmolive (UK) Ltd
Crest Nicholson plc
Esso UK Ltd
Friends Provident plc
Gallaher Ltd
Gladedale Holdings Ltd
Mott MacDonald Ltd
Pfizer Ltd
Philips Electronics UK Ltd
Procter & Gamble UK
S C Johnson Ltd
Samsung Electronics (UK) Ltd
Siemens plc
Sony United Kingdom Ltd
Thales UK Ltd
Toshiba Information Systems (UK) Ltd
TT Electronics plc
Unilever UK
Unum
W S Atkins plc
Wates Group Ltd

Tyne & Wear

Arriva plc
Bellway plc
eaga plc
Fenwick Ltd
Greggs plc
Newcastle Building Society
Nike (UK) Ltd
Northern Rock plc
The Go Ahead Group plc

Warwickshire

Calor Gas Ltd
CEF Holdings Ltd
FKI plc
GAP (UK) Ltd
National Grid plc
TNT UK Ltd

West Midlands

Birmingham International Airport Ltd
Euro Packaging Ltd
Genting Stanley plc

IMI plc
LINPAC Group Ltd
Mitchells & Butlers plc
Severn Trent Plc
Wragge & Co LLP
Carillion plc
Coventry Building Society
E.ON UK plc
Geopost UK Ltd
Jaguar Cars Ltd
West Bromwich Building Society

West Sussex

G4S plc
Spirent plc
The Body Shop International plc
TUI UK Ltd

West Yorkshire

Alcoa UK Holdings Ltd
Arla Foods Ltd
ASDA Stores Ltd
Bradford & Bingley plc
Cattles plc
Clariant UK Ltd
Communisis plc
Congregational & General Insurance plc
Evans Property Group
Filtronic plc
Findel plc
HESCO Bastion Ltd
Kelda Group plc
Leeds Building Society
Northern Foods plc
Provident Financial plc
Wm Morrison Supermarkets plc
Yorkshire Building Society

Wiltshire

Avon Rubber plc
Dyson Ltd
Honda of the UK Manufacturing Ltd
Nationwide Building Society
RWE npower
WH Smith plc
Zurich Financial Services (UKISA) Ltd

Worcestershire

AT&T (UK) Ltd
GKN plc
Halfords Group plc

Scotland

Aberdeen

First plc
John Wood Group plc

Edinburgh

AEGON Scottish Equitable plc
HBOS plc
John Menzies plc
Johnston Press Plc
Miller Group Ltd
Scottish & Newcastle UK Ltd
Standard Life
The Royal Bank of Scotland Group plc

Fife
Tullis Russell Group Ltd

Glasgow
Clydesdale Bank plc
House of Fraser (Stores) Ltd
Robert Wiseman Dairies plc
ScottishPower plc
STV Group plc
The Weir Group plc

Lanarkshire
British Energy Group plc

Moray
Baxters Food Group Ltd

Perth
Scottish and Southern Energy plc
Stagecoach Group plc

West Lothian
Agilent Technologies UK Ltd

Wales

Cardiff
Admiral Group plc
Dwr Cymru Welsh Water
First Plus Financial Group plc
Julian Hodge Bank Ltd
Principality Building Society

Flintshire
Redrow Group plc

Gwynnedd
Anglesey Aluminium Metals Ltd

Merthyr Tydfil
Hoover Ltd

Rhondda Cynon Taff
Celtic Energy Ltd

Vale of Glamorgan
Dow Corning Ltd

Northern Ireland

Belfast
Bombardier Aerospace Europe Ltd
First Trust Bank

In this section we list national agencies which may be helpful in the context of company giving, under the general headings employees/professional advice, sponsorship, enterprise and training, education, donations, promoting good practice, media, general company information and informal contacts.

Employees/professional advice

Business in the Community
137 Shepherdess Walk
London
N1 7RQ
Tel: 020 7566 8650
Web: www.bitc.org.uk

Chartered Surveyors Voluntary Service
RICS Contact Centre
Surveyor Court
Westwood Business Park
Westwood Way
Coventry
CV4 8JE
Tel: 0870 333 1600
Web: www.rics.org.uk

Community Service Volunteers (CSV)
237 Pentonville Road
London
N1 9NJ
Tel: 020 7278 6601
Web: www.csv.org.uk

Life Academy
9 Chesham Road
Guildford
Surrey
GU1 3LS
Tel: 01483 301 170
Web: www.life-academy.co.uk

ProHelp
c/o Business in the Community
137 Shepherdess Walk
London
N1 7RQ
Tel: 020 7566 8652
Web: www.bitc.org.uk

REACH (Retired Executives Action Clearing House)
89 Albert Embankment
London
SE1 7TP
Tel: 020 7582 6543
Web: www.volwork.org.uk

The Retirement Trust
The Retirement Trust
Silton Cottage
Chantlers Hill
Paddock Wood
Tonbridge
Kent
TN12 6LX
Tel: 01892 838474
Web: www.theretirementtrust.org.uk

Volunteering England
Regents Wharf
8 All Saints Street
London
N1 9RL
Tel: 0845 305 6979
Web: www.volunteering.org.uk

Sponsorship

Arts and Business
Nutmeg House
60 Gainsford Street
Butlers Wharf
London. SE1 2NY
Tel: 020 7378 8143
Web: www.aandb.org.uk

Community Links
Canning Town Public Hall
105 Barking Road
Canning Town
London
E16 4HQ
Tel: 020 7473 2270
Web: www.community-links.org

Groundwork UK
Lockside
5 Scotland Street
Birmingham
B1 2RR
Tel: 0121 236 8565
Web: www.groundwork.org.uk

Enterprise and training

Common Purpose UK
Common Purpose
Discovery House
28–42 Banner Street
London
EC1Y 8QE
Tel: 020 7608 8118
Web: www.commonpurpose.org.uk
There are regional offices throughout the UK.

Community Development Foundation (CDF)
Headquarters
Unit 5, Angel Gate
320–326 City Road
London
EC1V 2PT
Tel: 020 7833 1772
Web: www.cdf.org.uk

National Federation of Enterprise Agencies
12 Stephenson Court
Fraser Road
Priory Business Park
Bedford
MK44 3WJ
Tel: 01234 831623
Web: www.nfea.com

Education

Confederation of British Industry (CBI)
Centre Point
103 New Oxford Street
London
WC1A 1DU
Tel: 020 7395 8195
Web: www.cbi.org.uk

Council for Industry and Higher Education (CIHE)
Studio 11
Tiger House
Burton Street
London
WC1H 9BY
Tel: 020 7383 7667
Web: www.cihe-uk.com

The Work Foundation
The Work Foundation
21 Palmer Street
London
SW1H 0AD Tel: 020 7976 3500
Web: www.theworkfoundation.com

Donations

CAF (Charities Aid Foundation)
25 Kings Hill Avenue
Kings Hill
West Malling
Kent
ME19 4TA
Tel: 01732 520 000
Web: www.cafonline.org

Charities Trust
Suite 22
Century Building,
Brunswick Business Park,
Tower Street,
Liverpool,
L3 4BJ
Tel: 0870 708 7878
Web: www.chariticstrust.org

Charity Commission
London
Harmsworth House
13–15 Bouverie Street
London
EC4Y 8DP
Main Contact Centre: 0845 3000 218
Web: www.charitycommission.gov.uk
Liverpool
12 Princes Dock
Princes Parade
Liverpool
L3 1DE
Taunton
Woodfield House
Tangier
Taunton
Somerset
TA1 4BL
Newport
8th Floor
Clarence House
Clarence Place
Newport
South Wales
NP19 7AA

In Kind Direct
5th Floor
11–15 Monument Street
London
EC3R 8JU
Tel: 020 7714 3930
Web: www.inkinddirect.org

ShareGift
17 Carlton House Terrace
London
SW1Y 5AH
Tel: 020 7930 3737
Web: www.sharegift.org

Workplace Giving UK
2nd Floor
Cavendish House
369 Burnt Oak Broadway
Edgware
Middlesex
HA8 5AW
Tel: 020 8731 5125
Web: www.workplacegiving-uk.co.uk

Promoting good practice

Business in the Community
137 Shepherdess Walk
London
N1 7RQ
Tel: 020 7566 8650
Web: www.bitc.org.uk

Scottish Business in the Community
Livingstone House
First Floor (East)
43a Discovery Terrace
Heriott-Watt Research Park
Edinburgh
EH14 4AP
Tel 0131 451 1100
Web: www.sbcscot.com

Charities Tax Reform Group (CTRG)
Church House
Great Smith Street
London
SW1P 3AZ
Tel: 020 7222 1265
Web: www.ctrg.org.uk

The Corporate Responsibility Group
The Qube
90 Whitfield Street
London. W1T 4EZ
Tel: 020 7612 8830
Web: www.crguk.org

Directory of Social Change
London
24 Stephenson Way
London
NW1 2DP
Tel: 08450 77 77 07
Liverpool
Ground Floor
Federation House
Hope Street
Liverpool
L1 9BW
Research: 0151 708 0136
Training: 0151 708 0117

EIRIS (Ethical Investment Research Services)
The Ethical Investment Research Service
80–84 Bondway
London
SW8 1SF
Tel: 020 7840 5700
Web: www.eiris.org

Out of This World
106 High Street
Gosforth
Newcastle upon Tyne
NE3 1HB
Tel: 0191 213 5377
Web: www.ootw.co.uk

Corporate Citizenship
5th Floor Holborn Gate
330 High Holborn
London
WC1V 7QG
Tel: 020 7861 1616
Web: www.corporate-citizenship.com

The London Benchmarking Group
c/o Corporate Citizenship
5th Floor Holborn Gate
330 High Holborn
London
WC1V 7QG
Tel: 020 7861 1616
Web: www.corporate-citizenship.com

The Prince of Wales International Business Leaders Forum (IBLF)
15–16 Cornwall Terrace
Regent's Park
London
NW1 4QP
Tel: 020 7467 3600
Web: www.iblf.org

Media

BBC Charity Appeals Office
Room 5126
White City
201 Wood Lane
London
W12 7TS
Tel: 020 8008 1198
Web: www.bbc.co.uk/charityappeals

Campaign for Press & Broadcasting Freedom
2nd Floor
Vi & Garner Smith House
23 Orford Road
Walthamstow
London
E17 9NL
Tel: 020 8521 5932
Web: www.cpbf.org.uk

Channel Four Television Company
Channel 4 Enquiries
PO Box 1058
Belfast
BT1 9DU
Tel: 0845 076 0191
Web: www.channel4.com

CSV Media
237 Pentonville Road
London
N1 9NJ
Tel: 20 7278 6601
Web: www.csv.org.uk/Services/Media/media+homepage.htm

ITV Network Centre
200 Gray's Inn Road
London
WC1X 8HF
Tel: 020 7156 6000
Web: www.itv.com

Media Trust
Riverwalk House
157–161 Millbank
2nd floor
London
SW1P 4RR
Tel: 020 7217 3717
Web: www.mediatrust.org

General company information

Companies House
Crown Way
Maindy
Cardiff
CF 14 3UZ
Tel: 0303 1234 500
Web: www.companieshouse.gov.uk

Trades Union Congress (TUC)
Congress House
Great Russell Street
London
WC1B 3LS
Tel: 020 7636 4030
Web: www.tuc.org.uk

Co-operative and Community Finance
Brunswick Court
Brunswick Square
Bristol
BS2 8PE
Tel: 01179 166750
Web: www.icof.co.uk

British Urban Regeneration Association
4th Floor
63–66 Hatton Garden
London
EC1N 8LE
Tel: 020 7539 4030
Web: www.bura.org.uk

URBED (Urban and Economic Development Ltd)
26 Gray's Inn Road
London
WC1X 8HP
Tel: 020 7831 9986
Web: www.urbed.com

Young Enterprise UK
Peterley House
Peterley Road
Oxford
OX4 2TZ
Tel. 01865 776 845
Web: www.young-enterprise.org.uk

Informal contacts

Association of Inner Wheel Clubs in Great Britain & Ireland
51 Warwick Square
London
SW1V 2AT
Tel: 020 7834 4600
Web: www.associationinnerwheel.co.uk

Rotary International in Great Britain & Ireland
Kinwarton Road
Alcester
Warwickshire
B49 6PB
Tel: 01789 765 411
Web: www.rotary-ribi.org

Index

Note: companies named after a person are indexed under the *surname*.

3i Group plc *1*
3M United Kingdom plc *1*

A

Abbey *2*
Abbott Mead Vickers – BBDO Ltd *3*
Accenture UK Ltd *4*
ADC Krone (UK) *5*
Addleshaw Goddard *6*
adidas (UK) Ltd *7*
Admiral Group plc *8*
Adnams plc *8*
Adobe Systems UK *9*
AEA Technology plc *10*
Aegis Group plc *11*
AEGON Scottish Equitable plc *12*
Aggregate Industries Ltd *12*
Agilent Technologies UK Ltd *13*
Air Products Group Ltd *13*
Akzo Nobel UK Ltd *14*
Alcoa UK Holdings Ltd *15*
Allen & Overy LLP *16*
Alliance & Leicester plc *17*
Alliance Boots Holdings Ltd *18*
Allianz Insurance plc *20*
Allied London Properties Ltd *21*
AMEC plc *21*
Amey UK plc *22*
Anglesey Aluminium Metals Ltd *23*
Anglia Regional Co-operative Society Ltd *23*
Anglian Water Services Ltd *24*
Anglo American plc *25*
AOL UK Ltd *26*
Apax Partners LLP *27*
ARAMARK Ltd *27*
Archant *28*
Arla Foods Ltd *28*
Arriva plc *29*
Arup Group Ltd *30*
ASDA Stores Ltd *30*
Associated British Foods plc *32*
Associated British Ports Holdings Ltd *32*
AstraZeneca plc *33*
AT&T (UK) Ltd *34*
W S Atkins plc *35*
Aviva plc *35*
Avon Cosmetics Ltd *36*
Avon Rubber plc *37*

B

BAA plc *38*
BAE Systems *39*
Bain & Company Inc. UK *39*
J C Bamford Excavators Ltd *40*
Bank of England *41*
Bank of Ireland UK Financial Services *42*

The Banks Group *43*
Barclays plc *43*
Barrett Developments plc *45*
BASF plc *45*
Baxter Healthcare Ltd *46*
Baxters Food Group Ltd *46*
Bayer plc *47*
Bellway plc *48*
Berkeley Group plc *48*
Bestway (Holdings) Ltd *49*
BHP Billiton plc *49*
Birmingham International Airport Ltd *50*
Biwater plc *51*
Bloomsbury Publishing plc *51*
BMW UK Ltd *52*
The Body Shop International plc *53*
Bombardier Aerospace Europe Ltd *54*
Robert Bosch Ltd *55*
Boyer Allan Investment Investment Management LLP *55*
BP plc *56*
Bradford & Bingley plc *57*
Bristol-Myers Squibb Pharmaceuticals Ltd *58*
Brit Insurance Holdings plc *58*
Britannia Building Society *59*
British Airways plc *60*
British American Tobacco plc *61*
British Energy Group plc *62*
British Land Company plc *63*
British Nuclear Fuels plc *64*
British Sky Broadcasting Group plc *64*
British Sugar plc *65*
Brixton plc *66*
Broadland Properties Ltd *67*
N Brown Group plc *67*
Bruntwood Ltd *68*
BT Group plc *69*
Bunzl plc *70*
BUPA Ltd *71*

C

C E Electric UK Ltd *72*
CA plc *73*
Cable and Wireless plc *74*
Cadbury plc *75*
Cadogan Group Ltd *76*
Caledonia Investments *76*
Calor Gas Ltd *77*
Camelot Group plc *78*
Canary Wharf Group plc *79*
Canon (UK) Ltd *79*
Caparo Group Ltd *80*
Capita Group plc *80*
Capital One Holdings Ltd *81*
Cargill plc *82*
Carillion plc *83*

The Carphone Warehouse Group plc *83*
Catlin Group Ltd *84*
Cattles plc *85*
Caudwell Holdings Ltd *86*
Cazenove Group plc *86*
CEF Holdings Ltd *87*
Celtic Energy Ltd *88*
CEMEX UK Operations *88*
Centrica plc *89*
Charter plc *90*
Chelsea Building Society *91*
Cheshire Building Society *92*
Chevron Ltd *93*
Chrysalis Group plc *93*
Ciba UK plc *94*
CIBC World Markets plc *95*
Citibank International plc *96*
Citroën UK Ltd *97*
Clariant UK Ltd *97*
Clinton Cards plc *98*
Close Brothers Group plc *98*
Clydesdale Bank plc *98*
Coats plc *100*
Cobham plc *101*
Coca-Cola Great Britain *101*
Colgate-Palmolive (UK) Ltd *102*
Communisis plc *103*
Compass Group plc *103*
Congregational & General Insurance plc *104*
Thomas Cook Group plc *105*
Cookson Group plc *105*
Cooper Gay (Holdings) Ltd *106*
The Co-operative Group *106*
Cooper-Parry LLP *108*
Corus Group plc *108*
Costain Group plc *109*
Coutts & Co *110*
Coventry Building Society *111*
Credit Suisse *112*
Crest Nicholson plc *113*
Cummins Ltd *113*
P Z Cussons plc *114*

D

Daejan Holdings plc *114*
Daily Mail and General Trust plc *115*
Data Connection Ltd *116*
DDB UK Ltd *116*
De Beers *117*
De La Rue plc *117*
De Vere Group *118*
Deloitte *119*
Derbyshire Building Society *120*
Deutsche Bank *121*
Dhamecha Group Ltd *122*
Diageo plc *123*

Dow Chemical Company Ltd *124*
Dow Corning Ltd *124*
Dresdner Kleinwort Ltd *125*
DSG International plc *126*
Du Pont (UK) Ltd *127*
Dwr Cymru Welsh Water *128*
Dyson Ltd *129*

E

E.ON UK plc *129*
eaga plc *130*
East Midlands Airport *131*
Ecclesiastical Insurance Group plc *132*
Economist Newspaper Ltd *133*
EDF Energy plc *134*
Egg Ltd *135*
Electronic Data Systems Ltd *136*
EMI Group Ltd *137*
Ernst & Young LLP *138*
Esh Group *139*
Esso UK Ltd *139*
Euro Packaging Ltd *140*
Evans Property Group *141*
Execution Ltd *141*

F

F&C Asset Management plc *142*
Family Assurance Friendly Society Ltd *143*
Fenwick Ltd *143*
Fiat Group Automobiles UK Ltd *144*
Fidelity Investment Management Ltd *145*
Filtronic plc *146*
Financial Services Authority *146*
Findel plc *147*
First plc *148*
First Plus Financial Group plc *149*
First Trust Bank *149*
FKI plc *150*
Focus (DIY) Ltd *151*
Ford Motor Company Ltd *151*
Fortis Insurance Ltd *152*
Freshfields Bruuckhaus Deringer LLP *153*
Friends Provident plc *154*
Fujitsu Services Holdings plc *155*
Future plc *155*

G

G4S plc *156*
Galiform plc *156*
Gallaher Ltd *157*
GAP (UK) Ltd *158*
GE Healthcare *158*
General Motors UK Ltd *159*
Genting Stanley plc *160*
Geopost UK Ltd *161*
GKN plc *161*
Gladedale Holdings Ltd *162*
GlaxoSmithKline plc *162*
Glencore UK Ltd *164*
The Go Ahead Group plc *164*
Goldman Sachs International *165*
Great Portland Estates plc *166*
Greencore Group UK *166*
Greggs plc *167*
Grosvenor Group *168*
Guardian Media Group plc *169*

H

Halfords Group plc *170*
Hammerson plc *171*
Hanson Ltd *171*
Hasbro UK Ltd *172*
HBOS plc *173*
H J Heinz Company Ltd *174*
Henderson Group plc *175*
Herbert Smith LLP *176*
HESCO Bastion Ltd *177*
Hess Ltd *177*
Hewlett-Packard Ltd *178*
HFC Bank Ltd *179*
William Hill plc *179*
Hiscox plc *180*
Julian Hodge Bank Ltd *180*
Honda of the UK Manufacturing Ltd *181*
Hoover Ltd *181*
House of Fraser (Stores) Ltd *182*
HSBC Holdings plc *182*
Alan Hudson Ltd *183*
Hunting plc *183*
Huntsman / Tioxide Europe Ltd *184*

I

IBM United Kingdom Ltd *184*
ICAP plc *185*
IMI plc *186*
Imperial Tobacco Group plc *187*
Inchcape plc *187*
Informa plc *188*
Innocent Drinks *188*
Intercontinental Hotels Group plc *189*
Invensys plc *190*
Invesco Asset Management Ltd *190*
IPC Media Ltd *191*
ITV plc *192*

J

Jaguar Cars Ltd *192*
Jardine Lloyd Thompson Group plc *193*
JJB Sports plc *193*
S C Johnson Ltd *194*
Johnson Matthey plc *195*
Johnson Service Group plc *196*
Johnston Press plc *197*
Jones Lang LaSalle Ltd *197*

K

Kaupthing Singer & Friedlander Ltd *198*
Kelda Group plc *198*
Kellogg Company of Great Britain *199*
Kingfisher plc *200*
Kodak Ltd *202*
KPMG LLP *202*
Kraft Foods UK Ltd *204*
Kwik-Fit Group *204*

L

Ladbrokes plc *205*
Lafarge Aggregates & Concretes UK *206*
The Laird Group plc *207*
Land Securities Group plc *208*
Lazard & Co. Ltd *208*
Sara Lee UK Holdings Ltd *209*
Leeds Building Society *209*

Legal & General plc *210*
John Lewis Partnership plc *211*
Liberty International plc *212*
Eli Lilly and Company Ltd *213*
Lincoln Financial Group *214*
Linklaters *215*
LINPAC Group Ltd *216*
Littlewoods Shop Direct Home Shopping
   Ltd *217*
Liverpool Victoria *217*
Lloyd's *218*
Lloyds TSB Group plc *219*
Lockheed Martin *221*
Lofthouse of Fleetwood Ltd *221*
London Stock Exchange *222*
Low & Bonar plc *222*

M

Man Group plc *223*
The Manchester Airport Group plc *224*
Marks and Spencer Group plc *226*
Marsh Ltd *227*
Marshall of Cambridge (Holdings) Ltd
   228
Mascolo Ltd *228*
Bernard Matthews Ltd *229*
Mazars LLP *230*
Robert McAlpine Ltd *231*
McCain Foods (GB) Ltd *231*
McDonald's Restaurants Ltd *232*
Medtronic Ltd *232*
John Menzies plc *233*
Merck Sharp & Dohme Ltd *233*
The Mersey Docks and HarbourCompany
   234
Michelin Tyre Public Ltd Company *235*
Microsoft Ltd *235*
The Midcounties Co-operative *237*
Miller Group Ltd *238*
Misys plc *238*
Mitchells & Butlers plc *239*
J P Morgan Chase *240*
The Morgan Crucible Company plc *241*
Morgan Stanley International Ltd *241*
T J Morris Ltd *243*
Wm Morrison Supermarkets plc *243*
Mothercare plc *244*
Mott MacDonald Ltd *245*
Muir Group *245*

N

National Express Group plc *246*
National Grid plc *246*
National Magazine Co Ltd *248*
Nationwide Building Society *248*
Nestlé UK Ltd *249*
Network Rail Infrastructure Ltd *250*
Newcastle Building Society *250*
News International plc *251*
Next plc *252*
Nike (UK) Ltd *252*
Norbert Dentressangle *254*
Northern & Shell Network Ltd *254*
Northern Foods plc *255*
Northern Rock plc *256*
Northern Trust Group Ltd *257*

Northumbrian Water Group 257
Norwich & Peterborough Building Society 258
Nottingham Building Society 259
Novae Group plc 259

O

Old Mutual plc 260
Oracle Corporation UK Ltd 261
Orange PCS Ltd 261
Osborne & Little Ltd 262

P

Palmer & Harvey McLane Ltd 263
Panasonic UK Ltd 263
Pearson plc 264
Pennon Group plc 265
Pentland Group plc 266
PepsiCo UK 266
Persimmon plc 267
Personal Group Holdings plc 268
Pfizer Ltd 268
Philips Electronics UK Ltd 270
Pilkington Group Ltd 271
PKF (UK) LLP 271
Premier Foods plc 272
PricewaterhouseCoopers LLP 272
Principality Building Society 273
Private Equity Foundation 273
Procter & Gamble UK 274
Provident Financial plc 275
Prudential plc 276
Psion plc 277

Q

QinetiQ Group plc 278

R

RAB Capital plc 278
Rank Group plc 279
Ravensale Ltd 279
Reckitt Benckiser plc 280
Redrow Group plc 280
Reed Executive plc 281
Renishaw plc 281
Rentokil Initial plc 282
Rexam plc 283
Richer Sounds plc 283
Ridgesave Ltd 284
Rio Tinto plc 284
RM plc 285
Roche Products Ltd 286
Rolls–Royce plc 286
N M Rothschild & Sons Ltd 287
Royal & Sun Alliance Insurance Group plc 288
The Royal Bank of Scotland Group plc 288
The Royal London Mutual Insurance Society Ltd 289
Royal Mail Group plc 290
RWE npower 291

S

Saga Group Ltd 291
J Sainsbury plc 292
Samsung Electronics (UK) Ltd 293

Savills plc 294
Schroders plc 295
Scott Bader Company Ltd 295
Scottish & Newcastle UK Ltd 297
Scottish and Southern Energy plc 297
ScottishPower plc 298
SEGRO plc 299
Serco Group plc 300
Severn Trent plc 300
Shell 301
Shepherd Building Group Ltd 302
Shire Pharmaceuticals plc 303
Shoe Zone Ltd 304
Siemens plc 305
SIG plc 305
Simmons & Simmons 306
Slaughter and May 306
Smith & Nephew plc 307
D S Smith Holdings plc 308
WH Smith plc 309
Smiths Group plc 309
Sodexo Ltd 310
Sony United Kingdom Ltd 311
Southern Co-operatives Ltd 312
Spar (UK) Ltd 312
Spirax Sarco Engineering plc 313
Spirent plc 314
Sportech plc 314
SSL International plc 315
St James's Place plc 315
Stagecoach Group plc 316
Standard Chartered plc 316
Standard Life 317
Starbucks Coffee Company (UK) Ltd 318
Stemcor Holdings Ltd 319
Steria Ltd 319
J Stobart and Sons Ltd 320
Levi Strauss (UK) Ltd 321
STV Group plc 322
Swann-Morton Ltd 322
John Swire & Sons Ltd 323

T

Tate & Lyle plc 323
Taylor Woodrow Construction 324
TDG plc 325
Telefonica O2 Europe plc 325
Telegraph Media Group Ltd 326
Tesco plc 327
Thales UK Ltd 328
Thomson Reuters plc 329
Daniel Thwaites plc 330
TJX UK (formerly TK Maxx) 330
T-Mobile (UK) Ltd 331
TNT UK Ltd 331
Tomkins plc 332
Topps Tiles plc 333
Toshiba Information Systems (UK) Ltd 333
Total UK Ltd 334
Toyota Motor Manufacturing (UK) Ltd 334
Travelex Holdings Ltd 335
Travis Perkins plc 336
Trinity Mirror plc 336
TT Electronics plc 337

TUI UK Ltd 338
Tullis Russell Group Ltd 338

U

UBS 339
UIA (Insurance) Ltd 340
UK Coal plc 340
Unilever UK 341
Unipart Group of Companies Ltd 343
Uniq plc 343
Unisys Ltd 344
United Airlines 344
United Biscuits Ltd 345
United Business Media Ltd 346
United Utilities Group plc 346
Unum 347
UPS 348

V

Vodafone Group plc 348
VT Group plc 349

W

Warburtons Ltd 350
Wates Group Ltd 351
Weetabix Ltd 351
The Weir Group plc 352
Wessex Water Services Ltd 352
West Bromwich Building Society 353
Western Power Distribution 354
J D Wetherspoon plc 354
Whitbread plc 355
Wilkinson Hardware Stores Ltd 356
Willmott Dixon Ltd 356
Robert Wiseman Dairies plc 357
John Wood Group plc 358
WPP Group plc 358
Wragge & Co LLP 359
WSP Group plc 360
Wyevale Garden Centres Ltd 360

X

Xerox (UK) Ltd 361

Y

Yattendon Investment Trust plc 361
Yorkshire Building Society 362
Yule Catto & Co plc 363

Z

Zurich Financial Services (UKISA) Ltd 364